World Views: Classic and Contemporary Readings

Edited by Roger West, Elizabeth Hair, Richard Hartnett, Mike Kirst, and Ed Macy

Custom Edition for Trident Technical College

Eighth Edition

Pearson Learning Solutions, 330 Hudson Street, New York, New York 10013A
Pearson Education Company
www.pearsoned.com

Printed in the United States of America

1 2 3 4 5 6 7 8 9 10 V057 18 17 16 15

000200010271973891

ML/KC

ISBN 10: 1-323-14921-X
ISBN 13: 978-1-323-14921-8

Copyright Acknowledgments

Contents

Non-Fiction

Fiction

The Night of a Thousand Suicides

Teruhiko Asada

During World War II, on August 5, 1944, at a prisoner of war (POW) camp in Cowra, in New South Wales, Australia, over a thousand Japanese POWs attempted what is generally regarded as the largest POW escape in military history. Armed with such makeshift weapons as clubs, knives, baseball bats, and wire garroting, the Japanese attacked their Australian guards and attempted to cut through the wire fence surrounding the camp. Over three-hundred managed to escape, but all were eventually captured or died. According to most sources, a total of 234 Japanese prisoners lost their lives. Some were killed by guards, but many of the deaths were by suicide, since traditional Japanese culture regarded capture during wartime to be shameful, and it was expected that soldiers would die rather than submit to detention. The excerpt which follows is taken from a fictionalized account of the incident, a novel entitled The Night of a Thousand Suicides: The Outbreak at Cowra. *The novel was first published in Japan in 1967 before being translated into English in 1970. The author, Teruhiko Asada (1915–), was himself a POW at Cowra.*

Gradually, as I listened to the stories of the survivors, the details of that tragic night became clear in my mind. Having received the order concerning the movement of prisoners at our interview with Major Ramsay, Sergeant-major Kajima called a section leaders' meeting immediately on returning to the Japanese compound. The move was set down for the following day and it was imperative to decide at once whether to obey or disobey. Negotiation was now out of the question.

There was considerable stir created in the camp. Such a snap action on the part of the Australian authorities had not been expected.

All had been busy getting ready for a concert to be held the next day. Technicians were decorating the stage and making costumes while Matchan (Cpl. Matsuoka), the entertainment group leader, and Miyasan (Private First Class Tsuruoka) were rehearsing lines from "Kirare Yosaburo." Home-made samisen, flute and drum were to make it a really professional performance complete with the correct musical accompaniment and all were looking forward eagerly to the occasion. Cooking too was in progress, with a few old hands battling along covered in flour, baking cakes to be distributed to everyone after the concert.

In the midst of all this suddenly came the news of the move order, and chief cook Sgt Kikuchi, with flour all over his face, and Matchan, still wearing the Yosaburo costume, raced into the section leaders' meeting.

Knowing the determination of Major Ramsay, none put forward a very positive opinion, but simply allowed time to be taken up with grumblings and criticism of the injustice of the Australian order. To a man they wanted to reject the order, but every mouth was stopped when asked point blank if disobedience of the order could be maintained at the point of a bayonet. Unless considerable unity of purpose were achieved, they could be carted off in ones and twos until none were left. To disobey meant that a man had to be ready to offer his life.

The camp leader closed the meeting with the request that the section leaders report again as soon as a decision had been reached in the sections. However, the situation was the same in each section—simply that the order for the move was distasteful in the extreme but there was an unwillingness to go to the point of risking death in disobeying it.

At the second meeting of section leaders Section Leader Ishikawa reported that his section had decided that no matter how much the order was resented, the only course left open was to obey. Most of the section leaders silently indicated agreement and all appeared to have been waiting for such a proposal. Ishikawa went on to continue putting the case with some feeling:

"This is not purely and simply because of a fear of death. There is the intention to bear before the world the responsibility for having become prisoners but I don't think that time is now." The order for the move, he added, seemed the logical step for the Australian Army to take in the circumstances.

"Shut up, you old fool!" Cpl. Hotei was on his feet as he shouted the words, his face flushed from drinking.

"There's not one single coward of that kind in my section. We're all ready to die defying any such order. That's the fighting spirit of Japan!"

Flight-sergeant Tobé was the next up, also full of "jungle juice."

"There are no cowards in my section, either. Dying or living they're going to stick by me, they said. Are you going to tell men like that to pack off to Hay?

Before the men are 'done' like that, how about an attack? There will never be another chance. Now is the time. We will die together like the falling blossoms."

"Hear, hear!" came from outside the window where more than a dozen quite crazy drunk men belonging to the extremists had gathered to peer in and note the trend of the meeting.

The atmosphere of the meeting changed radically.

"Have you forgotten the Field Service Code?"

"The way of the samurai is the way of death."

Met with these cries, none could demur.

After getting the men away from the immediate vicinity, the camp leader said, "It's all very well to talk of an attack, but we don't have a single weapon."

Before he could go on, Cpl. Hotei stuck out a huge fist and asserted, "We do have weapons—these! We're going to fight with our bare hands. We'll beat the Australians to death and take their weapons!"

The delirium was contagious.

"We've got the baseball bats and knives and forks. If each one kills one we can account for a thousand of the enemy," put in an other section leader. "How about it?"

"All right then, let's get going."

The meeting was in a ferment.

"Hold on now." W. O. Ishikawa was on his feet. "The members of my section are certainly not a bunch of cowards and if all really agreed with the sentiments just expressed my men would naturally follow the will of the majority in spite of their own misgivings. But I think we have to be sure if this is really the will of the whole body after all. I don't think it ought to be decided at a section leaders' meeting only but that every man in the compound should take part in a secret ballot on the matter and that a simple majority so obtained should be decisive."

The camp leader adopted this plan. There was to be another recess, the next meeting to take place when results of the secret ballot were known.

The matter of voting was by no means simple. It involved a decision on a general attack—in effect, death for honour or, to put it another way, mass suicide. All were continually thinking of death, but now when faced with the challenge to get ready to die, they tended to waver. Only a very small minority had definite opinions. Most were ready to follow the lead of the majority, but it was not easy to make out just what majority opinion was after all.

Violent arguments broke out in every section, so that it was difficult to obtain a decision by which all would abide. Night fell but it wasn't possible to enjoy the evening meal. Now with shrill voices they continued the debate.

The extremists had the most to say, keen to remove the shame of imprisonment by carrying out an unarmed attack, a valiant, appealing concept.

By contrast, the case that the moderates put forward seemed so lacking in life that they were liable to be regarded as miserable and cowardly. It took considerable courage to be a spokesman for such a cause. It was necessary to have a well grounded and thought-out argument that would withstand the barbs of, "Have you forgotten the Field Service Code?" or, "Call yourself a Japanese soldier?"

Logic is not the strong point of the Japanese. They are inclined to be carried away with an atmosphere and also to submit their wills to that of a superior. In the case of the section leaders of the moderate persuasion the voices against the attack were the stronger. For all that, there was an increasing tendency for the majority in the compound to favour carrying out the attack. As the night wore on, an abnormal excitement seemed to take over, resulting in a desire to take part in vengeful acts of destruction.

For the third time the section leaders met and the votes from all the sections were totalled up. Over half were in favour of the attack, and the die was cast.

There was room for doubt that this was a true representation of the will of the entire body of prisoners. It looked very much as though they had been carried away with the admonitions of the extremists. No ballot was carried out in the sections led by Flight-sergeant Tobé and Cpl. Hotei. They maintained that voices expressing a willingness to leave the decision to the section leader constituted a vote in favour of the attack. By contrast, a proper secret ballot was carried out in W. O. Ishikawa's section and the count showed two-thirds against the charge. It was quite likely that, if strict secret ballots had been carried out in all sections, those against might have been in the majority. All feared death, but feared the name coward even more. They wanted to appear patriotic, loyal soldiers before the world and they could not have it said that they would suffer any shame in order to preserve their lives.

The majority decision to take part in the attack was thus announced in a crazed atmosphere. It was already after lights out but nothing was further from the men's minds than the thought of sleep. The section leaders' meeting was discussing what form the attack should take. No matter how it was carried out it could have little effect against machinegun bullets. They would all die together and the time was now only a few hours away.

All the home brew was brought out and consumed, the cakes made for the occasion of the concert were eaten freely, and enough cigarettes smoked to make the head spin. Knives and forks were sharpened on cement-rendered surfaces; and bats, iron pipes, motor vehicle springs and the like were kept at hand for use as weapons. An atmosphere of near frenzy was maintained; a readiness to go just as soon as the camp leader's order came.

There were, however, some who were not carried away with this mood, going through torture of soul because they lacked the resolve to take action to avoid the death now facing them. They walked about the compound with arms folded debating within themselves the meaning of this death—a violent conflict going on within the heart of every man.

The searchlights were turned on them. It seemed that the Australians found evidence of disquiet in the fact that although it was now past lights out the prisoners had not turned their lights off and there was continual moving to and fro by many of them. It was, of course, possible to put it down partly to preparations for the move to take place the following morning. No doubt the possibility of an attack by unarmed men was not even considered.[1]

It had been decided that a bugle call at midnight would signal the start of the attack. Sections 1 to 10 were to get through the front gate and escape in a northerly direction; sections 11 to 20 to surmount the barricades on the north-cast; sections 21 to 27 were to escape from the south-west corner of the Japanese compound and into the wide road through the centre of the greater camp area ("Broadway") and head south. Sections 27 to 36 would escape to the south-east. In this way prisoners would head in four different directions for the attack. The sick and those wounded who could not be expected to scale the barricades were not forced to take part. Civilian employees of the Japanese forces among the prisoners were not judged to be as guilty as soldiers taken prisoner and each was allowed to make up his own mind about taking part.

Huts were to be burned down at the time of the attack as a sign of the determination of the prisoners never to return to the place. Each man was to take one blanket to be used in protecting the body from barbed wire when climbing over the barricades. Further protection was afforded by wearing baseball gloves or by wrapping the hands in pieces of blankets. A small amount of food, including biscuits, was also to be carried. Attention was paid to a number of details of this kind in preparing for the attack.

But as to what was to be done once the men had escaped across the barricades, nothing was yet definitely decided. The attack was to be like a mass suicide but there was no way of estimating exactly the strength of Australian firepower likely to be encountered so that it was not possible to say that none of the prisoners would succeed in getting through; and some indication of what should then be done must be given. But there was no longer enough time to attend to such details of planning. It was decided simply that any who got out alive should gather in a suitable place, choose a leader, and attempt to attack Australian camps and airfields; and since none could really expect to get out alive, planning for that eventuality did not occupy the mind very much.

The section leaders passed to their men these instructions from the camp leader. Despite the fact that the men had made up their minds to take part in the attack, when the time finally came there was a certain amount of disorder and confusion. The decision had been reached by a majority vote and differed quite a deal from a military command. While it was a general attack, exemptions were to be permitted and the will of the individual respected, with the result that it was difficult to get orderly conduct. So much time was consumed in preparations for the battle, farewelling comrades, and in prevailing on those opposed to the plan to change their minds, that zero hour came and went without the sounding of the bugle. The officers had been contacted about the planned attack but had not answered to say whether they were for or against. Because I had not been there, the N.C.Os and men had not taken the officers into account in their deliberations except to pass on news of the decision reached and to leave the officers to make up their own minds.

It seemed that Lt. Kimura had turned up during the deliberations, probably noting the air of unrest and desiring to persuade the men to act more sanely, but the extremists outside the window refused to let him go inside and turned him back with, "Beat it!" and, "Chicken-hearted officer!"

A full two hours after the set time, all sections were at last ready, with mattresses piled up in the fireplaces ready to set on fire and it was then that Camp Leader Kajima gave the order to blow the bugle.

Choking tension prevailed while waiting for its sound. Every face was pale and none could remain still. There was a rush on the toilets and when they became full quite a large number of men defecated by the huts.

"Buck up, men."

"See you at the Yasukuni Shrine."

As comrades gripped each other's hands and exchanged words of farewell, tears welled up in their eyes spontaneously. It has been said that a person facing death sees, as in a kaleidoscope, a recapitulation of events dating back to his infancy, and so it was here; many felt a constricting of the chest as though it were held in a tight band, and a sudden emptiness of the mind—a vacuum, and an unaccountable loss of the power to think clearly. The atmosphere of frenzy created by a crowd of a thousand men prompted all to run about and shout wildly.

The state of those wounded and sick who were unable to join the attack and must later find another way to die was pathetic. It was their desire to choose a glorious end like this. Delirious malaria cases and men with artificial limbs begged to be taken along and it wasn't easy for Section Leader Ishikawa and the others to pacify them. They ordered not only these wounded but also the civilians to remain behind and even allowed servicemen to make up their minds individually concerning participation. But, in an atmosphere of this kind, it took a lot of courage to express such an opinion, if it conflicted with the feeling of the majority. Section Leader Tobé refused to acknowledge the right to such freedom.

"We're all joining the attack and will go down fighting. The sick are to offer themselves nobly at this time and if they lack the guts to die of their own accord then I'll kill them with my own hands." Now drunk to the point being quite crazed, Tobé had been all for the idea of the attack from the beginning but was actually without previous battle experience and had never been face to face with death before, so that despite his brave talk his heart was in a state of agitation.

"We apologize for our inability to join you. We shall go ahead of you to the Yasukuni Shrine." So saying, three of the sick faced the north, gave three cheers of "Banzai" for the Emperor, and suicided by cutting their carotid arteries with razor blades.

In Cpl. Hotei's section was one man who, though fit, said, "I agree with the plan to die but I am against the attack. I don't want to kill anyone, but just die on my own." A number agreed with these sentiments and before the huts were set alight they lined up beneath a beam and hanged themselves from ropes tied to it, their final request to their comrades being that, since some had opposed the idea of bodies being left hanging, they should be cut down and burned. As each one prepared to go he was encouraged by the others assuring him that they would soon follow.

Suicides took place in the other sections also, most of the physically incapacitated men choosing this way out. They died ahead of the others because they regretted not being fit enough to take part in the attack and were convinced that life as survivors would be meaningless for them. As many as twenty belonged to this group.

The compound office was the first to blaze up and on seeing this the men in the other huts immediately set fire to the blankets they had piled up. Oil that had been poured over the mattresses gave off black smoke as flames filled the huts in a matter of moments and came through the windows.

Shouts from the guards on the towers showed that they were aware of trouble in the compound and the light of searchlights directed onto the compound from all directions showed the seriousness of the incident. The alarm siren roared as machineguns were trained on the compound and the forms of Australian soldiers on the point of firing could be seen.

The trumpet sounded the charge, but what should have been a rhythmical call was faltering and broken, more like a shriek than anything else. In battle normally there would be the order, "Charge!" answered by the war cry of the men, but here there was neither, just the tumult created by animal-like gasps wrung from the bodies of a thousand men, a sound that shook the night air.

The men charged in four directions as planned, caught in the beams of the searchlights as they made for the barricades.

They split up and ran at a half crouch, or almost crawling, fast along the ground. Firing broke out from the towers and all instinctively dropped to the ground and remained motionless. The fear experienced when exposed to machinegun fire was greater than anticipated. Even those who had raged and boasted that they would kill two or three of the enemy before going down to Australian bullets now found that their legs were suddenly unwilling to carry them forward and they flattened themselves on the ground with their eyes closed. When the firing ceased they were relieved to find that they were free from pain or sign of injury. But it wasn't possible to remain flat on the ground indefinitely, and, aiming to revive each other's shaken wills with shouts of, "Let us go!" and "Let us die!", a number began to race forward again but, as soon as heavy firing recommenced, no amount of self-respect was able to prevent them from flattening to the ground once more.

The absence of casualties up to this point was explained by the fact that the Australians were not aiming to hit the prisoners but merely sending warning shots whistling over their heads. Strangely enough the discovery of this seemed to anger the escapees who now shouted defiantly in the direction of the gunners, challenging them to shoot to kill. Wave after wave now rushed the barricades, threw the blankets, and clambered over. At this the firing grew more intense and now was directed at the prisoners. The whistling sound changed to a thudding and splashing as frost columns and mud were kicked up by the bullets, and men on the barricades were hit in rapid succession, sending up curses and cries as they were struck. With their last breath they called on Emperor or mother or repeated the name of a friend over and over.

The attack had been momentarily checked and all the remaining men could do was to remain flattened on the ground and wait. Some who had succeeded in getting to the other side of the barricades turned to berate their fellows for their tardiness. This only increased the feeling of impotence.

The threat of being regarded as timid was enough to get the men on the move once again.

Since the firing was mostly concentrated on the front gate of the compound, casualties were heaviest here. Camp Leader Kajima's and W. O. Ishikawa's sections were in this area. They had climbed over the inner barricade but, stopped at the outer, had now taken shelter in the stormwater drain at the foot of the barricade to avoid being cut down by an impassable curtain of fire coming in from both left and right.

Half the escaping prisoners were by now dead or wounded and most of the living were covered in scratches caused by contact with the barbed wire.

During a break in the firing, W. O. Ishikawa raised himself up from the drain to see about a dozen or more Australian soldiers feverishly erecting a machinegun emplacement. The Australians' cry of "Come on, you Japs!" was answered by shouts of "Bakayaro!" [fools!] from this side.

Suddenly flares turned night into day and once more heavy firing began. The only thing to do was crouch, breathless, in the drain, with a blanket for covering. To move meant to receive a bullet.

The sections in the south-east corner including those led by Deputy Camp Leader Tobé and by Cpl. Matsuoka faced less concentrated fire and succeeded in breaking out into the wide road between compounds to find themselves on a thirty-yard-wide asphalt strip with no place to hide and where they all came under fire together. The end result of a rash charge in the direction of the Australian positions was annihilation.

Seeing this from the other side of the barricade, W. O. Ishikawa found himself unable to remain immobile in his place of safety, and, calling on the men of his section to follow the example of those who had just offered themselves, started to clamber up the barricade, only to be dragged off the wire and pinned to the ground by a young airman, Imanishi.

Although he was in Ishikawa's section, this Imanishi had been a member of the extremist group and a most intractable character. That one so strongly in favour of the general attack and a last-ditch stand should now restrain Ishikawa was indeed an unexpected development. The warrant officer no longer felt capable of breaking free from Imanishi and climbing the barricade, and remained where he was clenching his teeth in vexation. He had come thus far only to have his spirit broken as he witnessed the fall of his comrades. The availability of the stormwater drain in which to take refuge had been the means to turn him into a miserable coward. "A man's no good as long as he's got something to cling to for support, even if he has made up his mind to die. His reason can't be trusted."

It was some time later that he asked Imanishi the reason for his action.

"I can't tell you, really. Just overwhelming fear, I suppose. Fear that you'd be killed and a desire to keep you alive with us." Here was one who had called on his comrades to die, making an about-face at the last moment and calling on those same men to live.

As with a would-be suicide who shuns the idea of a second attempt, to live through the mad moments of the attack took away the desire to die and W.O. Ishikawa and his men made no further attempt to scale the barricades, but lay on the ground still as death. "No need to face the bullets now. We'll die before a firing squad anyway."

The eastern sky brightened and the sun came up as though to signal the end of an episode.

The Australian interpreter was making an announcement. "Listen carefully, you Japanese prisoners who have just rioted. As soldiers we respect the bravery you have shown in the attack but most of you have fallen. Further resistance is useless. Those of you remaining are to throw away your weapons, raise both your hands in the air and make your way back inside the compound. No man who has his hands raised will be fired on. The commandant has given his word that none will be punished. Go back into the compound immediately."

"They're telling us to go back into the compound. Better go, then, I suppose." They slowly got up and made their way into the compound, moving like puppets without a will of their own. Fatigue and cold seemed to make both spirit and body seem remote. Nothing remained but an overwhelming desire to lie down and go to sleep. Tears flowed at the thought of how shameful the men looked marching back into the compound with their hands raised above their heads.

The most spectacular fight was put up by those at the northeast corner of the compound.[2] Sgt. Kikuchi and Aoyama took part in this attack. The usually quiet Sgt. Kikuchi was right in the lead going over the barricades and headed for the watchtower. Because they broke out so early they avoided coming under fire almost altogether, being at a dead angle to the guns. He called together about fifteen men and climbed a tower, whereupon the four guards, taken by surprise, tried to get away but were beaten to death with pieces of iron pipe. With a shout the prisoners took the machinegun, only to find it inoperative because the Australians had removed vital working parts on retreating.

Guards in the nearby towers had no sooner taken in the situation than they directed a withering fire at the captured tower, mowing the captors down in quick succession. The members of this group who had not fallen, now made off up a hill towards the east, on the slopes of which gum-trees grew here and there. The men ran from tree to tree for cover. Since the trunks of the trees were of such a size that an adult could barely encircle them with both arms, four or five men found cover by huddling close together and, for that very reason, became special targets.

A civilian, Shinagawa, lay writhing in agony on the ground after receiving a bullet in the abdomen, a pool of blood around him. Sgt. Kikuchi could bear to look at it no longer and ordered a soldier named Kameda, nearby, to put the wounded man at ease. Kameda failed to get the meaning of the statement.

"Choke him!" the sergeant bawled at the youngster.

Kameda didn't make a move but looked terrified. Kikuchi didn't coerce the lad further and couldn't bring himself to put an end to Shinagawa. Leaving him as he was, Kikuchi and the others ran on up the hill until they reached a place where they were no longer followed by the bullets.

The escapees instinctively made their way to low ground between the hills. There were over twenty men in all, and, following the orders given by the camp leader, they were to select a leader and attempt to attack Australian camps and airfields. But they lacked the energy for that kind of operation. They were limp and weak from the effects of fatigue, cold and hunger. The nightmare of coming out under the hail of bullets had taken so much out of them that they had absolutely no inclination to repeat that kind of action but now gathered together in almost an apathetic way. Those who, a short time ago, had professed themselves ready to make a brave last-ditch stand, had in fact suffered a rout and now indulged in the luxury of this place of rest out of the reach of the bullets.

The men crouched on the ground shivering in the extreme pre-dawn cold.

"I can't stand this cold. Let's light a fire." The one who made the suggestion found himself unopposed. A fire would be sure to reveal their position to the Australians but they no longer cared and anyway they looked like perishing with the cold. A stockman on a white horse appeared over the hill just above them and, on seeing the group of Japanese around the fire, hurriedly wheeled his horse about and made off.

"We've been spotted."

"Can't waste any more time here."

It wasn't really possible to do much at this stage however. To move away from their present location they would have to travel across land where there was scarcely a tree in sight which they could use to take cover.

"What will we do when the enemy comes? Each man try to account for one of them? Or just surrender?" When Sgt. Kikuchi put this to them there wasn't a single answer; a sign that they were in favour of surrender.

An hour later jeeps carrying Australian troops converged on the place from three sides. A truck fitted with wire panels, prison van style, was standing ready and the prisoners were forced, at bayonet-point, to board it.

"What, prisoners again!"

"What did we break out for after all?"

"We don't deserve to be called Japanese soldiers."

"We're a miserable bunch when we compare ourselves with those who died."

Every man was on the point of making such an outburst, but, knowing that such charges would apply also to the speaker, faces were turned aside from each other.

As the truck descended the hill toward the camp, one of the prisoners clambered up the side of the truck and jumped onto the road, not out of a desire to escape but in order to commit suicide. The body bounced two or three times on the frozen surface and was still. It was Sgt. Kikuchi. Nobody had a chance to stop him, the incident having taken place too quickly.

Endnotes

1. "Information was received at Group headquarters early in August that the Japanese were planning a mass outbreak. . . . That night the guards were alert and tense." (*Australia in the War of 1939–45: The Final Campaigns.*)

2. "The strongest group of Japanese—about 400—broke through the wire on the north-west. Here Privates Hardy and Jones punched their way through the prisoners, manned a Vickers gun and fired it until they were knifed and clubbed to death. The Japanese swung the gun round to fire on the Australians' huts but it jammed, and its Japanese crew was killed. . . . Including those who killed themselves, 234 Japanese died and 108 were wounded. Thirty-one killed themselves and 12 were burnt to death in huts set on fire by Japanese. Sixteen of the wounded showed signs of attempted suicide. The 22nd Garrison Battalion lost 3 killed and 3 wounded." (*Australia in the War of 1939–45: The Final Campaigns.*)

The Barking[1]

Ingeborg Bachmann

Ingeborg Bachmann was born on June 25, 1926, in Klagenfort, Austria. She has marked the end of her childhood as the day the Nazi army marched into Klagenfort in 1938, when she was just twelve years old. Despite the Nazi occupation, she was able to graduate from school in 1944 and enter the University of Vienna in 1946.

During her lifetime, Bachmann published several novels and collections of short stories and lectured on the work of other twentieth century writers like Franz Kafka and William Faulkner at universities throughout Europe. She also became politically active, protesting the acquisition of nuclear weapons by the West German army, arguing against a statute of limitations for Nazi war crimes, and demonstrating against the Vietnam War. One of her major concerns, however, was that of the plight of women in a patriarchal society and what she saw as a fascist relationship between the sexes, one in which men exercised control over women, which is depicted in many of her stories.

Bachmann died on October 23, 1973, after her apartment was destroyed by fire and she was badly burned.

Bachmann's short story, "The Barking," relates the story of a husband and his wife, as well as a son and his mother. It explores the dynamics of those relationships and the psychological effects of the feelings of powerlessness of the women.

Old Frau[2] Jordan had been called "old Frau Jordan" for the past three decades because there had been first one and now another young Frau Jordan, and although she did live in Hietzing,[3] she had only a one-room apartment in a dilapidated villa, with a tiny kitchen and no more than half a tub in the bathroom. From her distinguished son Leo, the professor, she received 1,000 schillings[4] per month, and somehow she managed to make do, although those 1,000 schillings had depreciated so much over the last twenty years that she was just barely able to pay an older woman, a certain Frau Agnes, who "looked in" on her twice a week, to tidy up a little, just "the bare minimum." She even saved some of the money for birthday and Christmas presents for her son and grandson from her son's first marriage, whom the first young wife sent over punctually every Christmas to pick up his present. Leo on the other hand was too busy to notice, and since he had become famous and his local prestige had blossomed into international renown, he was busier than ever. Things only changed when the latest young Frau Jordan began to visit the old woman as often as she could, a really nice, likable girl, as the old woman soon admitted to herself, but at each visit she said only: But *Franziska*, it's not right, you shouldn't come so often, it's such a waste. You two surely have enough expenses as it is, *but Leo is just such a good son!*

Franziska always brought something with her, delicacies and sherry, some pastries, because she had guessed that the old woman liked to take a sip now and then and, moreover, attached great importance to having something in the house "for the company." After all, Leo might drop by, and he mustn't notice how much she was missing and that all day long she wondered how to allocate her money and how much she could put aside for presents. Her apartment was meticulously clean, but gave off a *faint "old-woman" smell* which she was not aware of and which put Leo Jordan to flight, apart from the fact that he had no time to lose and *no idea what to talk* about with his eighty-five-year-old mother. Sometimes, seldom, he had been amused—that much Franziska knew—namely, when he was having a relationship with a married woman, because then old Frau Jordan had gone without sleep and made strange, convoluted allusions, trembling for his safety: she believed that the married men whose wives Leo Jordan was living with were dangerous and jealous and bloodthirsty, and she wasn't able to calm down until he married Franziska, who did not have a jealous husband lurking in the bushes but was young and cheerful, an orphan, admittedly not from an educated family, but at least with a brother who had gone to college. Families of the educated classes and educated men in general carried great weight with Frau Jordan, although she didn't do much socializing; she only heard about things. But her son had the right to marry into an educated family. The old woman and Franziska talked almost exclusively about Leo, because he was the only productive topic the two of them had, and Franziska was shown the photo album over and over again. Leo in a stroller, Leo at the beach, and Leo through the years, taking hikes, pasting stamps in his collection, and so on until his military service.

The Leo she came to know through the old woman was a completely different Leo from the man she had married, and when the two women sat drinking their sherry the old woman would say: He was a complicated child, a strange boy, actually you could tell all along that he was destined for great things.

For a while Franziska was happy to hear these assertions, that Leo was so good to his mother and had always done everything conceivable to help her, but then she noticed that something was wrong, and with dismay she realized—the old woman was afraid of her son. It began with the old woman saying, sometimes hastily and parenthetically (she believed it to be a clever tactic that Franziska would never see through because she was blinded by admiration for her husband): But please don't mention a word of it to Leo, you know how concerned he is, it might upset him, whatever you do, please don't tell him that something is wrong with my knee, it's such a little thing, he might get upset about it.

Although Franziska had since learned that Leo never got upset at all, certainly not because of his mother, and only listened to her reports with half an ear, she suppressed this first realization. Unfortunately she had already told him about the knee but swore to the old woman she wouldn't say a word. Leo had reacted with annoyance and then, to placate her, had explained that he really couldn't drive out to Hietzing because of such a trifle. Just tell her—he rattled off some medical terminology—she should buy this and that and do and walk as little as possible. Franziska bought the medication without further comment and claimed in Hietzing that she had secretly spoken with one of her husband's assistants without mentioning any names and that he had given her this advice, although she was at a loss as to how to keep the old woman in bed without the help of a nurse. But she no longer had enough courage to approach Leo about it, because a nurse cost money, and now she was caught in the middle. On the one hand Frau Jordan didn't want anything to do with it, and on the other Leo Jordan—albeit for completely different reasons—simply didn't want to hear about it. When Frau Jordan's knee was swollen, Franziska lied to her husband several times; she drove quickly to Hietzing, allegedly to the hairdresser's, and straightened up the little apartment, bringing all sorts of things with her. She purchased a radio but was uneasy afterward: Leo was bound to notice the expenditure, so she quickly transferred the money back and broke into the meager savings she had set aside for some sort of emergency which would hopefully never arise and could only be a minor emergency at any rate. She and her brother had divided what little remained after the death of their entire family, with the exception of a cottage in southern Carinthia[5] which was slowly falling into disrepair. In the end she called a general practitioner in the neighborhood, and asked him to treat the old woman for a while, paying him out of her own savings. More importantly, she didn't dare reveal to the doctor who she was and who the old woman was, because that would only have hurt Leo's reputation, and protecting Leo's reputation was also in Franziska's best interest. But the old woman thought much more selflessly: there was no way she could ask her famous son to go so far as to come and take a look at her knee. She had used a cane before on occasion, but after this knee problem she really needed it, so Franziska sometimes drove her to town. Shopping with the old woman was a somewhat laborious undertaking: once she had only needed a comb, but there were no combs like the ones "in her day," and although the old woman was polite, standing in the store with erect dignity, she annoyed the little saleswoman by eyeing the price tags suspiciously, unable to refrain from telling Franziska in a clearly audible whisper that the prices here were outrageous, they'd better go somewhere else. The saleswoman, who was in no position to judge how important buying this comb was to the old woman, replied rudely that they wouldn't find this comb cheaper anywhere in town. Franziska launched into embarrassed negotiations with the mother, took the comb the old woman wanted but looked on as costing a fortune and quickly paid for it, saying: Just consider it a Christmas present from us, a present in advance. Prices have really gone up horrendously everywhere. The old woman didn't say a word, she sensed her defeat, but still, if prices really were so outrageous—a comb like this used to cost two schillings and nowadays it cost sixty—well then there wasn't much left for her to understand in this world.

After a while the topic "the good son" had been exhausted and Franziska repeatedly steered the conversation to the old woman herself, because the only thing she knew was that Leo's father had died young of a heart attack or stroke, quite suddenly, on a staircase, and that must have been a long time ago, because if you stopped to figure it out this woman had been a widow for almost half a century. First she had worked for years to raise her only child, and then she was suddenly an old woman nobody cared about anymore. She never spoke about her marriage, only in connection with Leo who had had a very difficult life, without a father, and she was so preoccupied with Leo that she failed to see the parallel to Franziska, who had lost both her parents when she was young. Her son was the only one who could have had a difficult time, and then it turned out that it hadn't been so bad after all, because a distant cousin had paid for his education, a certain Johannes about whom Franziska had heard very little, merely a few derogatory, critical references to some eternal—now aging—loafer who was swimming in money and supposedly led a life of idleness with all its ridiculous affectations. He dabbled a little in art, collected Chinese lacquerware, and was just another one of those freeloaders found in every family. Franziska knew also that he was homosexual, but she was really amazed how someone like Leo, whose very profession obliged him to uphold a neutral and scientific attitude toward homosexuality and phenomena of a quite different magnitude, could go on and on about this cousin as though he had somehow, through his own negligence, fallen prey to works of art, homosexuality, and an inheritance to boot, but at that time Franziska still admired her husband too much to be more than irritated and hurt. With relief she heard from the old woman, in discussing those hard times, that Leo was infinitely grateful and had been a big help to this Johannes, who was then in the throes of a number of personal crises—which were better left untold. The old woman hesitated and then added, because she was, after all, sitting opposite the wife of a psychiatrist: I think you should know that Johannes is sexual.

Franziska controlled herself and suppressed a laugh, it was surely the most daring revelation the old woman had roused herself to in years, but with Franziska she was opening up more and more. She told her how Leo had often given Johannes advice, naturally free of charge, but Johannes was a hopeless case, and if a person didn't have the willpower to change it was understandable that he would be at his wits' end, and from what she heard, Johannes just kept on with it, the same as always. Franziska carefully translated this native story into reality and understood even less why Leo talked about this cousin in such a disparaging and malicious way. At that time the obvious reason escaped her, namely, that Leo was reluctant to be reminded of his mother and his former wives and lovers who were nothing to him but a conspiracy of creditors from whom he could escape only by belittling them to himself and others. His tirades about his first wife were similar: she had been the epitome of everything diabolical, unappreciative and spiteful, traits that had not been revealed in depth until the divorce when her aristocratic father had hired a lawyer for her to secure some of the money for the child, money she'd given him when he was a young doctor and hard times had struck again. It was an alarmingly large sum to Franziska but, as she was told, one could expect nothing less from the "baroness," as Leo ironically called her, because the family had always treated him like an upstart, without having the slightest idea who was dwelling in their midst. It amused him to note that the "baroness" had never remarried and lived in total seclusion. After him she hadn't been able to find another fool—young and gullible and poor, as he had been—who would have married such a deserving Fräulein. She had understood nothing about his work, absolutely nothing, and although she behaved fairly in respect to the agreement about their son, sending him for regular visits and teaching him to respect his father, she obviously did it for no other reason than to prove to the world how generous she was.

The brilliant doctor's rise to fame along the thorny path of suffering had already become Franziska's religion at that time, and again and again she reproached herself with the image of him making his way, against indescribable odds and despite the obstacle that dreadful marriage posed, all the way to the top. And the cross he was forced to bear because of his mother, the financial and moral burden, was no light one for him, but that at least Franziska could take off his shoulders. Although it otherwise might not have occurred to her to spend her free hours with an old woman the time became something special when she thought of Leo: a helping hand, evidence of her love for him, allowing him to devote his undivided attention to his work.

Leo was just too good to her, he told her that she was overdoing it, the way she took care of his mother, a telephone call now and again would have sufficed. For the past few years the old woman had had a telephone which she feared more than loved: she didn't like to talk on the phone and always shouted into the mouthpiece and couldn't hear what the other party said, and besides that, the phone was too expensive, but of course Franziska wasn't to mention that to Leo. Once the old woman—prompted by Franziska and a second glass of sherry—did in fact begin to talk about the old days, the very old days, and it turned out that she wasn't from an educated family, her father had knit gloves and socks in a small factory in Lower Austria and she had been the oldest of eight children, but then she'd had a wonderful time when she took up employment with a Greek family, immensely rich people with a little boy, *the most beautiful child she had ever laid eyes* on, and she was his nursemaid. Being a nursemaid was a really good job, nothing degrading about it, and the Greek's young wife had had servants aplenty, oh yes, she'd had a real stroke of luck, such a good position had been hard to find back then. The child's name was KiKi, at least everyone had called him Kiki. When the old woman began talking about Kiki more and more frequently, remembering every detail— what Kiki had said, how cute and affectionate he was, the walks they'd taken together—her eyes lit up as they never did when she spoke of her own child. Kiki had simply been a little angel, never naughty, she stressed, never naughty at all, and the separation must have been terrible, they hadn't told Kiki that the Fräulein was leaving, and she had cried all night long, and once, years later, she had tried to find out what had become of the family. First she'd heard that they were traveling, then that they were back in Greece, and now she had no idea whatsoever what had happened to Kiki, who must be over sixty by now, yes, over sixty she said pensively, and she had been forced to leave because the Greek family had planned their first major trip and couldn't take her along, and when they left the young wife had given her a wonderful present. The old woman stood up and rummaged in a jewelry box, then showed her the brooch from Kiki's mother, it was the real thing, with diamonds, but she still asked herself today if they hadn't let her go because the wife had noticed that Kiki was more attached to her than to his own mother, she could understand that all right, but it had been the hardest blow of all, and she had never completely recovered from it. Franziska regarded the brooch thoughtfully; perhaps it really was quite valuable, she didn't know much about jewelry, but she was beginning to realize something else: this Kiki must have meant more to the old woman than Leo. She often hesitated to talk about Leo's childhood, or she began only to break off in fright saying abruptly: It was just childish nonsense, you know boys are so hard to raise, he didn't do it on purpose, he was just having such a bad time and it was all I could do to make ends meet. But you get everything back a hundredfold when a child has grown up and made his own way and become so famous, he takes after his father more than me, you know.

Franziska carefully handed back the brooch, and once again the old woman started in fear. Please Franziska, don't mention a word of this to Leo, it could annoy him. I have my plans, you know, if I get sick I could sell it so that I won't become even more of a burden to him. Franziska embraced the old woman with a hug that was both timid and fierce. Don't ever do that, promise me you'll never sell this brooch. You're not a burden to us at all!

On the way home she made one detour after the other, in a state of inner turmoil, this poor woman shouldn't sell her brooch while she and Leo spent money freely, went on trips, entertained. She kept debating what she should say to Leo, but a first, faint alarm sounded inside her, because even though the old woman had her quirks and exaggerated things, she must be right about something, and so in the end she didn't say a word about it at home and only reported cheerfully that his mother was doing very well. But before they left for a conference in London she arranged a contract with a garage which ran a private taxi service, made a downpayment. and said to the old woman: An idea has occurred to us, because you shouldn't walk too far by yourself. Just call a taxi when you want to go out, it hardly costs a thing, it's just a favor from an old patient, but don't say anything about it, especially not to Leo, you know how he is, he doesn't like it when you thank him and everything, and you just ride to town when you need something, and have the taxi wait, but always have Herr Pineider take you, the young one. He doesn't know that his father was one of Leo's patients though, that comes under professional secrecy, you know, I was just there and talked to him, and you have to promise me, for Leo's sake, that you'll take the taxi, it would ease our minds. In the beginning, the old woman made little use of the taxi, and Franziska scolded her for it when she returned from England; her leg had worsened and the old woman had naturally done all her shopping on foot, once even going so far as to take the streetcar into town because one could hardly get anything in Hietzing, and Franziska said firmly, as if to a stubborn child: This is definitely not to happen again.

They exhausted one topic after another: Kiki, the life of a young nurse-maid in Vienna before the First World War and before her marriage, and sometimes it was only Franziska who talked, especially when she had just returned from a trip with Leo, a brilliant talk he'd delivered at the conference, and that he had given her this offprint for his mother. The old woman labored through the title with an effort: "The Significance of Endogenous and Exogenous Factors in Connection with the Occurrence of Paranoid and Depressive Psychoses in Former Concentration Camp Inmates and Refugees." Franziska assured her it was merely the groundwork for a much larger study he was working on, and he was even letting her help him with it. It would probably become the most significant and the first really important book in the field. A work of incalculable impact.

The old woman was strangely mute, surely she didn't understand the implications of these studies, maybe nothing at all of what her son was doing. Then she said, surprisingly: I hope he won't make too many enemies with it, here in Vienna, and then there's that other thing . . .

Franziska grew agitated: But that's exactly the point, that would be a very good thing, it's a provocation, too, and Leo isn't afraid of anyone, for him it's the only thing that counts, that has a purpose far beyond its scientific significance.

Yes, of course, the old woman said quickly, and he knows how to defend himself, and if you're famous you always have enemies. I was just thinking about Johannes, but that's so long ago now. Did you know that he was in a concentration camp for a year and a half before the war ended? Franziska was surprised, she hadn't known, but she failed to see the connection. The old woman didn't want to say any more but then continued: It meant a certain amount of danger for Leo, having a relative who, well, you know what I mean. Yes, of course, said Franziska, still somewhat confused; sometimes the old woman had such a roundabout way of saying things without really saying them, and she couldn't make head or tail of it, although suddenly she was bursting with pride that a member of Leo's family had been through something so terrible and that Leo, in his tactful, modest way, had never said anything about it to her, not even about the danger he must have faced as a young doctor. That afternoon the old woman didn't want to go on talking; she merely asked disjointedly: Do you hear it, too?

What?

The dogs, the old woman said. There were never so many dogs in Hietzing, I've heard them barking again, and they bark at night, too. Frau Schönthal next door has a poodle now. It doesn't bark much though, it's such a nice dog, I see her almost every day when I go shopping, but we only say hello, her husband doesn't have much of an education.

Franziska drove home as quickly as she could; this time she wanted to ask Leo if there was anything to the fact that his mother had suddenly begun talking about dogs, if it was an alarming symptom, maybe it had something to do with her age. She had also noticed that the old woman had been upset once about ten schillings which had been lying on the table and then disappeared when Frau Agnes left, all this excitement about ten missing schillings, certainly she had only imagined it anyway, weren't those all signs of the process of aging? It couldn't possibly have been the cleaning woman, she was what people in certain circles—that is, in better circles—called a "God-fearing" woman who came more out of pity than for the money, which she didn't need anyway—she did it as a favor and nothing more, And old Frau Jordan's pitiful presents—an ancient, threadbare purse or some other useless paraphernalia—would hardly have induced Frau Agnes to come; she had realized long ago that she had nothing to expect from the old woman or from her son, and she knew nothing of Franziska's enthusiastic plans for improving the situation; Franziska had chided the old woman as though she were a child, because she didn't want to lose this valuable help over a bout of senile obstinacy and an unfounded suspicion.

More and more often she found the old woman at the window when she arrived, and they no longer sat together when Franziska came to drink sherry and nibble on pastries. The business with the dogs continued, although at the same time her hearing problem grew worse, and Franziska was at a loss. Something had to be done, and Leo, whom she bothered with none of this, was not going to avoid devoting some attention to his mother one of these days. Only then things started becoming complicated between Leo and herself, and she discovered that he had so intimidated her that she was afraid of him. But at least once, in a fit of her old courage, she overcame her inexplicable fear and suggested at dinner: Why don't we invite your mother to come and stay with us, we have enough room, and then our Rosi could always be with her and you would never have to worry, besides, she's so quiet and undemanding, she would never disturb you, and certainly not me, I'm suggesting it for your sake because I know how much you worry. Leo was in a good mood that evening and secretly happy about something. She didn't realize what it was but had decided to make use of the opportunity, and he answered, laughing: What an idea, you have no feel for the situation, my dear, you can't uproot an elderly person after a while, it would only depress her and she needs her freedom, she's a strong woman who has lived alone for decades. You don't know her the way I do, she would die of fright here, just from the kind of people who come over. She'd probably debate for hours on end whether to use the bathroom, out of fear that one of us just might want to use it. Come on, my little Franziska, please don't make such a face, I think your impulse is touching and admirable, but that wonderful idea of yours would be the death of her. Believe me, it's just that I happen to know more about these things.

But this business with the dogs . . . ? Franziska began to stutter, she hadn't wanted to talk about it and would gladly have immediately taken back what she'd said. She was no longer capable of putting her apprehension into words.

What, her husband asked in a completely different tone of voice, she doesn't still want a mutt, does she? I don't understand, Franziska answered. Why should she—you don't mean she wants to have a dog, do you?

Of course I do, and I'm more than glad that this childish interlude has blown over so quickly, at her age she just couldn't handle a dog, she should take care of herself, that's more important to me, a dog is such a nuisance, she has no idea what they would mean, with her advancing senility. She never said anything about it, Franziska replied half-heartedly, I don't think she wants a dog. I wanted to say something entirely different, but it's not important, sorry. Would you like a cognac, are you going to work later, should I type anything for you?

At her next visit Franziska didn't know how to persuade the old woman, who was always on the alert, to give her answers she needed to know. She approached the subject in a roundabout way, remarking casually: Incidentally, I saw Frau Schönthal's dog today, really a cute dog, I like poodles a lot, actually all animals, because I grew up in the country, you know, we always had dogs, I mean my grandparents and everyone in the village, and cats, too, of course. Wouldn't it be good for you to have a dog or a cat, now that you have trouble reading. I mean, certainly that kind of thing passes, but I for one would absolutely love to have a dog. But you know, in the city it's just a bother and not really fair to the dog, but here in Hietzing, where it can frisk around in the yard and you can go for walks . . .

The old woman exclaimed in agitation: A dog, no, no, I don't want a dog! Franziska realized she had done something wrong, but felt at the same time that she hadn't offended the old woman as she might have had she suggested a parrot or canaries: it must have been something else entirely that had put her in such a state of agitation. After a while the old woman said very quietly: Nuri was a really nice dog, and I got along well with him, that was, let me think, it must have been five years ago, but then I had to give him away, to a home or a place where they resell them. Leo doesn't like dogs. No, what am I saying, it was different, there was something in that dog I can't really understand, he couldn't stand Leo, he always jumped at him and barked madly whenever Leo made the slightest move toward the door, and then once he almost bit him, and Leo was so indignant, of course that's understandable, when a dog is that wild, but he was never like that otherwise, not even with strangers, and then naturally I gave him away. I couldn't let Leo be barked at and bitten by Nuri, no, that would have been too much,

Leo should be able to feel at home when he visits me and not have to get angry about some poorly trained dog.

Franziska thought that, although there was no longer a dog who jumped at him and disliked him, Leo came seldom enough as it was, and even less often since Franziska came instead. How long had it been anyway since his last visit? Once the three of them had gone for a short ride along the Weinstrasse and into the Helenenthal and lunched at an inn with his mother; otherwise Franziska always came alone.

Be sure not to say anything to Leo, though, that business with Nuri really hurt his feelings, he's very sensitive, you know, and to this day I can't forgive myself for being so selfish as to want to have Nuri, but old people are very selfish, dear Franziska, you can't understand that yet, you're still so young and good, but when you're very old you get all these selfish desires, and you can't just let yourself give in to them. What would have become of me if Leo hadn't taken care of me, his father died all of a sudden like that and there was no time to make any arrangements, and there wasn't any money, either, my husband was a little careless, no, not a spendthrift, but he had a hard time of it and didn't have much of a knack with money, Leo doesn't take after him in that respect. In those days I could still work, the boy was a reason to keep going, and I was still young, but what would I do nowadays? My one fear has always been having to go to an old people's home, but Leo would never stand for that, and if I didn't have this apartment I'd have to go to some home, and I guess a dog isn't worth all that. Franziska listened to her, clenched up inside, and she said to herself: So that's it, that's it, she gave her dog away for his sake. And she asked herself: What kind of people are we?—because she was incapable of thinking: What kind of a man is my husband!—we're just so cruel, and she thinks she's selfish, and all the time we have everything we want! In order to hide her tears she quickly unpacked a small package from Meinl, little things, and acted as though she hadn't understood. Oh, by the way, I'm so scatterbrained today, I've only brought you the tea and coffee and a little smoked salmon and Russian salad. Actually it doesn't go together all that well, but I was really flustered at the store because Leo is leaving and one of the manuscripts isn't finished yet. But he'll give you a call tonight, and he'll be back in a week anyway.

He needs a break, the old woman said, see to it that he gets one if you can, you two haven't had any vacation at all yet this year. Franziska said brightly: That's a good idea, I'll convince him some way or another, I just need to think of a strategy, but thanks a lot, that's really a good piece of advice, he's constantly overworked, you know, and at some point I have to make him slow down.

What Franziska did not know was that this was her last visit to the old woman and she no longer needed the strategy, because other things came to pass, events of such hurricane force that she almost forgot the old woman and a great many other things as well.

In her fear, the old woman didn't ask her son on the phone why Franziska had stopped coming. She was worried, but her son sounded cheerful and unconcerned, and once he even came over and stayed for twenty minutes. He didn't touch the pastries, he didn't finish the sherry and he didn't talk about Franziska, but he did talk quite a bit about himself, and that made her ecstatic because it had been such a long time since he had spoken about himself. So he was leaving on vacation now, he needed a break, but the word "Mexico" gave the old woman a mild shock, wasn't that the place where they had scorpions and revolutions and savages and earth-quakes, but he laughed reassuringly, kissed her and promised to write. He sent a few postcards, which she read religiously. Franziska hadn't added her regards. Once Franziska called her from Carinthia. Really, the money these young people throw out the window! Franziska had only called to ask if everything was okay. Then they talked about Leo, but the old woman kept' shouting at the most inappropriate times: It's getting too expensive, child, but Franziska kept talking, yes, she had finally succeeded, he was finally taking a break, and she had had to go to her brother's, there was something to settle here, that was why she hadn't been able to accompany Leo. Family matters in Carinthia. Because of the house. Then the old woman received a strange envelope with a few lines from Franziska. She didn't say anything, just sent her regards and wrote that she would like her to have this photo she had taken herself, the photograph was of Leo, apparently on the Sem-mering Pass,[6] laughing in a snowy landscape in front of a large hotel. The old woman decided not to say anything to Leo; he wouldn't have asked her anyway. She hid the photograph under the brooch in her jewelry box.

She could no longer read books and was bored by the radio; newspapers were all she wanted, and Frau Agnes got them for her. It took her hours to decipher them, she read the obituaries and always felt a certain satisfaction when someone younger than herself had passed away. Well, look at that, Pro-fessor Haderer too, he could hardly have been more than seventy. Frau Schön-thal's mother had died, too, of cancer, she wasn't even sixty-five. The old woman stiffly offered her condolences in the grocery store and didn't even look at the poodle, and then she went home and stood at the window. She slept more than old people are said to sleep, but she often awoke, only to hear the dogs again. She was startled whenever the cleaning woman came: since Franziska's visits had ended, it bothered her when anyone came over, and she had the impression that she was changing. Now she actually was frightened of suddenly collapsing in the street or losing control of herself when she had to go to town for something, and so she obediently called young Herr Pineider, who drove her around. And she became accustomed to this small precaution for her own safety. She completely lost her sense of time, and when Leo once came by to see her, deeply tanned, she no longer knew if he was returning from Mexico or when he had been there at all. But she was careful not to ask, and gathered from something he said that he had just arrived from Ischia,[7] back from a trip to Italy. Confused, she said: Good, good. That was good for you. And while he was telling her something the dogs began to bark, several of them, all at once, very near, and she was so completely encircled by the barking and a very gentle, gentle terror that she was no longer afraid of her son. The fear of an entire lifetime suddenly left her.

When he said on his way out: Next time I'll bring Elfi over, you have to meet her one of these days! she had no idea what he was talking about. Wasn't he married to Franziska anymore, how long had it been, how many wives was that now anyway, she could no longer remember how long he had lived with Franziska and when, and she said: Go ahead and bring her over. Fine. Whatever is best for you. The barking was so close now that for an instant she was certain that Nuri was with her again and would jump at him and bark. She wished he would finally leave, she wanted to be alone. She thanked him out of habit, just in case, and he asked in astonishment: Whatever for? Now I really did go and forget to bring you my book after all. A phenomenal success. I'll have it sent.

Well then, thank you so much my child. Send it over, but unfortunately your dumb old mother can hardly read anymore and doesn't understand much anyway.

She let him embrace her and found herself alone again surrounded by the barking. It came from every garden and house in Hietzing, an invasion of the beasts had begun, the dogs came closer, barking to her, and she stood erect, as always, no longer dreaming of the time with Kiki and the Greeks, no longer thinking of the day when the last ten schillings had disappeared and Leo had lied to her. Instead she redoubled her efforts to hide things better, wishing she could throw them away, especially the brooch and the photograph, so that Leo wouldn't find anything after she died. But she couldn't think of a good hiding place, maybe the bucket with the scraps, but she trusted Frau Agnes less and less, too, because she would have had to give her the rubbish, and she suspected that the woman would rummage through it and find the brooch. Once she said, a little too harshly: At least you could give the bones and the leftovers to the dogs.

The cleaning woman looked at her in amazement and asked: What dogs? To the dogs, of course, insisted the old woman in an imperious tone, I want the dogs to have them!

She was a suspicious looking creature, a thief. She probably took the bones home with her.

To the dogs, I said. Can't you understand me, are you deaf or something? No wonder, at your age.

Then the barking diminished, and she thought: someone has chased the dogs off or given them away, because now it was no longer that same powerful, recurrent, barking. The fainter the barking, the more adamant she became: she was only biding her time until the louder barking resumed. One had to be able to wait, and she could wait. All at once it was no longer a barking sound, although there was no doubt it came from the dogs in the neighborhood. It wasn't a growling either, just now and again the great, wild triumphant howling of a single dog, then a whimpering, the faint barking of all the others fading into the distance.

One day nearly two years after the death of his sister Franziska, Dr. Martin Ranner received a bill from a company by the name of Pineider for taxi services listed separately by date, for which Frau Franziska Jordan had made a downpayment and signed a contract. But because only very few trips had been made while Franziska was alive and the majority after her death he called the company for an explanation of this mysterious bill. Although the explanation actually explained very little, he had no desire to call his former brother-in-law or ever see him again, so he paid the fares, in installments, for a woman he had never known and never had anything to do with. He came to the conclusion that the old Frau Jordan must have passed away some time ago; the company had let several months go by since her last trip, perhaps out of reverence, before asserting its claims.

Endnotes

1. Translated by Mary Fran Gilbert.
2. Mrs. (German).
3. A suburb west of Vienna, Austria.
4. The basic Austrian unit of currency.
5. A southwestern province of Austria.
6. In the Alps in southern Austria, known as a tourist resort and center for winder sports.
7. An island vacation spot north of the Bay of Naples.

This Way for the Gas, Ladies and Gentlemen

Tadeusz Borowski

All of us walk around naked. The delousing is finally over, and our striped suits are back from the tanks of Cyclone B solution, an efficient killer of lice in clothing and of men in gas chambers. Only the inmates in the blocks cut off from ours by the "Spanish goats" I still have nothing to wear. But all the same, all of us walk around naked: the heat is unbearable. The camp has been sealed off tight. Not a single prisoner, not one solitary louse, can sneak through the gate. The labour Kommandos have stopped working. All day, thousands of naked men shuffle up and down the roads, cluster around the squares, or lie against the walls and on top of the roofs. We have been sleeping on plain boards, since our mattresses and blankets are still being disinfected. From the rear block-houses we have a view of the F.K.L.—*Frauen Konzentration Lager*,[2] there too the delousing is in full swing. Twenty-eight thousand women have been stripped naked and driven out of the barracks. Now they swarm around the large yard between the blockhouses.

The heat rises, the hours are endless. We are without even our usual diversion: the wide roads leading to the crematoria are empty. For several days now, no new transports have come in. Part of "Canada"[3] has been liquidated and detailed to a labour Kommando—one of the very toughest—at Harmenz. For there exists in the camp a special brand of justice based on envy: when the rich and mighty fall, their friends see to it that they fall to the very bottom. And Canada, our Canada, which smells not of maple forests but of French perfume, has amassed great fortunes and currency from all over Europe.

Several of us sit on the top bunk, our legs dangling over the edge. We slice the neat loaves of crisp, crunchy bread. It is a bit coarse to the taste, the kind that stays fresh for days. Sent all the way from Warsaw—only a week ago my mother held this white loaf in her hands . . . dear Lord . . .

We unwrap the bacon, the onion, we open a can of evaporated milk. Henri, the fat Frenchman, dreams aloud of the French wine brought by the transports from Strasbourg, Paris, Marseille . . . Sweat streams down his body.

"Listen, *mon ami,*[4] next time we go up on the loading ramp, I'll bring you real champagne. You haven't tried it before, eh?"

"No. But you'll never be able to smuggle it through the gate, so stop teasing. Why not try and 'organize' some shoes for me instead—you know, the perforated kind, with a double sole, and what about that shirt you promised me long ago?"

"*Patience, patience.* When the new transports come, I'll bring all you want. We'll be going on the ramp again!"

"And what if there aren't any more 'cremo' transports?" I say spitefully. "Can't you see how much easier life is becoming around here: no limit on packages, no more beatings? You even write letters home . . . One hears all kind of talk, and, dammit, they'll run out of people!"

"Stop talking nonsense." Henri's serious fat face moves rhythmically, his mouth is full of sardines. We have been friends for a long time, but I do not even know his last name. "Stop talking nonsense," he repeats, swallowing with effort. "They can't run out of people, or we'll starve to death in this blasted camp. All of us live on what they bring."

"All? We have our packages . . ."

"Sure, you and your friend, and ten other friends of yours. Some of you Poles get packages. But what about us, and the Jews, and the Russkis? And what if we had no food, no 'organization' from the transports, do you think you'd be eating those packages of yours in peace? We wouldn't let you!"

"You would, you'd starve to death like the Greeks. Around here, whoever has grub, has power."

"Anyway, you have enough, we have enough, so why argue?"

Right, why argue? They have enough, I have enough, we eat together and we sleep on the same bunks. Henri slices the bread, he makes a tomato salad. It tastes good with the commissary mustard.

Below us, naked sweat-drenched men crowd the narrow barracks aisles or lie packed in eights and tens in the lower bunks. Their nude, withered bodies stink of sweat and excrement; their cheeks are hollow. Directly beneath me, in the bottom bunk, lies a rabbi. He has covered head with a piece of rag torn off a blanket and reads from a Hebrew prayer book (there is no shortage of this type of literature at the camp), wailing loudly, monotonously.

"Can't somebody shut him up? He's been raving as if he'd caught God himself by the feet."

"I don't feel like moving. Let him rave. They'll take him to the oven that much sooner."

"Religion is the opium of the people," Henri, who is a Communist and a *rentier*,[5] says sententiously. "If they didn't believe in God and eternal life, they'd have smashed the crematoria long ago."

"Why haven't you done it then?"

The question is rhetorical; the Frenchman ignores it.

"Idiot," he says simply, and stuffs a tomato in his mouth.

Just as we finish our snack, there is a sudden commotion at the door. The Muslims[6] scurry in fright to the safety of their bunks, a messenger runs into the Block Elder's shack. The Elder, his face solemn, steps out at once.

"Canada! *Antreten!*[7] There's a transport coming!"

"Great God!" yells Henri, jumping off the bunk. He swallows the rest of his tomato, snatches his coat, screams "*Raus*"[8] at the men below, and in a flash is at the door. We can hear a scramble in the other bunks. Canada is leaving for the ramp.

"Henri, the shoes!" I call after him.

"*Keine Angst!*"[9] he shouts back, already outside.

I proceed to put away the food. I tie a piece of rope around the suitcase where the onions and the tomatoes from my garden in Warsaw mingle with Portuguese sardines, bacon from Lublin (that's from my brother), and authentic sweetmeats from Salonica. I tie it all up, pull on my trousers, and slide off the bunk.

"*Platz!*"[10] yell, pushing my way through the Greeks. They step aside. At the door I bump into Henri.

"*Was ist los?*"[11]

"Want to come with us on the ramp?"

"Sure, why not?"

"Come along then, grab your coat! We're short a few men. I've already told the Kapo," and he shoves me out of the barracks door.

We line up. Someone has marked down our numbers, someone up ahead yells, "March, march," and now we are running towards the gate accompanied by the shouts of a multilingual throng that is already being pushed back to the barracks. Not everybody is lucky enough to be going on the ramp . . . We have almost reached the gate. *Links, zwei, drei, vier! Mützen ab!*[12] Erect, arms stretched stiffly along our hips, we march past the gate briskly, smartly, almost grace-fully. A sleepy S.S. man with a large pad in his hand checks us off, waving us ahead in groups of five.

"*Hundert!*"[13] he calls after we have all passed.

"*Stimmt!*"[14] hoarse answer from out front.

We march fast, almost at a run. There are guards all around, young men with automatics. We pass camp II B, then some deserted barracks and a clump of unfamiliar green—apple and pear trees. We cross the circle of watchtowers and, running, burst on to the highway. We have arrived. Just a few more yards. There surrounded by trees, is the ramp.

A cheerful little station, very much like any other provincial railway stop: a small square framed by tall chestnuts and paved with yellow gravel. Not far off, beside the road, squats a tiny wooden shed, uglier and more flimsy than the ugliest and flimsiest railway shack; farther along lie stacks of old rails, heaps of wooden beams, barracks parts, bricks, paving stones. This is where they load freight for Birkenau: supplies for the construction of the camp, and people for the gas chambers. Trucks drive around, load up lumber, cement, people—a regular daily routine.

And now the guards are being posted along the rails, across the beams, in the green shade of the Silesian chestnuts, to form a tight circle around the ramp. They wipe the sweat from their faces and sip out of their canteens. It is unbearably hot; the sun stands motionless at its zenith.

"Fall out!"

We sit down in the narrow streaks of shade along the stacked rails. The hungry Greeks (several of them managed to come along, God only knows how) rummage underneath the rails. One of them finds some pieces of mildewed bread, another a few half-rotten sardines. They eat.

"*Schweinedreck*,"[15] spits a young, tall guard with corn-coloured hair and dreamy blue eyes. "For God's sake, any minute you'll have so much food to stuff down your guts, you'll bust!" He adjusts his gun, wipes his face with a handkerchief.

"Hey you, fatso!" His boot lightly touches Henri's shoulder. "*Pass mal auf*"[16] want a drink?"

"Sure, but I haven't got any marks," replies the Frenchman with a profes-sional air.

"*Schade*, too bad."

"Come, come, Herr Posten, isn't my word good enough any more? Haven't we done business before? How much?"

"One hundred. *Gemacht?*"[17]

"*Gemacht.*"

We drink the water, lukewarm and tasteless. It will be paid for by the people who have not yet arrived.

"Now you be careful," says Henri, turning to me. He tosses away the empty bottle. It strikes the rails and bursts into tiny fragments. "Don't take any money, they might be checking. Anyway, who the hell needs money? You've got enough to eat. Don't take suits, either, or they'll think you're planning to escape. Just get a shirt, silk only, with a collar. And a vest. And if you find something to drink, don't bother calling me. I know how to shift for myself, but you watch your step or they'll let you have it."

"Do they beat you up here?"

"Naturally. You've got to have eyes in your ass. *Arschaugen.*[18]

Around us sit the Greeks, their jaws working greedily, like huge human insects. They munch on stale lumps of bread. They are restless, wondering what will happen next. The sight of the large beams and the stacks of rails has them worried. They dislike carrying heavy loads.

"*Was wir arbeiten?*"[19] they ask.

"*Niks. Transport kommen, alles Krematorium, compris?*"[20]

"*Alles verstehen,*"[21] they answer in crematorium Esperanto. All is well—they will not have to move the heavy rails or carry the beams.

In the meantime, the ramp has become increasingly alive with activity, increasingly noisy. The crews are being divided into those who will open and unload the arriving cattle cars and those who will be posted by the wooden steps. They receive instructions on how to proceed most efficiently. Motor cycles drive up, delivering S.S. officers, bemedalled, glittering brass, beefy men with highly polished boots and shiny brutal faces. Some have brought their briefcases, others hold thin, flexible whips. This gives them an air of military readiness and agility. They walk in and out of the commissary—for the miserable little shack by the road serves as their commissary, where in the summertime they drink mineral water, *Studentenquelle,* and where in winter they can warm up with a glass of hot wine. They greet each other in the state-approved way, raising an arm Roman fashion, then shake hands cordially, exchange warm smiles, discuss mail from home their children, their families. Some stroll majestically on the ramp. The silver squares on their collars glitter, the gravel crunches under their boots, their bamboo, whips snap impatiently.

We lie against the rails in the narrow streaks of shade, breathe unevenly, occasionally exchange a few words in our various tongues, and gaze listlessly at the majestic men in green uniforms, at the green trees, and at the church steeple of a distant village.

"The transport is coming," somebody says. We spring to our feet, all eyes turn in one direction. Around the bend, one after another, the cattle cars begin rolling in. The train backs into the station, a conductor leans out, waves his hand, blows a whistle. The locomotive whistles back with a shrieking noise, puffs, the train rolls slowly alongside the ramp. In the tiny barred windows appear pale wilted exhausted human faces, terror-stricken women with tangled hair, unshaven men. They gaze at the station in silence. And then, suddenly, there is a stir inside the cars and a pounding against the wooden boards.

"Water! Air!"—weary, desperate cries.

Heads push through the windows, mouths gasp frantically for air. They draw a few breaths, then disappear; others come in their place, then also disappear. The cries and moans grow louder.

A man in a green uniform covered with more glitter than any of the others jerks his head impatiently, his lips twist in annoyance. He inhales deeply, then with a rapid gesture throws his cigarette away and signals to the guard. The guard removes the automatic from his shoulder, aims, sends a series of shots along the train. All is quiet now. Meanwhile, the trucks have arrived, steps are being drawn up, and the Canada men stand ready at their posts by the train doors. The S.S. officer with the briefcase raises his hand.

"Whoever takes gold, or anything at all besides food, will be shot for stealing Reich property. Understand? *Verstanden?*"

"*Jawohl!*"[22] we answer eagerly.

"*Also los!* Begin!"

The bolts crack, the doors fall open. A wave of fresh air rushes inside the train. People . . . inhumanly crammed, buried under incredible heaps of luggage, suitcases, trunks, packages, crates, bundles of every description (everything that had been their past and was to start their future). Monstrously squeezed together, they have fainted from heat, suffocated, crushed one another. Now they push towards the opened doors, breathing like fish cast out on the sand.

"Attention! Out, and take your luggage with you! Take out everything. Pile all your stuff near the exits. Yes, your coats too. It is summer. March to the left. Understand?"

"Sir, what's going to happen to us?" They jump from the train on to the gravel, anxious, worn-out.

"Where are you people from?"

"Sosnowiec-Bedzin. Sir, what's going to happen to us?" They repeat the question stubbornly, gazing into our tired eyes.

"I don't know. I don't understand Polish."

It is the camp law: people going to their death must be deceived to the very end. This is the only permissible form of charity. The heat is treamendous. The sun hangs directly over our heads, the white, hot sky quivers, the air vibrates, an occasional breeze feels like a sizzling blast from a furnace. Our lips are parched, the mouth fills with the salty taste of blood, the body is weak and heavy from lying in the sun. Water!

A huge, multicoloured wave of people loaded down with luggage pours from the train like a blind, mad river trying to find a new bed. But before they have a chance to recover, before they can draw a breath of fresh air and look at the sky, bundles are snatched from their hands, coats ripped off their backs, their purses and umbrellas taken away.

"But please, sir, it's for the sun, I cannot . . ."

"*Verboten!*"[23] one of us barks through clenched teeth. There is an S.S. man standing behind your back, calm, efficient, watchful.

"*Meine Herrschaften*,[24] this way, ladies and gentlemen, try not to throw your things around, please. Show some goodwill," he says courteously, his restless hands playing with the slender whip.

"Of course, of course," they answer as they pass, and now they walk alongside the train somewhat more cheerfully. A woman reaches down quickly to pick up her handbag. The whip flies, the woman screams, stumbles, and falls under the feet of the surging crowd. Behind her, a child cries in a thin little voice "Mamele!"—a very small girl with tangled black curls.

The heaps grow. Suitcases, bundles, blankets, coats, handbags that open as they fall, spilling coins, gold, watches; mountains of bread pile up at the exits, heaps of marmalade, jams, masses of meat, sausages; sugar spills on the gravel. Trucks, loaded with people, start up with a deafening roar and drive off amidst the wailing and screaming of the women separated from their children, and the stupefied silence of the men left behind. They are the ones who had been ordered to step to the right—the healthy and the young who will go to the camp. In the end, they too will not escape death, but first they must work.

Trucks leave and return, without interruption, as on a monstrous conveyor belt. A Red Cross van drives back and forth, incessantly: it transports the gas that will kill these people. The enormous cross on the hood, red as blood, seems to dissolve in the sun.

The Canada men at the trucks cannot stop for a single moment, even to catch their breath. They shove the people up the steps, pack them in tightly, sixty per truck, more or less. Near by stands a young, cleanshaven "gentleman," an S.S. officer with a notebook in his hand. For each departing truck he enters a mark; sixteen gone means one thousand people, more or less. The gentleman is calm, precise. No truck can leave without a signal from him, or a mark in his notebook: *Ordnung muss sein*.[25] The marks swell into thousands, the thousands into whole transports, which afterwards we shall simply call "from Salonica," "from Strasbourg," "from Rotterdam." This one will be called "Sosnowiec-Bedzin." The new prisoners from Sosnowiec-Bedzin will receive serial numbers 131–2—thousand, of course, though afterwards we shall simply say 131–2, for short.

The transports swell into weeks, months, years. When the war is over, they will count up the marks in their notebooks—all four and a half million of them. The bloodiest battle of the war, the greatest victory of the strong, united Germany. *Ein Reich, ein Volk, ein Führer*[26] and four crematoria.

The train has been emptied. A thin, pock-marked S.S. man peers inside, shakes his head in disgust, and motions to our group, pointing his finger at the door.

"*Rein*. Clean it up!"

We climb inside. In the corners amid human excrement and abandoned wrist-watches he squashed, trampled infants, naked little monsters with enormous heads and bloated bellies. We carry them out like chickens, holding several in each hand.

"Don't take them to the trucks, pass them on to the women," says the S.S. man, lighting a cigarette. His cigarette lighter is not working properly; he examines it carefully.

"Take them, for God's sake!" I explode as the women run from me in horror, covering their eyes.

The name of God sounds strangely pointless, since the women and the infants will go on the trucks, every one of them, without exception. We all know what this means, and we look at each other with hate and horror.

"What, you don't want to take them?" asks the pock-marked S.S. man with a note of surprise and reproach in his voice, and reaches for his revolver.

"You mustn't shoot, I'll carry them." A tall grey-haired woman takes the little corpses out of my hands and for an instant gazes straight into my eyes.

"My poor boy," she whispers and smiles at me. Then she walks away, staggering along the path. I lean against the side of the train. I am terribly tired. Someone pulls at my sleeve.

"*En avant*, to the rails, come on!"

I look up, but the face swims before my eyes, dissolves, huge and transparent, melts into the motionless trees and the sea of people . . . I blink rapidly: Henri.

"Listen, Henri, are we good people?"

"That's stupid. Why do you ask?"

"You see, my friend, you see, I don't know why, but I am furious, simply furious with these people—furious because I must be here because of them. I feel no pity. I am not sorry they're going to the gas chamber. Damn them all! I could throw myself at them, beat them with my fists. It must be pathological, I just can't understand . . ."

"Ah, on the contrary, it is natural, predictable, calculated. The ramp exhausts you, you rebel—and the easiest way to relieve your hate is to turn against someone weaker. Why, I'd even call it healthy. It's simple logic, *compris?*"[27] He props himself up comfortably against the heap of rails. "Look at the Greeks, they know how to make the best of it! They stuff their bellies with anything they find. One of them has just devoured a full jar of marmalade."

"Pigs! Tomorrow half of them will die of the shits."

"Pigs? You've been hungry."

"Pigs!" I repeat furiously. I close my eyes. The air is filled with ghastly cries, the earth trembles beneath me. I can feel sticky moisture on my eyelids. My throat is completely dry.

The morbid procession streams on and on—trucks growl like mad dogs. I shut my eyes tight, but I can still see corpses dragged from the train, trampled infants, cripples piled on top of the dead, wave after wave . . . freight cars roll in, the heaps of clothing, suitcases, and bundles grow, people climb out, look at the sun, take a few breaths, beg for water, get into the trucks, drive away. And again freight cars roll in, again people . . . The scenes become confused in my mind—I am not sure if all of this is actually happening, or if I am dreaming. There is a humming inside my head; I feel that I must vomit.

Henri tugs at my arm.

"Don't sleep, we're off to load up the loot."

All the people are gone. In the distance, the last few trucks roll along the road in clouds of dust, the train has left, several S.S. officers promenade up and down the ramp. The silver glitters on their collars. Their boots shine, the red, beefy faces shine. Among them there is a woman—only now I realize she has been here all along—withered, flat-chested, bony, her thin, colourless hair pulled back and tied in a "Nordic" knot; her hands are in the pockets in her wide skirt. With a rat-like, resolute smile glued on her thin lips she sniffs around the corners of the ramp. She detests feminine beauty with the hatred of a woman who is herself repulsive, and knows it. Yes, I have seen her many times before and I know her well: she is the commandant of the F.K.L. She has come to look over the new crop of women, for some of them, instead of going on the trucks, will go on foot—to the concentration camp. There our boys, the barbers from Zauna, will shave their heads and will have a good laugh at their "outside world" modesty.

We proceed to load the loot. We lift huge trunks, heave them on to the trucks. There they are arranged in stacks, packed tightly. Occasionally somebody slashes one open with a knife, for pleasure or in search of vodka and perfume. One of the crates falls open; suits, shirts, books drop out on ground . . . I pick up a small, heavy package. I unwrap it—gold, about two handfuls, bracelets, rings, brooches, diamonds . . .

"*Gib hier*,"[28] an S.S. man says calmly, holding up his briefcase already full of gold and colourful foreign currency. He locks the case, hands it to an officer, takes another, an empty one, and stands by the next truck, waiting. The gold will go to the Reich.

It is hot, terribly hot. Our throats are dry, each word hurts. Anything for a sip of water! Faster, faster, so that it is over, so that we may rest. At last we are done, all the trucks have gone. Now we swiftly clean up the remaining dirt: there must be "no trace left of the *Schweinerei*."[29] But just as the last truck disappears behind the trees and we walk, finally, to rest in the shade, a shrill whistle sounds around the bend. Slowly, terribly slowly, a train rolls in, the engine whistles back with a deafening shriek. Again weary, pale faces at the windows, flat as though cut out of paper, with huge, feverishly burning eyes. Already trucks are pulling up, already the composed gentleman with his notebook is at his post, and the S.S. men emerge from the commissary carrying briefcases for the gold and money. We unseal the train doors.

It is impossible to control oneself any longer. Brutally we tear suitcases from their hands, impatiently pull off their coats. Go on, go on, vanish! They go, they vanish. Men, women, children. Some of them know.

Here is a woman—she walks quickly, but tries to appear calm. A small child with a pink cherub's face runs after her and, unable to keep up, stretches out his little arms and cries: "Mama! Mama!"

"Pick up your child, woman!"

"It's not mine, sir, not mine!" she shouts hysterically and runs on, covering her face with her hands. She wants to hide, she wants to reach those who will not ride the trucks, those who will go on foot, those who will stay alive. She is young, healthy, good-looking, she wants to live.

But the child runs after her, wailing loudly: "Mama, mama, don't leave me!"

"It's not mine, not mine, no!"

Andrei, a sailor from Sevastopol, grabs hold of her. His eyes are glassy from vodka and the heat. With one powerful blow he knocks her off her feet, then, as she falls, takes her by the hair and pulls her up again. His face twitches with rage.

"Ah, you bloody Jewess! So you're running from your own child! I'll show you, you whore!" His huge hand chokes her, he lifts her in the air and heaves her on to the truck like a heavy sack of grain.

"Here! And take this with you, bitch!" and he throws the child at her feet.

"*Gut gemacht*, good work. That's the way to deal with degenerate mothers," says the S.S. man standing at the foot of the truck. "*Gut, gut, Russki.*"

"Shut your mouth," growls Andrei through clenched teeth, and walks away. From under a pile of rags he pulls out a canteen, unscrews the cork, takes a few deep swallows, passes it to me. The strong vodka burns the throat. My head swims, my legs are shaky, again I feel like throwing up.

And suddenly, above the teeming crowd pushing forward like a river driven by an unseen power, a girl appears. She descends lightly from the train, hops on to the gravel, looks around inquiringly, as if somewhat surprised. Her soft, blonde hair has fallen on her shoulders in a torrent, she throws it back impatiently. With a natural gesture she runs her hands down her blouse, casually straightens her skirt. She stands like this for an instant, gazing at the crowd then turns and with a gliding look examines our faces, as though searching for someone. Unknowingly, I continue to stare at her, until our eyes meet.

"Listen, tell me, where are they taking us?"

I look at her without saying a word. Here, standing before me, is a girl, a girl with enchanting blonde hair, with beautiful breasts, wearing a little cotton blouse, a girl with a wise, mature look in her eyes. Here she stands, gazing straight into my face, waiting. And over there is the gas chamber: communal death, disgusting and ugly. And over in the other direction is the concentration camp: the shaved head, the heavy Soviet trousers in sweltering heat, the sickening, stale odour of dirty, damp female bodies, the animal hunger, the inhuman labour, and later the same gas chamber, only an even more hideous, more terrible death . . .

Why did she bring it? I think to myself, noticing a lovely gold watch on her delicate wrist. They'll take it away from her anyway.

"Listen, tell me," she repeats.

I remain silent. Her lips tighten.

"I know," she says with a shade of proud contempt in her voice, tossing her head. She walks off resolutely in the direction of the trucks. Someone tries to stop her; she boldly pushes him aside and runs up the steps. In the distance I can only catch a glimpse of her blonde hair flying in the breeze.

I go back inside the train; I carry out dead infants; I unload luggage. I touch corpses, but I cannot overcome the mounting, uncontrollable terror. I try to escape from the corpses, but they are everywhere: lined up on gravel, on the cement edge of the ramp, inside the cattle cars. Babies, hideous naked women, men twisted by convulsions. I run off as far as I can go, but immediately a whip slashes across my back. Out of the corner of my eye I see an S.S. man, swearing profusely. I stagger forward and run, lose myself in the Canada group. Now, at last, I can once more rest against the stack of rails. The sun has leaned low over the horizon and illuminates the ramp with a reddish glow; the shadows of the trees have become elongated, ghostlike. In the silence that settles over nature at this time of day, the human cries seem to rise all the way to the sky.

Only from this distance does one have a full view of the inferno on the teeming ramp. I see a pair of human beings who have fallen to the ground locked in a last desperate embrace. The man has dug his fingers into the woman's flesh and has caught her clothing with his teeth. She screams hysterically, swears, cries, until at last a large boot comes down over her throat and she is silent. They are pulled apart and dragged like cattle to the truck. I see four Canada men lugging a corpse: a huge, swollen female corpse. Cursing, dripping wet from the strain, they kick out of their way some stray children who have been running all over the ramp, howling like dogs. The men pick them up by the collars, heads, arms, and toss them inside the trucks on top of the heaps. The four men have trouble lifting the fat corpse on to the car, they call others for help, and all together they hoist up the mound of meat. Big, swollen, puffed-up corpses are being collected from all over the ramp; on top of them are piled the invalids, the smothered, the sick, the unconscious. The heap seethes, howls, groans. The driver starts the motor, the truck begins rolling.

"Halt! Halt!" an S.S. man yells after them. "Stop, damn you!"

They are dragging to the truck an old man wearing tails and a band around his arm. His head knocks against the gravel and pavement; he moans and wails in an uninterrupted monotone: "*Ich will mit dem Herrn Kommandanten sprechen*—I wish to speak with the commandant . . ." With senile stubbornness he keeps repeating these words all the way. Thrown on the truck, trampled by others, choked, he still wails: "*Ich will mit dem . . .*"

"Look here, old man!" a young S.S. man calls, laughing jovially. "In half an hour you'll be talking with the top commandant! Only don't forget to greet him with a *Heil Hitler!*"

Several other men are carrying a small girl with only one leg, They hold her by the arms and the one leg. Tears are running down her face and she whispers faintly: "Sir, it hurts, it hurts . . ." They throw her on the truck of the corpses. She will burn alive along with them.

The evening has come, cool and clear. The stars are out. We lie against the rails. It is incredibly quiet. Anaemic bulbs hang from the top of the high lampposts; beyond the circle of light stretches an impenetrable darkness. Just one step, and a man could vanish for ever. But the guards are watching, their automatics ready.

"Did you get the shoes?" asks Henri.

"No."

"Why?"

"My God, man, I am finished, absolutely finished!"

"So soon? After only two transports? Just look at me, I . . . since Christmas, at least a million people have passed through my hands. The worst of all are the transports from around Paris—one is always bumping into friends."

"And what do you say to them?"

"That first they will have a bath, and later we'll meet at the camp. What would you say?"

I do not answer. We drink coffee with vodka; somebody opens a tin of cocoa and mixes it with sugar. We scoop it up by the handful, the cocoa sticks to the lips. Again coffee, again vodka.

"Henri, what are we waiting for?"

"There'll be another transport."

"I'm not going to unload it! I can't take any more."

"So, it's got you down? Canada is nice, eh?" Henri grins indulgently and disappears into the darkness. In a moment he is back again.

"All right. Just sit here quietly and don't let an S.S. man see you. I'll try to find you your shoes."

"Just leave me alone. Never mind the shoes." I want to sleep. It is very late.

Another whistle, another transport. Freight cars emerge out of the darkness, pass under the lamp-posts, and again vanish in the night. The ramp is small, but the circle of lights is smaller. The unloading will have to be done gradually. Somewhere the trucks are growling. They back up against the steps, black, ghostlike, their searchlights flash across the trees. *Wasser! Luft!* The same all over again, like a late showing of the same film: a volley of shots, the train falls silent. Only this time a little girl pushes herself halfway through the small window and, losing her balance, falls out on to the gravel. Stunned, she lies still for a moment, then stands up and begins walking around in a circle, faster and faster, waving her rigid arms in the air, breathing loudly and spasmodically, whining in a faint voice. Her mind has given way in the inferno inside the train. The whining is hard on the nerves: an S.S. man approaches calmly, his heavy boot strikes between her shoulders. She falls. Holding her down with his foot, he draws his revolver, fires once, then again. She remains face down, kicking the gravel with her feet, until she stiffens. They proceed to unseal the train.

I am back on the ramp, standing by the doors. A warm, sickening smell gushes from inside. The mountain of people filling the car almost halfway up to the ceiling is motionless, horribly tangled, but still steaming.

"*Ausladen!*"[30] comes the command. An S.S. man steps out from the darkness. Across his chest hangs a portable searchlight. He throws a stream of light inside.

"Why are you standing about like sheep? Start unloading!" His whip flies and falls across our backs. I seize a corpse by the hand; the fingers close tightly around mine. I pull back with a shriek and stagger away. My heart pounds, jumps up to my throat. I can no longer control the nausea. Hunched under the train I begin to vomit. Then, like a drunk, I weave over to the stack of rails.

I lie against the cool, kind metal and dream about returning to the camp, about my bunk, on which there is no mattress, about sleep among comrades who are not going to the gas tonight. Suddenly I see the camp as a haven of peace. It is true, others may be dying, but one is somehow still alive, one has enough food, enough strength to work . . .

The lights flicker with a spectral glow, the wave of people—feverish, agitated, stupefied people—flows on and on, endlessly. They think that now they will have to face a new life in the camp, and they prepare themselves emotionally for the hard struggle ahead. They do not know that in just a few moments they will die, that the gold, money, and diamonds which they have so prudently hidden in their clothing and on their bodies will now be useless to them. Experienced professionals will probe into every recess of their flesh, will pull the gold from under the tongue and the diamonds from the uterus and the colon. They will rip out gold teeth. In tightly sealed crates they will ship them to Berlin.

The S.S. men's black figures move about, dignified, businesslike. The gentleman with the notebook puts down his final marks, rounds out the figures: fifteen thousand.

Many, very many, trucks have been driven to the crematoria today.

It is almost over. The dead are being cleared off the ramp and piled into the last truck. The Canada men, weighed down under a load of bread, marmalade, and sugar, and smelling of perfume and fresh linen, line up to go. For several days the entire camp will live off this transport. For several days the entire camp will talk about "Sosnowiec-Bedzin." "Sosnowiec-Bedzin" was a good, rich transport.

The stars are already beginning to pale as we walk back to the camp. The sky grows translucent and opens high above our heads—it is getting light.

Great columns of smoke rise from the crematoria and merge up above into a huge black river which very slowly floats across the sky over Birkenau and disappears beyond the forests in the direction of Trzebinia. The "Sosnowiec-Bedzin" transport is already burning.

We pass a heavily armed S.S. detachment on its way to change guard. The men march briskly, in step, shoulder to shoulder, one mass, one will.

"*Und morgen die ganze Welt . . .*"[31] they sing at the top of their lungs.

"*Rechts ran!* To the right march!" snaps a command from up front. We move out of their way.

[1948]

Endnotes

1 Crossed wooden beams covered in barbed wire.

2 German: Women's concentration camp [all foreign terms are German unless otherwise noted.]

3 A term indicating desirable working and living conditions in the camp.

4 French: my friend.

5 French: someone who lives on the income from investments or property.

6 A term indicating a prisoner who has been broken and is sure to be sent to the gas chamber.

7 Get moving!

8 Get out

9 Don't worry!

10 Take your places!

11 What's the matter?

12 Left, two, three, four! Hats off!

13 A hundred!

14 Okay!

15 Filthy pigs

16 Pay attention

17 Done

18 Ass eyes

19 What will we be working on?

20 Nothing. Transport coming, all crematorium, understand?

21 We understand

22 Yes!

23 Forbidden!

24 Distinguished ladies and gentlemen.

25 There must be order.

26 One empire, one people, one leader.

27 French: Understand?

28 Give it here.

29 Obscenity

30 Unload

31 And tomorrow, the whole world . . .

The Fall River Axe Murders

Angela Carter

*Angela Carter (1940–1992) was born in Eastbourne, Sussex, England. She was
an English novelist and journalist, known for her works of magical realism, in which
magical elements appear in an otherwise realistic setting. Born Angela Olive Stalker,
she first worked as a journalist for the* Croydon Advertiser. *At 20, she married
Paul Carter but, after winning the Somerset Maugham Award for literature, she left
him and spent two years living in Tokyo; she felt Maugham would have been pleased
to know that she used the money to run away from her husband and British culture.
Carter then explored the United States, Asia, and Europe. In 1977, Carter married Mark Pearce, and they settled down in Balham in south London. She spent much
of the late 1970s and the 1980s as a writer in residence at various universities,
including the University of Sheffield, Brown University, the University of Adelaide,
and the University of East Anglia. One of Carter's early works,* The Bloody
Chamber *(1979), is a collection of feminist fairytales in which she took on the
role of Old Mother Goose to tell the tales of Bluebeard, Little Red Riding Hood,
and Alice in Wonderland. The selection below, "Fall River Axe Murders"—Carter's
reworking of the infamous Lizzie Borden murders—uses fairy-tale fragments rem-
iniscent of the tales in* The Bloody Chamber, *particularly Carter's retelling of
"Little Red Riding Hood," to tell its story of a woman who kills her parents. Two
films, for which she wrote the screenplays,* The Company of Wolves *(1984)
and* The Magic Toyshop *(1987), have been adapted from her work. Carter
died of cancer 1992.*

Lizzie Borden with an axe
Gave her father forty whacks
When she saw what she had done
She gave her mother forty-one.

—*Children's rhyme*

Early in the morning of the fourth of August 1892, in the city of Fall River, Massachusetts.

Hot, hot, hot. Even though it is early in the morning, well before the factory whistle issues its peremptory summons from the dark, satanic mills to which the city owes its present pre-eminence in the cotton trade, the white, furious sun already shimmers and quivers high in the still air.

Nobody could call the New England summer a lovable thing; the inhabitants of New England have never made friends with it. More than the heat, it is the humidity that makes it scarcely tolerable. The weather clings, like a low fever you cannot shake off. The Indians who first lived here had the sense to take off their buckskins as soon as things hotted up and sit, thereafter, up to their necks in ponds. This behavior is no longer permissible in the "City of Spindles."

However, as in most latitudes with similar summers, everything slows down in these dog days. The blinds are drawn, the shutters closed; all indoors becomes drowsy penumbra in which to nap away the worst heat of the day, and when they venture out again in the refreshed evening, they put on thin clothes loose enough to let cool air circulate refreshingly between the muslin and the skin, so that the warm weather, as nature intended, is a sweet, sensual, horizontal thing.

But the descendants of the industrious, self-mortifying saints who imported the Protestant ethic wholesale into a land intended for the siesta are proud of flying in the face of nature. The moment the factory whistle blares—bustle! Bustle! Bustle! And the stern fathers of Fall River will step briskly forth into the furnace, well wrapped up in flannel underclothes, linen shirts, vests and coats and trousers of good, thick wool, and—final touch—a strangulatory neck tie, as if discomfort were next to godliness.

On this burning morning when, after breakfast and the performance of a few household duties, Lizzie Borden will murder her parents, she will, on rising, don a simple cotton frock that, if worn by itself, might be right for the weather. But, underneath, has gone a long, starched cotton petticoat; another starched cotton petticoat, a short one; long drawers; woolen stockings; a chemise; and a whalebone corset that takes her viscera in an unkind hand and squeezes them very tightly.

There is also a heavy linen napkin strapped between her legs because she is menstruating.

In all these clothes, out of sorts and nauseous as she is, in this dementing heat, her belly in a vice, she will heat up a flatiron on a stove and press handkerchiefs with the heated iron until it is time for her to go down to the cellar wood-pile to collect the hatchet with which our imagination—"Lizzie Borden with an axe"—always equips her, just as we always visualize Saint Catherine rolling along her wheel, the emblem of her passion.

Soon, in just as many clothes as Miss Lizzie wears, if less fine, Bridget, the servant girl, will slop kerosene on a sheet of last night's newspaper, rumpled around a stick or two of kindling. When the fire settles down, she will cook breakfast. The fire will keep her company as she washes up afterward, when the mercury pauses briefly at eighty-five before recommencing its giddy ascent upwards.

In a blue serge suit one look at which would be enough to bring you out in prickly heat, old Andrew Borden will perambulate the perspiring town truffling for money like a pig until he will return home mid-morning when he will find his death, unannounced, waiting for him.

In a mean house on Second Street in the smoky city of Fall River, five living creatures are sleeping in the still, warm early morning. They comprise two old men and three women. The first old man owns all the women by either marriage, birth, or contract. His house is narrow as a coffin and that was how he made his fortune—he used to be an undertaker but he has recently branched out in several directions and all his branches bear fruit of the most fiscally gratifying kind.

But you would never think, to look at his house, that he is a successful and prosperous man. His house is cramped, comfortless—"unpretentious," you might say, if you were sycophantic, while Second Street itself saw better days some time ago. The Borden house—see "Andrew J. Borden" in flowing script on the brass plate next to the door—stands by itself with a few scant feet of yard on either side.

On the left is a stable, out of use since he sold the horse. In the back lot grow a few pear trees, laden at this season.

On this particular morning, as luck would have it, only one of the two Borden girls sleeps in their father's house. Emma Lenora, his oldest daughter, has taken herself off to nearby New Bedford for a few days, to catch the ocean breeze.

Few of their social class stay in sweltering Fall River in the sweating months of June, July, and August. But then, few of their social class live on Second Street, in the low part of town where heat gathers like fog. Lizzie was invited away, too, to a summer house by the sea to join a merry band of girls but, as if on purpose to mortify her flesh, as if important business kept her in the exhausted town, as if a wicked fairy spelled her on Second Street, she did not go.

The other old man is some kind of kin of Borden's. He doesn't belong here; he is a chance bystander, he is irrelevant.

Write him out of the script.

Even though his presence in the doomed house is historically unimpeachable, the colouring of this domestic apocalypse must be crude and the design profoundly simplified for the maximum emblematic effect.

Write John Vinnicum Morse out of the script.

One old man and three of his women sleep in the house on Second Street. These women comprise his second wife, his youngest daughter and his servant girl.

The City Hall clock whirs and sputters the prolegomena to the first stroke of six and Bridget's alarm clock gives a sympathetic skip and click as the minute hand stutters on the hour; back the little hammer jerks, about to hit the bell on top of her clock, but Bridget's damp eyelids do not shudder with premonition as she lies in her sticking flannel nightgown under one thin sheet on an iron bedstead, lies on her back, as the good nuns taught her in her Irish girlhood, in case she dies during the night, to make less trouble for the one who lays her out.

She is a good girl, on the whole, although her temper is sometimes uncertain and then she will talk back to the missus, sometimes, and will be forced to confess the sin of impatience to the priest. Overcome by heat and nausea everyone in the house is going to wake up sick today—she will return to this little bed later on in the morning to snatch a few moments' rest. Fateful forty winks! While she indulges in them, the massacre takes place.

A rosary of brown glass beads, a cardboard-backed colour print of the Virgin bought from a Portuguese shop, a flyblown photograph of her solemn mother in Donegal—these lie or are propped on the mantelpiece that, however sharp the Massachusetts winter, has never seen a lit stick. A banged tin trunk at the foot of the bed holds all Bridget's worldly goods.

There is a stiff chair beside the bed with, upon it, a candlestick, matches, the alarm clock that resounds the room with a dyadic, metallic clang for it is a joke between Bridget and her mistress that the girl could sleep through anything, anything, and so she needs the alarm clock as well as all the factory whistles that are just about to blast off, just this very second about to blast off. . . .

A splintered pine washstand holds the jug and bowl she never uses; she isn't going to lug water all the way up to the third floor just to wipe herself down, is she? Not when there's water enough in the kitchen, where, in the sink, all will clean their teeth this morning.

Old Borden sees no necessity for baths. He does not believe in total immersion. To lose his natural oils would be to rob his body. Since he does not approve of baths, it goes without saying they do not maintain a bathroom.

A frameless square of mirror reflects in corrugated waves a cracked, dusty soap dish containing a quantity of black metal hair pins.

On bright rectangles of paper blinds move the beautiful shadows of the pear trees.

Although Bridget left the door open a crack in forlorn hopes of coaxing a draught into the room, all the spent heat of the previous day has packed itself tightly into her attic. A dandruff of spent whitewash flakes from the ceiling where a fly drearily whines.

Bridget's lopsided shoes stand together on a hand-braided rug of aged rags. The dress she wears for Mass on Sundays hangs from the hook on the back of the door. The calico dress she will wear for the morning's chores is folded up on the trunk where she left it last night, along with soiled under-things that will do another day.

The house is thickly redolent of sleep, that sweetish smell. Still, all still; in all the house nothing moves except the droning fly and the stillness on the staircase crushes him, he falls still. Stillness pressing against the blinds, still-ness, mortal stillness in the room below, where Master and Mistress share the matrimonial bed.

Were the drapes open or the lamp lit, one could better observe the differ-ences between this room and the austerity of the maid's room. Here is a carpet splashed with vigorous flowers even if the carpet is of the cheap and cheerful variety; there are mauve, ochre, and cerise flowers on the wallpaper, even though the wallpaper was old when the Bordens arrived in the house. A dresser with another distorting mirror; no mirror in this house does not take your face and twist it out of shape for you. On the dresser, a runner embroidered with forget-me-nots; on the runner, a bone comb missing three teeth and lightly threaded with grey hairs, a hairbrush backed with ebonized wood, and a number of lace mats underneath small china boxes holding safety pins, hairnets, et cetera. The little hairpiece that Mrs. Borden attaches to her balding scalp for daytime wear is curled up like a dead squirrel.

But of Borden's male occupation of this room there is no trace because he has a dressing-room of his own, through that door, on the left. . . .

What about the other door, the one next to it?

It leads to the back stairs.

And that yet other door, partially concealed behind the head of the heavy mahogany bed?

If it were not kept securely locked, it would take you into Miss Lizzie's room.

It is a peculiarity of the house, that the rooms are full of doors and—a further peculiarity—all these doors are always kept locked. A house full of locked doors that open only into other rooms with other locked doors. Upstairs and downstairs, all the rooms lead in and out of one another like a maze in a bad dream. It is a house without passages. There is no part of the house that has not been marked out as some inmate's personal territory; it is a house with no shared, no common spaces between one room and the next. It is a house of privacies sealed as close as if they had been sealed with wax on a legal document.

The only way to Emma's room is through Lizzie's. There is no way out of Emma's room. It is a dead end.

The Bordens' custom of locking all the doors, inside and outside, dates from a time, a few years ago, shortly before Bridget came to work for them, when the house was burgled. A person unknown came in through the side door while Borden and his wife had taken one of their rare trips out together. He had loaded her into a trap and set out for a farm they owned outside town, a surprise visit to ensure his tenant, a dour Swede, was not bilking him. The girls stayed at home in their rooms, napping on their beds or repairing ripped hems, or sewing loose buttons more securely, or writing letters, or contemplating acts of charity among the deserving poor, or staring vacantly into space.

I can't imagine what else they might do.

What the girls do when they are on their own is unimaginable to me.

Emma is even more of a mystery than Lizzie because we know less about her. She is a blank space. She has no life. The door from her room leads only into the room of her younger sister.

"Girls" is, of course, a courtesy term. Emma is well into her forties, Lizzie, her thirties, but they did not marry and so live on in their father's house, where they remain in a fictive, protracted childhood, "girls" for good.

In this city of working women, the most visible sign of the status of the Borden girls is that they toil not. "Clickety clack, clickety clack, You're got to work till it breaks your back!" the looms sing to the girls they lured here, the girls fresh from Lancashire, the dark-browed Portuguese, the French Canadian farmers' daughters, the up-country girls, the song whose rhythms now govern the movements of their dexterous fingers. But the Borden girls are deaf to it.

Strange, that endless confinement of these perpetual "girls" who do not labour in the mean house of the rich man. Strange, marginal life that those who lived it believed to be the very printing on the page, to be just exactly why the book was printed in the first place, to be the way all decent folks lived.

While the master and mistress were away and the girls asleep or otherwise occupied, some person or persons unknown tiptoed up the back stairs to the matrimonial bedroom and pocketed Mrs. Borden's gold watch and chain, the collar necklace and silver bangle of her remote childhood, and a roll of dollar bills old Borden kept under his clean union suits in the third drawer of the bureau on the left. The intruder attempted to force the lock of the safe, that featureless block of black iron like a slaughtering block or an altar sitting squarely next to the bed on Old Borden's side, but it would have taken a crowbar to adequately penetrate the safe and the intruder tackled it with a pair of nail scissors that were lying handy on the dresser, so that didn't come off.

Then the intruder pissed and shitted on the cover of the Bordens' bed, knocked the clutter of this and that on the dresser to the floor, smashing a brace of green and violet porcelain parakeets into a thousand fragments in the process, swept into Old Borden's dressing room, there to maliciously assault his funeral coat as it hung in the moth-balled dark of his closet with the self-same nail scissors that had been used on the safe, which now split in two and were abandoned on the closet floor, retired to the kitchen, smashed the flour crock and the treacle crock, and then scrawled an obscenity or two on the parlour window with the cake of soap that lived beside the scullery sink.

What a mess! Lizzie stared with vague surprise at the parlor window; she heard the soft bang of the open screen door, swinging idly, although there was no breeze. What was she doing, standing clad only in her corset in the middle of the sitting room? How had she got there? Had she crept down when she heard the screen door rattle? She did not know. She could not remember.

It was well known in polite circles in Fall River that Lizzie suffered from occasional "peculiar spells," as the idiom of the place and time called odd lapses of behaviour, unexpected, involuntary trances, moments of disconnection—those times when the mind misses a beat.

The Indians cursed the land with madness and death.

Even on the sunniest days, you could not say the landscape smiled; the ragged woodland, the ocean beaten out of steel. Not much, here, to cheer the heart, and all beneath the avenging light. The Indians stuck a few flints of their hard-cornered language onto the map, those names like meals of stone-Massachusetts, Pawtuxet, Woonsocket. And there are certain fruits of the region, such as the corn, especially those strange ears of crimson corn-some of the kernels are black, they dry out and rattle, you cannot eat them but people, nowadays, like to hang them on their doors for decoration in the fall—that strange, archaic-looking corn; and various squashes, the long-necked, pale yellow butternut, and the squat, whorled acorn squash, pine-green with a splatter of orange on one flanksquash and pumpkin that look and feel like votive objects carved from wood; you must boil them for hours to make them soft and then they taste flat, insipid, alien. These fruits have the ineradicable somberness of the aborigines.

From puberty, she had been troubled by these curious lapses of consciousness that often, though not always, came at the time of her menses; at these times, everyday things appeared to her with a piercing, appalling clarity that rendered them mysterious beyond words, so that the harsh, serrated leaves knocking against the window were those of a tree whose name she did not know in which sat birds whose names were not yet invented, whirring, clicking, and chucking like no birds known before, while a sputtering radiance emanated from everything. All the familiar things, at those times, seemed to her not only unknown but also unknowable, always unknowable.

So the strangers must have felt after they watched the boat that brought them slide away from them over the horizon and, abandoned, turned their faces inland towards the wilderness with the anguish of the newborn confronted with infinite space.

Time opened in two; suddenly she was not continuous any more.

Dull headaches announced the approaches of these trances, from which she returned as from an electric elsewhere. She would quiver with exhaustion; her sister would bathe her temples with a handkerchief moistened with eau de cologne, she lying on her bedroom sofa.

She had no words with which to describe the over-clarity with which she had seen the everyday things around her, even had she wished to do so. She kept the knowledge that she was discrete because the notion had no meaning to her, or, perhaps, too much meaning for her to assimilate since she believed that either a person was, or else was not. But don't think because she believed this that she believed it in so many words . . . she believed it in the same way that she believed she lived in Fall River, Massachusetts, and in the same way that she believed the second Mrs. Borden had married her father for his money. She did not believe she believed in these things; she thought she knew them for a fact, just as she knew the Portuguese were pigs and God was the Father Almighty.

Therefore these intermittent lapses in day-to-day consciousness, in which she was and was not at the same time, were unaccountable in every way and she did not dare to think of them once she came back to herself. So she remained a stranger to herself.

A trap rattled by in the street outside. A child burst out crying in a house across the way. Lizzie experienced the departure of vision as though it were the clearing of a haze.

"Help! We have been burgled! Help!"

I cannot tell you what effect the burglary had on Borden. It utterly disconcerted him; he was a man stunned. It violated him, even. He was a man raped. It took away his hitherto unshakeable confidence in the integrity inherent in things.

The family broke its habitual silence with one another in order to discuss the burglary, it moved them so. They blamed it on the Portuguese, mostly, but sometimes on the Canucks. If their outrage remained constant and did not diminish with time, the focus of it varied according to their moods, although they always pointed the finger of suspicion at the strangers who lived in the dark ramparts of the company housing a few stinking blocks away. They did not always suspect the dark strangers exclusively; sometimes they thought the culprit might very well have been one of the mill hands fresh from saucy Lancashire across the ocean who did the deed, for a slum landlord has few friends among the criminal classes. Sometimes Lizzie voiced the notion that the lugubrious and monosyllabic Swede out on Old Borden's bit of property at Swansea might have been harbouring a grudge against her father for some reason and, when the old man gruffly reminded her the Swede had the unshakeable alibi of Borden's own presence at the time of the offence, she would fall silent and fix upon the middle distance the large, accusing, blue stare of her pale eyes.

The possibility of a poltergeist occurred to Mrs. Borden, although she does not know the word; she knows, however, that her younger step-daughter could make the plates jump out of sheer spite, if she wanted to. But the old man adores his daughter. Perhaps it is then, after the shock of the burglary, that he decided she needed a change of scene, a dose of sea air, a long voyage.

The only defense against further depredation was to lock everything and then lock it again, to lock and relock everything and then lock it up once more for luck.

After the burglary, the front door and the side door were always locked three times if one of the inhabitants of the house left it for just so long as to go into the yard and pick up a basket of fallen pears when pears were in season, or if the maid went out to hang a bit of washing or Old Borden, after supper, took a piss under a tree.

From this time dated the custom of locking all the bedroom doors on the inside when one was on the inside oneself or on the outside when one was on the outside. Old Borden locked his bedroom door in the morning, when he left it, and put the key in sight of all on the kitchen shelf.

The burglary awakened Old Borden to the evanescent nature of private property. He thereafter undertook an orgy of investment. He would forthwith invest his surplus in good brick and mortar for who can make away with an office block?

A number of leases fell in simultaneously at just this time on a certain street in the downtown area of the city and Borden snapped them up. When he owned the block, he pulled it down. He planned the Borden building, an edifice of shops and offices, dark red brick, deep tan stone, with cast iron detail, from whence, in perpetuity, he might reap a fine harvest of unsaleable rents, and this monument, like that of Ozymandias, would long survive him—indeed, still stands, foursquare and handsome, the Andrew Borden Building on South Main Street.

Not bad for a fish peddler's son, eh? To turn yourself into a solid piece of real estate?

For, although "Borden" is an ancient name in New England and the Borden clan between them owned the better part of Fall River, our Borden, Old Borden, these Bordens, did not spring from a wealthy branch of the family. There were Bordens and Bordens and he was the son of a man who sold fresh fish in a wicker basket from house to house. Old Borden's parsimony was bred of poverty but learned to thrive best on prosperity for thrift has a different meaning for the poor; they get no joy of it, it is stark necessity to them. But a penniless miser is a contradiction in terms.

Morose and gaunt, this self-made man is one of few pleasures. His vocation is capital accumulation.

What is his hobby?

Why, grinding the faces of the poor.

First, Andrew Borden was an undertaker and death, recognizing an accomplice, did well by him. In the city of spindles, few made old bones, the little children who laboured in the mills died with especial frequency. When he was an undertaker, no!—it was not true he cut the feet of corpses to fit into a job lot of coffins bought cheap as Civil War surplus! That was a rumour put about by his enemies!

With the profits from his coffins, he bought up a tenement or two and made fresh profit from the living. He bought shares in the mills. Then he invested in a brace of banks, so that now he makes a profit on money itself, which is the purest form of profit of all.

Foreclosures and evictions are meat and drink to him. He loves nothing better than a little usury. He is halfway on the road to his first million.

At night, to save the kerosene, he sits in lampless dark. He waters the pear trees with his own urine; waste not, want not. As soon as the daily newspapers are done with, he rips them into squares and stores them in the cellar privy so that they can wipe their arses with them. He mourns the loss of a good organic waste that goes down the privy. He would like to charge the very cockroaches in the kitchen rent. And yet he has not grown fat on all this; the pure flame of his passion has melted off his flesh, his skin sticks to his bones out of sheer parsimony. Perhaps it is from his first profession that he has acquired his bearing, for he walks with the stately dignity of a hearse.

To watch Old Borden bearing down the street toward you was to be filled with an instinctual respect for morality, whose gaunt ambassador he seemed to be. And it made you think, too, what a triumph over nature it was when we rose up to walk on two legs instead of four, in the first place! For he held himself upright with such ponderous assertion it was a perpetual reminder to all who witnessed his progress how it is not natural to be upright, it is a triumph of the will over gravity, in itself a transcendence of the spirit over matter.

His spine is like an iron rod, forged, not born, impossible to imagine that spine of Old Borden's curled up in the womb in the big C-shape of the fetus; he walks as if his legs had joints at neither knee or ankle so that his feet strike at the trembling earth like a bailiff pounding a door with an iron bar.

He has a white, chin-strap beard, old-fashioned already in those days. His lips are so thin it looks as if he'd gnawed them off. He is at peace with his god for he has used his talents as the Good Book says he should.

Yet do not think he has no soft spot. Like Old Lear, like Old Goriot, his heart and, more than that, his cheque-book—is putty in his youngest daughter's hands. On his pinky—you cannot see it, it lies under the covers— he wears a gold ring, not a wedding ring but a high school ring, a singular trinket for a fabulously misanthropic miser. His youngest daughter gave it to him when she left school and asked him to wear it, always, and so he always does, and will wear it to the grave.

He sleeps fully dressed in a flannel nightshirt over his long-sleeved under-wear, and a flannel nightcap, and his back is turned toward his wife of thirty years, as is hers to his.

They are Mr. and Mrs. Jack Spratt in person, he, tall and gaunt as a hanging judge and she, such a spreading, round little doughball. He is a miser, while she is a glutton, a solitary eater, most innocent of vices and yet the shadow or parodic vice of his, for he would like to eat up all the world, or, failing that, since fate has not spread him a sufficiently large table for his ambi-tions—he is a mute, inglorious Napoleon, he does not know what he might have done because he never had the opportunity—since he has not access to the entire world, he would like to gobble up the city of Fall River. But she, well, she just gently, continuously stuffs herself, doesn't she; she's always nib-bling away at something, at the cud, perhaps.

Not that she gets much pleasure from it, either; no gourmet, she, forever meditating the exquisite difference between a mayonnaise sharpened with a few drops of Orleans vinegar or one pointed up with a squeeze of fresh lemon juice. No. Abby never aspired so high, nor would she ever think to do so even if she had the option; she is satisfied to stick to simple gluttony and she eschews all overtones of the sensuality of consumption. Since she relishes not one single mouthful of the food she eats, she knows her ceaseless gluttony is no transgression.

Here they lie in bed together, living embodiments of two of the Seven Deadly Sins, but he knows his avarice is no offence because he never spends any money and she knows she is not greedy because the grub she shovels down gives her dyspepsia. Gives her dyspepsia and worse; in those days, great-grand-mother's days, summer and salmonella came in together.

Refrigeration is, perhaps, the only unmitigated blessing that the Age of Technology has brought us, a blessing that has brought no bane in tow, a wholly positive good that can be welcomed without reluctance or qualifica-tion. The white-enameled refrigerator is the genius of every home, the friendly chill of whose breath has banished summer sickness and the runs for good! How often, nowadays, in summer does your milk turn into a sour jelly, or your butter separate itself out into the liquid fat and the corrupt-smelling whey? When did you last see the waxy clusters of the seed-pearl eggs of the blowfly materialise disgustingly on the left-over joint? Perhaps, perfect child of the

Frigidaire, you've known none of all this! In those days, however, you took your life in your hands each time you picked up your knife and fork.

On the Saturday preceding the murders, for dinner, at twelve, the Bordens had a big joint of roast mutton, hot. Bridget cooked it. They must have had potatoes with it. Mashed, probably. With flour gravy. I don't know if they had greens or not. The documents don't say. But we know the main items of the Bordens' diet during their last week living because the police thoroughly investigated the rumour that the parents had been poisoned before they had been butchered and so the week's dolorous bill of fair was recorded in full.

On Saturday, they had more mutton, cold, for supper. They ate their roast on Saturdays because they were Sabbatarians and did not believe work should be done on Sundays, so Bridget had Sunday off, to go to church.

Because Bridget had Sundays off, they ate more cold mutton for Sunday dinner, with bread and butter, I dare say, and pickles, perhaps.

On Monday, they had mutton for midday dinner. I don't know how Bridget fixed the mutton; perhaps she warmed it up in left-over gravy, to make a change from having it cold. They had mutton for breakfast on Tuesday, too. It must have been a veritably gargantuan joint of mutton—or did the fault lie with Old Borden; did he carve thin as paper money and lay the slice on the plate with as much disinclination as if he'd been paying back a loan, so the eaters felt he grudged each bite?

There was a ice-box of the old-fashioned, wooden kind, the doors of which must be kept tightly shut at all times or else the ice melts and everything inside goes rotten. Every morning, Bridget put out the pan for the ice-man and filled up the dripping ice-compartment.

In this ice-box, she lodged the remains of the mutton.

On Tuesday, it was time for a change. They had sword-fish for midday dinner. Bridget bought the thick steaks of sword-fish in a fish-market that smelled like a brothel after a busy night. She put the sword-fish in the ice-box until it was time to grill it. Then the left-over sword-fish went back into the ice-box until supper time, when she warmed it up again. That was the night they vomited again and again.

Bridget kept back the knuckle from the leg of mutton in order to make broth; perhaps the broth was comforting to an upset stomach and perhaps not. They had the broth for Wednesday dinner, followed by mutton, again. Was that warmed over, too? On Wednesday, they had cold mutton for supper, again.

There is nothing quite like cold mutton. The sinewy, grey, lean meat amidst the veined lumps of congealed fat, varicosed with clotted blood; it must be the sheep's Pyrrhic vengeance on the carnivore! Considering that which lay upon her plate, Mrs. Borden's habitual gluttony takes on almost a heroic quality. Undeterred by the vileness of the table, still she pigs valiantly away while the girls look on, push their own plates away, wince to see the grease on her chin.

Oh, how she loves to eat! She is Mrs. Jack Spratt in person, round as a ball, fat as butter . . . the heavy fare of New England, the chowders, the cornmeal puddings, the boiled dinners, have shaped her, and continue to shape her.

See her rub her bread round her plate. "Is there a little more gravy, Bridget, just to finish up my bread?" She pours cold gravy, lumpy with flour, onto her plate, so much gravy she's forced, in the end, to cut herself just another little corner of bread with which to finish up the gravy.

The sisters think, she eats and eats and eats; she eats everything, she will eat up every single thing, crunch up the plate from which she eats when no more gravy is forthcoming, munch through the greenbacks in father's safe for a salad, for dessert she will polish off the gingerbread house in which they live.

If the old woman thought to deceive them as to her true nature by affecting to confine her voracity only to comestibles, Lizzie knew better; her guzzling stepmother's appetite terrified and appalled her, for it was the only thing within the straight and narrow Borden home that was not kept within confinement.

There had never been any conversation at table; that was not their style. Their stiff lips would part to request the salt, the bread, the butter, yes; but, apart from that, only the raucous squawk of knife on plate and private sounds of chewing and swallowing amplified and publicised and rendered over-intimate, obscene, by the unutterable silence of the narrow dining room. A strip of flypaper hung from a nail over the table, bearing upon it a mourning band of dead flies. A stopped clock of black marble, shaped like a Greek mausoleum, stood on the sideboard, becalmed. Father sat at the head of the table and shaved the meat. Mrs. Borden sat at the foot and ate it.

"I won't eat with her; I won't," said Lizzie. "I refuse to sit at the trough with that sow."

After this little explosion of ill temper, Bridget served the meal twice, once for Mr. and Mrs. Borden, then kept all warm and brought it out again for Lizzie and Emma, since Emma knew it was her duty to take the part of her little sister, her little dearest, the tender and difficult one. After this interruption, calm returned to the household; calm continued to dominate the household.

Saturday, Sunday, Monday, Tuesday, Wednesday. In and out of the ice-box went the slowly dwindling leg of mutton until Thursday dinner was cancelled because corpses and not places were laid out on the table as if the eaters had become the meal.

Back to back they lie. You could rest a sword in the space between the old man and his wife, between the old man's backbone, the only rigid thing he ever offered her, and her soft, warm, enormous bum. Her flannel nightdress is cut on the same lines as his nightshirt except for the limp flannel frill around the neck. She weighs two hundred pounds. She is five feet nothing tall. The bed sags on her side. It is the bed in which his first wife died.

Last night, they dosed themselves with castor oil, due to the indisposition that kept them both awake and vomiting the whole night before that; the copious results of their purges brim the chamberpots beneath the bed.

Their purges flailed them. Their faces show up decomposing green in the dim, curtained room, in which the air is too thick for flies to move.

The youngest daughter dreams behind the locked door.

She threw back the top sheet and her window is wide open but there is no breeze outside this morning to deliciously shiver the screen. Bright sun floods the blinds so that the linen-coloured light shows us how Lizzie has gone to bed as for a levee in a pretty, ruffled nightdress of starched white muslin with ribbons of pastel pink satin threaded through the eyelets of the lace, for is it not the "naughty nineties" everywhere but dour Fall River? Don't the gilded steamships of the Fall River Line signify all the squandered luxury of the Gilded Age within their mahogany and chandeliered interiors? Elsewhere, it is the Belle Epoque. In New York, Paris, London, champagne corks pop and women fall backwards in a crisp meringue of petticoats for fun and profit but not in Fall River. Oh, no. So, in the immutable privacy of her bedroom, for her own delight, Lizzie puts on a rich girl's pretty nightdress, although she lives in a mean house, because she is a rich girl.

But she is plain.

The hem of her nightdress is rucked up above her knees because she is a restless sleeper. Her light, dry, reddish hair, crackling with static, slipping loose from the nighttime plait, crisps and stutters over the square pillow at which she clutches as she sprawls on her stomach, having rested her cheek on the starched pillowcase for coolness's sake at some earlier hour.

Lizzie was not an affectionate diminutive but the name with which she had been christened. Since she would always be known as "Lizzie," so her father reasoned why burden her with the effete and fancy prolongation of "Elizabeth"? A miser in everything, he even cropped off half her name before he gave it to her. So "Lizzie" it was, stark and unadorned, and she is a motherless child, orphaned at two years old, poor thing.

Now she is two-and thirty and yet the memory of that mother whom she cannot remember remains an abiding source of grief: "If mother had lived, everything would have been different."

How? Why? Different in what way? She wouldn't have been able to answer that, lost in nostalgia for lost affection. Yet how could she have been loved better than by her sister, Emma, who lavished the pent-up treasures of a New England spinster's heart upon the little thing? Different, perhaps, because her natural mother, the first Mrs. Borden, subject as she was to fits of sudden, wild, inexplicable rage, might have taken the hatchet to Old Borden on her own account? But Lizzie loves her father. All are agreed on that. Lizzie adores the adoring father who, after her mother died, took to himself another wife.

Her bare feet twitch a little, like those of a dog dreaming of rabbits. Her sleep is thin and unsatisfying, full of vague terrors and indeterminate menaces to which she cannot put a name or form once she is awake. Sleep opens within her a disorderly house. But all she knows is, she sleeps badly, and this last, stifling night has been troubled, too, by vague nausea and the gripes of her female pain; her room is harsh with the metallic smell of menstrual blood.

Yesterday evening she slipped out of the house to visit a woman friend. Lizzie was agitated; she kept picking nervously at the shirring on the front of her dress.

"I am afraid . . . that somebody . . . will do something," said Lizzie.

"Mrs. Borden . . ." and here Lizzie lowered her voice and her eyes looked everywhere in the room except at Miss Russell . . . "Mrs. Borden—oh! Will you ever believe? Mrs. Borden thinks somebody is trying to poison us!"

She used to call her stepmother "mother," as duty bade, but after a quarrel about money after her father deeded half a slum property to her stepmother five years before, Lizzie always, with cool scrupulosity, spoke of "Mrs. Borden" when she was forced to speak of her and called her "Mrs. Borden" to her face, too.

"Last night, Mrs. Borden and poor father were so sick! I heard them, through the wall. And, as for me, I haven't felt myself all day, I have felt so strange. So very . . . strange."

Miss Russell hastened to discover an explanation within reason; she was embarrassed to mention the "peculiar spells." Everyone knew there was nothing odd about the Borden girls. It was Lizzie's difficult time of the month, too; her friend could tell by a certain haggard, glazed look on Lizzie's face when it was happening. Yet her gentility forbade her to mention that.

"Something you ate? It must have been something you have eaten. What was yesterday's supper?" solicitously enquired Miss Russell.

"Warmed-over swordfish. We had it hot for dinner though I could not take much. Then Bridget heated up the left-overs for supper but, again, for myself, I could only get down a forkful. Mrs. Borden ate up the remains and scoured her plate with her bread. She smacked her lips but then was sick all night." (Note of smugness, here.)

"Oh, Lizzie! In all this heat, this dreadful heat! Twice-cooked fish! You know how quickly fish goes off in this heat! Bridget should have known better than to give you twice-cooked fish!"

"There have been threats," Lizzie pursued remorselessly, keeping her eyes on her nervous fingertips. "So many people, you understand, dislike father."

This cannot be denied. Miss Russell politely remained mute.

"Mrs. Borden was so very sick she called the doctor in and Father was abusive toward the doctor and shouted at him and told him he would not pay a doctor's bills whilst we had our own good castor oil in the house. He shouted at the doctor and all the neighbours heard and I was so ashamed. There is a man, you see . . ." and here she ducked her head, while her short, pale eyelashes beat on her cheekbones . . . "such a man, a dark man, Portuguese, Italian, I've seen him outside the house at odd, at unexpected hours, early in the morning, late at night, whenever I cannot sleep in this dreadful heat if I raise the blind and peep out, there I see him in the shadows of the pear trees, in the yard . . . perhaps he puts poison in the milk, in the mornings, after the milk-man fills his can."

"Perhaps he poisons the ice, when the ice-man comes."

"How long has he been haunting your house?" asked Miss Russell, properly dismayed.

"Since . . . the burglary," said Lizzie and suddenly looked Miss Russell full in the face with a kind of triumph. How large her eyes were, prominent, yet veiled. And her well-manicured fingers went on pecking away at the front of her dress as if she were trying to unpick the shirring.

Miss Russell knew, she just knew, this dark man was a figment of Lizzie's imagination. All in a rush, she lost patience with the girl; dark men standing outside her bedroom window, indeed! Yet she was kind and cast about for ways to reassure her.

"But Bridget is up and about when the milk-man and the ice-man call and the whole street is busy and bustling, too; who would dare to put poison in either milk or ice-bucket while half of Second Street looks on? Oh, Lizzie, it is the dreadful summer, the heat, the intolerable heat that's put us all out of sorts, makes us fractious and nervous, makes us sick. So easy to imagine things in this terrible weather, that taints the food and sows worms in the mind. . . . I thought you'd planned to go away, Lizzie, to the ocean. Didn't you plan to take a little holiday, by the sea? Oh, do go! Sea air would blow away all these silly fancies!"

Lizzie neither nods nor shakes her head but continues to worry at her shirring. For does she not have important business in Fall River? Only that morning, had she not been down to the drug-store to try to buy some prussic acid? But how can she tell kind Miss Russell she is gripped by an imperious need to stay in Fall River and murder her parents?

Had all that talk of poison in the vomiting house put her in mind of poison? She went to the drug-store on the corner of Main Street in order to buy prussic acid but nobody would sell it to her so she came home empty-handed. When she asked the corner pharmacist only that morning for a little prussic acid to kill the moth in her seal-skin cape, the man looked at her oddly. "Moths don't breed in seal-skin," he opined. The autopsy will reveal no trace of poison in the stomachs of either parent. She did not try to poison them; she only had it in mind to poison them.

"And this dark man," she pursued to the unwilling Miss Russell, "oh! I have seen the moon glint upon his knife!"

When she wakes up, she can never remember her dreams; she only remembers she slept badly.

Hers is a pleasant room of not ungenerous dimensions, seeing the house is so very small. Besides the bed and the dresser, there is a sofa and a desk; it is her bedroom and also her sitting room and her office, too, for the desk is stacked with account books of various charitable organizations with which she occupies her ample spare time. The Fruit and Flower Mission, under whose auspices she visits the indigent old in the hospital with gifts; the Women's Christian Temperance Union, for whom she extracts signatures for petitions against the Demon Drink; Christian Endeavour, whatever that is—this is the golden age of good works and she flings herself into committees with a vengeance. What would the daughters of the rich do with themselves if the poor ceased to exist?

Then there is the Newsboys Thanksgiving Dinner Fund; and the Horse-trough Association; and the Chinese Conversion Association—no class nor kind is safe from her merciless charity.

She used to teach a Sunday school class of little Chinese children but they did not like her; they teased her, they played an unpleasant trick on her, one Sunday afternoon they put a dead dog inside her desk, a trick of which would have thought the Chinese were incapable because they are so impassive and did not even giggle when she shrieked.

First, she shrieked; then she caught hold of the shoulder of the little Chinese boy sitting at the end of the front row—the nearest child she could get at—and started in on hitting him but then the class instantly abandoned its impassivity and let out such a racket the superintendent came before much damage was done. The children were severely punished. They were forbidden to come to Sunday school again.

Bureau; dressing-table; closet; bed; sofa. She spends her days in this room, moving between each of these dull items of furniture in a circumscribed, undeviating, planetary round. She loves her privacy, she loves her room, she locks herself up in it all day. A shelf contains a book or two: Heros of the Mission Field, The Romance of Trade. On the walls, framed photographs of high school friends, sentimentally inscribed, with, tucked inside one frame, a picture postcard showing a black kitten peeking through a horseshoe. A water-colour of a Cape Cod seascape executed with poignant amateur incompetence. A monochrome photograph of two works of art, a Della Robbia madonna and the Mona Lisa; these she bought in the Uffizi and the Louvre, respectively, when she went to Europe.

Europe!

For don't you remember What Katy Did Next? The storybook heroine took the steamship to smoky old London, to elegant, fascinating Paris, to sunny, antique Rome and Florence; the storybook heroine sees Europe reveal itself before her like an interesting series of magic lantern slides on a gigantic screen. All is present and all unreal. The Tower of London; click. Notre Dame; click. The Sistine Chapel; click. Then the lights go out and she is in the dark again.

Of this journey she retained only the most circumspect of souvenirs, that madonna, that Mona Lisa, reproductions of objects of art consecrated by a universal approval of taste. If she came back with a bag full of memories stamped "Never to be Forgotten," she put the bag away under the bed on which she had dreamed of the world before she set out to see it and on which, at home again, she continued to dream, the dream having been transformed not into lived experience but into memory, which is only another kind of dreaming.

Wistfully: "When I was in Florence . . ."

But then, with pleasure, she corrects herself: "When we were in Florence . . ."

Because a good deal, in fact, most of the gratification the trip gave her came from having set out from Fall River with a select group of the daughters of respectable and affluent mill owners. Once away from Second Street, she was able to move comfortably in the segment of Fall River society to which she belonged by right of old name and new money but from which, when she was at home, her father's plentiful personal eccentricities excluded her. Sharing bedrooms, sharing staterooms, sharing berths, the girls travelled together in a genteel gaggle that bore its doom already upon it for they were girls who would not marry, now, and any pleasure they might have obtained from the variety and excitement of the trip was spoiled in advance by the knowledge they were eating up what might have been their own wedding-cake, using up what should have been, if they'd had any luck, their marriage settlements.

All girls pushing thirty, privileged to go out and look at the world before they resigned themselves to the thin condition of New England spinsterhood; but it was a case of look, don't touch. They knew they must not get their hands dirtied or their dresses crushed by the world, while their affectionate companionship en route had a certain steadfast, determined quality about it as they bravely made the best of the second-best.

It was a sour tour, in some ways, and it was a round trip; it ended at the sour place from which it had set out. Home, again, the narrow house, the rooms all locked like those in Bluebeard's Castle, and the fat, white stepmother whom nobody loves sitting in the middle of the spider web; she has not budged a single inch while Lizzie was away but she has grown fatter.

This stepmother oppressed her like a spell. Lizzie will immediately correct the judge at her trial: "She is not my mother, sir; she is my stepmother: my mother died when I was a child." But Old Borden brought his new bride home when his younger girl was five!

Another mystery—how the Bordens contrived to live together for twenty, nearly thirty years without generating amongst themselves a single scrap of the grumbling, irritable, everyday affection without which proximity becomes intolerable; yet their life cannot have been truly intolerable, because they lived it for so long. They bore it. They did not rub along together, somehow; they rubbed each other up the wrong way all the time, and yet they lived in each other's pockets.

Correction: they lived in Old Borden's pocket and all they had in common was the contents of that pocket.

The days open their cramped spaces into other cramped spaces and old furniture and never anything to look forward to, nothing. Empty days. Oppressive afternoons. Nights stalled in calm. Empty days.

When Old Borden dug in his pocket to shell out for Lizzie's trip to Europe, the eye of God on the pyramid blinked to see daylight but no extravagance is too excessive for the miser's younger daughter who is the wild card in this house and, it seems, can have anything she wants, play ducks and drakes with her father's silver dollars if it so pleases her. He pays all her dressmakers' bills on the dot and how she loves to dress up fine! In her unacknowledged, atrocious solitude, she has become addicted to dandyism. He gives her each week in pin money the same as the cook gets for wages and Lizzie gives that which she does not spend on personal adornment to the deserving poor.

He would give his Lizzie anything, anything in the world that lives under the green sign of the dollar.

She would like a pet, a kitten or a puppy; she loves small animals and birds, too, poor, helpless things. She piles high the bird-table all winter. She used to keep some white pouter pigeons in the disused stable, the kind that look like shuttlecocks and go "vroo croo" soft as a cloud.

Surviving photographs of Lizzie Borden show a face it is difficult to look at as if you knew nothing about her; coming events cast their shadow across her face, or else you see the shadows these events have cast—something terrible, something ominous in this face with its jutting, rectangular jaw and those mad eyes of the New England saints, eyes that belong to a person who does not listen . . . fanatic's eyes, you might say, if you knew nothing about her. If you were sorting through a box of old photographs in a junk shop and came across this particular sepia, faded face above the choker collars of the eighteen-nineties, you might murmur when you saw her: "Oh, what big eyes you have!" as Red Riding Hood said to the wolf, but then you might not even pause to pick her out and look at her more closely, for hers is not, in itself, a striking face.

But as soon as the face has a name, once you recognise her, when you know who she is and what it was she did, the face becomes as if of one possessed, and now it haunts you, you look at it again and again, it secretes mystery.

This woman, with her jaw of a concentration camp attendant; and such eyes . . .

In her old age, she wore pince-nez and truly with the years the mad light has departed from those eyes or else is deflected by her glasses—if, indeed, it was a mad light, in the first place, for don't we all conceal somewhere photographs of ourselves that make us look like crazed assassins? And, in those early photographs of her young womanhood, she herself does not look so much like a crazed assassin as somebody in extreme solitude, oblivious of that camera in whose direction she obscurely smiles, so that it would not surprise you to learn that she is blind.

There is a mirror on the dresser in which she sometimes looks at those times when time snaps in two and then she sees herself with clairvoyant eyes, as though she were another person.

"Lizzie is not herself, today."

At those times, those irremediable times, she could have raised her muzzle to an aching moon and howled.

At other times, she watches herself doing her hair and trying her clothes on. The distorting mirror reflects her with the queasy fidelity of water. She puts on dresses and then she takes them off. She looks at herself in her corset. She measures herself with the tape measure. She pulls the measure tight. She pats her hair. She tries on a hat, a little hat, a chic little straw toque. She punctures it with a hatpin. She pulls the veil down. She pulls it up. She takes the hat off. She drives the hatpin into it with a vivacious strength she did not know she possessed.

Time goes by and nothing happens.

She traces the outlines of her face with an uncertain hand as if she were thinking of unfastening the bandages on her soul but it isn't time to do that, yet; her new face isn't ready to be seen, yet.

She is a girl of Sargasso calm.

She used to keep her pigeons in the loft above the disused stable and feed them grain out of the palms of her cupped hands. She liked to feel the soft scratch of their little beaks. They murmured "vroo croo" with infinite tenderness. She changed their water every day and cleaned up their leprous messes but Old Borden took a dislike to their cooing, it got on his nerves—who'd have thought he had any nerves? But he invented some, they got on them, and one afternoon he took out the hatchet from the wood-pile in the cellar and chopped the pigeons' heads off.

Abby fancied the slaughtered pigeons for a pie but Bridget the servant girl put her foot down at that; What? Make a pie out of Miss Lizzie's beloved turtledoves? Jesus Mary and Joseph!!! she claimed with characteristic impetuousness; what can they be thinking of! Miss Lizzie so nervy with her funny turns and all! (The maid is the only one in the house with any sense and that's the truth of it.) Lizzie came home from the Fruit and Flowers Mission where she had been reading a tract to an old woman in a poorhouse: "God bless you, Miss Lizzie." At home all was blood and feathers.

She doesn't weep, this one, it isn't her nature, she is still waters, but, when moved, she changes colour, her face flushes, it goes dark, angry, mottled red, marbling up like the marbling on the inner covers of the family Bible. The old man loves his daughter this side of idolatry and pays for everything she wants but all the same he killed her pigeons when his wife wanted to gobble them up.

That is how she sees it. That is how she understands it. Now she cannot bear to watch her stepmother eat. Each bite the woman takes seems to go "vroo croo."

Old Borden cleaned off the hatchet and put it back in the cellar, next to the wood-pile. The red receding from her face, Lizzie went down to inspect the instrument of destruction. She picked it up and weighed it in her hand.

That was a few weeks before, at the beginning of the spring.

Her hands and feet twitch in her sleep; the nerves and muscles of this complicated mechanism won't relax, just won't relax; she is all twang, all tension; she is as taut as the strings of a wind-harp from which random currents of air pluck out tunes that are not our tunes.

At the first stroke of the City Hall clock, the first factory hooter blares, and then, on another note, another, and another, the Metacomet Mill, the American Mill, the Mechanics Mill . . . until every mill in the entire town sings out aloud in a common anthem of summoning and the hot alleys where the factory folk live blacken with the hurrying throng, hurry! scurry! to loom, to bobbin, to spindle, to dye-shop as to places of worship, men, and women, too, and children, the street blackens, the sky darkens as the chimneys now belch forth, the clang, bang, and clatter of the mills commences.

Bridget's clock leaps and shudders on its chair, about to sound its own alarm. Their day, the Bordens' fatal day, trembles on the brink of beginning.

Outside, above, in the already burning air, see! The angel of death roosts on the roof-tree.

Désirée's Baby

Kate Chopin

Kate Chopin, born February 8, 1850 in St. Louis Missouri, is now often considered an early feminist writer. However, by all accounts, she would never have considered herself a feminist. It is likely, though, that the circumstances of her formative years contributed to the themes of women's independence and rebellion against socially constructed gender norms that tend to characterize a significant portion of her body of work. Kate Chopin, born Catherine O'Flaherty to an Irish immigrant father, was raised by her French-American mother after her father's sudden death in 1855. Young Kate O'Flaherty and her widowed mother moved in with her grandmother and great-grandmother, both also widowed. Spending her childhood and adolescence in a household without a male head-of-house, in many ways shaped how she would understand gender roles, as she never witnessed traditional female submission to a dominant male.

In 1870, she married Oscar Chopin, a prosperous New Orleans cotton broker. Despite what one might glean from the female characters in many of her stories, Kate Chopin's marriage was a happy one. She and her husband had six children. Financial troubles would cause the young family to leave New Orleans in 1879 for a small rural community in Cloutierville, Louisiana. The family's economic instability would be magnified by Oscar's sudden death in 1882. Chopin and her children soon left Louisiana for Missouri and moved in with her mother. Back in St. Louis, Kate Chopin would finally begin her career as a writer at age 39, in-part as a means to provide for her family.

Chopin's reputation as writer rose quickly. She wrote her first short story in 1889. That same year she began work on her first novel At Fault, which she would publish on her own in 1890. Four years later, she published Bayou Folk, her first collection of stories. In 1897, she published her second collection of stories under the title A Night in Acadie. Though her writings were highly controversial, often tackling socially shunned topics such as women's sexuality, interracial relationships, and the defiance of class divisions, Chopin's work became increasingly popular. However, her literary career would fall even quicker than it rose. The publication of her second novel, The Awakening (1899), would be met with such harsh criticism that Chopin would essentially lay down her pen and end her literary career.

It would not be until the 1960s that Kate Chopin's work would once again enjoy a rise in popularity. The discussions of race, class, gender, and sexuality that typify Chopin's stories were mirrored in the social movements of the American landscape in the 1960s and 70s. "Désirée's Baby," originally published in Vogue magazine in 1893, is an excellent example of the way in which Chopin is able to present issues of race and sexuality without imparting her own criticism of social mores.

As the day was pleasant, Madame Valmondé drove over to L'Abri to see Désirée and the baby.

It made her laugh to think of Désirée with a baby. Why, it seemed but yesterday that Désirée was little more than a baby herself; when Monsieur in riding through the gateway of Valmondé had found her lying asleep in the shadow of the big stone pillar.

The little one awoke in his arms and began to cry for "Dada." That was as much as she could do or say. Some people thought she might have strayed there of her own accord, for she was of the toddling age. The prevailing belief was that she had been purposely left by a party of Texans, whose canvas-covered wagon, late in the day, had crossed the ferry that Coton Maïs kept, just below the plantation. In time Madame Valmondé abandoned every speculation but the one that Désirée had been sent to her by a beneficent Providence to be the child of her affection, seeing that she was without child of the flesh. For the girl grew to be beautiful and gentle, affectionate and sincere,—the idol of Valmondé.

It was no wonder, when she stood one day against the stone pillar in whose shadow she had lain asleep, eighteen years before, that Armand Aubigny riding by and seeing her there, had fallen in love with her. That was the way all the Aubignys fell in love, as if struck by a pistol shot. The wonder was that he had not loved her before; for he had known her since his father brought him home from Paris, a boy of eight, after his mother died there. The passion that awoke in him that day, when he saw her at the gate, swept along like an avalanche, or like a prairie fire, or like anything that drives headlong over all obstacles.

Monsieur Valmondé grew practical and wanted things well considered: that is, the girl's obscure origin. Armand looked into her eyes and did not care. He was reminded that she was nameless. What did it matter about a name when he could give her one of the oldest and proudest in Louisiana? He ordered the *corbeille* from Paris, and contained himself with what patience he could until it arrived; then they were married.

Madame Valmondé had not seen Désirée and the baby for four weeks. When she reached L'Abri she shuddered at the first sight of it, as she always did. It was a sad looking place, which for many years had not known the gentle presence of a mistress, old Monsieur Aubigny having married and buried his wife in France, and she having loved her own land too well ever to leave it. The roof came down steep and black like a cowl, reaching out beyond the wide galleries that encircled the yellow stuccoed house. Big, solemn oaks grew close to it, and their thick-leaved, far-reaching branches shadowed it like a pall. Young Aubigny's rule was a strict one, too, and under it his negroes had forgotten how to be gay, as they had been during the old master's easy-going and indulgent lifetime.

The young mother was recovering slowly, and lay full length, in her soft white muslins and laces, upon a couch. The baby was beside her, upon her arm, where he had fallen asleep, at her breast. The yellow nurse woman sat beside a window fanning herself.

Madame Valmondé bent her portly figure over Désirée and kissed her, holding her an instant tenderly in her arms. Then she turned to the child.

"This is not the baby!" she exclaimed, in startled tones. French was the language spoken at Valmondé in those days.

"I knew you would be astonished," laughed Désirée, "at the way he has grown. The little *cochon de lait!* Look at his legs, mamma, and his hands and finger-nails,—real finger-nails. Zandrine had to cut them this morning Is n't it true, Zandrine?"

The woman bowed her turbaned head majestically, "Mais si, Madame."

"And the way he cries," went on Désirée, "is deafening. Armand heard him the other day as far away as La Blanche's cabin."

Madame Valmondé had never removed her eyes from the child. She lifted it and walked with it over to the window that was lightest. She scanned the baby narrowly, then looked as searchingly at Zandrine, whose face was turned to gaze across the fields.

"Yes, the child has grown, has changed;" said Madame Valmondé, slowly, as she replaced it beside its mother. "What does Armand say?"

Désirée's face became suffused with a glow that was happiness itself.

"Oh, Armand is the proudest father in the parish, I believe, chiefly because it is a boy, to bear his name; though he says not,—that he would have loved a girl as well. But I know it is n't true I know he says that to please me.

And mamma," she added, drawing Madame Valmondé's head down to her, and speaking in a whisper, "he has n't punished one of them—not one of them—since baby is born. Even Négrillon, who pretended to have burnt his leg that he might rest from work—he only laughed, and said Négrillon was a great scamp. Oh, mamma, I'm so happy; it frightens me."

What Désirée said was true. Marriage, and later the birth of his son had softened Armand Aubigny's imperious and exacting nature greatly. This was what made the gentle Désirée so happy, for she loved him desperately. When he frowned she trembled, but loved him. When he smiled, she asked no greater blessing of God. But Armand's dark, handsome face had not often been disfigured by frowns since the day he fell in love with her.

When the baby was about three months old, Désirée awoke one day to the conviction that there was something in the air menacing her peace. It was at first too subtle to grasp. It had only been a disquieting suggestion; an air of mystery among the blacks; unexpected visits from far-off neighbors who could hardly account for their coming. Then a strange, an awful change in her husband's manner, which she dared not ask him to explain. When he spoke to her, it was with averted eyes, from which the old love-light seemed to have gone out. He absented himself from home; and when there, avoided her presence and that of her child, without excuse. And the very spirit of Satan seemed suddenly to take hold of him in his dealings with the slaves. Désirée was miserable enough to die.

She sat in her room, one hot afternoon, in her *peignoir*, listlessly drawing through her fingers the strands of her long, silky brown hair that hung about her shoulders. The baby, half naked, lay asleep upon her own great mahogany bed, that was like a sumptuous throne, with its satin-lined half-canopy. One of La Blanche's little quadroon boys—half naked too— stood fanning the child slowly with a fan of peacock feathers. Désirée's eyes had been fixed absently and sadly upon the baby, while she was striving to penetrate the threatening mist that she felt closing about her. She looked from her child to the boy who stood beside him, and back again; over and over. "Ah!" It was a cry that she could not help; which she was not conscious of having uttered. The blood turned like ice in her veins, and a clammy moisture gathered upon her face.

She tried to speak to the little quadroon boy; but no sound would come, at first. When he heard his name uttered, he looked up, and his mistress was pointing to the door. He laid aside the great, soft fan, and obediently stole away, over the polished floor, on his bare tiptoes.

She stayed motionless, with gaze riveted upon her child, and her face the picture of fright. Presently her husband entered the room, and without noticing her, went to a table and began to search among some papers which covered it.

"Armand," she called to him, in a voice which must have stabbed him, if he was human. But he did not notice. "Armand," she said again. Then she rose and tottered towards him. "Armand," she panted once more, clutching his arm, "look at our child. What does it mean? tell me."

He coldly but gently loosened her fingers from about his arm and thrust the hand away from him. "Tell me what it means!" she cried despairingly.

"It means," he answered lightly, "that the child is not white; it means that you are not white."

A quick conception of all that this accusation meant for her nerved her with unwonted courage to deny it. "It is a lie; it is not true, I am white! Look at my hair, it is brown; and my eyes are gray, Armand, you know they are gray. And my skin is fair," seizing his wrist. "Look at my hand; whiter than yours, Armand," she laughed hysterically.

"As white as La Blanche's," he returned cruelly; and went away leaving her alone with their child.

When she could hold a pen in her hand, she sent a despairing letter to Madame Valmondé.

"My mother, they tell me I am not white. Armand has told me I am not white. For God's sake tell them it is not true. You must know it is not true. I shall die. I must die. I cannot be so unhappy, and live."

The answer that came was as brief:

"My own Désirée: Come home to Valmondé; back to your mother who loves you. Come with your child."

When the letter reached Désirée she went with it to her husband's study, and laid it open upon the desk before which he sat. She was like a stone image: silent, white, motionless after she placed it there.

In silence he ran his cold eyes over the written words. He said nothing. "Shall I go, Armand?" she asked in tones sharp with agonized suspense.

"Yes, go."

"Do you want me to go?"

"Yes, I want you to go."

He thought Almighty God had dealt cruelly and unjustly with him; and felt, somehow, that he was paying Him back in kind when he stabbed thus into his wife's soul. Moreover he no longer loved her, because of the unconscious injury she had brought upon his home and his name.

She turned away like one stunned by a blow, and walked slowly towards the door, hoping he would call her back.

"Good-by, Armand," she moaned.

He did not answer her. That was his last blow at fate.

Désirée went in search of her child. Zandrine was pacing the sombre gallery with it. She took the little one from the nurse's arms with no word of explanation, and descending the steps, walked away, under the live-oak branches.

It was an October afternoon; the sun was just sinking. Out in the still fields the negroes were picking cotton.

Desiree had not changed the thin white garment nor the slippers which she wore. Her hair was uncovered and the sun's rays brought a golden gleam from its brown meshes. She did not take the broad, beaten road which led to the far-off plantation of Valmondé. She walked across a deserted field, where the stubble bruised her tender feet, so delicately shod, and tore her thin gown to shreds.

She disappeared among the reeds and willows that grew thick along the banks of the deep, sluggish bayou; and she did not come back again.

Some weeks later there was a curious scene enacted at L'Abri. In the centre of the smoothly swept back yard was a great bonfire. Armand Aubigny sat in the wide hallway that commanded a view of the spectacle; and it was he who dealt out to a half dozen negroes the material which kept this fire ablaze.

A graceful cradle of willow, with all its dainty furbishings, was laid upon the pyre, which had already been fed with the richness of a priceless *layette*. Then there were silk gowns, and velvet and satin ones added to these; laces, too, and embroideries; bonnets and gloves; for the *corbeille* had been of rare quality.

The last thing to go was a tiny bundle of letters; innocent little scribblings that Désirée had sent to him during the days of their espousal. There was the remnant of one back in the drawer from which he took them. But it was not Désirée's; it was part of an old letter from his mother to his father. He read it. She was thanking God for the blessing of her husband's love:—

"But, above all," she wrote, "night and day, I thank the good God for having so arranged our lives that our dear Armand will never know that his mother, who adores him, belongs to the race that is cursed with the brand of slavery."

Kate Chopin wrote "Désirée's Baby" on November 24, 1892. It was published in *Vogue* (the same magazine that is sold today) on January 14, 1893, the first of nineteen Kate Chopin stories that *Vogue* published. It was reprinted in Chopin's collection of stories, *Bayou Folk*, in 1894.

You can find complete composition dates and publication dates for all Chopin's works on pages 1003 to 1032 of *The Complete Works of Kate Chopin*, edited by Per Seyersted (Baton Rouge: Louisiana State University Press, 1969, 2006).

http://www.KateChopin.org

The Perfect Bride

Dandin

translated by J.A.B. van Buitenen

Sri Dandin (6th–7th century) was an Indian Sanskrit writer. Dandin, who is best known for writing the Kavyadarsa (Mirror of Poetry), *the handbook of classical Sanskrit poetics, or* kavya, *also wrote a prose romance,* Dasakumāracarita (Tales of Ten Princes). *The* Dasakumāracarita, *considered to be a precursor to the modern novel in India, tells the stories of ten princes as they pursue love and royal power. Set in the time of the Guptan Empire (ca. A.D. 320–550), an era of great political and cultural achievement in India, these stories accurately depict Indian society during the period. The following selection, which tells the story of the son of a merchant prince who searches for a wife, is one of the tales from the* Dasakumāracarit.

In Tamil Land in a city called Kañci lived the millionaire son of a merchant prince. His name was Saktikumara and when he was about eighteen years old, he began to worry.

"There is no happiness without a wife," he reflected, "nor with a wife if she is disagreeable. But how to find a wife who has all the wifely virtues?"

Distrusting the purely accidental aspect of marriage with a wife taken at the recommendation of others, he became an astrologer and palmist and, tucking two pounds of unthreshed rice in the hem of his garment, wandered through the land. Everyone who had daughters displayed them before him, saying, "Here is a fortune teller!" But however well marked and suitable the girl was, Saktikumara would ask, "Are you able, my dear, to prepare a complete meal for us with these two pounds of rice?" Thus he roamed from house to house, entering only to be laughed at and thrown out.

One day, in a hamlet on the southern bank of the Kaveri in Sibi country, an ayah[1] showed him a young girl with but a few jewels, who, together with her parents, had gone through a large fortune of which only a decrepit house was left. He stared at her.

"Here is a girl," he thought, "with a perfectly proportioned figure—not too heavy, not too thin, neither too short nor too tall—with regular features and a fair complexion. Her toes are pink inside; the soles are marked with auspicious lines, of barley grain, fish, lotus, and pitcher; her ankles are symmetrical and the feet well rounded and not muscular. The calves are perfectly curved, and the knees are hardly noticeable, as though they were swallowed by the sturdy thighs. The loin dimples are precisely parallel and square and shed lustre upon buttocks round as chariot wheels. Her abdomen is adorned by three folds and is slender around the deep navel, even a little caved. The broad-based breasts with proud nipples fill the full region of her chest. Her copper-red fingers, straight and well rounded, with long, smooth, polished nails like glistening gems, adorn hands which show the happy signs of abundance of grain, wealth, and sons. Her arms, which start from sloping shoulders and taper to the wrists, are very delicate. Her slender neck is curved and bent like a seashell. Her lotus-like face shows unblemished red lips that are rounded in the middle, a lovely and unabbreviated chin, firm but fully rounded cheeks, dark brows that arch a little but do not meet, and a nose like a haughty Sesamum blossom. The wide eyes, jet black, dazzling white, and reddish brown, are radiant and tender and profound and languidly roving. Her forehead is shapely like the crescent moon, her locks darkly alluring like a mine of sapphires. The long ears are twice adorned, by a fading lotus and a playful stalk. Her long, abundant, and fragrant locks are glossy black, every single hair of them, and do not fade to brown even at the ends.

"When her figure is so beautiful, her character cannot be different. My heart goes out to her. However, I shall not marry her before I have tried her: for those who act without circumspection inevitably reap repentance in abundance."

So he asked with a kindly look, "Would you be able, my dear, to make me a complete meal with this rice?"

The girl gave her old servant a meaningful glance; whereupon the woman took the two pounds of rice from him and placed it on the terrace before the door after sprinkling and scrubbing it thoroughly. Then she washed the girl's feet. The girl then dried the sweet-smelling rice measure by measure, repeatedly turning it over in the sun, and when it was thoroughly dry, she spread it on a hard, smooth part of the floor, threshed it very, very gently with the edge of a reed-stalk, and finally took all the rice grains out of the husks without breaking them.

Then she said to her ayah: "Mother, jewelers want these husks; they use them to polish jewelry. Sell it to them and, with the pennies they give you, you must buy good hard firewood sticks, neither too dry nor too damp, a small-sized pan, and two shallow bowls."

When the servant had done that, the girl placed the rice grains in a shallow mortar of kakubha wood with a flat, wide bottom and began pounding them with a long, heavy, iron-tipped, smooth-bodied pestle of khadira wood that was slightly recessed in the middle to form a grip. She tired her arms in a charming play of raising and dropping, picking up and picking out single grains, which she then cleaned of chaff and awn in a winnowing basket, washed repeatedly in water, and, after a small offering to the fireplace, dropped in boiling water, five parts water to one part rice.

As the grains softened and started to jump and swelled to the size of a bud, she lowered the fire and, holding the lid on the pot, poured out the scum. Then she plunged her spoon in the rice, turned the grains with the spoon, and, having satisfied herself that they were evenly boiled, turned the pot upside down on its lid to let the rice steam. She poured water over those fire-sticks which had not burned up entirely, and when the fire had died and the heat was gone, she sent this charcoal to the dealers: "Buy with the coin you receive as much of vegetables, ghee, curds, oil, myrobalan, and tamarinds as you can get."

When this had been done, she added two or three kinds of spices, and once the rice broth was transferred to a new bowl placed on wet sand, she cooled it with gentle strokes of a palmleaf fan, added salt, and scented it with fragrant smoke. Then she ground the myrobalan to a fine lotus-sweet powder, and finally relayed through her servant the invitation to a bath. The old nurse, clean from a bath herself, gave Saktikumara myrobalan and oil, whereupon he bathed. After his bath he sat down on a plank placed on sprinkled and swept stones. He touched the two bowls that were placed on a light, green banana-tree leaf from her own garden—a quarter of one leaf was used—and she set the rice broth before him. He drank it and, feeling happy and content after his journey, let a sweet lassitude pervade his body. Then she served him two spoonsful of rice porridge and added a serving of butter, soup, and condiment. Finally, she served him the remaining boiled rice with curds mixed with mace, cardamon and cinnamon, and fragrant cool buttermilk and fermented rice gruel. He finished all the rice and side dishes. Then he asked for water. From a new pitcher with water that was scented with the incense of aloe wood, permeated with the fragrance of fresh Bignonia blossoms and perfumed with lotus buds, she poured out an even thin stream. He held his mouth close to the vessel; and while the snow-cold spattering drops bristled and reddened his eyelashes, his ears rejoiced in the tinkling sound of the stream, his cheeks tickled and thrilled at the pleasurable touch, his nostrils opened to the fragrance of the lotus buds, and his sense of taste delighted in the delicious flavor, he drank the water to his heart's content. With a nod of his head he indicated that she stop pouring, and she gave him, from another vessel, fresh water to rinse his mouth. When the old woman had removed the scraps of the meal and had cleaned the stone floor with yellow cowdung, he spread his ragged upper cloth on the ground and took a short nap.

Highly satisfied, he married the girl with proper rites and took her with him. Once he had brought her home, he ignored her and wooed a courtesan; the bride treated even that woman as her dear friend. She waited on her husband as if he were a god, untiringly. She did the household chores without fail and, wonder of tact, won the affection of the servants. Conquered by her virtues, her husband put the entire household in her charge and, depending body and soul on her alone, applied himself to the pursuit of Virtue, Wealth, and Love. Thus, I say, a wife's virtue is a man's happiness.

Endnote

1. Household servant.

King of the Bingo Game

Ralph Ellison

Ralph Ellison was born in Oklahoma in 1914. He attended the Tuskegee Institute in Alabama to study music, which was the school's most highly esteemed program. He was named after transcendentalist poet and essayist Ralph Waldo Emerson.

Ellison's most well-known work is Invisible Man, *published in 1952. This book won the National Book Award in 1953. It is about the "invisibility" caused by race, and the socio-intellectual problems facing African-Americans in the early twentieth century, including Black Nationalism and a cultural identity crisis.*

Ellison's good friend and colleague, Richard Wright, became an open member of the Communist Party, and Ellison also became "quietly affiliated" with the group, editing Communist publications. Both Wright and Ellison became disillusioned with the Communist Party during World War II. Both men felt the party had betrayed African Americans and replaced Marxism with social reformism. In the wake of his disillusionment with the Communist Party, Ellison began to write his novel Invisible Man, *partly in response to the party's betrayal.*

Ellison's other works include his second novel, Juneteenth, *which was published posthumously five years after his death. He also wrote* Shadow and Act *(1964), a collection of political, social and critical essays, and* Going to the Territory *(1986).*

Ellison was awarded a special achievement award from the Anisfield-Wolf Book Awards in 1992. He was also an accomplished sculptor, musician, and photographer. Ellison taught at Bard College, Rutgers University, the University of Chicago, and New York University. Ellison is also a charter member of the Fellowship of Southern Writers.

"King of the Bingo Game" (1944) was one of the last stories Ellison wrote before Invisible Man. The short story integrates politics, history, and ritual with a foundation of African-American folklore. In writing about "King of the Bingo Game," Ellison scholar Robert G. O'Meally stated it was Ellison's "use of black sermons, tales, games, jokes, boasts, dozens, blues, and spirituals that set his work apart from that of other mid-century African-American writers."

Ellison died of pancreatic cancer in 1994 at the age of 80.

The woman in front or him was eating roasted peanuts that smelled so good that he could barely contain his hunger. He could not even sleep and wished they'd hurry and begin the bingo game. There, on his right, two fellows were drinking wine out of a bottle wrapped in a paper bag, and he could hear soft gurgling in the dark. His stomach gave a low, gnawing growl. "If this was down South," he thought, "all I'd have to do is lean over and say, 'Lady, gimme a few of those peanuts, please ma'am,' and she'd pass me the bag and never think nothing of it." Or he could ask the fellows for a drink in the same way. Folks down South stuck together that way; they didn't even have to know you. But up here it was different. Ask somebody for something, and they'd think you were crazy. Well, I ain't crazy. I'm just broke, 'cause I got no birth certificate to get a job, and Laura 'bout to die 'cause we got no money for a doctor. But I ain't crazy. And yet a pinpoint of doubt was focused in his mind as he glanced toward the screen and saw the hero stealthily entering a dark room and sending the beam of a flashlight along a wall of bookcases. This is where he finds the trapdoor, he remembered. The man would pass abruptly through the wall and find the girl tied to a bed, her legs and arms spread wide, and her clothing torn to rags. He laughed softly to himself. He had seen the picture three times, and this was one of the best scenes.

On his right the fellow whispered wide-eyed to his companion, "Man, look ayonder!"

"Damn!"

"Wouldn't I like to have her tied up like that . . ."

"Hey! That fool's letting her loose!"

"Aw, man, he loves her."

"Love or no love!"

The man moved impatiently beside him, and he tried to involve himself in the scene. But Laura was on his mind. Tiring quickly of watching the picture he looked back to where the white beam filtered from the projection room above the balcony. It started small and grew large, specks of dust dancing in its whiteness as it reached the screen. It was strange how the beam always landed right on the screen and didn't mess up and fall somewhere else. But they had it all fixed. Everything was fixed. Now suppose when they showed that girl with her dress torn the girl started taking off the rest of her clothes, and when the guy came in he didn't untie her but kept her there and went to taking off his own clothes? *That* would be something to see. If a picture got out off hand like that those guys up there would go nuts. Yeah, and there'd be so many folks in here you couldn't find a seat for nine months! A strange sensation played over his skin. He shuddered. Yesterday he'd seen a bedbug on a woman's neck as they walked out into the bright street. But exploring his thigh through a hole in his pocket he found only goose pimples and old scars.

The bottle gurgled again. He closed his eyes. Now a dreamy music was accompanying the film and train whistles were sounding in the distance, and he was a boy again walking along a railroad trestle down South, and seeing the train coming, and running back as fast as he could go, and hearing the whistle blowing, and getting off the trestle to solid ground just in time, with the earth trembling beneath his feet, and feeling relieved as he ran down the cinder-strewn embankment onto the highway, and looking back and seeing with terror that the train had left the track and was following him right down the middle of the street, and all the white people laughing as he ran screaming . . .

"Wake up there, buddy! What the hell do you mean hollering like that? Can't you see we trying to enjoy this here picture?"

He stared at the man with gratitude.

"I'm sorry, old man," he said. "I musta been dreaming."

"Well, here, have a drink. And don't be making no noise like that, damn!"

His hands trembled as he tilted his head. It was not wine, but whiskey. Cold rye whiskey. He took a deep swoller, decided it was better not to take another, and handed the bottle back to its owner.

"Thanks, old man," he said.

Now he felt the cold whiskey breaking a warm path straight through the middle of him, growing hotter and sharper as it moved. He had not eaten all day, and it made him light-headed. The smell of the peanuts stabbed him like a knife, and he got up and found a seat in the middle aisle. But no sooner did he sit than he saw a row of intensefaced young girls, and got up again, thinking, "You chicks musta been Lindy-hopping[1] somewhere." He found a seat several rows ahead as the lights came on, and he saw the screen disappear behind a heavy red and gold curtain; then the curtain rising, and the man with the microphone and a uniformed attendant coming on the stage.

He felt for his bingo cards, smiling. The guy at the door wouldn't like it if he knew about his having *five* cards. Well, not everyone played the bingo game; and even with five cards he didn't have much of a chance. For Laura, though, he had to have faith. He studied the cards, each with its different numerals, punching the free center hole in each and spreading them neatly across his lap; and when the lights faded he sat slouched in his seat so that he could look from his cards to the bingo wheel with but a quick shifting of his eyes.

Ahead, at the end or the darkness, the man with the microphone was pressing a button attached to a long cord and spinning the bingo wheel and calling out the number each time the wheel came to rest. And each time the voice rang out his finger raced over the cards for the number. With five cards he had to move fast. He became nervous, there were too many cards, and the man went too fast with his grating voice. Perhaps he should just select one and throw the others away. But he was afraid. He became warm. Wonder how much Laura's doctor would cost? Damn that, watch the cards! And with despair he heard the man call three in a row which he missed on all five cards. This way he'd never win . . .

When he saw the row of holes punched across the third card, he sat paralyzed and heard the man call three more numbers before he stumbled forward, screaming,

"Bingo! Bingo!"

"Let that fool up there," someone called.

"Get up there, man!"

He stumbled down the aisle and up the steps to the stage into a light so sharp and bright that for a moment it blinded him, and he felt that he had moved into the spell of some strange, mysterious power. Yet it was as familiar as the sun, and he knew it was the perfectly familiar bingo.

The man with the microphone was saying something to the audience as he held out his card. A cold light flashed from the man's finger as the card left his hand. His knees trembled. The man stepped closer, checking the card against the numbers chalked on the board. Suppose he had made a mistake? The pomade on the man's hair made him feel faint, and he backed away. But the man was checking the card over the microphone now, and he had to stay. He stood tense, listening.

"Under the O, forty-four," the man chanted. 'Under the I, seven. Under the G, three. Under the B, ninety-six. Under the N, thirteen!"

His breath came easier as the man smiled at the audience.

"Yes sir, ladies and gentlemen, he's one of the chosen people!"

The audience rippled with laughter and applause.

"Step right up to the front of the stage."

He moved slowly forward, wishing that the light was not so bright.

"To win tonight's jackpot of $36.90 the wheel must stop between the double zero, understand?"

He nodded, knowing the ritual from the many days and nights he had watched the winners march across the stage to press the button that controlled the spinning wheel and receive the prizes. And now he followed the instructions as though he'd crossed the slippery stage a million prize-winning times.

The man was making some kind of a joke, and he nodded vacantly. So tense had he become that he felt a sudden desire to cry and shook it away. He felt vaguely that his whole life was determined by the bingo wheel, not only that which would happen now that he was at last before it, but all that had gone before, since his birth and his mother's birth and the birth of his father. It had always been there even though he had not been aware of it, handing out the unlucky cards and numbers of his days. The feeling persisted, and he started quickly away. I better get down from here before I make a fool of myself he thought.

"Here, boy," the man called. "You haven't started yet."

Someone laughed as he went hesitantly back.

"Are you all reet?"

He grinned at the man's jive talk, but no words would come, and he knew it was not a convincing grin. For suddenly he knew that he stood on the slippery brink of some terrible embarrassment.

"Where are you from, boy?" the man asked.

"Down South."

"He's from down South, ladies and gentlemen," the man said. "Where from? Speak right into the mike."

"Rocky Mont," he said. "Rock' Mont, North Car'lina."

"So you decided to come down off that mountain to the U.S.," the man laughed. He felt that the man was making a fool of him, but then something cold was placed in his hand, and the lights were no longer behind him.

Standing before the wheel he felt alone, but that was somehow right, and he remembered his plan. He would give the wheel a short quick twirl. Just a touch of the button. He had watched it many times, and always it came close to double zero when it was short and quick. He steeled himself; the fear had left, and he felt a profound sense of promise, as though he were about to be repaid for all the things he'd suffered all his life. Trembling, he pressed the button. There was a whirl of lights, and in a second he realized with finality that though he wanted to, he could not stop. It was as though he held a high-powered line in his naked hand. His nerves tightened. As the wheel increased its speed it seemed to draw him more and more into its power, as though it held his fate; and with it came a deep need to submit, to whirl, to lose himself in its swirl of color. He could not stop it now. So let it be.

The button rested snugly in his palm where the man had placed it. And now he became aware of the man beside him, advising him through the microphone, while behind the shadowy audience hummed with noisy voices. He shifted his feet. There was still that feeling of helplessness within him, making part of him desire to turn back, even now that the jackpot was right in his hand. He squeezed the button until his fist ached. Then, like the sudden shriek of a subway whistle, a doubt tore through his head. Suppose he did not spin the wheel long enough? What could he do, and how could he tell? And then he knew even as he wondered, that as long as he pressed the button, he could control the jackpot. He and only he could determine whether or not it was to be his. Not even the man with the microphone could do anything about it now. He felt drunk. Then, as though he had come down from a high hill into a valley of people, he heard the audience yelling.

"Come down from there, you jerk!"

"Let somebody else have a chance . . ."

"Ole Jack thinks he done found the end of the rainbow . . ."

The last voice was not unfriendly, and he turned and smiled dreamily into the yelling mouths. Then he turned his back squarely on them.

"Don't take too long, boy," a voice said.

He nodded. They were yelling behind him. Those folks did not understand what had happened to him. They had been playing the bingo game day in and night out for years, trying to win rent money or hamburger change. But not one of those wise guys had discovered this wonderful thing. He watched the wheel whirling past the numbers and experienced a burst of exaltation: This is God! This is the really truly God! He said it aloud, "This is God!"

He said it with such absolute conviction that he feared he would fall fainting into the footlights. But the crowd yelled so loud that they could not hear. These fools, he thought. I'm here trying to tell them the most wonderful secret in the world, and they're yelling like they gone crazy. A hand fell upon his shoulder.

"You'll have to make a choice now, boy. You've taken too long."

He brushed the hand violently away.

"Leave me alone, man. I know what I'm doing!"

The man looked surprised and held on to the microphone for support. And because he did not wish to hurt the man's feelings he smiled, realizing with a sudden pang that there was no way of explaining to the man just why he had to stand there pressing the button forever.

"Come here," he called tiredly.

The man approached, rolling the heavy microphone across the stage.

"Anybody can play this bingo game, right?" he said.

"Sure, but . . ."

He smiled, feeling inclined to be patient with this slick looking white man with his blue shirt and his sharp gabardine suit.

"That's what I thought," he said. "Anybody can win the jackpot as long as they get the lucky number, right?"

"That's the rule, but after all . . ."

"That's what I thought," he said. "And the big prize goes to the man who knows how to win it?"

The man nodded speechlessly.

"Well then, go on over there and watch me win like I want to. I ain't going to hurt nobody," he said, "and I'll show you how to win. I mean to show the whole world how it's got to be done."

And because he understood, he smiled again to let the man know that he held nothing against him for being white and impatient. Then he refused to see the man any longer and stood pressing the button, the voices of the crowd reaching him like sounds in distant streets. Let them yell. All the Negroes down there were just ashamed because he was black like them. He smiled inwardly, knowing how it was. Most of the time he was ashamed of what Negroes did himself. Well, let them be ashamed for something this time. Like him. He was like a long thin black wire that was being stretched and wound upon the bingo wheel; wound until he wanted to scream; wound, but this time himself controlling the winding and the sadness and the shame, and because he did, Laura would be all right. Suddenly the lights flickered. He staggered backwards. Had something gone wrong? All this noise. Didn't they know that although he controlled the wheel, it also controlled him, and unless he pressed the button forever and forever and ever it would stop, leaving him high and dry, dry and high on this hard high slippery hill and Laura dead? There was only one chance; he had to do whatever the wheel demanded. And gripping the button in despair, he discovered with surprise that it imparted a nervous energy. His spine tingled. He felt a certain power.

Now he faced the raging crowd with defiance, its screams penetrating his eardrums like trumpets shrieking from a juke-box. The vague faces glowing in the bingo lights gave him a sense of himself that he had never known before. He was running the show, by God! They had to react to him, for he was their luck. This is *me*, he thought. Let the bastards yell. Then someone was laughing inside him, and he realized that somehow he had forgotten his own name. It was a sad, lost feeling to lose your name, and a crazy thing to do. That name had been given him by the white man who had owned his grandfather a long lost time ago down South. But maybe those wise guys knew his name.

"Who am I?" he screamed.

"Hurry up and bingo, you jerk!"

They didn't know either, he thought sadly. They didn't even know their own names, they were all poor nameless bastards. Well, he didn't need that old name; he was reborn. For as long as he pressed the button he was The-man-who-pressed-the-button-who-held-the-prize-who-was-the-King-of-Bingo. That was the way it was, and he'd have to press the button even if nobody understood, even though Laura did not understand.

"Live!" he shouted.

The audience quieted like the dying of a huge fan.

"Live, Laura, baby. I got holt of it now, sugar. Live!"

He screamed it tears streaming down his face. "I got nobody but YOU!"

The screams tore from his very guts. He felt as though the rush of blood to his head would burst out in baseball seams of small red droplets, like a head beaten by police clubs. Bending over he saw a trickle of blood splashing the toe of his shoe. With his free hand he searched his head. It was his nose. God, suppose something has gone wrong? He felt that the whole audience had somehow entered him and was stamping its feet in his stomach and he was unable to throw them out. They wanted the prize, that was it. They wanted the secret for themselves. But they'd never get it; he would keep the bingo wheel whirling forever, and Laura would be safe in the wheel. But would she? It had to be, because if she were not safe the wheel would cease to turn; it could not go on. He had to get away, *vomit* all, and his mind formed an image of himself running with Laura in his arms down the tracks of the subway just ahead of an A train, running desperately *vomit* with people screaming for him to come out but knowing no way of leaving the tracks because to stop would bring the train crushing down upon him and to attempt to leave across the other tracks would mean to run into a hot third rail as high as his waist which threw blue sparks that blinded his eyes until he could hardly see.

He heard singing and the audience was clapping its hands.

> Shoot the liquor to him, Jim boy!
> Clap-clap-clap
> Well a-calla the cop
> He's blowing his top!
> Shoot the liquor to him, Jim, boy!

Bitter anger grew within him at the singing. They think I'm crazy. Well let 'em laugh. I'll do what I got to do.

He was standing in an attitude of intense listening when he saw that they were watching something on the stage behind him. He felt weak. But when he turned he saw no one. If only his thumb did not ache so. Now they were applauding. And for a moment he thought that the wheel had stopped. But that was impossible, his thumb still pressed the button. Then he saw them. Two men in uniform beckoned from the end of the stage. They were coming toward him, walking in step, slowly, like a tap-dance team returning for a third encore. But their shoulders shot forward, and he backed away, looking wildly about. There was nothing to fight them with. He had only the long black cord which led to a plug somewhere back stage, and he couldn't use that because it operated the bingo wheel. He backed slowly, fixing the men with his eyes as his lips stretched over his teeth in a tight, fixed grin; moved toward the end of the stage and realizing that he couldn't go much further, for suddenly the cord became taut and he couldn't afford to break the cord. But he had to do something. The audience was howling. Suddenly he stopped dead, seeing the men halt, their legs lifted as in an interrupted step of a slow-motion dance. There was nothing to do but run in the other direction and he dashed forward, slipping and sliding. The men fell back, surprised. He struck out violently going past.

"Grab him!"

He ran, but all too quickly the cord tightened, resistingly, and he turned and ran back again. This time he slipped them, and discovered by running in a circle before the wheel he could keep the cord from tightening. But this way he had to flail his arms to keep the men away. Why couldn't they leave a man alone? He ran, circling.

"Ring down the curtain," someone yelled. But they couldn't do that. If they did the wheel flashing from the projection room would be cut off. But they had him before he could tell them so, trying to pry open his fist, and he was wrestling and trying to bring his knees into the fight and holding on to the button, for it was his life. And now he was down, seeing a foot coming down, crushing his wrist cruelly, down, as he saw the wheel whirling serenely above.

"I can't give it up," he screamed. Then quietly, in a confidential tone, "Boys, I really can't give it up."

It landed hard against his head. And in the blank moment they had it away from him, completely now. He fought them trying to pull him up from the stage as he watched the wheel spin slowly to a stop. Without surprise he saw it rest at double-zero.

"You see," he pointed bitterly.

"Sure, boy, sure, it's O.K.," one of the men said smiling.

And seeing the man bow his head to someone he could not see, he felt very, very happy; he would receive what all the winners received.

But as he warmed in the justice of the man's tight smile he did not see the man's slow wink, nor see the bow-legged man behind him step clear of the swiftly descending curtain and set himself for a blow. He only felt the dull pain exploding in his skull, and he knew even as it slipped out of him that his luck had run out on the stage.

Endnote

1. Dancing.

Saboteur

Ha Jin

Ha Jin was born in Liaoning, China in 1956. When he was thirteen, Jin joined the People's Liberation Army during the Cultural Revolution in China. After his military stint, he attended Heilongjiang University and earned a bachelor's degree in English studies, followed by a master's degree in Anglo-American literature at Shandong University.

Jin grew up in the tumult and uncertainty of early communist China. He was at Brandeis University in Massachusetts on a scholarship when the 1989 Tiananmen Square Massacre happened. The Chinese government's censorship crackdown cemented Jin's decision to stay in the United States. It was also the reason for his choice to write in English.

Jin won the National Book Award for Fiction and the PEN/Faulkner Award for his 1999 novel, Waiting. *Jin's works also include* Under the Red Flag *(1997), which won the Flannery O'Connor Award for Short Fiction, and* Ocean of Words *(1996), which was awarded the PEN/Hemingway Award. His Korean War novel* War Trash *(2004) won a second PEN/Faulkner Award for Jin, and was also a finalist for the Pulitzer Prize. Many of Jin's short stories have appeared in* The Best American Short Stories *anthologies.*

Many of Jin's stories and novels are set in China, specifically in the fictional Muji City. This includes his short story "Saboteur," set amidst the humiliation, fear and paranoia of early Communist China. Thematically, the story is about the overwhelming power of government and the realities and ramifications of revenge

Jin currently teaches at Boston University in Massachusetts.

Mr. Chiu and his bride were having lunch in the square before Muji Train Station. On the table between them were two bottles of soda spewing out brown foam, and two paper boxes of rice and sauteed cucumber and pork. "Let's eat," he said to her, and broke the connected ends of the chopsticks. He picked up a slice of streaky pork and put it into his mouth. As he was chewing, a few crinkles appeared on his thin Jaw.

To his right, at another table two railroad policemen were drinking tea and laughing; it seemed that the stout, middle-aged man was telling a joke to his young comrade, who was tall and of athletic build. Now and again they would steal a glance at Mr. Chiu's table.

The air smelled of rotten melon. A few flies kept buzzing above the couple's lunch. Hundreds of people were rushing around to get on the platform or to catch buses to downtown. Food and fruit vendors were crying for customers in lazy voices. About a dozen young women, representing the local hotels, held up placards which displayed the daily prices and words as large as a palm, like Free Meals, Air-Conditioning, and On the River. In the center of the square stood a concrete statue of Chairman Mao, at whose feet peasants were napping with their backs on the warm granite and with their faces toward the sunny sky. A flock of pigeons perched on the chairman's raised hand and forearm.

The rice and cucumber tasted good and Mr. Chiu was eating unhurriedly. His sallow face showed exhaustion. He was glad that the honeymoon was finally over and that he and his bride were heading for Harbin. During the two weeks' vacation, he had been worried about his liver because three months ago he had suffered from acute hepatitis; he was afraid he might have a relapse. But there had been no severe symptom, despite his liver being still big and tender. On the whole he was pleased with his health, which could even endure the strain of a honeymoon; indeed, he was on the course of recovery. He looked at his bride, who took off her wire glasses, kneading the root of her nose with her fingertips. Beads of sweat coated her pale cheeks.

"Are you all right, sweetheart?" he asked.

"I have a headache. I didn't sleep well last night."

"Take an aspirin, will you?"

"It's not that serious. Tomorrow is Sunday and I can sleep longer. Don't worry."

As they were talking, the stout policeman at the next table stood up and threw a bowl of tea in their direction. Both Mr. Chiu's and his bride's sandals were wet instantly.

"Hooligan!" she said in a low voice.

Mr. Chiu got to his feet and said out loud, "Comrade policeman, why did you do this?" He stretched out his right foot to show the wet sandal.

"Do what?" the stout man asked huskily, glaring at Mr. Chiu while the young fellow was whistling.

"See, you dumped water on our feet."

"You're lying. You wet your shoes yourself."

"Comrade policeman, your duty is to keep order, but you purposely tortured us common citizens. Why violate the law you are supposed to enforce?" As Mr. Chiu was speaking, dozens of people began gathering around.

With a wave of his hand, the man said to the young fellow, "Let's get hold of him!"

They grabbed Mr. Chiu and clamped handcuffs around his wrists. He cried, "You can't do this to me. This is utterly unreasonable."

"Shut up!" The man pulled out his pistol. "You can use your tongue at our headquarters."

The young fellow added, "You're a saboteur, you know? You're disrupting public order."

The bride was too terrified to say anything coherent. She was a recent college graduate, had majored in fine arts, and had never seen the police make an arrest. All she could say now was, "Oh please, please!"

The policemen were pulling Mr. Chiu, but he refused to go with them, holding the corner of the table and shouting, "We have a train to catch. We already bought the tickets."

The stout man punched him in the chest. "Shut up. Let your ticket expire." With the pistol butt he chopped Mr. Chiu's hands, which at once released the table. Together the two men were dragging him away to the police station.

Realizing he had to go with them, Mr. Chiu turned his head and shouted to his bride, "Don't wait for me here. Take the train. If I'm not back by tomorrow morning, send someone over to get me out."

She nodded, covering her sobbing mouth with her palm.

After removing his shoelaces, they locked Mr. Chiu into a cell in the back of the Railroad Police Station. The single window in the room was blocked by six steel bars; it faced a spacious yard in which stood a few pines. Beyond the trees two swings hung from an iron frame, swaying gently in the breeze. Somewhere in the building a cleaver was chopping rhythmically. There must be a kitchen upstairs, Mr. Chiu thought.

He was too exhausted to worry about what they would do to him, so he lay down on the narrow bed, with his eyes shut. He wasn't afraid. The Cultural Revolution was over already, and recently the Party had been propagating the idea that all citizens were equal before the law. The police ought to be a law-abiding model for common people. As long as he remained coolheaded and reasoned with them, they might not harm him.

Late in the afternoon he was taken to the Interrogation Bureau on the second floor. On his way there, in the stairwell, he ran into the middle-aged policeman who had manhandled him. The man grinned, rolling his bulgy eyes and pointing his fingers at him like firing a pistol. Egg of a tortoise! Mr. Chiu cursed mentally.

The moment he sat down in the office, he burped, his palm shielding his mouth. In front of him, across a long desk, sat the chief of the bureau and a donkey-faced man. On the glass desktop was a folder containing information on his case. He felt it bizarre that in just a matter of hours they had accumulated a small pile of writing about him. On second thought he began to wonder whether they had kept a file on him all the time. How could this have happened? He lived and worked in Harbin, more than three hundred miles away, and this was his first time in Muji City.

The chief of the bureau was a thin, bald man, who looked serene and intelligent. His slim hands handled the written pages in the folder like those of a lecturing scholar. To Mr. Chiu's left sat a young scribe, with a clipboard on his knee and a black fountain pen in his hand.

"Your name?" the chief asked, apparently reading out the question from a form.

"Chiu Maguang."

"Age?"

"Thirty-four."

"Profession?"

"Lecturer."

"Work unit?"

"Harbin University."

"Political status?"

"Communist Party member."

The chief put down the paper and began to speak. "Your crime is sabotage, although it hasn't induced serious consequences yet. Because you are a Party member, you should be punished more. You have failed to be a model for the masses and you——"

"Excuse me, sir," Mr. Chiu cut him off.

"What?"

"I didn't do anything. Your men are the saboteurs of our social order. They threw hot tea on my feet and my wife's feet. Logically speaking, you should criticize them, if not punish them."

"That statement is groundless. You have no witness. How could I believe you?" the chief said matter-of-factly.

"This is my evidence." He raised his right hand. "Your man hit my fingers with a pistol."

"That can't prove how your feet got wet. Besides, you could hurt your fingers by yourself."

"But I told the truth!" Anger flared up in Mr. Chiu. "Your police station owes me an apology. My train ticket has expired, my new leather sandals are ruined, and I am late for a conference in the provincial capital. You must compensate me for the damage and losses. Don't mistake me for a common citizen who would tremble when you sneeze. I'm a scholar, a philosopher, and an expert in dialectical materialism. If necessary, we will argue about this in the Northeastern Daily, or we will go to the highest People's Court in Beijing. Tell me, what's your name?" He got carried away by his harangue, which was by no means trivial and had worked to his advantage on numerous occasions.

"Stop bluffing us," the donkey-faced man broke in. "We have seen a lot of your kind. We can easily prove you are guilty. Here are some of the statements given by the eyewitnesses." He pushed a few sheets of paper toward Mr. Chiu.

Mr. Chiu was dazed to see the different handwritings, which all stated that he had shouted in the square to attract attention and refused to obey the police. One of the witnesses had identified herself as a purchasing agent from a shipyard in Shanghai. Something stirred in Mr. Chiu's stomach, a pain rising to his ribs. He gave out a faint moan.

"Now, you have to admit you are guilty," the chief said. "Although it's a serious crime, we won't punish you severely, provided you write out a self-criticism and promise that you won't disrupt public order again. In other words, whether you will be released will depend on your attitude toward this crime."

"You're daydreaming," Mr. Chiu cried. "I won't write a word, because I'm innocent. I demand that you provide me with a letter of apology so I can explain to my university why I'm late."

Both the interrogators smiled with contempt. "Well, we've never done that," said the chief, taking a puff at his cigarette.

"Then make this a precedent."

"It's unnecessary. We are pretty certain that you will comply with our wishes." The chief blew a column of smoke at Mr. Chiu's face.

At the tilt of the chiefs head, two guards stepped forward and grabbed the criminal by the arms. Mr. Chiu meanwhile went on saying, "I shall report you to the provincial administration. You'll have to pay for this! You are worse than the Japanese military police."

They dragged him out of the room.

After dinner, which consisted of a bowl of millet porridge, a corn bun, and a piece of pickled turnip, Mr. Chiu began to have a fever, shaking with a chill and sweating profusely. He knew that the fire of anger had got into his liver and that he was probably having a relapse. No medicine was available, because his briefcase had been left with his bride. At home it would have been time for him to sit in front of their color TV, drinking jasmine tea and watching the evening news. It was so lonesome in here. The orange bulb above the single bed was the only source of light, which enabled the guards to keep him under surveillance at night. A moment ago he had asked them for a newspaper or a magazine to read, but they had turned him down.

Through the small opening on the door noises came in. It seemed that the police on duty were playing poker or chess in a nearby office; shouts and laughter could be heard now and then. Meanwhile, an accordion kept coughing from a remote corner in the building. Looking at the ballpoint and the letter paper left for him by the guards when they took him back from the Interrogation Bureau, Mr. Chiu remembered the old saying, "When a scholar runs into soldiers, the more he argues, the muddier his point becomes." How ridiculous this whole thing was. He ruffled his thick hair with his fingers.

He felt miserable, massaging his stomach continually. To tell the truth, he was more upset than frightened, because he would have to catch up with his work once he was back home—a paper that was to meet the publishing deadline next week, and two dozen books he ought to read for the courses he was going to teach in the fall.

A human shadow flitted across the opening. Mr. Chiu rushed to the door and shouted through the hole, "Comrade guard, comrade guard!"

"What do you want?" a voice rasped.

"I want you to inform your leaders that I'm very sick. I have heart disease and hepatitis. I may die here if you keep me like this without medication."

"No leader is on duty on the weekend. You have to wait till Monday."

"What? You mean I'll stay in here tomorrow?"

"Yes."

"Your station will be held responsible if anything happens to me."

"We know that. Take it easy, you won't die."

It seemed illogical that Mr. Chiu slept quite well that night, though the light above his head had been on all the time, and the straw mattress was hard and infested with fleas. He was afraid of ticks, mosquitoes, cockroaches—any kind of insect but fleas and bedbugs. Once in the countryside, where his school's faculty and staff had helped the peasants harvest crops for a week, his colleagues had joked about his flesh, which they said must have tasted nonhuman to fleas. Except for him, they were all afflicted with hundreds of bites.

More amazing now, he felt he didn't miss his bride a lot. He even enjoyed sleeping alone, perhaps because the honeymoon had tired him out and he needed more rest.

The back yard was quiet on Sunday morning. Pale sunlight streamed through the pine branches. A few sparrows were jumping on the ground, catching caterpillars and ladybugs. Holding the steel bars, Mr. Chiu inhaled the morning air, which smelled meaty. There must be a restaurant or a delicatessen nearby. He reminded himself that he should take this detention with ease. A sentence that Chairman Mao had written to a hospitalized friend rose in his mind: "Since you are already in here, you may as well stay and make the best of it."

His desire for peace of mind originated from his fear that his hepatitis might get worse. He tried to remain unperturbed. However, he was sure that his liver was swelling up, since the fever still persisted. For a whole day he lay in bed, thinking about his paper on the nature of contradictions. Time and again he was overwhelmed by anger, cursing aloud, "A bunch of thugs!" He swore that once he was out, he would write an article about this experience. He had better find out some of the policemen's names.

It turned out to be a restful day for the most part; he was certain that his university would send somebody to his rescue. All he should do now was remain calm and wait patiently. Sooner or later the police would have to release him, although they had no idea that he might refuse to leave unless they wrote him an apology. Damn those hoodlums, they had ordered more than they could eat!

When he woke up on Monday morning, it was already light. Somewhere a man was moaning; the sound came from the back yard. After a long yawn, and kicking off the tattered blanket, Mr. Chiu climbed out of bed and went to the window. In the middle of the yard, a young man was fastened to a pine, his wrists handcuffed from behind around the trunk. He was wriggling and swearing loudly, but there was no sign of anyone else in the yard. He looked familiar to Mr. Chiu.

Mr. Chiu squinted his eyes to see who it was. To his astonishment, he recognized the man, who was Fenjin, a recent graduate from the Law Department at Harbin University. Two years ago Mr. Chiu had taught a course in Marxist materialism, in which Fenjin had been enrolled. Now, how on earth had this young devil landed here?

Then it dawned on him that Fenjin must have been sent over by his bride. What a stupid woman! What a bookworm, who knew only how to read foreign novels. He had expected that she would talk to the school's security section, which would for sure send a cadre here. Fenjin held no official position; he merely worked in a private law firm that had just two lawyers; in fact, they had little business except for some detective work for men and women who suspected their spouses of having extramarital affairs. Mr. Chiu was overcome with a wave of nausea.

Should he call out to let his student know he was nearby? He decided not to, because he didn't know what had happened. Fenjin must have quarreled with the police to incur such a punishment. Yet, this would not have occurred if Fenjin hadn't come to his rescue. So no matter what, Mr. Chiu had to do something. But what could he do?

It was going to be a scorcher. He could see purple steam shimmering and rising from the ground among the pines. Poor devil, he thought, as he raised a bowl of corn glue to his mouth, sipped, and took a bite of a piece of salted celery.

When a guard came to collect the bowl and the chopsticks, Mr. Chiu asked him what had happened to the man in the back yard. "He called our boss 'bandit,'" the guard said. "He claimed he was a lawyer or something. An arrogant son of a rabbit."

Now it was obvious that Mr. Chiu had to do something to help his rescuer. Before he could figure out a way, a scream broke out in the back yard. He rushed to the window and saw a tall policeman standing before Fenjin, an iron bucket on the ground. It was the same young fellow who had arrested Mr. Chiu in the square two days before. The man pinched Fenjin's nose, then raised his hand, which stayed in the air for a few seconds, then slapped the lawyer across the face. As Fenjin was groaning, the man lifted up the bucket and poured the water on his head.

"This will keep you from getting sunstroke, boy. I'll give you some more every hour," the man said loudly.

Fenjin kept his eyes shut, yet his wry face showed that he was struggling to hold back from cursing the policeman or that he was probably sobbing in silence. He sneezed, then raised his face and shouted, "Let me go take a piss."

"Oh yeah?" the man bawled. "Pee in your pants."

Still Mr. Chiu didn't make any noise, holding the steel bars with both hands, his fingers white. The policeman turned and glanced at the cell's window; his pistol, partly holstered, glittered in the sun. With a snort he spat his cigarette butt to the ground and stamped it into the dust.

Then the door opened and the guards motioned Mr. Chiu to come out. Again they took him upstairs to the Interrogation Bureau.

The same men were in the office, though this time the scribe was sitting there empty-handed. At the sight of Mr. Chiu the chief said, "Ah, here you are. Please be seated."

After Mr. Chiu sat down, the chief waved a white silk fan and said to him, "You may have seen your lawyer. He's a young man without manners, so our director had him taught a crash lesson in the back yard."

"It's illegal to do that. Aren't you afraid to appear in a newspaper?"

"No, we are not, not even on TV. What else can you do? We are not afraid of any story you make up. We call it fiction. What we do care is that you cooperate with us; that's to say, you must admit your crime."

"What if I refuse to cooperate?"

"Then your lawyer will continue his education in the sunshine."

A swoon swayed Mr. Chiu, and he held the arms of the chair to steady himself. A numb pain stung him in the upper stomach and nauseated him, and his head was throbbing. He was sure that the hepatitis was finally attacking him. Anger was flaming up in his chest, his throat was tight and clogged.

The chief resumed, "As a matter of fact, you don't have to write out your self-criticism. We had your crime described clearly here. What we need is just your signature."

Holding back his rage, Mr. Chiu said, "Let me look at that."

With a smirk the donkey-faced man handed him a sheet, which carried these words: "I hereby admit that on July 13 I disrupted public order at Muji Train Station, and that I refused to listen to reason when the railroad police issued their warning. Thus I myself am responsible for my arrest. After two days' detention, I have realized the reactionary nature of my crime. From now on, I shall continue to educate myself with all my effort and shall never commit this kind of crime again."

A voice started screaming in Mr. Chiu's head, "Lie, lie!" But he shook his head and forced the voice away. He asked the chief, "If I sign this, will you release both my lawyer and me?"

"Of course, we'll do that." The chief was drumming his fingers on the blue folder—their file on him.

Mr. Chiu signed his name and put his thumbprint under his signature.

"Now you are free to go," the chief said with a smile, and handed him a piece of paper to wipe his thumb with.

Mr. Chiu was so sick that he didn't stand up from the chair at the first try. Then he doubled his effort and rose to his feet. He staggered out of the building to meet his lawyer in the back yard. In his chest he felt as though there were a bomb. If he were able to, he would have razed the entire police station and eliminated all their families. Though he knew he could do nothing like that, he made up his mind to do something.

"Sorry about this torture, Fenjin," Mr. Chiu said when they met.

"It doesn't matter. They are savages." The lawyer brushed a patch of dirt off his jacket with his trembling fingers. Water was still dribbling from the bottoms of his trouser legs.

"Let's go now," the teacher said.

The moment they came out of the police station, Mr. Chiu caught sight of a tea stand. He grabbed Fenjin's arm and walked over to the old woman at the table. "Two bowls of black tea," he said and handed her a one-yuan note.

After the first bowl, they each had another one. Then they set out for the train station. But before they walked fifty yards, Mr. Chiu insisted on eating a bowl of tree-ear soup at a food stand. Fenjin agreed. He told his teacher, "Don't treat me like a guest."

"No, I want to eat something myself."

As if dying of hunger, Mr. Chiu dragged his lawyer from restaurant to restaurant near the police station, but at each place he ordered no more than two bowls of food. Fenjin wondered why his teacher wouldn't stay at one place and eat his fill.

Mr. Chiu bought noodles, wonton, eight-grain porridge, and chicken soup, respectively, at four restaurants. While eating, he kept saying through his teeth, "If only I could kill all the bastards!" At the last place he merely took a few sips of the soup without tasting the chicken cubes and mushrooms.

Fenjin was baffled by his teacher, who looked ferocious and muttered to himself mysteriously, and whose jaundiced face was covered with dark puckers. For the first time Fenjin thought of Mr. Chiu as an ugly man.

Within a month over eight hundred people contracted acute hepatitis in Muji. Six died of the disease, including two children. Nobody knew how the epidemic had started.

(originally published in the *Antioch Review*, Volume: 59. Issue 2, Spring 2001)

All That You Love
Will Be Carried Away

Stephen King

In 2003, Stephen King (1947——) was awarded the Medal for Distinguished Contribution for American Letters by the National Book Foundation. He was perhaps one of the most recognized names in contemporary fiction by this time. All of his fifty novels had been bestsellers and most of his books and many of his short stories had been made into movies. Stephen King was a household name. He was the "King of Horror" and he has been most associated with that genre. However, he has often stepped outside of straightforward "fright-writing" into writing stories that, though they bear the characteristic stamp of his style, distinguish themselves from the main body of his work. The following short story is an example of one of these. Though dark, it is not exactly a "horror" story.

"All That You Love Will Be Carried Away" is a story about writing—writing as a record, as therapy, as a legacy, as a reason to live. Among other things, as you will see, it describes one man's writing process. Elsewhere in this book you will find a sample of King's non-fiction. That excerpt is from a book called On Writing, *in which King describes his own writing process. King's success as a writer naturally led to a demand for such a book, and it was well-received by many readers (another NEW YORK TIMES bestseller!).*

However, King's writing is not universally admired. In response to winning the National Book Award, literary critic Harold Bloom railed against King as "an immensely inadequate writer on a sentence-by-sentence, paragraph-by-paragraph, book-by-book basis" and questioned what good King's writing does "for humanity."

Consider the story that you are about to read, and the sort of writing it describes in light of our ideas of "good" and "bad" writing. How do we judge the value of writing, any writing, to humanity, as people like the judges for The National Book Foundation, or Harold Bloom, or even King himself might try to do?

Though most successful at writing novels, King claims to consider the short story to be the highest form of his craft. "All That You Love Will Be Carried Away" is perhaps one of his most finely crafted examples. The story was originally published in The New Yorker *magazine in 2001 and later in a collection of short stories by King called* Everything's Eventual *in 2002. In* Everything's Eventual, *King describes writing the story and admits that his was not the only hand involved in crafting it. King points to the ending of this story, or the lack thereof, as intentionally "ambiguous" (it is similar to that of another well-known short story by Frank R. Stockton called "The Lady or the Tiger"). He gives credit to the* New Yorker *editor Bill Buford for suggesting that he change his original ending to the one that you are about to read, before publishing it.*

It was a Motel 6 on I-80 just west of Lincoln, Nebraska. The snow that began at midafternoon had faded the sign's virulent yellow to a kinder pastel shade as the light ran out of the January dusk. The wind was closing in on that quality of empty amplification one encounters only in the country's flat midsection, usually in wintertime. That meant nothing but discomfort now, but if big snow came tonight—the weather forecasters couldn't seem to make up their minds—then the interstate would be shut down by morning. That was nothing to Alfie Zimmer.

He got his key from a man in a red vest and drove down to the end of the long cinder-block building. He had been selling in the Midwest for twenty years, and had formulated four basic rules about securing his night's rest. First, always reserve ahead. Second, reserve at a franchise motel if possible—your Holiday Inn, your Ramada Inn, your Comfort Inn, your Motel 6. Third, always ask for a room on the end. That way, the worst you could have was one set of noisy neighbors. Last, ask for a room that begins with a one. Alfie was forty-four, too old to be fucking truck-stop whores, eating chicken-fried steak, or hauling his luggage upstairs. These days, the rooms on the first floor were usually reserved for non-smokers. Alfie rented them and smoked anyway.

Someone had taken the space in front of room 190. All the spaces along the building were taken. Alfie wasn't surprised. You could make a reservation, guarantee it, but if you arrived late (late on a day like this was after 4 P.M.), you had to park and walk. The cars belonging to the early birds were nestled up to the gray cinder block and the bright-yellow doors in a long line, their windows already covered with a scrim of light snow.

Alfie drove around the corner and parked with the nose of his Chevrolet pointed at the white expanse of some farmer's field, swimming deep into the gray of day's end. At the farthest limit of vision he could see the spark lights of a farm. In there, they would be hunkered down. Out here, the wind blew hard enough to rock the car. Snow skated past, obliterating the farm lights for a few moments.

Alfie was a big man with a florid face and a smoker's respiration. He was wearing a topcoat, because when you were selling that was what people liked to see. Not a jacket. Storekeepers sold to people wearing jackets and John Deere caps, they didn't buy from them. The room key lay on the seat beside him. It was attached to a diamond of green plastic. The key was a real key, not a MagCard. On the radio Clint Black was singing "Nothin' but the Tail Lights." It was a country song. Lincoln had an FM rocker now, but rock-and-roll music didn't seem right to Alfie. Not out here, where if you switched over to AM you could still hear angry old men calling down hellfire.

He shut off the engine, put the key to 190 in his pocket, and checked to make sure he still had his notebook in there, too. His old pal. "Save Russian Jews," he said, reminding himself. "Collect valuable prizes."

He got out of the car and a gust of wind hit him hard, rocking him back on his heels, flapping his pants around his legs, making him laugh a smoker's surprised rattle-box laugh.

His samples were in the trunk, but he wouldn't need them tonight. No, not tonight, not at all. He took his suitcase and his briefcase out of the back-seat, shut the door, then pushed the black button on his key fob. That one locked all the doors. The red one set off an alarm, what you were supposed to use if you were going to get mugged. Alfie had never been mugged. He guessed that few salesmen of gourmet foods were, especially in this part of the country. Ther+e was a market for gourmet foods in Nebraska, Iowa, Oklahoma, and Kansas; even in the Dakotas, although many might not believe it. Alfie had done quite well, especially over the last two years as he got to know the market's deeper creases—but it was never going to equal the market for, let's say, fertilizer. Which he could smell now on the winter wind that was freezing his cheeks and turning them an even darker shade of red.

He stood where he was a moment longer, waiting for the wind to drop. It did, and he could see the spark lights again. The farmhouse. And was it possible that behind those lights, some farmer's wife was even now heating up a pot of Cottager Split Pea Soup or perhaps microwaving a Cottager Shepherd's Pie or Chicken Français? It was. It was as possible as hell. While her husband watched the early news with his shoes off and his sock feet on a hassock, and overhead their son played a video game on his GameCube and their daughter sat in the tub, chin-deep in fragrant bubbles, her hair tied up with a ribbon, reading *The Golden Compass*, by Philip Pullman, or perhaps one of the Harry Potter books, which were favorites of Alfie's daughter, Carlene. All that going on behind the spark lights, some family's universal joint turning smoothly in its socket, but between them and the edge of this parking lot was a mile and a half of flat field, white in the running-away light of a low sky, comatose with the season. Alfie briefly imagined himself walking into that field in his city shoes, his briefcase in one hand and his suitcase in the other, working his way across the frozen furrows, finally arriving, knocking; the door would be opened and he would smell pea soup, that good hearty smell, and hear the KETV meteorologist in the other room saying, "But now look at this low-pressure system just coming over the Rockies."

And what would Alfie say to the farmer's wife? That he just dropped by for dinner? Would he advise her to save Russian Jews, collect valuable prizes? Would he begin by saying, "Ma'am, according to at least one source I've read recently, all that you love will be carried away"? That would be a good conversation opener, sure to interest the farmer's wife in the wayfaring stranger who had just walked across her husband's east field to knock on her door. And when she invited him to step in, to tell her more, he could open his briefcase and give her a couple of his sample books, tell her that once she discovered the Cottager brand of quickserve gourmet delicacies she would almost certainly want to move on to the more sophisticated pleasures of Ma Mère. And, by the way, did she have a taste for caviar? Many did. Even in Nebraska.

Freezing. Standing here and freezing.

He turned from the field and the spark lights at the far end of it and walked to the motel, moving in careful duck steps so he wouldn't go ass over teakettle. He had done it before, God knew. Whoops-a-daisy in a half a hundred motel parking lots. He had done most of it before, actually, and supposed that was at least part of the problem.

There was an overhang, so he was able to get out of the snow. There was a Coke machine with a sign saying, USE CORRECT CHANGE. There was an ice machine and a Snax machine with candy bars and various kinds of potato chips behind curls of metal like bedsprings. There was no USE CORRECT CHANGE sign on the Snax machine. From the room to the left of the one where he intended to kill himself, Alfie could hear the early news, but it would sound better in that farmhouse over yonder, he was sure of that. The wind boomed. Snow swirled around his city shoes, and then Alfie let himself into his room. The light switch was to the left. He turned it on and shut the door.

He knew the room; it was the room of his dreams. It was square. The walls were white. On one was a picture of a small boy in a straw hat, asleep with a fishing pole in his hand. There was a green rug on the floor, a quarter-inch of some nubbly synthetic stuff. It was cold in here right now, but when he pushed the Hi Heat button on the control panel of the Climatron beneath the window the place would warm up fast. Would probably become hot. A counter ran the length of one wall. There was a TV on it. On top of the TV was a piece of cardboard with ONE-TOUCH MOVIES! printed on it.

There were twin double beds, each covered with bright-gold spreads that had been tucked under the pillows and then pulled over them, so the pillows looked like the corpses of infants. There was a table between the beds with a Gideon Bible, a TV-channel guide, and a flesh-colored phone on it. Beyond the second bed was the door to the bathroom. When you turned on the light in there, the fan would go on, too. If you wanted the light, you got the fan, too. There was no way around it. The light itself would be fluorescent, with the ghosts of dead flies inside. On the counter beside the sink there would be a hot plate and a Proctor-Silex electric kettle and little packets of instant coffee. There was a smell in here, the mingling of some harsh cleaning fluid and mildew on the shower curtain. Alfie knew it all. He had dreamed it right down to the green rug, but that was no accomplishment, it was an easy dream. He thought about turning on the heater, but that would rattle, too, and, besides, what was the point?

Alfie unbuttoned his topcoat and put his suitcase on the floor at the foot of the bed closest to the bathroom. He put his briefcase on the gold coverlet. He sat down, the sides of his coat spreading out like the skirt of a dress. He opened his briefcase, thumbed through the various brochures, catalogues, and order forms; finally, he found the gun. It was a Smith & Wesson revolver, .38 caliber. He put it on the pillows at the head of the bed.

He lit a cigarette, reached for the telephone, then remembered his notebook. He reached into his right coat pocket and pulled it out. It was an old Spiral, bought for a buck forty-nine in the stationery department of some forgotten five-and-dime in Omaha or Sioux City or maybe Jubilee, Kansas. The cover was creased and almost completely innocent of any printing it might once have borne. Some of the pages had pulled partially free of the metal coil that served as the notebook's binding, but all of them were still there. Alfie had been carrying this notebook for almost seven years, ever since his days selling Universal Product Code readers for Simonex.

There was an ashtray on the shelf under the phone. Out here, some of the motel rooms still came with ashtrays, even on the first floor. Alfie fished for it, put his cigarette on the groove, and opened his notebook. He flipped through pages written with a hundred different pens (and a few pencils), pausing to read a couple of entries. One read: "I suckt Jim Morrison's cock w/my poutie boy mouth (LAWRENCE KS)." Restrooms were filled with homosexual graffiti, most of it tiresome and repetitive, but "poutie boy mouth" was pretty good. Another was "Albert Gore is my favorite whore (MURDO S DAK)."

The last page, three quarters of the way through the book, had just two entries. "Don't chew the Trojan Gum it taste's just like rubber (A VOCA IA)." And: "Poopie doopie you so loopy (PAPILLION NEB)." Alfie was crazy about that one. Something about the "-ie,-ie," and then, boom, you got "-y." It could have been no more than an illiterate's mistake (he was sure that would have been maura's take on it) but why think like that? What fun was that? No, Alfie preferred, (even now) to believe that "-ie,-ie," . . . wait for it . . . "-y" was an intended construction. Something sneaky but playful, with the feel of an e.e. cummings poem.

He rummaged through the stuff in his inside coat pocket, feeling papers, an old toll-ticket, a bottle of pills—stuff he had quit taking—and at last finding the pen that always hid in the litter. Time to record today's finds. Two good ones, both from the same rest area, one over the urinal he had used, the other written with a Sharpie on the map case beside the Hav-A-Bite machine. (Snax, which in Alfie's opinion vended a superior product line, had for some reason been disenfranchised in the I-80 rest areas about four years ago.) These days Alfie sometimes went two weeks and three thousand miles without seeing anything new, or even a viable variation on something old. Now, two in one day. Two on the *last* day. Like some sort of omen.

His pen had COTTAGER FOODS THE *GOOD* STUFF! written in gold along the barrel, next to the logo, a thatched hut with smoke coming out of the quaintly crooked chimney.

Sitting there on the bed, still in his topcoat, Alfie bent studiously over his old notebook so that his shadow fell on the page. Below "Don't chew the Trojan Gum" and "Poopie doopie you so loopy," Alfie added "Save Russian Jews, collect valuable prizes (WALTON NEB)" and "All that you love will be carried away (WALTON NEB)." He hesitated. He rarely added notes, liking his finds to stand alone. Explanation rendered the exotic mundane (or so he had come to believe; in the early years he had annotated much more freely), but from time to time a footnote still seemed to be more illuminating than demystifying.

He starred the second entry—"All that you love will be carried away (WALTON NEB)"—and drew a line two inches above the bottom of the page, and wrote.*

*"To read this you must also look at the exit ramp from the Walton Rest Area back to highway, i.e. at departing transients."

He put the pen back in his pocket, wondering why he or anyone would continue anything this close to ending everything. He couldn't think of a single answer. But of course you went on breathing, too. You couldn't stop it without rough surgery.

The wind gusted outside. Alfie looked briefly toward the window, where the curtain (also green, but a different shade from the rug) had been drawn. If he pulled it back, he would be able to see chains of light on Interstate 80, each bright bead marking sentient beings running on the rod of the highway. Then he looked back down at his book. He meant to do it, all right. This was just . . . well . . .

"Breathing," he said, and smiled. He picked his cigarette out of the ash-tray, smoked, returned it to its groove, and thumbed back through the book again. The entries recalled thousands of truck stops and roadside chicken shacks and highway rest areas the way certain songs on the radio can bring back specific memories of a place, a time, the person you were with, what you were drinking, what you were thinking.

"Here I sit, brokenhearted, tried to shit but only farted." Everyone knew that one, but there was an interesting variation from Double D Steaks in Hooker, Oklahoma: "Here I sit, I'm at a loss, trying to shit out taco sauce. I know I'm going to drop a load, only hope I don't explode." And from Casey, Iowa, where SR 25 crossed I-80: "My mother made me a whore." To which someone had added in very different penmanship: If I supply the yarn will she make me one?"

He had started collecting when he was selling the UPCs, noting various bits of graffiti in the Spiral notebook without at first knowing why he was doing it. They were just amusing, or disconcerting, or both at the same time. Yet little by little he had become fascinated with these messages from the interstate, where the only other communication seemed to be dipped head-lights when you passed in the rain, or maybe somebody in a bad mood flip-ping you the bird when you went by in the passing lane pulling a rooster-tail of snow behind you. He came gradually to see—or perhaps only to hope—that something was going on here. The e.e. cummings lilt of "Poopie doopie you so loopy," for instance, or the inarticulate rage of "I 380 West Avenue kill my mother TAKE HER JEWELS."

Or take this oldie: "Here I sit, cheeks a-flexin', giving birth to another Texan." The meter, when you considered it, was odd. Not iambs but some odd triplet formula with the stress on the third: "Here I *sit*, cheeks a-*flexin'*, giving *birth* to *another Tex*an." Okay, it broke down a little at the end, but that somehow added to it memorability, gave it that final mnemonic twist of the tail. He had thought on many occasions that he could go back to school, take some course, get all that feet-and-meter stuff down pat. Know what he was talking about instead of running on a tightrope of intuition. All he really remembered clearly from school was iambic pentameter: "To be or not to be, that is the question." He had seen that in a men's room on I-70, actually, to which someone had added, "The real question is who your father was, dipstick."

These triplets, now. What were *they* called? Was that trochaic? He didn't know. The fact that he could find out no longer seemed important, but he could find out, yes. It was something people taught; it was no big secret.

Or take this variation, which Alfie had also seen all over the country: "Here I sit, on the pooper, giving birth to a Maine state trooper." It was always

Maine, no matter where you were it was always Maine State Trooper, and why? Because no other state would scan. Maine was the only one of the fifty whose name consisted of a single syllable. Yet again, it was in triplets: "Here I *sit*, on the *pooper*."

He had thought of writing a book. Just a little one. The first title to occur to him had been "Don't Look Up Here, You're Pissing on Your Shoes," but you couldn't call a book that. Not and reasonably hope that someone would put it out for sale in a store, anyway. And, besides, that was light. Frothy. He had become convinced over the years that something was going on here, and it wasn't frothy. The title he had finally decided on was an adaptation of something he'd seen in a rest area toilet stall outside Fort Scott, Kansas, on Highway 54. "I Killed Ted Bundy: The Secret Transit Code of America's Highways." By Alfred Zimmer. That sounded mysterious and ominous, almost scholarly. But he hadn't done it. And although he had seen "If I supply the yarn, will she make me one" added to "My mother made me a whore" all over the country, he had never expounded (at least in writing) on the startling lack of sympathy, the "just deal with it" sensibility, of the response. Or what about "Mammon is the King of new Jersey"? How did one explain why New Jersey made it funny and the name of some other state probably wouldn't? Even to try seemed almost arrogant. He was just a little man, after all, with a little man's job. He sold things. A line of frozen dinners, currently.

And now, of course . . . now . . .

Alfie took another deep drag on his cigarette, mashed it out, and called home. He didn't expect to get Maura and didn't. It was his own recorded voice that answered him, ending with the number of his cell-phone. A lot of good that would do; the cell-phone was in the trunk of the Chevrolet, broken. He had never had good luck with gadgets.

After the beep he said, "Hi, it's me. I'm in Lincoln. It's snowing. Remember the casserole you were going to take over to my mother. She'll be expecting it. And she asked for the Red Ball coupons. I know you think she's crazy on that subject, but humor her, okay? She's old. Tell Carlene Daddy says hi." He paused, then for the first time in about five years he added, "I love you."

He hung up, thought about another cigarette—no worries about lung cancer, not now—and decided against it. He put the notebook, open to the last page, beside the telephone. He picked up the gun and rolled out the cylinder. Fully loaded. He snapped the cylinder back with a flick of his wrist, then slipped the short barrel into his mouth. It tasted of oil and metal. He thought, *Here I* SIT, *about to* COOL *it, my plan to* EAT *a fuckin'* BOOL-*it*. He grinned around the barrel. That was terrible. He never would have written that down in his book.

Then another thought occurred to him and he put the gun back in its trench on the pillow, and drew the phone to him again, and once more dialed home.

He waited for his voice to recite the useless cell-phone number, then said, "Me again. Don't forget Rambo's appointment at the vet day after tomorrow, okay? Also, the sea-jerky strips at night. They really do help his hips. Bye."

He hung up and raised the gun again. Before he could put the barrel in his mouth, his eye fell on the notebook. He frowned and put the gun down. The book was open to the last four entries. The first thing anyone responding to the shot would see would be his dead body, sprawled across the bed closest to the bathroom, his head hanging down and bleeding on the nubbly green rug. The second thing, however, would be the Spiral notebook, open to the final written page.

Alfie imagined some cop, some Nebraska state trooper who would never be written about on any bathroom wall due to the disciplines of scansion, reading those final entries, perhaps turning the battered old notebook toward him with the tip of his own pen. He would read the first three entries— "Trojan Gum," "Poopie doopie," "Save Russian Jews"—and dismiss them as insanity. He would read the last line, "All that you love will be carried away," and decide that the dead guy had regained a little rationality at the end, just enough to write a halfway sensible suicide note.

Alfie didn't like the idea of people thinking he was crazy (further examination of the book, which contained such information as "Medger Evers is alive and well in Disneyland," would only confirm that impression). He was not crazy, and the things he had written here over the years weren't crazy, either. He was convinced of it. And if he was wrong, if these were the rantings of lunatics, they needed to be examined even more closely. That thing about don't look up here, you're pissing on your shoes, for instance, was that humor? Or a growl of rage?

He considered using the john to get rid of the notebook, then shook his head. He'd end up on his knees with his shirtsleeves rolled back, fishing around in there trying to get the damn thing back out. While the fan rattled and the fluorescent buzzed. And although immersion might blur some of the ink, it wouldn't blur all of it. Not enough. Besides, the notebook had been with him so long, riding in his pocket across so many flat and empty Midwest miles. He hated the idea of just flushing it away.

The last page, then? Surely one page, balled up, would go down. But that would leave the rest of them (there was always a them) to discover, all that clear evidence of an unsound mind. They'd say, "Lucky he didn't decide to visit a schoolyard with an AK-47. Take a bunch of little kids with him." And it would follow Maura like a tin can tied to a dog's tail. "Did you hear about her husband?" they'd ask each other in the supermarket. "Killed himself in a motel. Left a book full of crazy stuff. Lucky he didn't kill *her.*" Well, he could afford to be a little hard about that. Maura was an adult, after all. Carlene, on the other hand . . . Carlene was . . .

Alfie looked at his watch. At her j.v. basketball game, that's where Carlene was right now. Her teammates would say most of the same things the supermarket ladies would say, only within earshot and accompanied by those chilling seventh-grade giggles. Eyes full of glee and horror. Was that fair? No, of course not, but there was nothing fair about what had happened to him, either. Sometimes when you were cruising along the highway, you saw big curls of rubber that had unwound from the recap tires some of the independent truckers used. That was what he felt like now: thrown tread. The pills made it worse. They cleared your mind just enough to see what a colossal jam you were in.

"But I'm not crazy," he said. "That doesn't make me crazy." No. Crazy might actually be better.

Alfie picked up the notebook, flipped it closed much as he had flipped the cylinder back into the .38, and sat there tapping it against his leg. This was ludicrous.

Ludicrous or not, it nagged him. The way thinking a stove burner might still be on sometimes nagged him when he was home, nagged until he finally got up and checked and found it cold. Only this was worse. Because he loved the stuff in the notebook. Amassing graffiti—thinking about graffiti—had been his real work these last years, not selling price-code readers or frozen dinners that were really not much more than Swansons or Freezer Queens in fancy microwavable dishes. The daffy exuberance of "Helen Keller fucked her feller!" for instance. Yet the notebook might be a real embarrassment once he was dead. It would be like accidentally hanging yourself in the closet because you were experimenting with a new way of jacking off and got found that way with your shorts under your feet and shit on your ankle. Some of the stuff in his notebook might show up in the newspaper, along with his picture. Once upon a time he would have scoffed at the idea, but in these days, when even Bible Belt newspapers routinely speculated about a mole on the President's penis, the notion was hard to dismiss.

Burn it, then? No, he'd set off the goddamned smoke detector.

Put it behind the picture on the wall? The picture of the little boy with the fishing pole and the straw hat?

Alfie considered this, then nodded slowly. Not a bad idea at all. The Spiral notebook might stay there for years. Then, someday in the distant future, it would drop out. Someone—perhaps a lodger, more likely a maid—would pick it up, curious. Would flip through it. What would that person's reaction be? Shock? Amusement? Plain old head-scratching puzzlement? Alfie rather hoped for this last. Because things in the notebook were puzzling. "Elvis killed Big Pussy," someone in Hackberry, Texas, had written. "Serenity is being square," someone in Rapid City, South Dakota, had opined. And below that, someone had written, "No, stupid, serenity $= (va)^2 + b$, if $v =$ serenity, $a =$ satisfaction, and $b =$ sexual compatibility."

Behind the picture, then.

Alfie was halfway across the room when he remembered the pills in his coat pocket. And there were more in the glove compartment of the car, different kinds but for the same thing. They were prescription drugs, but not the sort the doctor gave you if your were feeling . . . well . . . sunny. So the cops would search this room thoroughly for other kinds of drugs and when they lifted the picture away from the wall the notebook would drop out onto the green rug. The things in it would look even worse, even crazier, because of the pains he had taken to hide it.

And they'd read the last thing as a suicide note, simply because it *was* the last thing. No matter where he left the book, that would happen. Sure as shit sticks to the ass of America, as some East Texas turnpike poet had once written.

"If they find it," he said, and just like that the answer came to him.

The snow had thickened, the wind had grown even stronger, and the spark lights across the field were gone. Alfie stood beside his snow-covered car at the edge of the parking lot with his coat billowing out in front of him. At the farm, they'd all be watching TV by now. The whole fam' damly. Assuming the satellite dish hadn't blown off the barn roof, that was. Back at his place, his wife and daughter would be arriving at home from Carlene's basketball game. Maura and Carlene lived in a world that had little to do with interstates, or fast food boxes blowing down the breakdown lanes and the sound of semis passing you at seventy and eighty and even ninety miles an hour like a Doppler whine. He wasn't complaining about it (or hoped he wasn't); he was just pointing it out. "Nobody here even if there is," someone in Chalk Level, Missouri, had written on a shithouse wall, and sometimes in those rest-area bathrooms there was blood, mostly just a little, but once he had seen a grimy basin under a scratched steel mirror half filled with it. Did anyone notice? Did anyone report such things?

In some rest areas the weather report fell constantly from overhead speakers, and to Alfie the voice giving it sounded haunted, the voice of a ghost running through the vocal chords of a corpse. In Candy, Kansas, on Route 283, in Ness County, someone had written, "Behold, I stand at the door and knock," to which someone else had added, "If your not from Pudlishers Cleering House go away you Bad Boy."

Alfie stood at the edge of the pavement, gasping a little because the air was so cold and full of snow. In his left hand he held the Spiral notebook, bent almost double. There was no need to destroy it, after all. He would simply throw it into Farmer John's east field, here on the west side of Lincoln. The wind would help him. The notebook might carry twenty feet on the fly, and the wind could tumble it even farther before it finally fetched up against the side of the furrow and was covered. It would lie there buried all winter, long after his body had been shipped home. In the spring, Farmer John would come out this way on his tractor, the cab filled with the music of patty loveless or George Jones or maybe even Clint Black, and he would plow the Spiral notebook under without seeing it and it would disappear into the scheme of things. Always supposing there was one. "Relax, it's all just the rinse cycle," someone had written beside a pay phone on I-35 not far from Cameron, Missouri.

Alfie drew the book back to throw it, then lowered his arm. He hated to let it go, that was the truth of it. That was the bottom line everyone was always talking about. But things were bad, now. He raised his arm again and then lowered it again. In his distress and indecision he began to cry without being aware of it. The wind rushed around him, on its way to wherever. He couldn't go on living the way he had been living, he knew that much. Not one more day. And a shot in the mouth would be easier than any living change, he knew that, too. Far easier than struggling to write a book few people (if any at all) were likely to read. He raised his arm again, cocked the hand with the notebook in it back to his ear like a pitcher preparing to throw a fastball, then stood like that. An idea occurred to him. He would count to sixty. If the spark lights of the farmhouse reappeared at any time during that count, he would try to write the book.

To write a book like that, he thought, you'd have to begin by talking about how it was to measure distance in green mile markers, and the very width of the land, and how the wind sounded when you got out of your car at one of those rest areas in Oklahoma or North Dakota. How it sounded almost like words. You'd have to explicate the silence, and how the bathroom always smelled of piss and the great hollow farts of departed travelers, and how in that silence the voices on the walls began to speak. The voices of those who had written and then moved on. The telling would hurt, but if the wind dropped and the spark lights of the farm came back, he'd do it anyway.

If they didn't he'd throw the notebook into the field, go back into Room 190 (just hang a left at the Snax machine), and shoot himself, as planned.

Either way. Either way.

Alfie stood there counting to sixty inside his head, waiting to see if the wind would drop.

The Daydreams of a Drunk Woman[1]

Clarice Lispector

Clarice Lispector was born in December 1925 in the small Ukrainian town of Tchetchelik while her Russian-Jewish parents were in the process of immigrating to Brazil, where they settled in the little town of Recife. At the age of twelve, she had already graduated from secondary school and published her first short story. While working on a law degree, she also became the first female reporter for a major Brazilian newspaper, and in 1944, she published her first novel, Close to the Savage Heart, *the same year that she graduated from law school.*

During law school, she married a Brazilian diplomat and was able to travel extensively throughout Europe and live in Washington, DC. After a divorce from her husband, she returned to Brazil with her two sons, where she lived the rest of her life, until she died from an extended battle with cancer on December 9, 1977.

One of the major influences on Lispector is the existential theories and literature of Jon Paul Sartre, which argues that each of us is the product of our own choices. In "Daydreams of a Drunk Woman," the protagonist struggles with the reality that it is her choices that have created the nightmare that is her life.

It seemed to her that the trolley cars were about to cross through the room as they caused her reflected image to tremble. She was combing her hair at her leisure in front of the dressing table with its three mirrors, and her strong white arms shivered in the coolness of the evening. Her eyes did not look away as the mirrors trembled, sometimes dark, sometimes luminous. Outside, from a window above, something heavy and hollow fell to the ground. Had her husband and the little ones been at home, the idea would already have occurred to her that they were to blame. Her eyes did not take themselves off her image, her comb worked pensively, and her open dressing gown revealed in the mirrors the intersected breasts of several women.

"Evening News" shouted the newsboy to the mild breeze in Riachuelo Street,[2] and something trembled as if foretold. She threw her comb down on the dressing table and sang dreamily: "Who saw the little spar-row . . . it passed by the window . . . and flew beyond Minho!"[3]—but, suddenly becoming irritated, she shut up abruptly like a fan.

She lay down and fanned herself impatiently with a newspaper that rustled in the room. She clutched the bedsheet, inhaling its odor as she crushed its starched embroidery with her red-lacquered nails. Then, almost smiling, she started to fan herself once more. Oh my!—she sighed as she began to smile. She beheld the picture of her bright smile, the smile of a woman who was still young, and she continued to smile to herself, closing her eyes and fanning herself still more vigorously. Oh my!—she would come fluttering in from the street like a butterfly.

"Hey there! Guess who came to see me today?" she mused as a feasible and interesting topic of conversation. "No idea, tell me," those eyes asked her with a gallant smile, those sad eyes set in one of those pale faces that make one feel so uncomfortable. "Maria Quiteria, my dear!" she replied coquettishly with her hand on her hip. "And who, might we ask, would she be?" they insisted gallantly, but now without any expression. "You!" she broke off, slightly annoyed. How boring!

Oh what a succulent room! Here she was, fanning herself in Brazil. The sun, trapped in the blinds, shimmered on the wall like the strings of a guitar. Riachuelo Street shook under the gasping weight of the trolley cars which came from Mem de Sá Street. Curious and impatient, she listened to the vibrations of the china cabinet in the drawing room. Impatiently she rolled over to lie face downward, and, sensuously stretching the toes of her dainty feet, she awaited her next thought with open eyes. "Whosoever found, searched," she said to herself in the form of a rhymed refrain, which always ended up by sounding like some maxim. Until eventually she fell asleep with her mouth wide open, her saliva staining the pillow.

She only woke up when her husband came into the room the moment he returned from work. She did not want to eat any dinner nor to abandon her dreams, and she went back to sleep: let him content himself with the leftovers from lunch.

And now that the kids were at the country house of their aunts in Jacarepaguá,[4] she took advantage of their absence in order to begin the day as she pleased: restless and frivolous in her bed . . . one of those whims perhaps. Her husband appeared before her, having already dressed, and she did not even know what he had prepared for his breakfast. She avoided examining his suit to see whether it needed brushing . . . little did she care if this was his day for attending to his business in the city. But when he bent over to kiss her, her capriciousness crackled like a dry leaf.

"Don't paw me!"

"What the devil's the matter with you?" the man asked her in amazement, as he immediately set about attempting some more effective caress.

Obstinate, she would not have known what to reply, and she felt so touchy and aloof that she did not even know where to find a suitable reply. She suddenly lost her temper. "Go to hell! . . . prowling round me like some old tomcat."

He seemed to think more clearly and said, firmly, "You're ill, my girl."

She accepted his remark, surprised, and vaguely flattered.

She remained in bed the whole day long listening to the silence of the house without the scurrying of the kids, without her husband who would have his meals in the city today. Her anger was tenuous and ardent. She only got up to go to the bathroom, from which she returned haughty and offended.

The morning turned into a long enormous afternoon, which then turned into a shallow night, which innocently dawned throughout the entire house.

She was still in bed, peaceful and casual. She was in love. . . . She was anticipating her love for the man whom she would love one day. Who knows, this sometimes happened, and without any guilt or injury for either partner. Lying in bed thinking and thinking, and almost laughing as one does over some gossip. Thinking and thinking. About what? As if she knew. So she just stayed there.

The next minute she would get up, angry. But in the weakness of that first instant she felt dizzy and fragile in the room which swam round and round until she managed to grope her way back to bed, amazed that it might be true. "Hey, girl, don't you go getting sick on me!" she muttered suspiciously. She raised her hand to her forehead to see if there was any fever.

That night, until she fell asleep, her mind became more and more delirious—for how many minutes?—until she flopped over, fast asleep, to snore beside her husband.

She awoke late, the potatoes waiting to be peeled, the kids expected home that same evening from their visit to the country. "God, I've lost my self-respect, I have! My day for washing and darning socks.... What a lazy bitch you've turned out to be!" she scolded herself, inquisitive and pleased ... shopping to be done, fish to remember, already so late on a hectic sunny morning.

But on Saturday night they went to the tavern in Tiradentes Square[5] at the invitation of a rich businessman, she with her new dress which didn't have any fancy trimmings but was made of good material, a dress that would last her a lifetime. On Saturday night, drunk in Tiradentes Square, inebriated but with her husband at her side to give her support, and being very polite in front of the other man who was so much more refined and rich—striving to make conversation, for she was no provincial ninny and she had already experienced life in the capital. But so drunk that she could no longer stand.

And if her husband was not drunk it was only because he did not want to show disrespect for the businessman, and, full of solicitude and humility, he left the swaggering to the other fellow. His manner suited such an elegant occasion, but it gave her such an urge to laugh! She despised him beyond words! She looked at her husband stuffed into his new suit and found him so ridiculous ... so drunk that she could no longer stand, but without losing her self-respect as a woman. And the green wine[6] from her native Portugal slowly being drained from her glass.

When she got drunk, as if she had eaten a heavy Sunday lunch, all things which by their true nature are separate from each other—the smell of oil on the one hand, of a male on the other; the soup tureen on the one hand, the waiter on the other—became strangely linked by their true nature and the whole thing was nothing short of disgraceful ... shocking!

And if her eyes appeared brilliant and cold, if her movements faltered clumsily until she succeeded in reaching the toothpick holder, beneath the surface she really felt so far quite at ease ... there was that full cloud to transport her without effort. Her puffy lips, her teeth white, and her body swollen with wine. And the vanity of feeling drunk, making her show such disdain for everything, making her feel swollen and rotund like a large cow.

Naturally she talked, since she lacked neither the ability to converse nor topics to discuss. But the words that a woman uttered when drunk were like being pregnant—mere words on her lips which had nothing to do with the secret core that seemed like a pregnancy. God, how queer she felt! Saturday night, her every-day soul lost, and how satisfying to lose it, and to remind her of former days, only her small, ill-kempt hands—and here she was now with her elbows resting on the white and red checked tablecloth like a gambling table, deeply launched upon a degrading and revolting existence. And what about her laughter? ... this outburst of laughter which mysteriously emerged from her full white throat, in response to the polite manners of the businessman, an outburst of laughter coming from the depths of that sleep, and from the depths of that security of someone who has a body. Her white flesh was as sweet as lobster, the legs of a live lobster wriggling slowly in the air . . . that urge to be sick in order to plunge that sweetness into something really awful . . . and that perversity of someone who has a body.

She talked and listened with curiosity to what she herself was about to reply to the well-to-do businessman who had so kindly invited them out to dinner and paid for their meal. Intrigued and amazed, she heard what she was on the point of replying, and what she might say in her present state would serve as an augury for the future. She was no longer a lobster, but a harsher sign—that of the scorpion. After all, she had been born in November.

A beacon that sweeps through the dawn while one is asleep, such was her drunkenness which floated slowly through the air.

At the same time, she was conscious of such feelings! Such feelings! When she gazed upon that picture which was so beautifully painted in the restaurant, she was immediately overcome by an artistic sensibility. No one would get it out of her head that she had really been born for greater things. She had always been one for works of art.

But such sensibility! And not merely excited by the picture of grapes and pears and dead fish with shining scales. Her sensibility irritated her without causing her pain, like a broken fingernail. And if she wanted, she could allow herself the luxury of becoming even more sensitive, she could go still further, because she was protected by a situation, protected like everyone who had attained a position in life. Like someone saved from misfortune. I'm so miserable, dear God! If she wished, she could even pour more wine into her glass, and, protected by the position which she had attained in life, become even more drunk just so long as she did not lose her self-respect. And so, even more drunk, she peered round the room, and how she despised the barren people in that restaurant. Not a real man among them. How sad it really all seemed. How she despised the barren people in that restaurant, while she was plump and heavy and generous to the full. And everything in the restaurant seemed so remote, the one thing distant from the other, as if the one might never be able to converse with the other. Each existing for itself, and God existing there for everyone.

Her eyes once more settled on that female whom she had instantly detested the moment she had entered the room. Upon arriving, she had spotted her seated at a table accompanied by a man and all dolled up in a hat and jewelry, glittering like a false coin, all coy and refined. What a fine hat she was wearing! . . . Bet you anything she isn't even married for all that pious look on her face . . . and that fine hat stuck on her head. A fat lot of good her hypocrisy would do her, and she had better watch out in case her airs and graces proved her undoing! The more sanctimonious they were, the bigger frauds they turned out to be. And as for the waiter, he was a great nitwit, serving her, full of gestures and finesse, while the sallow man with her pretended not to notice. And that pious ninny so pleased with herself in that hat and so modest about her slim waistline, and I'll bet she couldn't even bear her man a child. All right, it was none of her business, but from the moment she arrived she felt the urge to give that blonde prude of a woman playing the grand lady in her hat a few good slaps on the face. She didn't even have any shape, and she was flat-chested. And no doubt, for all her fine hats, she was nothing more than a fishwife trying to pass herself off as a duchess.

Oh, how humiliated she felt at having come to the bar without a hat, and her head now felt bare. And that madam with her affectations, playing the refined lady! I know what you need, my beauty, you and your sallow boy friend! And if you think I envy you with your flat chest, let me assure you that I don't give a damn for you and your hats. Shameless sluts like you are only asking for a good hard slap on the face.

In her holy rage, she stretched out a shaky hand and reached for a toothpick.

But finally, the difficulty of arriving home disappeared; she now bestirred herself amidst the familiar reality of her room, now seated on the edge of the bed, a slipper dangling from one foot.

And, as she had half closed her blurred eyes, everything took on the appearance of flesh, the foot of the bed, the window, the suit her husband had thrown off, and everything became rather painful. Meanwhile, she was becoming larger, more unsteady, swollen and gigantic. If only she could get closer to herself, she would find she was even larger. Each of her arms could be explored by someone who didn't even recognize that they were dealing with an arm, and someone could plunge into each eye and swim around without knowing that it was an eye. And all around her everything was a bit painful. Things of the flesh stricken by nervous twinges. The chilly air had caught her as she had come out of the restaurant.

She was sitting up in bed, resigned and sceptical. And this was nothing yet, God only knew—she was perfectly aware that this was nothing yet. At this moment things were happening to her that would only hurt later and in earnest. When restored to her normal size, her anesthetized body would start to wake up, throbbing, and she would begin to pay for those big meals and drinks. Then, since this would really end up by happening. I might as well open my eyes right now (which she did) and then everything looked smaller and clearer, without her feeling any pain. Everything, deep down, was the same, only smaller and more familiar. She was sitting quite upright in bed, her stomach so full, absorbed and resigned, with the delicacy of one who sits waiting until her partner awakens. "You gorge yourself and I pay the piper," she said sadly, looking at the dainty white toes of her feet. She looked around her, patient and obedient. Ah, words, nothing but words, the objects in the room lined up in the order of words, to form those confused and irksome phrases that he who knows how will read. Boredom . . . such awful boredom. . . . How sickening! How very annoying! When all is said and done, heaven help me—God knows best. What was one to do? How can I describe this thing inside me? Anyhow, God knows best. And to think that she had enjoyed herself so much last night . . . and to think of how nice it all was—a restaurant to her liking—and how she had been seated elegantly at table. At table! The world would exclaim. But she made no reply, drawing herself erect with a bad-tempered click of her tongue . . . irritated . . . "Don't come to me with your endearments" . . . disenchanted, resigned, satiated, married, content, vaguely nauseated.

It was at this moment that she became deaf; one of her senses was missing. She clapped the palm of her hand over her ear, which only made things worse . . . suddenly filling her eardrum with the whirr of an elevator . . . life suddenly becoming loud and magnified in its smallest movements. One of two things: either she was deaf or hearing all too well. She reacted against this new suggestion with a sensation of spite and annoyance, with a sigh of resigned satiety. "Drop dead," she said gently . . . defeated.

"And when in the restaurant . . ." she suddenly recalled when she had been in the restaurant her husband's protector had pressed his foot against hers beneath the table, and above the table his face was watching her. By coincidence or intentionally? The rascal. A fellow, to be frank, who was not unattractive. She shrugged her shoulders.

And when above the roundness of her low-cut dress—right in the middle of Tiradentes Square! she thought, shaking her head incredulously—that fly had settled on her bare bosom. What cheek!

Certain things were good because they were almost nauseating . . . the noise like that of an elevator in her blood, while her husband lay snoring at her side . . . her chubby little children sleeping in the other room, the little villains. Ah, what's wrong with me! she wondered desperately. Have I eaten too much? Heavens above! What is wrong with me?

It was unhappiness.

Her toes playing with her slipper . . . the floor not too clean at that spot. "What a slovenly, lazy bitch you've become."

Not tomorrow, because her legs would not be too steady, but the day after tomorrow that house of hers would be a sight worth seeing: she would give it a scouring with soap and water which would get rid of all the dirt! "You mark my words," she threatened in her rage. Ah, she was feeling so well, so strong, as if she still had milk in those firm breasts. When her husband's friend saw her so pretty and plump he had immediately felt respect for her. And when she started to get embarrassed she did not know which way to look. Such misery! What was one to do? Seated on the edge of the bed, blinking in resignation. How well one could see the moon on these summer nights. She leaned over slightly, indifferent and resigned. The moon! How clearly one could see it. The moon high and yellow gliding through the sky, poor thing. Gliding, gliding . . . high up, high up. The moon! Then her vulgarity exploded in a sudden outburst of affection; "you slut", she cried out, laughing.

Endnotes

1. Translated by Giovanni Pontiero.
2. A street in Rio de Janeiro that intersects with Mem de Sá Street. Riachuelo is the name of a large department store: Mem de Sá was a sixteenth-century Portuguese governor-general of Brazil and the founder of Rio de Janeiro.
3. A river in northwest Portugal.
4. A quiet neighborhood in Rio de Janeiro with a beach where families would gather to picnic.
5. A square in Rio de Janeiro named after the Brazilian revolutionary patriot; he was executed by the Portuguese in 1792.
6. *Vinho Verde*, literally "green wine," is a soft wine produced in Portugal and often drunk cold before meals.

Diary of a Madman

Lu Xun

Considered one of the most important writers in the development of modern Chinese literature, Lu Xun, the pen name of Zhou Shuren, addressed the failure of traditional Chinese literature and society in most of his stories. Lu was born in 1881 into a family of Confucian scholars and received a traditional education based on Confucian classical literature, something he would challenge later in his life through his short stories. Lu was among the Chinese intellectuals who left the restrictive social environment to study abroad, especially in Japan. While attending medical school in Tokyo, Lu saw a photograph of the execution by beheading of a Chinese man convicted of being a spy. The apathy he saw in the faces of the onlookers to the execution led him to give up the study of medicine and become a writer because he felt the spirits of the people needed more healing than did their bodies. Lu's story "Diary of a Madman" addresses Lu's perception of the adverse effects social stultification and Confucianism have had on Chinese culture. Lu believed that the strict ways in which Confucianism regulated social, familial, and personal behaviors limited or denied individual expression. Instead it created a society of "cannibals" who devoured those who dared to deviate from social and philosophical norms. This belief is encapsulated in the story when the narrator tells a group of people he fears are coming after him, "If you don't change, you're going to devour each other anyway." Lu died in 1936 and remains one of China's most celebrated writers.

There was once a pair of male siblings whose actual names I beg your indulgence to withhold. Suffice it to say that we three were boon companions during our school years. Subsequently, circumstances contrived to rend us asunder so that we were gradually bereft of knowledge regarding each other's activities.

Not too long ago, however, I chanced to hear that one of them had been hard afflicted with a dread disease. I obtained this intelligence at a time when I happened to be returning to my native haunts and, hence, made so bold as to detour somewhat from my normal course in order to visit them. I encountered but one of the siblings. He apprised me that it had been his younger brother who had suffered the dire illness. By now, however, he had long since become sound and fit again; in fact he had already repaired to other parts to await a substantive official appointment.[1]

The elder brother apologized for having needlessly put me to the inconvenience of this visitation, and concluding his disquisition with a hearty smile, showed me two volumes of diaries which, he assured me, would reveal the nature of his brother's disorder during those fearful days.

As to the *lapsus calami* that occur in the course of the diaries, I have altered not a word. Nonetheless, I have changed all the names, despite the fact that their publication would be of no great consequence since they are all humble villagers unknown to the world at large.

Recorded this 2nd day in the 7th year of the Republic.[2]

1

Moonlight's really nice tonight. Haven't seen it in over thirty years. Seeing it today, I feel like a new man. I know now that I've been completely out of things for the last three decades or more.

But I've still got to be *very* careful. Otherwise, how do you explain those dirty looks the Zhao family's dog gave me?

I've got good reason for my fears.

2

No moonlight at all tonight—something's not quite right. When I made my way out the front gate this morning—ever so carefully—there was something funny about the way the Venerable Old Zhao looked at me: seemed as though he was afraid of me and yet, at the same time, looked as though he had it in for me. There were seven or eight other people who had their heads together whispering about me. They were afraid I'd see them too! All up and down the the street people acted the same way. The meanest looking one of all spread his lips out wide and actually *smiled* at me! A shiver ran from the top of my head clear down to the tips of my toes, for I realized that meant they already had their henchmen well deployed, and were ready to strike.

But I wasn't going to let that intimidate *me*. I kept right on walking. There was a group of children up ahead and they were talking about me too. The expressions in their eyes were just like the Venerable Old Zhao's, and their faces were iron gray. I wondered what grudge the children had against me that they were acting this way too. I couldn't contain myself any longer and shouted, "Tell me, tell me!" But they just ran away.

Let's see now, what grudge can there be between me and the Venerable Old Zhao, or the people on the street for that matter? The only thing I can think of is that twenty years ago I trampled the account books kept by Mr. Antiquity, and he was hopping mad about it too. Though the Venerable Old Zhao doesn't know him, he must have gotten wind of it somehow. Probably decided to right the injustice I had done Mr. Antiquity by getting all those people on the street to gang up on me. But the children? Back then they hadn't even come into the world yet. Why should they have given me those funny looks today? Seemed as though they were afraid of me and yet, at the same time, looked as though they would like to do me some harm. That really frightens me. Bewilders me. Hurts me.

I have it! Their fathers and mothers have *taught* them to be like that!

3

I can never get to sleep at night. You really have to study something before you can understand it.

Take all those people: some have worn the cangue on the district magistrate's order, some have had their faces slapped by the gentry, some have had their wives ravished by *yamen* clerks,[3] some have had their dads and moms dunned to death by creditors; and yet, right at the time when all those terrible things were taking place, the expressions on their faces were never as frightened, or as savage, as the ones they wore yesterday.

Strangest of all was that woman on the street. She slapped her son and said: "Damn it all, you've got me so riled up I could take a good bite right out of your hide!" She was talking to him, but she was looking at me! I tried, but couldn't conceal a shudder of fright. That's when that ghastly crew of people, with their green faces and protruding fangs, began to roar with laughter. Old Fifth Chen ran up, took me firmly in tow, and dragged me away.

When we got back, the people at home all pretended not to know me. The expressions in their eyes were just like all the others too. After he got me into the study. Old Fifth Chen bolted the door from the outside—just the way you would pen up a chicken or a duck! That made figuring out what was at the bottom of it all harder than ever.

A few days back one of our tenant farmers came in from Wolf Cub Village to report a famine. Told my elder brother the villagers had all ganged up on a "bad" man and beaten him to death. Even gouged out his heart and liver. Fried them up and ate them to bolster their own courage! When I tried to horn in on the conversation, Elder Brother and the tenant farmer both gave me sinister looks. I realized for the first time today that the expression in their eyes was just the same as what I saw in those people on the street.

As I think of it now, a shiver's running from the top of my head clear down to the tips of my toes.

If they're capable of eating people, then who's to say they won't eat *me?*

Don't you see? That woman's words about "taking a good bite," and the laughter of that ghastly crew with their green faces and protruding fangs, and the words of our tenant farmer a few days back—it's perfectly clear to me now that all that talk and all that laughter were really a set of secret signals. Those words were poison! That laughter, a knife! Their teeth are bared and waiting—white and razor sharp! Those people are cannibals!

As I see it myself, though I'm not what you'd call an evil man, still, ever since I trampled the Antiquity family's account books, it's hard to say *what* they'll do. They seem to have something in mind, but I can't begin to guess what. What's more, as soon as they turn against someone, they'll *say* he's evil anyway. I can still remember how it was when Elder Brother was teaching me composition. No matter how good a man was, if I could find a few things wrong with him he would approvingly underline my words; on the other hand, if I made a few allowances for a bad man, he'd say I was "an extraordinary student, an absolute genius." When all is said and done, how can I possibly guess what people like *that* have in mind, especially when they're getting ready for a cannibals' feast?

You have to *really* go into something before you can understand it. I seemed to remember, though not too clearly, that from ancient times on people have often been eaten, and so I started leafing through a history book to look it up. There were no dates in this history, but scrawled this way and that across every page were the words BENEVOLENCE, RIGHTEOUSNESS, and MORALITY. Since I couldn't get to sleep anyway, I read that history very carefully for most of the night, and finally I began to make out what was written *between* the lines; the whole volume was filled with a single phrase: EAT PEOPLE!

The words written in the history book, the things the tenant farmer said—all of it began to stare at me with hideous eyes, began to snarl and growl at me from behind bared teeth!

Why sure, *I'm* a person too, and they want to eat *me!*

4

In the morning I sat in the study for a while, calm and collected. Old Fifth Chen brought in some food—vegetables and a steamed fish. The fish's eyes were white and hard. Its mouth was wide open, just like the mouths of those people who wanted to eat human flesh. After I'd taken a few bites, the meat felt so smooth and slippery in my mouth that I couldn't tell whether it was fish or human flesh. I vomited.

"Old Fifth," I said, "tell Elder Brother that it's absolutely stifling in here and that I'd like to take a walk in the garden." He left without answering, but sure enough, after a while the door opened. I didn't even budge—just sat there waiting to see what they'd do to me. I *knew* that they wouldn't be willing to set me loose.

Just as I expected! Elder Brother came in with an old man in tow and walked slowly toward me. There was a savage glint in the old man's eyes. He was afraid I'd see it and kept his head tilted toward the floor while stealing sidewise glances at me over the temples of his glasses. "You seem to be fine today," said Elder Brother.

"You bet!" I replied.

"I've asked Dr. He to come and examine your pulse today."

"He's welcome!" I said. But don't think for one moment that I didn't know the old geezer was an executioner in disguise! Taking my pulse was nothing but a ruse; he wanted to feel my flesh and decide if I was fat enough to butcher yet. He'd probably even get a share of the meat for his troubles. I wasn't a *bit* afraid. Even though I don't eat human flesh, I still have a lot more courage than those who do. I thrust both hands out to see how the old buzzard would make his move.[4] Sitting down, he closed his eyes and felt my pulse for a good long while. Then he froze. Just sat there without moving a muscle for another good long while. Finally he opened his spooky eyes and said: "Don't let your thoughts run away with you. Just convalesce in peace and quiet for a few days and you'll be all right."

Don't let my thoughts run away with me? Convalesce in peace and quiet? If I convalesce till I'm good and fat, they get more to eat, but what do *I* get out of it? How can I possibly be *all right?* What a bunch! All they think about is eating human flesh, and then they go sneaking around, thinking up every which way they can to camouflage their real intentions. They were comical enough to crack *anybody* up. I couldn't hold it in any longer and let out a good loud laugh. Now *that* really felt good. I knew in my heart of hearts that my laughter was *packed* with courage and righteousness. And do you know what? They were so completely subdued by it that the old man and my elder brother both went pale!

But the more *courage* I had, the more that made them want to eat me so that they could get a little of it for free. The old man walked out. Before he had taken many steps, he lowered his head and told Elder Brother. "To be eaten as soon as possible!" He nodded understandingly. So, Elder Brother, you're in it too! Although that discovery seemed unforeseen, it really wasn't, either. My own elder brother had thrown in with the very people who wanted to eat me!

My elder brother is a cannibal!

I'm brother to a cannibal.

Even though I'm to be the victim of cannibalism, I'm *brother* to a cannibal all the same!

5

During the past few days I've taken a step back in my thinking. Supposing that old man wasn't an executioner in disguise but really was a doctor—well, he'd still be a cannibal just the same. In *Medicinal . . . something or other* by Li Shizhen, the grandfather of the doctor's trade, it says quite clearly that human flesh can be eaten, so how can that old man say that *he's* not a cannibal too?[5]

And as for my own elder brother, I'm not being the least bit unfair to him. When he was explaining the classics to me, he said with his very own tongue that it was all right to *exchange children and eat them*. And then there was another time when he happened to start in on an evil man and said that not only should the man be killed, but his *flesh should be eaten* and *his skin used as a sleeping mat* as well.[6]

When our tenant farmer came in from Wolf Cub Village a few days back and talked about eating a man's heart and liver, Elder Brother didn't seem to see anything out of the way in that either—just kept nodding his head. You can tell from that alone that his present way of thinking is every bit as malicious as it was when I was a child. If it's all right to exchange *children* and eat them, then *anyone* can be exchanged, anyone can be eaten. Back then I just took what he said as explanation of the classics and let it go at that, but now I realize that while he was explaining, the grease of human flesh was smeared all over his lips, and what's more, his mind was filled with plans for further cannibalism.

6

Pitch black out. Can't tell if it's day or night. The Zhao family's dog has started barking again.

Savage as a lion, timid as a rabbit, crafty as a fox . . .

7

I'm on to the way they operate. They'll never be willing to come straight out and kill me. Besides, they wouldn't dare. They'd be afraid of all the bad luck it might bring down on them if they did. And so, they've gotten everyone into cahoots with them and have set traps all over the place so that I'll do *myself* in. When I think back on the looks of those men and women on the streets a few days ago, coupled with the things my elder brother's been up to recently, I can figure out eight or nine tenths of it. From their point of view, the best thing of all would be for me to take off my belt, fasten it around a beam, and hang myself. They wouldn't be guilty of murder, and yet they'd still get everything they're after. Why, they'd be so beside themselves with joy, they'd sob with laughter. Or if they couldn't get me to do that, maybe they could torment me until I died of fright and worry. Even though I'd come out a bit leaner that way, they'd still nod their heads in approval.

Their kind only know how to eat dead meat. I remember reading in a book somewhere about something called the *hai-yi-na*. Its general appearance is said to be hideous, and the expression in its eyes particularly ugly and malicious. Often eats carrion, too. Even chews the bones to a pulp and swallows them down. Just thinking about it's enough to frighten a man.

The *hai-yi-na* is kin to the wolf.[7] The wolf's a relative of the dog, and just a few days ago the Zhao family dog gave me a funny look. It's easy to see that he's in on it too. How did that old man expect to fool *me* by staring at the floor?

My elder brother's the most pathetic of the whole lot. Since he's a human being too, how can he manage to be so totally without qualms, and what's more, even gang up with them to eat me? Could it be that he's been used to this sort of thing all along and sees nothing wrong with it? Or could it be that he's lost all conscience and just goes ahead and does it even though he knows it's wrong?

If I'm going to curse cannibals, I'll have to start with him. And if I'm going to *convert* cannibals, I'll have to start with him too.

8

Actually, by now even they should long since have understood the truth of this . . .

Someone came in. Couldn't have been more than twenty or so. I wasn't able to make out what he looked like too clearly, but he was all smiles. He nodded at me. His smile didn't look like the real thing either. And so I asked him, "Is this business of eating people right?"

He just kept right on smiling and said, "Except perhaps in a famine year, how could anyone get eaten?" I knew right off that he was one of them—one of those monsters who devour people!

At that point my own courage increased a hundredfold and I asked him, "Is it right?"

"Why are you talking about this kind of thing anyway? You really know how to . . . uh . . . how to pull a fellow's leg. Nice weather we're having."

"The weather *is* nice. There's a nice moon out, too, but I *still* want to know if it's right."

He seemed quite put out with me and began to mumble, "It's not—"

"Not right? Then how come they're still eating people?"

"No one's eating anyone."

"No one's *eating* anyone? They're eating people in Wolf Cub Village this very minute. And it's written in all the books, too, written in bright red blood!"

His expression changed and his face went gray like a slab of iron. His eyes started out from their sockets as he said, "Maybe they are, but it's always been that way, it's—"

"Just because it's always been that way, does that make it *right?*"

"I'm not going to discuss such things with you. If you insist on talking about that, then *you're* the one who's in the wrong!"

I leaped from my chair, opened my eyes, and looked around—but the fellow was nowhere to be seen. He was far younger than my elder brother, and yet he was actually one of them. It must be because his mom and dad taught him to be that way. And he's probably already passed it on to his own son. No wonder that even the children give me murderous looks.

9

They want to eat others and at the same time they're afraid that other people are going to eat them. That's why they're always watching each other with such suspicious looks in their eyes.

But all they'd have to do is give up that way of thinking, and then they could travel about, work, eat, and sleep in perfect security. Think how happy they'd feel! It's only a threshold, a pass. But what do they do instead? What is it that these fathers, sons, brothers, husbands, wives, friends, teachers, students, enemies, and even people who don't know each other *really* do? Why they all join together to hold each other back, and talk each other out of it!

That's it! They'd rather *die* than take that one little step.

10

I went to see Elder Brother bright and early. He was standing in the courtyard looking at the sky. I went up behind him so as to cut him off from the door back into the house. In the calmest and friendliest of tones, I said, "Elder Brother, there's something I'd like to tell you."

"Go right ahead." He immediately turned and nodded his head.

"It's only a few words," really, but it's hard to get them out.

Elder Brother, way back in the beginning, it's probably the case that primitive peoples *all* ate some human flesh. But later on, because their ways of thinking changed, some gave up the practice and tried their level best to improve themselves; they kept on changing until they became human beings, *real* human beings. But the others didn't; they just kept right on with their cannibalism and stayed at that primitive level.

"You have the same sort of thing with evolution in the animal world. Some reptiles, for instance, changed into fish, and then they evolved into birds, then into apes, and then into human beings.[8] But the others didn't want to improve themselves and just kept right on being reptiles down to this very day.

"Think how ashamed those primitive men who have remained cannibals must feel when they stand before *real* human beings. They must feel even more ashamed than reptiles do when confronted with their brethren who have evolved into apes.

"There's an old story from ancient times about Yi Ya boiling his son and serving him up to Jie Zhou. But if the truth be known, people have *always* practiced cannibalism, all the way from the time when Pan Gu separated heaven and earth down to Yi Ya's son, down to Xu Xilin, and on down to the man they killed in Wolf Cub Village.[9] And just last year when they executed a criminal in town, there was even someone with T.B. who dunked a steamed bread roll in his blood and then licked it off.[10]

"When they decided to eat me, by yourself, of course, you couldn't do much to prevent it, but why did you have to go and *join* them? Cannibals are capable of anything! If they're capable of eating me, then they're capable of eating *you* too! Even within their own group, they think nothing of devouring each other. And yet all they'd have to do is turn back—*change*—and then everything would be fine. Even though people may say, 'It's always been like this,' we can still do our best to improve. And we can start today!

"You're going to tell me it can't be done! Elder Brother, I think you're very likely to say that. When that tenant wanted to reduce his rent the day before yesterday, wasn't it you who said it couldn't be done?"

At first he just stood there with a cold smile, but then his eyes took on a murderous gleam. (I had exposed their innermost secrets.) His whole face had gone pale. Some people were standing outside the front gate. The Venerable Old Zhao and his dog were among them. Stealthily peering this way and that, they began to crowd through the open gate. Some I couldn't make out too well—their faces seemed covered with cloth. Some looked the same as ever—smiling green faces with protruding fangs. I could tell at a glance that they all belonged to the same gang, that they were all cannibals. But at the same time I also realized that they didn't all think the same way. Some thought *it's always been like this* and that they really should eat human flesh. Others knew they shouldn't but went right on doing it anyway, always on the lookout for fear someone might give them away. And since that's exactly what I had just done, I knew they must be furious. But they were all *smiling* at me—cold little smiles!

At this point Elder Brother suddenly took on an ugly look and barked, "Get out of here! All of you! What's so funny about a madman?"

Now I'm on to *another* of their tricks: not only are they unwilling to change, but they're already setting me up for their next cannibalistic feast by labeling me a "madman." That way, they'll be able to eat me without getting into the slightest trouble. Some people will even be grateful to them. Wasn't that the very trick used in the case that the tenant reported? Everybody ganged up on a "bad" man and ate him. It's the same old thing.

Old Fifth Chen came in and made straight for me, looking mad as could be. But he wasn't going to shut *me* up! I was going to tell that bunch of cannibals off, and no two ways about it!

"You can change! You can change from the bottom of your hearts! You ought to know that in the future they're not going to allow cannibalism in the world anymore. If you don't change, you're going to devour each other anyway. And even if a lot of you *are* left, a real human being's going to come along and eradicate the lot of you, just like a hunter getting rid of wolves—or reptiles!"

Old Fifth Chen chased them all out. I don't know where Elder Brother disappeared to. Old Fifth talked me into going back to my room.

It was pitch black inside. The beams and rafters started trembling overhead. They shook for a bit, and then they started getting bigger and bigger. They piled themselves up into a great heap on top of my body!

The weight was incredibly heavy and I couldn't even budge—they were trying to kill me! But I knew their weight was an illusion, and I struggled out from under them, my body bathed in sweat. I was still going to have my say. "Change this minute! Change from the bottom of your hearts! You ought to know that in the future they're not going to allow cannibals in the world anymore . . . "

II

The sun doesn't come out. The door doesn't open. It's two meals a day.

I picked up my chopsticks and that got me thinking about Elder Brother. I realized that the reason for my younger sister's death lay entirely with him. I can see her now—such a lovable and helpless little thing, only five at the time. Mother couldn't stop crying, but *he* urged her to stop, probably because he'd eaten sister's flesh himself and hearing mother cry over her like that shamed him! But if he's still capable of feeling shame, then maybe . . .

Younger Sister was eaten by Elder Brother. I have no way of knowing whether Mother knew about it or not.

I think she *did* know, but while she was crying she didn't say anything about it. She probably thought it was all right, too. I can remember once when I was four or five, I was sitting out in the courtyard taking in a cool breeze when Elder Brother told me that when parents are ill, a son, in order to be counted as a really good person, should slice off a piece of his own flesh, boil it, and let them eat it.[11] At the time Mother didn't come out and say there was anything wrong with that. But if it was all right to eat one piece, then there certainly wouldn't be anything wrong with her eating the whole body. And yet when I think back to the way she cried and cried that day, it's enough to break my heart. It's all strange—very, very strange.

12

Can't think about it anymore. I just realized today that I too have muddled around for a good many years in a place where they've been continually eating people for four thousand years. Younger Sister happened to die at just the time when Elder Brother was in charge of the house. Who's to say he didn't slip some of her meat into the food we ate?

Who's to say I didn't eat a few pieces of my younger sister's flesh without knowing it? And now it's my turn . . .

Although I wasn't aware of it in the beginning, now that I *know* I'm someone with four thousand years' experience of cannibalism behind me, how hard it is to look real human beings in the eye!

13

Maybe there are some children around who still haven't eaten human flesh.
    Save the children . . .
    APRIL 1918

Endnotes

1. When there were too many officials for the number of offices to be filled, a man might well be appointed to an office that already had an incumbent. The new appointee would proceed to his post and wait until said office was vacated. Sometimes there would be a number of such appointees waiting their turns.

2. April 2, 1918. This introduction is written in classical Chinese, while the diary entries that follow are all in the colloquial language.

3. The cangue was a split board, hinged at one end and locked at the other; holes were cut out to accommodate the prisoner's neck and wrists. *Yamen* was the term for local government offices. The petty clerks who worked in them were notorious for relying on their proximity to power in order to bully and abuse the common people.

4. In Chinese medicine the pulse is taken at both wrists.

5. *Taxonomy of Medicinal Herbs*, a gigantic work, was the most important pharmacopoeia in traditional China. Li Shizhen lived from 1518 to 1593.

6. Both italicized expressions are from the *Zuozhuan* (Zuo Commentary [to the *Spring and Autumn Annals*]), a historical work which dates from the third century B.C. In 448 B.C., an officer who was exhorting his own side not to surrender is recorded as having said, "When the army of Chu besieged the capital of Song [in 603 B.C.], the

people exchanged their children and ate them, and used the bones for fuel; and still they would not submit to a covenant at the foot of their walls. For us who have sustained no great loss, to do so is to cast our state away" (Legge 5.817). It is also recorded that in 551 B.C. an officer boasting of his own prowess before his ruler, pointed to two men whom his ruler considered brave and said, "As to those two, they are like beasts, whose flesh I will eat, and then sleep upon their skins" (Legge 5.492).

7. Three Chinese characters are used here for phonetic value only—that is, *hai yi na* is a transliteration into Chinese of the English word "hyena."

8. Darwin's theory of evolution was immensely important to Chinese intellectuals during Lu Xun's lifetime and the common coin of much discourse.

9. An early philosophical text, *Guan Zi*, reports that the famous cook, Yi Ya, boiled his son and served him to his ruler, Duke Huan of Qi (685-643 B.C.), because the meat of a human infant was one of the few delicacies the duke had never tasted. Jie and Zhou were the last evil rulers of the Shang (1776-1122 B.C.) and Zhou (1122-221 B.C.) dynasties. The madman has mixed up some facts here. Pan Gu (literally, Coiled-up Antiquity) was born out of an egg. As he stood up he separated heaven and earth. The world, as we know it, was formed from his body. Xu Xilin (1873–1907) was from Lu Xun's hometown, Shaoxing. After studies in Japan he returned to China and served as head of the Anhui Police Academy. When a high Qing official, En Ming, participated in a graduation ceremony at the academy, Xu assassinated him, hoping that this spark would touch off the revolution. After the assassination, he and some of his students at the academy occupied the police armory and managed, for a while, to hold off En Ming's troops. When Xu was finally captured, En Ming's personal bodyguards dug out his heart and liver and ate them.

10. A similar incident is the basis for Lu Xun's story "Medicine." Human blood was believed to be a cure for tuberculosis.

11. In traditional literature stories about such gruesome acts of filial piety were not unusual.

The Dignity of Begging

William "Bloke" Modisane

William "Bloke" Modisane was born on August 28, 1923, and grew up in Johannesburg, South Africa. As a boy, Modisane witnessed his father's murder and his young sister's death from malnutrition. In 1951, Modisane wrote for the investigative South African magazine Drum, *contributing "The Dignity of Begging" among other works. He also worked as a jazz critic for the* Golden City Post, *a Johannesburg weekly newspaper. Modisane moved to England in 1959 and in 1963 published his moving autobiography* Blame Me on History, *a passionate recording of the dehumanization and oppression of blacks living under South African apartheid.* Blame Me on History *was banned in South Africa in 1966. While in exile, Modisane worked as a writer, broadcaster, and actor for both stage and film until his death in Dortmund, West Germany, in 1986. The current selection, "The Dignity of Begging," has been praised for its satire and humor while exploring the serious subject of the main character's responses to racial and economic oppression.*

The Magistrate raises his eyes above the documents and plunges them like daggers into my heart. His blue eyes are keen: my heart pounds like the bass of a boogie-woogie.

"I'm sick to death of you ... heartily sick. There's not a native beggar on the streets whose full story I don't know," the Magistrate says. "I've watched some of you grow up. There isn't one I haven't tried to rehabilitate many times. Some I was forced to send to jail, but they always come back ... they come back to the goose that lays the golden egg."

These are fighting words. The Magistrate sounds as though he's going to put us away for a few weeks. My only regret is that Richard Serurubele has to share my fate. If only the Magistrate knew that he is not a parasite like the rest of us, that he's what is called an exploited beggar. He was crippled by an automobile accident, and since then his parents have made capital out of it. They use him to beg so they can balance the family budget. They never show him the comfort of love. Relentlessly they drive him, like an animal that has to work for its keep and feed. He is twenty-one. Dragging one foot along, he is an abject sight who has all the sadness of the world in his face. He looks many times older than my mother-in-law.

"You beggars make it difficult for me to do my duty, and in spite of my failure to rehabilitate you, I always believe in giving you another chance . . . A fresh start, you might call it."

"But I'm almost certain that you'll be back here in a few days."

The Magistrate is getting soft; I can see my freedom at a distance of an arm's stretch. Here is my chance to put on my act. A look of deep compunction and a few well-chosen words can do the trick. I clear my throat and squeeze out a tear or two.

"Your Honor, most of us beg because we've been ostracized by our families; they treat us as though we were lepers," I say, wiping off a tear. "They want us to look up to them for all the things we need. They never encourage us to earn our own keep. Nobody wants to employ us, people are more willing to offer us alms, rather than give us jobs. All they do is show us pity . . . We don't want to be pitied, we want to be given a chance to prove that we're as good as anybody else."

I can see from the silence in the court that everybody is deceived . . . Everybody is filled with a sense of self-reproach. The Magistrate is as mute as the undertaker's parlor. I can read pity on the faces of all the people in the court; perhaps the most pathetic is my own. I am magnificent . . . an answer to every film director's dream. I know I have said enough . . . enough to let us out, that is.

"I understand you have matriculated, your name is Nathaniel, isn't it?" He turns a page of the report prepared by a worker in the Non-European Affairs Department. "Yes, here we are, Nathaniel Mokgomare, the department recommends that you be sent to a place where you will be taught some useful trade. I want you to report to Room 14 at the department's building tomorrow morning."

This is not what I had bargained for; my brilliant idea has boomeranged. Why must I take a job when I can earn twice a normal wage begging? After all, what will horses do if I take a job? I *must* uphold the dignity of begging. Professional ethics forbid all beggars from working.

"As for you, Richard Serurubele, I'll let you go this time, but mark my words: the next time you appear before me, I'll have you sent to the Bantu Refuge. Now get out of here, both of you."

If the Magistrate had seen the big grin on my face as we leave the court, he would have thrown my deformed carcass in jail and deliberately lost the key. He does not see it though.

With the exception of a few loose ends everything has gone according to schedule, but my friend Serurubele is just about the most miserable man on earth. The trouble with him is he lacks imagination, but then of course, not everybody is as bright as I am. He always seems to be looking at the dull side of life, a vice coupled with an appalling brand of honesty most bishops would swear didn't exist.

"One of these days, I'm going to kill myself," Serurubele says. "I can't go on like this; I'm tired of living off other people. Why did this have to happen to me? Tell me, Nathan. Why?"

How this man expects me to answer a question like this is beyond me. For one unguarded moment I almost tell him to send his Maker a telegram and ask Him all about it, but my gentler nature sees the harm such an answer might do.

"I don't know," I say, abruptly. "Things like this just happen; it's not in us to question why. Nature has a way of doing things, but even then she gives something in return ... at least I think so ... But how should I know, anyway?"

This is the one time I cannot find something concrete to say; I want to show him that there is compensation for his disability, but I just cannot lay my hands on it. This, I remember, is what made me leave home.

I left because my parents did not understand. They almost made a neurotic out of me; but today I wonder if it wasn't my own sensitivity which gave their actions then their seemingly absurd proportions. They seemed afraid to walk about freely; everybody sat down as if the house were full of cripples. I was treated like a babe in arms. All the things I wanted were brought to me, I was not even allowed to get myself water to drink. This excessive kindness gradually began to irritate me ... It became a constant reminder that I didn't belong, that I was an invalid. It then became apparent that they would soon put the food into my mouth which they had already chewed for me, and push it down my throat. These thoughts of inadequacy drove me from home.

A new life opened for me. I got myself a wife, two bouncing boys and a property at Pampoenfontein, also a room at Sophiatown complete with piano. Within two years I had begged well over a few hundred pounds. The money had been used wisely. Only one problem confronts me now, I want enough money to provide for my old age ... The two boys are also to be considered.

"For Christ's sake, Nathaniel," Serurubele says, "what's wrong with you? Why are you always so wrapped up in your thoughts ... this is where I stay, remember?"

I say good-bye to him and go to my room. After having something to eat I settle down to some hard thinking. There are all sorts of insurances and societies, unions and what have you, which protect workers. Why not a beggars' union? I could rally all the beggars of the city into one union with some professional name like The United Beggars' Union, into whose funds every beggar would contribute ten shillings a week. In the city of Johannesburg alone, there are over a hundred beggars and if they could all be talked over, a capital of about two thousand four hundred pounds could be realized in one year.

What a brilliant idea . . . an inspiration of genius. Sometimes I feel depressed that the world has not had the vision to realize the potentialities of my genius . . . possibly it cannot accommodate Einstein and myself in the same generation. Anyway, so much for that.

I could promise to offer each a bonus of ten pounds a year. That would be smart . . . No beggar could resist such an offer. Maybe I should promise to buy each a property somewhere cheap, say, buy one property a year for the needy ones like Serurubele, equip him with third-rate tools and interest him in turning out junk that nobody will care to give a second look at. The scheme would be costly, but at least it would go far in enlisting their confidence. Only one would get the property; the others would wait patiently until I get religion.

The following morning I'm at Room 14 bright and early. A white man with a bored expression on his face is sitting behind a big mahogany desk. I tell him my name. He takes some paper and writes on it. He tells me to go to the address written on the paper.

The faint showers that were falling outside have become heavier, and as I go out I say something nasty about the weather. A brilliant idea strikes me as a well-dressed lady is walking toward me. She looks like a mobile gold mine ready to be tapped . . . in fact, I can almost see the gold nuggets in her teeth. I put on a gloomy face, bend lower than usual and let my deformed carcass shiver. She stops and looks at me as if she's responsible for my deformity.

"Why, you poor boy, you're freezing to death," she says, with melodrama. "Here, go buy yourself something to eat."

I feel the half-crown piece in my hand and give her the usual line of how the good Lord will bless her, and send her tons and tons of luck: but from the way she's dressed, she appears to have had more than her share of luck.

I play this trick all the way to the address I'm given, and by the time I get there, I count well over ten half-crowns. Not bad, I say to myself; at this rate I can become the richest and most famous beggar in the city. To think the department wants to pin me behind a desk! The idea is criminal, to say the least.

One of these days when I'm on my annual leave, I hope to write a book on begging, something like a treatise on the subject. It will be written with sensitivity and charm, brimful with sketches from life, and profusely illustrated with colored photographs, with easy-to-follow rules on the noblest and oldest occupation in the world: begging! It will be a textbook for all aspiring beggars, young and old, who will reap a wealth of knowledge from my personal experience and genius. In fact, it will be the only one of its kind in world literature. Even millionaires will take up begging as a pastime to color their humdrum existence.

It will naturally begin with a history of the art from its ancient crudity of maiming children as a preparation in their education, right up to the contemporary age of beggars who are driven to the city in the latest American cars ... beggars with a bank balance big enough to impress the Receiver of Revenue. I can almost see it on the best-seller list for several months. This reverie almost causes me to lose my way.

I find the place and go in. My heart just misses a beat when I see the large number of people inside. Some, if not most, are deformed monstrosities like myself. What could be sweeter? I can see my plan taking shape.

The man in charge starts explaining the elementary principles of the typewriter. I pretend to be interested and ask many unnecessary questions, but intelligent enough to impress him. By five o'clock I'm running over the keyboard like a brilliant amateur.

On my way home I go via Serurubele's corner. He is still there and looking as miserable as ever. I suggest that we go home. I lure him to my room and when we get there I begin playing a certain tarantella like Rubinstein, only my rendering is in A flat Major. Either my piano recital is good or my friend just loves bad sounds.

"You can have a house like this and everything that goes with it; it's yours for the taking. Why beg for other people when you can do it for yourself?"

"I've got to help with the rent and the food," he says. "How do you think I'm going to get a house like this? I can't just wish for it."

"You don't have to, you must plan and work for it like I did. I have a plan that will give it to you in less than a year ... Listen."

I then start explaining to him about the society with particular emphasis on the good it will do to all beggars. I see his teeth sparkling behind thick lips. I put him in charge of organizing them for our first meeting.

Last night I dreamt I was at the race course and I saw the winning double as plain as I see my twisted leg. I raid my savings in the room and make my way to Turfontein. When I get there I start scouting around for policemen. None are about and a soothing satisfaction comes with the realization that I shall not bother myself with police badges. I put a pound win on two and seven, a double in the first leg. As I'm making my bet, a man with eyes as big and lethargic as an owl's is standing next to me and beaming like a blushing groom.

I'm too nervous to watch the race, so I decide to walk about and appreciate the scenery. Suddenly I feel as though someone is staring at me. I turn round and look straight at Miss Gallovidian, a welfare worker, who has the uncanny habit of showing up at the most unexpected places. I don't need a fortune-teller to tell me I'm in trouble. She has a notorious record of having safely deposited more than twelve beggars in the Refuge. My only chance is to get out of here before she can find a beefy policeman. I'm walking to the gate when I hear people talking about two and seven. I even forget the trouble Miss Gallovidian is going to bring me. I run as fast as a man with a twisted leg can to the Bookie. Only six tickets were sold, the loudspeaker was saying, only I'm not interested.

As the Bookie is handing me the money Blushing Groom seems even happier than I am. His crooked teeth, which are dulled by tobacco, click every time the Bookie counts a hundred. His greasy lips are watering while a pair of bloodshot eyes are blinking with a dull brilliance. It hurts my eyes to look at him. I have hardly put the money in my pocket, when Gruesome pats me on the back and says, nice and loud: "We make it!"

I must have been a fool not to have been wise as to why Blushing Groom was acting the perfect chaperon.

"That's fine," I say. "What have *we* made?"

"Don't be bashful," he says, "we caught the richest double. Come, this calls for a celebration." He extends a hand, and all the time he's smiling as if his wife has given birth to quadruplets.

"Look, pal," I say. "It's a good try. I couldn't have done better myself. This is the perfect setup, isn't it? Well, I've got news for you: I caught that double alone, I don't know you and I don't care to. Go get yourself another piece of cheese . . . I'm not that easy."

This ape suddenly stops smiling and looks at me like I had the plague. His broad, flat nose starts puffing out steam like an angry Spanish bull (only I'm not in the mood to make fancy passes like a toreador). All in all, he looks positively fierce, like the animal in the simile.

"Six hundred and seventy pounds is a lot of money," he shouts. "Nobody's going to cheat me out of my share. You being a cripple . . . "

"Shut up!" I yell. "Never call me that again, you . . . You!" I swing a right cross to his face, but this ape is smart. He blocks it and lands a hard one on my chin. I rock back and land flat on my sitters, while jungle tom-toms beat out a solid conga in my head. After a while my head clears and I get up, burning with rage. If I only had the strength, I would tear this ape apart.

Blushing Groom has put on quite a show; we have a good audience. Some white folk are threatening to beat his brains out . . . I sincerely hope they do.

Suddenly I see a police badge jostling its way through. This is no place for me! I dash and start zigzagging through the people. A junior confusion starts, with everybody trying to give way. I run a few minutes, stumble and fall on my face. The policeman bends down and grabs me firmly by the arm and whispers: "Look, John, let's not have trouble. Come along quietly and everything will be just fine."

Under these circumstances I have no choice but to submit. My mother always told me never to resist arrest, let alone striking a uniformed officer of the law. Me and my money part company after Blushing Groom had proferred charges. My submission causes me to spend a not-so-glorious weekend at the Bantu Refuge. My transfer there being arranged by the thoughtful sergeant in the charge office, who out of pure love could not have me thrown in with hardened criminals . . . what with the place filled with housebreakers, extortioners, professional pickpockets and a generous assortment of other unsavory characters. Frankly, I hoped he would mind his own business. I might even have started a craps game and made me some money.

"I am almost certain that you will be back here in a few days," the Magistrate had said. Somebody ought to tell him he has a great future . . . reading palms. He looks at me and a grin spreads over his pancakelike face. This place must be short of Magistrates; why has it got to be the same one all the time?

"Beggars who play the horses are a dangerous nuisance. They misuse kindness that is shown to them."

Just my luck: now I have to listen to a lecture on morals. The Magistrate looks pleased with himself, and I don't like it. Miss Gallovidian looks at me and smiles like a proud victress. She probably expects a promotion for this. I'm called onto the stand.

Some man with a thin face asks me to raise my right hand and swear to tell the truth. After saying my piece, the prosecutor starts questioning me as if he's promised thirty percent of Blushing Groom's cut. After his session with me, he calls Blushing Groom to the stand.

"Do you know this man?" the prosecutor says.

"No, sir."

"How was it then you put up ten shillings to bet the horses with him?"

"I was losing all morning when I decided to try somebody's guesses. I met him and we started talking."

"Did anybody see you talking to him?"

"I don't know, but somebody must have."

"Then what happened?"

"I asked him if he had a tip. He said he had one straight from the horse's mouth . . . A sure thing, he said. I then asked him if I could put up ten shillings. He agreed. I was afraid to make the bet, so I gave him the money and walked over to the Bookie's stand with him where he placed a pound win on two and seven."

"Why were you afraid to make the bet?"

"I thought he was luckier than I was ... besides, I had been losing all morning."

"Why did you strike him?"

"He was trying to cheat me out of my share, and tried to hit me when he couldn't."

The Magistrate looks at me with something like contempt in his eyes. I won't have to put on a show for him this time. I might just as well kiss half my money good-bye. Blushing Groom's story is watertight.

"I'm thoroughly disappointed with you," the Magistrate says. "I didn't know you were a thief too. I don't believe you could have made that bet alone; beggars haven't got so much money. I believe his story, things like this do happen. The money will be shared equally between the two of you."

"I don't believe you could have made that bet alone." What a cheek! I'll have that hobo know I make more money in one week than he does in a month. I don't believe you ... Good God!

I feel like committing mass murder as the court hands Blushing Groom three hundred and thirty-five pounds of my money. This prehistoric beast has a swell racket. A few more jobs like this and he can retire and buy himself a villa on the Riviera.

Blushing Groom is magnificent, inspiring awe. He is completely uncompromising, thoroughly unscrupulous, without qualms or a conscience. He has wholly realized the separateness of good and evil and attained a purity in evil worthy of honest appraisal. He would not allow himself to be swayed from cheating me by my being a cripple. If I were allowed to choose a brother, he would be my only choice.

I take my share of the money and clear out before the Magistrate and Miss Gallovidian cook up another charge against me. On my way home I find it difficult to resist the temptation of stopping at some busy corner and doing my stuff. I might make up for some of the money, but I just happen to be wearing my best and have been a beggar long enough to know that people don't give money away to beggars who are dressed better than they. People who give alms to beggars do so to establish their superiority over the receiver, and like I said: I'm not an apprentice beggar.

When I get home I find a letter from my wife.

> Our son Tommy is sick. Please come home ...

I become afraid and anxious for my Tommy, and even the kind words of my outsize landlady fail to move me.

I had to wait for something like this to show me the folly of my ways. A man's place is next to his wife and family. I had hoped that someday I would be able to provide my boys with a decent education, to grow them like normal boys, not just sons of a helpless cripple ... to find a place for them in the sun. I might be a big shot beggar but as a husband and father, I stink.

"If I should not see my friend Serurubele, will you ... "

"Yes, I'll explain to him. I'll always have your room for you if you should ever want it again."

Deep down I know that I will want it again. I have three hundred and thirty-five reasons why I should. Blushing Groom and the gullible public of Johannesburg will live in my mind forever ... I have to come back. I owe it to the profession.

Management of Grief

Bharati Mukherjee

Bharati Mukherjee was born in Calcutta, India, on July 27, 1940, to an upper-class Hindu Brahmin family. Her family's affluence allowed her the opportunity to receive an excellent education. She graduated with her MFA in 1961 from the prestigious Writer's Workshop at the University of Iowa, where she also earned her doctorate in Comparative Literature in 1969. Mukherjee later lived with her husband and two sons in Canada, but the family finally left to live in the United States after experiencing extreme prejudice and ill-treatment because she was Hindu. She has lived in the United States since 1980 and has become an American citizen. She later became a Distinguished Professor of English at the University of California, Berkeley.

Mukherjee's Story, "Management of Grief," is based on an actual terrorist bombing of an Air India flight by Sikh terrorists, an act that was in retaliation for the attack by the Indian government on The Golden Temple, the holiest shrine of the Sikh religion. The story examines the cultural gap between a Canadian social worker and the Indian immigrants she is attempting to help as they deal with the deaths of relatives who were on the flight.

A woman I don't know is boiling tea the Indian way in my kitchen. There are a lot of women I don't know in my kitchen, whispering and moving tactfully. They open doors, rummage through the pantry, and try not to ask me where things are kept. They remind me of when my sons were small, on Mother's Day or when

Vikram and I were tired, and they would make big, sloppy omelets. I would lie in bed pretending I didn't hear them.

Dr. Sharma, the treasurer of the Indo-Canada Society, pulls me into the hallway. He wants to know if I am worried about money. His wife, who has just come up from the basement with a tray of empty cups and glasses, scolds him. "Don't bother Mrs. Bhave with mundane details." She looks so monstrously pregnant her baby must be days overdue. I tell her she shouldn't be carrying heavy things. "Shaila," she says, smiling, "this is the fifth." Then she grabs a teenager by his shirttails. He slips his Walkman off his head. He has to be one of her four children; they have the same domed and dented foreheads. "What's the official word now?" she demands. The boy slips the headphones back on. "They're acting evasive, Ma. They're saying it could be an accident or a terrorist bomb."

All morning, the boys have been muttering, Sikh bomb, Sikh bomb. The men, not using the word, bow their heads in agreement. Mrs. Sharma touches her forehead at such a word. At least they've stopped talking about space debris and Russian lasers.

Two radios are going in the dining room. They are tuned to different stations. Someone must have brought the radios down from my boys' bedrooms. I haven't gone into their rooms since Kusum came running across the front lawn in her bathrobe. She looked so funny, I was laughing when I opened the door.

The big TV in the den is being whizzed through American networks and cable channels.

"Damn!" some man swears bitterly. "How can these preachers carry on like nothing's happened?" I want to tell him we're not that important. You look at the audience, and at the preacher in his blue robe with his beautiful white hair, the potted palm trees under a blue sky, and you know they care about nothing.

The phone rings and rings. Dr. Sharma's taken charge. "We're with her," he keeps saying. "Yes, yes, the doctor has given calming pills. Yes, yes, pills are having necessary effect." I wonder if pills alone explain this calm. Not peace, just a deadening quiet. I was always controlled, but never repressed. Sound can reach me, but my body is tensed, ready to scream. I hear their voices all around me. I hear my boys and Vikram cry, "Mommy, Shaila!" and their screams insulate me, like headphones.

The woman boiling water tells her story again and again. "I got the news first. My cousin called from Halifax before six A.M., can you imagine? He'd gotten up for players and his son was studying for medical exams and heard on a rock channel that something had happened to a plane. They said first it had disappeared from the radar, like a giant eraser just reached out. His father called me, so I said to him, what do you mean, 'something bad'? You mean a hijacking? And he said, *Behn*, there is no confirmation of anything yet, but check with your neighbors because a lot of them must be on that plane.

So I called poor Kusum straight-away. I knew Kusum's husband and daughter were booked to go yesterday."

Kusum lives across the street from me. She and Satish had moved in less than a month ago. They said they needed a bigger place. All these people, the Sharmas and friends from the Indo-Canada Society, had been there for the housewarming. Satish and Kusum made tandoori on their big gas grill and even the white neighbors piled their plates high with that luridly red, charred, juicy chicken. Their younger daughter had danced, and even our boys had broken away from the Stanley Cup telecast to put in a reluctant appearance. Everyone took pictures for their albums and for the community newspapers— another of our families had made it big in Toronto—and now I wonder how many of those happy faces are gone. "Why does God give us so much if all along He intends to take it away?" Kusum asks me.

I nod. We sit on carpeted stairs, holding hands like children. "I never once told him that I loved him," I say. I was too much the well-brought-up woman. I was so well brought up I never felt comfortable calling my husband by his first name.

"It's all right," Kusum says. "He knew. My husband knew. They felt it. Modern young girls have to say it because what they feel is fake."

Kusum's daughter Pam runs in with an overnight case. Pam's in her McDonald's uniform. "Mummy! You have to get dressed!" Panic makes her cranky. "A reporter's on his way here."

"Why?"

"You want to talk to him in your bathrobe?" She starts to brush her mother's long hair. She's the daughter who's always in trouble. She dates Canadian boys and hangs out in the mall, shopping for tight sweaters. The younger one, the goody-goody one according to Pam, the one with a voice so sweet that when she sang *bhajans* for Ethiopian relief even a frugal man like my husband wrote out a hundred-dollar check, *she* was on that plane. *She* was going to spend July and August with grandparents because Pam wouldn't go. Pam said she'd rather waitress at McDonald's. "If it's a choice between Bombay and Wonderland, I'm picking Wonderland," she'd said.

"Leave me alone," Kusum yells. "You know what I want to do? If I didn't have to look after you now, I'd hang myself."

Pam's young face goes blotchy with pain. "Thanks," she says, "don't let me stop you."

"Hush," pregnant Mrs. Sharma scolds Pam. "Leave your mother alone. Mr. Sharma will tackle the reporters and fill out the forms. He'll say what has to be said."

Pam stands her ground. "You think I don't know what Mummy's thinking? *Why her?* That's what. That's sick! Mummy wishes my little sister were alive and I were dead."

Kusum's hand in mine is trembly hot. We continue to sit on the stairs.

She calls before she arrives, wondering if there's anything I need. Her name is Judith Templeton and she's an appointee of the provincial government. "Multiculturalism?" I ask, and she says "partially," but that her mandate is bigger. "I've been told you knew many of the people on the flight," she says. "Perhaps if you'd agree to help us reach the others . . . ?"

She gives me time at least to put on tea water and pick up the mess in the front room. I have a few *samosas* from Kusum's housewarming that I could fry up, but then I think, why prolong this visit?

Judith Templeton is much younger than she sounded. She wears a blue suit with a white blouse and a polka-dot tie. Her blond hair is cut short, her only jewelry is pearl-drop earrings. Her briefcase is new and expensive looking, a gleaming cordovan leather. She sits with it across her lap. When she looks out the front windows onto the street, her contact lenses seem to float in front of her light blue eyes.

"What sort of help do you want from me?" I ask. She has refused the tea, out of politeness, but I insist, along with some slightly stale biscuits.

"I have no experience," she admits. "That is, I have an M.S.W. and I've worked in liaison with accident victims, but I mean I have no experience with a tragedy of this scale—"

"Who could?" I ask.

"—and with the complications of culture, language, and customs. Someone mentioned that Mrs. Bhave is a pillar—because you've taken it more calmly."

At this, perhaps, I frown, for she reaches forward, almost to take my hand. "I hope you understand my meaning, Mrs. Bhave. There are hundreds of people in Metro directly affected, like you, and some of them speak no English. There are some widows who've never handled money or gone on a bus, and there are old parents who still haven't eaten or gone outside their bedrooms. Some houses and apartments have been looted. Some wives are still hysterical. Some husbands are in shock and profound depression. We want to help, but our hands are tied in so many ways. We have to distribute money to some people, and there are legal documents—these things can be done. We have interpreters, but we don't always have the human touch, or maybe the right human touch. We don't want to make mistakes, Mrs. Bhave, and that's why we'd like to ask you to help us."

"More mistakes; you mean," I say.

"Police matters are not in my hands," she answers.

"Nothing I can do will make any difference," I say. "We must all grieve in our own way."

"But you are coping very well. All the people said, Mrs. Bhave is the strongest person of all. Perhaps if the others could see you, talk with you, it would help them."

"By the standards of the people you call hysterical, I am behaving very oddly and very badly, Miss Templeton." I want to say to, *I wish I could scream, starve, walk into Lake Ontario, jump from a bridge.* "They would not see me as a model. I do not see myself as a model."

I am a freak. No one who has ever known me would think of me reacting this way. This terrible calm will not go away.

She asks me if she may call again, after I get back from a long trip that we all must make. "Of course," I say. "Feel free to call, anytime."

Four days later, I find Kusum squatting on a rock overlooking a bay in Ireland. It isn't a big rock, but it just sharply out over water. This is as close as we'll ever get to them. June breezes balloon out her sari and unpin her knee-length hair. She has the bewildered look of a sea creature whom the tides have stranded.

It's been one hundred hours since Kusum came stumbling and screaming across my lawn. Waiting around the hospital, we've heard many stories. The police, the diplomats, they tell us things thinking that we're strong, that knowledge is helpful to the grieving, and maybe it is. Some, I know, prefer ignorance, or their own versions. The plane broke into two, they say. Unconsciousness was instantaneous. No one suffered. My boys must have just finished their breakfasts. They loved eating on planes, they loved the smallness of plates, knives, and forks. Last year they saved the airline salt and pepper shakers. Half an hour more and they would have made it to Heathrow.

Kusum says that we can't escape our fate. She says that all those people—our husbands, my boys, her girl with the nightingale voice, all those Hindus, Christians, Sikhs, Muslims, Parsis, and atheists on that plane—were fated to die together off this beautiful bay. She learned this from a swami in Toronto.

I have my Valium.

Six of us "relatives"—two widows and four widowers—chose to spend the day today by the waters instead of sitting in a hospital room and scanning photographs of the dead. That's what they call us now: relatives. I've looked through twenty-seven photos in two days. They're very kind to us, the Irish are very understanding. Sometimes understanding means freeing a tourist bus for this trip to the bay, so we can pretend to spy our loved ones through the glassiness of waves or in sun-speckled cloud shapes.

I could die here, too, and be content.

"What is that, out there?" She's standing and flapping her hands, and for a moment I see a head shape bobbing in the waves. She's standing in the water, I on the boulder. The tide is low, and a round, black, head-sized rock has just risen from the waves. She returns, her sari end dripping and ruined, and her face is a twisted remnant of hope, the way mine was a hundred hours ago, still laughing but inwardly knowing that nothing but the ultimate tragedy could bring two women together at six o'clock on a Sunday morning. I watch her face sag into blankness.

"That water felt warm, Shaila," she says at length.

"You can't," I say. "We have to wait for our turn to come."

I haven't eaten in four days, haven't brushed my teeth.

"I know," she says. "I tell myself I have no right to grieve. They are in a better place than we are. My swami says depression is a sign of our selfishness."

Maybe I'm selfish. Selfishly I break away from Kusum and run, sandals slapping against stones, to the water's edge. What if my boys aren't lying pinned under the debris? What if they aren't stuck a mile below that innocent blue chop? What if, given the strong currents . . .

Now I've ruined my sari, one of my best. Kusum has joined me, knee deep in water that feels to me like a swimming pool. I could settle in the water, and my husband would take my hand and the boys would slap water in my face just to see me scream.

"Do you remember what good swimmers my boys were, Kusum?"

"I saw the medals," she says.

One of the widowers, Dr. Ranganathan from Montreal, walks out to us, carrying his shoes in one hand. He's an electrical engineer. Someone at the hotel mentioned his work is famous around the world, something about the place where physics and electricity come together. He has lost a huge family, something indescribable. "With some good luck," Dr. Ranganathan suggests to me, "a good swimmer could make it safely to some island. It is quite possible that there may be many, many microscopic islets scattered around."

"You're not just saying that?" I tell Dr. Ranganathan about Vinod, my elder son. Last year he took diving as well.

"It's a parent's duty to hope," he says. "It is foolish to rule out possibilities that have not been tested. I myself have not surrendered hope."

Kusum is sobbing once again. "Dear lady," he says, laying his free hand on her arm, and she calms down.

"Vinod is how old?" he asks me. He's very careful, as we all are. *Is*, not was.

"Fourteen. Yesterday he was fourteen. His father and uncle were going to take him down to the Taj and give him a big birthday party. I couldn't go with them because I couldn't get two weeks off from my stupid job in June." I process bills for a travel agent. June is a big travel month.

Dr. Ranganathan whips the pockets of his suit jacket inside out. Squashed roses, in darkening shades of pink, float on the water. He tore the roses off creepers in somebody's garden. He didn't ask anyone if he could pluck the roses, but now there's been an article about it in the local papers. When you see an Indian person, it says, please give them flowers.

"A strong youth of fourteen," he says, "can very likely pull to safety a younger one."

My sons, though four years apart, were very close. Vinod wouldn't let Mithun drown. *Electrical engineering*, I think, foolishly perhaps: this man knows important secrets of the universe, things closed to me. Relief spins me light-headed. No wonder my boys' photographs haven't turned up in the gallery of photos of the recovered dead. "Such pretty roses," I say.

"My wife loved pink roses. Every Friday I had to bring a bunch home. I used to say, Why? After twenty-odd years of marriage you're still needing proof positive of my love?" He has identified his wife and three of his children. Then others from Montreal, the lucky ones, intact families with no survivors. He chuckles as he wades back to shore. Then he swings around to ask me a question. "Mrs. Bhave, you are wanting to throw in some roses for your loved ones? I have two big ones left."

But I have other things to float. Vinod's pocket calculator; a half-painted model B-52 for my Mithun. They'd want them on their island. And for my husband? For him I let fall into the calm, glassy waters a poem I wrote in the hospital yesterday. Finally he'll know my feelings for him.

"Don't tumble, the rocks are slippery," Dr. Ranganathan cautions. He holds out a hand for me to grab.

Then it's time to get back on the bus, time to rush back to our waiting posts on hospital benches.

Kusum is one of the lucky ones. The lucky ones flew here, identified in multiplicate their loved ones, then will fly to India with the bodies for proper ceremonies. Satish is one of the few males who surfaced. The photos of faces we saw on the walls in an office at Heathrow and here in the hospital are mostly of women. Women have more body fat, a nun said to me matter-of-factly. They float better.

Today I was stopped by a young sailor on the street. He had loaded bodies, he'd gone into the water when—he checks my face for signs of strength—when the sharks were first spotted. I don't blush, and he breaks down. "It's all right," I say. "Thank you." I heard about the sharks from Dr. Ranganathan. In his orderly mind, science brings understanding, it holds no terror. It is the shark's duty. For every deer there is a hunter, for every fish a fisherman.

The Irish are not shy; they rush to me and give me hugs and some are crying. I cannot imagine reactions like that on the streets of Toronto. Just strangers, and I am touched. Some carry flowers with them and give them to any Indian they see.

After lunch, a policeman I have gotten to know quite well catches hold of me. He says he thinks he has a match for Vinod. I explain what a good swimmer Vinod is.

"You want me with you when you look at photos?" Dr. Ranganathan walks ahead of me into the picture gallery. In these matters, he is a scientist, and I am grateful. It is a new perspective. "They have performed miracles," he says. "We are indebted to them."

The first day or two the policemen showed us relatives only one picture at a time; now they're in a hurry, they're eager to lay out the possibles, and even the probables.

The face on the photo is of a boy much like Vinod; the same intelligent eyes, the same thick brows dipping into a V. But this boy's features, even his cheeks, are puffier, wider, mushier.

"No." My gaze is pulled by other pictures. There are five other boys who look like Vinod.

The nun assigned to console me rubs the first picture with a fingertip. "When they've been in the water for a while, love, they look a little heavier." The bones under the skin are broken, they said on the first day—try to adjust your memories. It's important.

"It's not him. I'm his mother. I'd know."

"I know this one!" Dr. Ranganathan cries out, and suddenly from the back of the gallery. "And this one!" I think he senses that I don't want to find my boys. "They are the Kutty brothers. They were also from Montreal." I don't mean to be crying. On the contrary, I am ecstatic. My suitcase in the hotel is packed heavy with dry clothes for my boys.

The policeman starts to cry. "I am so sorry. I am so sorry, ma'am. I really thought we had a match."

With the nun ahead of us and the policeman behind, we, the unlucky ones without our children's bodies, file out of the makeshift gallery.

From Ireland most of us go on to India. Kusum and I take the same direct flight to Bombay, so I can help her clear customs quickly. But we have to argue with a man in uniform. He has large boils on his face. The boils swell and glow with sweat as we argue with him. He wants Kusum to wait in line and he refuses to take authority because his boss is on a tea break. But Kusum won't let her coffins out of sight, and I shan't desert her though I know that my parents, elderly and diabetic, must be waiting in a stuffy car in a scorching lot.

"You bastard!" I scream at the man with the popping boils. Other passengers press closer. "You think we're smuggling contraband in those coffins!"

Once upon a time we were well-brought-up women; we were dutiful wives who kept our heads veiled, our voices shy and sweet.

In India, I become, once again, an only child of rich, ailing parents. Old friends of the family come to pay their respects. Some are Sikh, and inwardly, involuntarily, I cringe. My parents are progressive people; they do not blame communities for a few individuals.

In Canada it is a different story now.

"Stay longer," my mother pleads. "Canada is a cold place. Why would you want to be by yourself?" I stay.

Three months pass. Then another.

"Vikram wouldn't have wanted you to give up things!" they protest. They call my husband by the name he was born with. In Toronto he'd changed to Vik so the men he worked with at his office would find his name as easy as Rod or Chris. "You know, the dead aren't cut off from us!"

My grandmother, the spoiled daughter of a rich zamindar, shaved her head with rusty razor blades when she was widowed at sixteen. My grandfather died of childhood diabetes when he was nineteen, and she saw herself as the harbinger of bad luck. My mother grew up without parents, raised indifferently by an uncle, while her true mother slept in a hut behind the main estate house and took her food with the servants. She grew up a rationalist. My parents abhor mindless mortification.

The zamindar's daughter kept stubborn faith in Vedic rituals; my parents rebelled. I am trapped between two modes of knowledge. At thirty-six, I am too old to start over and too young to give up. Like my husband's spirit, I flutter between worlds.

Courting aphasia, we travel. We travel with our phalanx of servants and poor relatives. To hill stations and to beach resorts. We play contract bridge in dusty gymkhana clubs. We ride stubby ponies up crumbly mountain trails. At tea dances, we let ourselves be twirled twice round the ballroom. We hit the holy spots we hadn't made time for before. In Varanasi, Kalighat, Rishikesh, Hardwar, astrologers and palmists seek me out and for a fee offer me cosmic consolations.

Already the widowers among us are being shown new bride candidates. They cannot resist the call of custom, the authority of their parents and older brothers. They must marry; it is the duty of a man to look after a wife. The new wives will be young widows with children, destitute but of good family. They will make loving wives, but the men will shun them. I've had calls from the men over crackling Indian telephone lines. "Save me," they say, these substantial, educated, successful men of forty. "My parents are arranging a marriage for me." In a month they will have buried one family and returned to Canada with a new bride and partial family.

I am comparatively lucky. No one here thinks of arranging a husband for an unlucky widow.

Then, on the third day of the sixth month into this odyssey, in an abandoned temple in a tiny Himalayan village, as I make my offering of flowers and sweetmeats to the god of a tribe of animists, my husband descends to me.

He is squatting next to a scrawny sadhu in moth-eaten robes. Vikram wears the vanilla suit he wore the last time I hugged him. The sadhu tosses petals on a butter-fed flame, reciting Sanskrit mantras, and sweeps his face of flies. My husband takes my hands in his.

You're beautiful, he starts. Then, *What are you doing here?*

Shall I stay? I ask. He only smiles, but already the image is fading. *You must finish alone what we started together.* No seaweed wreathes his mouth. He speaks too fast, just as he used to when we were an envied family in our pink split-level. He is gone.

In the windowless altar room, smoky with joss sticks and clarified butter lamps, a sweaty hand gropes for my blouse. I do not shriek. The sadhu arranges his roe. The lamps hiss and sputter out.

When we come out of the temple, my mother says, "Did you feel something weird in there?"

My mother has no patience with ghosts, prophetic dreams, holy men, and cults. "No," I lie. "Nothing."

But she knows that she's lost me. She knows that in days I shall be leaving.

Kusum's put up her house for sale. She wants to live in an ashram in Hardwar. Moving to Hardwar was her swami's idea. Her swami runs two ashrams, the one in Hardwar and another here in Toronto.

"Don't run away," I tell her.

"I'm not running away," she says. "I'm pursuing inner peace. You think you or that Ranganathan fellow are better off?"

Pam's left for California. She wants to do some modeling, she says. She says when she comes into her share of the insurance money she'll open a yoga-cum-aerobics studio in Hollywood. She sends me postcards so naughty I daren't leave them on the coffee table. Her mother has withdrawn from her and the world.

The rest of us don't lose touch, that's the point. Talk is all we have, says Dr. Ranganathan, who has also resisted his relatives and returned to Montreal and to his job, alone. He says, Whom better to talk with than other relatives? We've been melted down and recast as a new tribe.

He calls me twice a week from Montreal. Every Wednesday night and every Saturday afternoon. He is changing jobs, going to Ottawa. But Ottawa is over a hundred miles away, and he is forced to drive two hundred and twenty miles a day from his home in Montreal. He can't bring himself to sell his house. The house is a temple, he says; the king-sized bed in the master bedroom is a shrine. He sleeps on a folding cot. A devotee.

There are still some hysterical relatives. Judith Templeton's list of those needing help and those who've "accepted" is in nearly perfect balance. Acceptance means you speak of your family in the past tense and you make active plans for moving ahead with your life. There are courses at Seneca and Ryerson we could be taking. Her gleaming leather briefcase is full of college catalogues and lists of cultural societies that need our help. She has done impressive work, I tell her.

"In the textbooks on grief management," she replies—I am her confidante, I realize, one of the few whose grief has not sprung bizarre obsessions—"there are stages to pass through: rejection, depression, acceptance, reconstruction." She has compiled a chart and finds that six months after the tragedy, none of us still rejects reality, but only a handful are reconstructing. "Depressed acceptance" is the plateau we've reached. Remarriage is a major step in reconstruction (though she's a little surprised, even shocked, over *how* quickly some of the men have taken on new families). Selling one's house and changing jobs and cities is healthy.

How to tell Judith Templeton that my family surrounds me, and that like creatures in epics, they've changed shapes? She sees me as calm and accepting but worries that I have no job, no career. My closest friends are worse off than I. I cannot tell her my days, even my nights, are thrilling.

She asks me to help with families she can't reach at all. An elderly couple in Agincourt whose sons were killed just weeks after they had brought their parents over from a village in Punjab. From their names, I know they are Sikh. Judith Templeton and a translator have visited them twice with offers of money for airfare to Ireland, with bank forms, power-of-attorney forms, but they have refused to sign, or to leave their tiny apartment. Their sons' money is frozen in the bank. Their sons' investment apartments have been trashed by tenants, the furnishings sold off. The parents fear that anything they sign or any money they receive will end the company's or the country's obligations to them. They fear they are selling their sons for two airline tickets to a place they've never seen.

The high-rise apartment is a tower of Indians and West Indians, with a sprinkling of Orientals. The nearest bus-stop kiosk is lined with women in saris. Boys practice cricket in the parking lot. Inside the building, even I wince a bit from the ferocity of onion fumes, the distinctive and immediate Indianness of frying ghee, but Judith Templeton maintains a steady flow of information. These poor old people are in imminent danger of losing their place and all their services.

I say to her, "They are Sikh. They will not open up to a Hindu woman." And what I want to add is, as much as I try not to, I stiffen now at the sight of beards and turbans. I remember a time when we all trusted each other in this new country, it was only the new country we worried about.

The two rooms are dark and stuffy. The lights are off, and an oil lamp sputters on the coffee table. The bent old lady has let us in, and her husband is wrapping a white turban over his oiled, hip-length hair. She immediately goes to the kitchen, and I hear the most familiar sound of an Indian home, tap water hitting and filling a teapot.

They have not paid their utility bills, out of fear and inability to write a check. The telephone is gone, electricity and gas and water are soon to follow. They have told Judith their sons will provide. They are good boys, and they have always earned and looked after their parents.

We converse a bit in Hindi. They do not ask about the crash and I wonder if I should bring it up. If they think I am here merely as a translator, then they may feel insulted. There are thousands of Punjabi speakers, Sikhs, in Toronto to do a better job. And so I say to the old lady, "I too have lost my sons, and my husband, in the crash."

Her eyes immediately fill with tears. The man mutters a few words which sound like a blessing. "God provides and God takes away," he says.

I want to say, But only men destroy and give back nothing. "My boys and my husband are not coming back," I say. "We have to understand that."

Now the old woman responds. "But who is to say? Man alone does not decide these things." To this her husband adds his agreement.

Judith asks about the bank papers, the release forms. With a stroke of the pen, they will have a provincial trustee to pay their bills, invest their money, send them a monthly pension.

"Do you know this woman?" I ask them.

The man raises his hand from the table, turns it over, and seems to regard each finger separately before he answers. "This young lady is always coming here, we make tea for her, and she leaves papers for us to sign." His eyes scan a pile of papers in the corner of the room. "Soon we will be out of tea, then will she go away?"

The old lady adds, "I have asked my neighbors and no one else gets *angrezi* visitors. What have we done?"

"It's her job," I try to explain. "The government is worried. Soon you will have no place to stay, no lights, no gas, no water."

"Government will get its money. Tell her not to worry, we are honorable people."

I try to explain the government wishes to give money, not take. He raises his hand. "Let them take," he says. "We are accustomed to that. That is no problem."

"We are strong people," says the wife. "Tell her that."

"Who needs all this machinery?" demands the husband. "It is unhealthy, the bright lights, the cold air on a hot day, the cold food, the four gas rings. God will provide, not government."

"When our boys return," the mother says.

Her husband sucks his teeth. "Enough talk," he says.

Judith breaks in. "Have you convinced them?" The snaps on her cordovan briefcase go off like firecrackers in that quiet apartment. She lays the sheaf of legal papers on the coffee table. "If they can't write their names, an X will do—I've told them that."

Now the old lady has shuffled to the kitchen and soon emerges with a pot of tea and two cups. "I think my bladder will go first on a job like this," Judith says to me, smiling. "If only there was some way of reaching them. Please thank her for the tea. Tell her she's very kind."

I nod in Judith's direction and tell them in Hindi, "She thanks you for the tea. She thinks you are being very hospitable but she doesn't have the slightest idea what it means."

I want to say, Humor her. I want to say, My boys and my husband are with me too, more than ever. I look in the old man's eyes and I can read his stubborn, peasant's message: *I have protected this woman as best I can. She is the only person I have left. Give to me or take from me what you will, but I will not sign for it. I will not pretend that I accept.*

In the car, Judith says, "You see what I'm up against? I'm sure they're lovely people, but their stubbornness and ignorance are driving me crazy. They think signing a paper is signing their sons' death warrants, don't they?"

I am looking out the window. I want to say, *In our culture, it is a parent's duty to hope.*

"Now Shaila, this next woman is a real mess. She cries day and night, and she refuses all medical help. We may have to—"

"Let me out at the subway," I say.

"I beg your pardon?" I can feel those blue eyes staring at me.

It would not be like her to disobey. She merely disapproves, and slows at a corner to let me out. Her voice is plaintive. "Is there anything I said? Anything I did?"

I could answer her suddenly in a dozen ways, but I choose not to. "Shaila? Let's talk about it," I hear, then slam the door.

A wife and mother begins her life in a new country, and that life is cut short. Yet her husband tells her: Complete what we have started. We, who stayed out of politics and came half way around the world to avoid religious and political feuding, have been the first in the New World to die from it. I no longer know what we started, nor how to complete it. I write letters to the editors of local papers and to members of Parliament. Now at least they admit it was a bomb. One MP answers back, with sympathy, but with a challenge. You want to make a difference? Work on a campaign. Work on mine. Politicize the Indian voter.

My husband's old lawyer helps me set up a trust. Vikram was a saver and a careful investor. He had saved the boys' boarding school and college fees.

I sell the pink house at four times what we paid for it and take a small apartment downtown. I am looking for a charity to support.

We are deep in the Toronto winter, gray skies, icy pavements. I stay indoors, watching television. I have tried to assess my situation, how best to live my life, to complete what we began so many years ago. Kusum has written me from Hardwar that her life is now serene. She has seen Satish and has heard her daughter sing again. Kusum was on a pilgrimage, passing through a village, when she heard a young girl's voice, singing one of her daughter's favorite *bhajans*. She followed the music through the squalor of a Himalayan village, to a hut where a young girl, an exact replica of her daughter, was fanning coals under the kitchen fire. When she appeared, the girl cried out, "Ma!" and ran away. What did I think of that?

I think I can only envy her.

Pam didn't make it to California, but writes me from Vancouver. She works in a department store, giving makeup hints to Indian and Oriental girls. Dr. Ranganathan has given up his commute, given up his house and job, and accepted an academic position in Texas, where no one knows his story and he has vowed not to tell it. He calls me now once a week.

I wait, I listen and I pray, but Vikram has not returned to me. The voices and the shapes and the nights filled with visions ended abruptly several weeks ago.

I take it as a sign.

One rare, beautiful, sunny day last week, returning from a small errand on Yonge Street, I was walking through the park from the subway to my apartment. I live equidistant from the Ontario Houses of Parliament and the University of Toronto. The day was not cold, but something in the bare trees caught my attention. I looked up from the gravel, into the branches and the clear blue sky beyond. I thought I heard the rustling of larger forms, and I waited a moment for voices. Nothing.

"What?" I asked.

Then as I stood in the path looking north to Queen's Park and west to the university, I heard the voices of my family one last time. *Your time has come,* they said. *Go, be brave.*

I do not know where this voyage I have begun will end. I do not know which direction I will take. I dropped the package on a park bench and started walking.

Wild Swans

Alice Munro

Alice Munro (1931–) was born Alice Laidlaw in Wingham, Ontario and grew up in a rural area of Ontario where her parents were farmers. After her marriage to James Munro, she began writing in the 1950s while raising three daughters and has explained her preference for writing short fiction to the hectic life she led when her children were young, when there was simply not enough time for writing novels. Thus, she has written only one novel but numerous volumes of short fiction and is now recognized as one of the modern masters of the short story. Among her best-known collections are Who Do You Think You Are? *(1978), from which the selection here is taken, and* The Progress of Love *(1986). Among her literary awards are the Canadian Governor General's Award, the U.S. PEN-Malamud Award, and Britain's prestigious Booker Prize. Much of her fiction focuses on the lives of ordinary people in rural Canada, characters whose lives are outwardly often noneventful, but who sometimes make surprising discoveries about themselves.*

Flo said to watch for White Slavers. She said this was how they operated: an old woman, a motherly or grandmotherly sort, made friends while riding beside you on a bus or train. She offered you candy, which was drugged. Pretty soon you began to droop and mumble, were in no condition to speak for yourself. Oh, help, the woman said, my daughter (granddaughter) is sick, please somebody help me get her off so that she can recover in the fresh air. Up stepped a polite gentleman, pretending to be a stranger, offering assistance. Together, at the next stop, they hustled you off the train or bus, and that was the last the ordinary world ever saw of you. They kept you a prisoner in the White Slave place (to which you had been transported drugged and bound so you wouldn't even know where you were), until such time as you were thoroughly degraded and in despair, your insides torn up by drunken men and invested with vile disease, your mind destroyed by drugs, your hair and teeth fallen out. It took about three years for you to get to this state. You wouldn't want to go home then; maybe couldn't remember home, or find your way if you did. So they let you out on the streets.

Flo took ten dollars and put it in a little cloth bag, which she sewed to the strap of Rose's slip. Another thing likely to happen was that Rose would get her purse stolen.

Watch out, Flo said as well, for people dressed up as ministers. They were the worst. That disguise was commonly adopted by White Slavers, as well as those after your money.

Rose said she didn't see how she could tell which ones were disguised.

Flo had worked in Toronto once. She had worked as a waitress in a coffee shop in Union Station. That was how she knew all she knew. She never saw sunlight, in those days, except on her days off. But she saw plenty else. She saw a man cut another man's stomach with a knife, just pull out his shirt and do a tidy cut, as if it was a watermelon not a stomach. The stomach's owner just sat looking down surprised, with no time to protest. Flo implied that that was nothing, in Toronto. She saw two bad women (that was what Flo called whores, running the two words together, like badminton) get into a fight, and a man laughed at them, other men stopped and laughed and egged them on, and they had their fists full of each other's hair. At last the police came and took them away, still howling and yelping.

She saw a child die of a fit too. Its face was black as ink.

"Well, I'm not scared," said Rose provokingly. "There's the police, anyway."

"Oh, them! They'd be the first ones to diddle you!"

She did not believe anything Flo said on the subject of sex. Consider the undertaker.

A little bald man, very neatly dressed, would come into the store some times and speak to Flo with a placating expression.

"I only wanted a bag of candy. And maybe a few packages of gum. And one or two chocolate bars. Could you go to the trouble of wrapping them?"

Flo in her mock-deferential tone would assure him that she could. She wrapped them in heavy-duty white paper, so they were something like presents. He took his time with the selection, humming and chatting, then dawdled for a while. He might ask how Flo was feeling. And how Rose was, if she was there.

"You look pale. Young girls need fresh air." To Flo he would say, "You work too hard. You've worked hard all your life."

"No rest for the wicked," Flo would say agreeably.

When he went out she hurried to the window. There it was—the old black hearse with its purple curtains.

"He'll be after them today!" Flo would say as the hearse rolled away at a gentle pace, almost a funeral pace. The little man had been an undertaker, but he was retired now. The hearse was retired too. His sons had taken over the undertaking and bought a new one. He drove the old hearse all over the country, looking for women. So Flo said. Rose could not believe it. Flo said he gave them the gum and the candy. Rose said he probably ate them himself. Flo said he had been seen, he had been heard. In mild weather he drove with the windows down, singing, to himself or to somebody out of sight in the back.

"Her brow is like the snowdrift
Her throat is like the swan . . ."

Flo imitated him singing. Gently overtaking some woman walking on a back road, or resting at a country crossroads. All compliments and courtesy and chocolate bars, offering a ride. Of course every woman who reported being asked said she had turned him down. He never pestered anybody, drove politely on. He called in at houses, and if the husband was home he seemed to like just as well as anything to sit and chat. Wives said that was all he ever did anyway but Flo did not believe it.

"Some women are taken in," she said. "A number." She liked to speculate on what the hearse was like inside. Plush. Plush on the walls and the roof and the floor. Soft purple, the color of the curtains, the color of dark lilacs.

All nonsense, Rose thought. Who could believe it, of a man that age?

Rose was going to Toronto on the train for the first time by herself. She had been once before, but that was with Flo, long before her father died. They took along their own sandwiches and bought milk from the vendor on the train. It was sour. Sour chocolate milk. Rose kept taking tiny sips, unwilling to admit that something so much desired could fail her. Flo sniffed it, then hunted up and down the train until she found the old man in his red jacket, with no teeth and the tray hanging around his neck. She invited him to sample the chocolate milk. She invited people nearby to smell it. He let her have some ginger ale for nothing. It was slightly warm.

"I let him know," Flo said, looking around after he had left. "You have to let them know."

A woman agreed with her but most people looked out the window. Rose drank the warm ginger ale. Either that, or the scene with the vendor, or the conversation Flo and the agreeing woman now got into about where they came from, why they were going to Toronto, and Rose's morning constipation which was why she was lacking color, or the small amount of chocolate milk she had got inside her, caused her to throw up in the train toilet. All day long she was afraid people in Toronto could smell vomit on her coat.

This time Flo started the trip off by saying, "Keep an eye on her, she's never been away from home before!" to the conductor, then looking around and laughing, to show that was jokingly meant. Then she had to get off. It seemed the conductor had no more need for jokes than Rose had, and no intention of keeping an eye on anybody. He never spoke to Rose except to ask for her ticket. She had a window seat, and was soon extraordinarily happy. She felt Flo receding, West Hanratty flying away from her, her own wearying self discarded as easily as everything else. She loved the towns less and less known. A woman was standing at her back door in her nightgown, not caring if everybody on the train saw her. They were travelling south, out of the snowbelt, into an earlier spring, a tenderer sort of landscape. People could grow peach trees in their back yards.

Rose collected in her mind the things she had to look for in Toronto. First, things for Flo. Special stockings for her varicose veins. A special kind of cement for sticking handles on pots. And a full set of dominoes.

For herself Rose wanted to buy hair-remover to put on her arms and legs, and if possible an arrangement of inflatable cushions, supposed to reduce your hips and thighs. She thought they probably had hair-remover in the drugstore in Hanratty, but the woman in there was a friend of Flo's and told everything. She told Flo who bought hair dye and slimming medicine and French safes. As for the cushion business, you could send away for it but there was sure to be a comment at the Post Office, and Flo knew people there as well. She also planned to buy some bangles, and an angora sweater. She had great hopes of silver bangles and powder-blue angora. She thought they could transform her, make her calm and slender and take the frizz out of her hair, dry her underarms and turn her complexion to pearl.

The money for these things, as well as the money for the trip, came from a prize Rose had won, for writing an essay called "Art and Science in the World of Tomorrow." To her surprise, Flo asked if she could read it, and while she was reading it, she remarked that they must have thought they had to give Rose the prize for swallowing the dictionary. Then she said shyly, "It's very interesting."

She would have to spend the night at Cela McKinney's. Cela McKinney was her father's cousin. She had married a hotel manager and thought she had gone up in the world. But the hotel manager came home one day and sat down on the dining-room floor between two chairs and said, "I am never going to leave this house again." Nothing unusual had happened, he had just decided not to go out of the house again, and he didn't, until he died. That had made

Cela McKinney odd and nervous. She locked her doors at eight o'clock. She was also very stingy. Supper was usually oatmeal porridge, with raisins. Her house was dark and narrow and smelled like a bank.

The train was filling up. At Brantford a man asked if she would mind if he sat down beside her.

"It's cooler out than you'd think," he said. He offered her part of his newspaper. She said no thanks.

Then, lest he think her rude, she said it really was cooler. She went on looking out the window at the spring morning. There was no snow left, down here. The trees and bushes seemed to have a paler bark than they did at home. Even the sunlight looked different. It was as different from home, here, as the coast of the Mediterranean would be, or the valleys of California.

"Filthy windows, you'd think they'd take more care," the man said. "Do you travel much by train?"

She said no.

Water was lying in the fields. He nodded at it and said there was a lot this year.

"Heavy snows."

She noticed his saying "snows," a poetic-sounding word. Anyone at home would have said "snow."

"I had an unusual experience the other day. I was driving out in the country. In fact, I was on my way to see one of my parishioners, a lady with a heart condition—"

She looked quickly at his collar. He was wearing an ordinary shirt and tie and a dark-blue suit.

"Oh, yes," he said. "I'm a United Church minister. But I don't always wear my uniform. I wear it for preaching in. I'm off duty today.

"Well, as I said, I was driving through the country and I saw some Canada geese down on a pond, and I took another look, and there were some swans down with them. A whole great flock of swans. What a lovely sight they were. They would be on their spring migration, I expect, heading up North. What a spectacle. I never saw anything like it."

Rose was unable to think appreciatively of the wild swans because she was afraid he was going to lead the conversation from them to Nature in general and then to God, the way a minister would feel obliged to do. But he did not, he stopped with the swans.

"A very fine sight. You would have enjoyed them."

He was between fifty and sixty years old, Rose thought. He was short, and energetic-looking, with a square ruddy face and bright waves of gray hair combed straight up from his forehead. When she realized he was not going to mention God she felt she ought to show her gratitude.

She said they must have been lovely.

"It wasn't even a regular pond, it was only some water lying in a field. It was just luck the water was lying there and they came down and I came driving by at the right time. Just luck. They come in at the east end of Lake Erie, I think. But I never was lucky enough to see them before."

She turned by degrees to the window, and he returned to his paper. She remained slightly smiling, so as not to seem rude, not to seem to be rejecting conversation altogether. The morning really was cool, and she had taken down her coat off the hook where she put it when she first got on the train; she had spread it over herself, like a lap robe. She had set her purse on the floor when the minister sat down, to give him room. He took the sections of the paper apart, shaking and rustling them in a leisurely, rather showy way. He seemed to her the sort of person who does everything in a showy way: A ministerial way. He brushed aside the sections he didn't want at the moment. A corner of newspaper touched her leg, just at the edge of her coat.

She thought for some time that it was the paper. Then she said to herself, What if it is a hand? That was the kind of thing she could imagine. She would sometimes look at men's hands, at the fuzz on their forearms, their concentrating profiles. She would think about everything they could do. Even the stupid ones. For instance, the driver-salesman who brought the bread to Flo's store. The ripeness and confidence of manner, the settled mixture of ease and alertness with which he handled the bread truck. A fold of mature belly over the belt did not displease her. Another time she had her eye on the French teacher at school. Not a Frenchman at all, really, his name was McLaren, but Rose thought teaching French had rubbed off on him, made him look like one. Quick and sallow; sharp shoulders; hooked nose and sad eyes. She saw him lapping and coiling his way through slow pleasures, a perfect autocrat of indulgences. She had a considerable longing to be somebody's object. Pounded, pleasured, reduced, exhausted.

But what if it was a hand? What if it really was a hand? She shifted slightly, moved as much as she could toward the window. Her imagination seemed to have created this reality, a reality she was not prepared for at all. She found it alarming. She was concentrating on that leg, that bit of skin with the stocking over it. She could not bring herself to look. Was there a pressure, or was there not? She shifted again. Her legs had been, and remained, tightly closed. It was. It was a hand. It was a hand's pressure.

Please don't. That was what she tried to say. She shaped the words in her mind, tried them out, then couldn't get them past her lips. Why was that? The embarrassment, was it, the fear that people might hear? People were all around them, the seats were full.

It was not only that.

She did manage to look at him, not raising her head but turning it cautiously. He had tilted his seat back and closed his eyes. There was his dark-blue suit sleeve, disappearing under the newspaper. He had arranged the paper so that it overlapped Rose's coat. His hand was underneath, simply resting, as if flung out in sleep.

Now, Rose could have shifted the newspaper and removed her coat. If he was not asleep, he would have been obliged to draw back his hand. If he was asleep, if he did not draw it back, she could have whispered *Excuse me* and set his hand firmly on his own knee. This solution, so obvious and foolproof, did not occur to her. And she would have to wonder, Why not? The minister's hand was not, or not yet, at all welcome to her. It made her feel uncomfortable, resentful, slightly disgusted, trapped and wary. But she could not take charge of it, to reject it. She could not insist that it was there, when he seemed to be insisting that it was not. How could she declare him responsible, when he lay there so harmless and trusting, resting himself before his busy day, with such a pleased and healthy face? A man older than her father would be, if he were living, a man used to deference, an appreciator of Nature, delighter in wild swans. If she did say *Please don't* she was sure he would ignore her, as if overlooking some silliness or impoliteness on her part. She knew that as soon as she said it she would hope he had not heard.

But there was more to it than that. Curiosity. More constant, more imperious, than any lust. A lust in itself, that will make you draw back and wait, wait too long, risk almost anything, just to see what will happen. *To see what will happen.*

The hand began, over the next several miles, the most delicate, the most timid, pressures and investigations. Not asleep. Or if he was, his hand wasn't. She did feel disgust. She felt a faint, wandering nausea. She thought of flesh: lumps of flesh, pink snouts, fat tongues, blunt fingers, all on their way trotting and creeping and lolling and rubbing, looking for their comfort. She thought of cats in heat rubbing themselves along the top of board fences, yowling with their miserable complaint. It was pitiful, infantile, this itching and shoving and squeezing. Spongy tissues, inflamed membranes, tormented nerve-ends, shameful smells; humiliation.

All that was starting. His hand, that she wouldn't ever have wanted to hold, that she wouldn't have squeezed back, his stubborn patient hand was able, after all, to get the ferns to rustle and the streams to flow, to waken a sly luxuriance.

Nevertheless, she would rather not. She would still rather not. Please remove this, she said out the window. Stop it, please, she said to the stumps and barns. The hand moved up her leg past the top of her stocking to her bare skin, had moved higher, under her suspender, reached her underpants and the lower part of her belly. Her legs were still crossed, pinched together. While her legs stayed crossed she could lay claim to innocence, she had not admitted anything. She could still believe that she would stop this in a minute. Nothing was going to happen, nothing more. Her legs were never going to open.

But they were. They were. As the train crossed the Niagara Escarpment above Dundas, as they looked down at the preglacial valley, the silverwooded rubble of little hills, as they came sliding down to the shores of Lake Ontario, she would make this slow, and silent, and definite declaration, perhaps disappointing as much as satisfying the hand's owner. He would not lift his eyelids, his face would not alter, his fingers would not hesitate, but would go powerfully and discreetly to work. Invasion, and welcome, and sunlight flashing far and wide on the lake water; miles of bare orchards stirring round Burlington.

This was disgrace, this was beggary. But what harm in that, we say to ourselves at such moments, what harm in anything, the worse the better, as we ride the cold wave of greed, of greedy assent. A stranger's hand, or root vegetables or humble kitchen tools that people tell jokes about; the world is tumbling with innocent-seeming objects ready to declare themselves, slippery and obliging. She was careful of her breathing. She could not believe this. Victim and accomplice she was borne past Glassco's Jams and Marmalades, past the big pulsating pipes of oil refineries. They glided into suburbs where bedsheets, and towels used to wipe up intimate stains, flapped leeringly on the clotheslines, where even the children seemed to be frolicking lewdly in the schoolyards, and the very truck drivers stopped at the railway crossings must be thrusting their thumbs gleefully into curled hands. Such cunning antics now, such popular visions. The gates and towers of the Exhibition Grounds came into view, the painted domes and pillars floated marvellously against her eyelids' rosy sky. Then flew apart in celebration. You could have had such a flock of birds, wild swans, even, wakened under one big dome together, exploding from it, taking to the sky.

She bit the edge of her tongue. Very soon the conductor passed through the train, to stir the travellers, warn them back to life.

In the darkness under the station the United Church minister, refreshed, opened his eyes and got his paper folded together, then asked if she would like some help with her coat. His gallantry was self-satisfied, dismissive. No, said Rose, with a sore tongue. He hurried out of the train ahead of her. She did not see him in the station. She never saw him again in her life. But he remained on call, so to speak, for years and years, ready to slip into place at a critical moment, without even any regard, later on, for husband or lovers. What recommended him? She could never understand it. His simplicity, his arrogance, his perversely appealing lack of handsomeness, even of ordinary grown-up masculinity? When he stood up she saw that he was shorter even than she had thought, that his face was pink and shiny, that there was something crude and pushy and childish about him.

Was he a minister, really, or was that only what he said? Flo had mentioned people who were not ministers, dressed up as if they were. Not real ministers dressed as if they were not. Or, stranger still, men who were not real ministers pretending to be real but dressed as if they were not. But that she had come as close as she had, to what could happen, was an unwelcome thing. Rose walked through Union Station feeling the little bag with the ten dollars rubbing at her, knew she would feel it all day long, rubbing its reminder against her skin.

She couldn't stop getting Flo's messages, even with that. She remembered, because she was in Union Station, that there was a girl named Mavis working here, in the gift shop, when Flo was working in the coffee shop. Mavis had warts on her eyelids that looked like they were going to turn into sties but they didn't, they went away. Maybe she had them removed, Flo didn't ask. She was very good-looking, without them. There was a movie star in those days she looked a lot like. The movie star's name was Frances Farmer.

Frances Farmer. Rose had never heard of her.

That was the name. And Mavis went and bought herself a big hat that dipped over one eye and a dress entirely made of lace. She went off for the weekend to Georgian Bay, to a resort up there. She booked herself in under the name of Florence Farmer. To give everybody the idea she was really the other one, Frances Farmer, but calling herself Florence because she was on holiday and didn't want to be recognized. She had a little cigarette holder that was black and mother-of-pearl. She could have been arrested, Flo said. For the *nerve*.

Rose almost went over to the gift shop to see if Mavis was still there and if she could recognize her. She thought it would be an especially fine thing to manage a transformation like that. To dare it; to get away with it, to enter on preposterous adventures in your own, but newly named, skin.

Where Are You Going, Where Have You Been?

Joyce Carol Oates

for Bob Dylan

Joyce Carol Oates (1938–), born in Lockport, New York, is among the most accomplished and prolific of contemporary writers. She completed her first (unpublished) novel at the age of fifteen. Since the early 1960s, she has published 40 novels under her own name and another eight under the pseudonym Rosamund Smith. She has also published 26 volumes of short stories, 15 volumes of poetry, and eleven volumes of essays, not to mention a number of plays and children's books. Even more remarkably, she writes in a number of different genres: domestic novels, gothic romance, crime fiction, and horror fiction. Her writings have won many literary prizes, including the National Book Award and the O. Henry Award (three times). Among the best known of her novels is Black Water *(1992), a fictionalization of Senator Ted Kennedy's tragic car accident at Chappaquiddick in 1969; and* We Were the Mulvaneys *(1996), the story of a family's downfall in the wake of sexual violence. In the short story included here, first published in* Epoch *(Fall 1966), the threat of sexual violence is combined with an insightful account of the psychology of adolescent rebellion.*

Her name was Connie. She was fifteen and she had a quick, nervous giggling habit of craning her neck to glance into mirrors or checking other people's faces to make sure her own was all right. Her mother, who noticed everything and knew everything and who hadn't much reason any longer to look at her own face, always scolded Connie about it. "Stop gawking at yourself. Who are you?

157

You think you're so pretty?" she would say. Connie would raise her eyebrows at these familiar old complaints and look right through her mother, into a shadowy vision of herself as she was right at that moment: she knew she was pretty and that was everything. Her mother had been pretty once too, if you could believe those old snapshots in the album, but now her looks were gone and that was why she was always after Connie.

"Why don't you keep your room clean like your sister? How've you got your hair fixed—what the hell stinks? Hair spray? You don't see your sister using that junk."

Her sister June was twenty-four and still lived at home. She was a secretary in the high school Connie attended, and if that wasn't bad enough—with her in the same building—she was so plain and chunky and steady that Connie had to hear her praised all the time by her mother and her mother's sisters. June did this, June did that, she saved money and helped clean the house and cooked and Connie couldn't do a thing, her mind was all filled with trashy daydreams. Their father was away at work most of the time and when he came home he wanted supper and he read the newspaper at supper and after supper he went to bed. He didn't bother talking much to them, but around his bent head Connie's mother kept picking at her until Connie wished her mother was dead and she herself was dead and it was all over. "She makes me want to throw up sometimes," she complained to her friends. She had a high, breathless, amused voice that made everything she said sound a little forced, whether it was sincere or not.

There was one good thing: June went places with girl friends of hers, girls who were just as plain and steady as she, and so when Connie wanted to do that her mother had no objections. The father of Connie's best girl friend drove the girls the three miles to town and left them at a shopping plaza so they could walk through the stores or go to a movie, and when he came to pick them up again at eleven he never bothered to ask what they had done.

They must have been familiar sights, walking around the shopping plaza in their shorts and flat ballerina slippers that always scuffed the sidewalk, with charm bracelets jingling on their thin wrists; they would lean together to whisper and laugh secretly if someone passed who amused or interested them. Connie had long dark blond hair that drew anyone's eye to it, and she wore part of it pulled up on her head and puffed out and the rest of it she let fall down her back. She wore a pull-over jersey blouse that looked one way when she was at home and another way when she was away from home. Everything about her had two sides to it, one for home and one for anywhere that was not home: her walk, which could be childlike and bobbing, or languid enough to make anyone think she was hearing music in her head; her mouth, which was pale and smirking most of the time, but bright and pink on these evenings out; her laugh, which was cynical and drawling at home—"Ha, ha, very funny,"—but highpitched and nervous anywhere else, like the jingling of the charms on her bracelet.

Sometimes they did go shopping or to a movie, but sometimes they went across the highway, ducking fast across the busy road, to a drive-in restaurant where older kids hung out. The restaurant was shaped like a big bottle, though squatter than a real bottle, and on its cap was a revolving figure of a grinning boy holding a hamburger aloft. One night in midsummer they ran across, breathless with daring, and right away someone leaned out a car window and invited them over, but it was just a boy from high school they didn't like. It made them feel good to be able to ignore him. They went up through the maze of parked and cruising cars to the bright-lit, fly-infested restaurant, their faces pleased and expectant as if they were entering a sacred building that loomed up out of the night to give them what haven and blessing they yearned for. They sat at the counter and crossed their legs at the ankles, their thin shoulders rigid with excitement, and listened to the music that made everything so good: the music was always in the background, like music at a church service; it was something to depend upon.

A boy named Eddie came in to talk with them. He sat backwards on his stool, turning himself jerkily around in semicircles and then stopping and turning back again, and after a while he asked Connie if she would like something to eat. She said she would and so she tapped her friend's arm on her way out—her friend pulled her face up into a brave, droll look—and Connie said she would meet her at eleven, across the way. "I just hate to leave her like that," Connie said earnestly, but the boy said that she wouldn't be alone for long. So they went out to his car, and on the way Connie couldn't help but let her eyes wander over the windshields and faces all around her, her face gleaming with a joy that had nothing to do with Eddie or even this place; it might have been the music. She drew her shoulders up and sucked in her breath with the pure pleasure of being alive, and just at that moment she happened to glance at a face just a few feet from hers. It was a boy with shaggy black hair, in a convertible jalopy painted gold. He stared at her and then his lips widened into a grin. Connie slit her eyes at him and turned away, but she couldn't help glancing back and there he was, still watching her. He wagged a finger and laughed and said, "Gonna get you, baby," and Connie turned away again without Eddie noticing anything.

She spent three hours with him, at the restaurant where they ate hamburgers and drank Cokes in wax cups that were always sweating, and then down an alley a mile or so away, and when he left her off at five to eleven only the movie house was still open at the plaza. Her girl friend was there, talking with a boy. When Connie came up, the two girls smiled at each other and Connie said, "How was the movie?" and the girl said, "You should know." They rode off with the girl's father, sleepy and pleased, and Connie couldn't help but look back at the darkened shopping plaza with its big empty parking lot and its signs that were faded and ghostly now, and over at the drive-in restaurant where cars were still circling tirelessly. She couldn't hear the music at this distance.

Next morning June asked her how the movie was and Connie said, "So-so."

She and that girl and occasionally another girl went out several times a week, and the rest of the time Connie spent around the house—it was summer vacation—getting in her mother's way and thinking, dreaming about the boys she met. But all the boys fell back and dissolved into a single face that was not even a face but an idea, a feeling, mixed up with the urgent insistent pounding of the music and the humid night air of July. Connie's mother kept dragging her back to the daylight by finding things for her to do or saying suddenly, "What's this about the Pettinger girl?"

And Connie would say nervously, "Oh, her. That dope." She always drew thick clear lines between herself and such girls, and her mother was simple and kind enough to believe it. Her mother was so simple, Connie thought, that it was maybe cruel to fool her so much. Her mother went scuffling around the house in old bedroom slippers and complained over the telephone to one sister about the other, then the other called up and the two of them complained about the third one. If June's name was mentioned her mother's tone was approving, and if Connie's name was mentioned it was disapproving. This did not really mean she disliked Connie, and actually Connie thought that her mother preferred her to June just because she was prettier, but the two of them kept up a pretense of exasperation, a sense that they were tugging and struggling over something of little value to either of them. Sometimes, over coffee, they were almost friends, but something would come up—some vexation that was like a fly buzzing suddenly around their heads—and their faces went hard with contempt.

One Sunday Connie got up at eleven—none of them bothered with church—and washed her hair so that it could dry all day long in the sun. Her parents and sister were going to a barbecue at an aunt's house and Connie said no, she wasn't interested, rolling her eyes to let her mother know just what she thought of it. "Stay home alone then," her mother said sharply. Connie sat out back in a lawn chair and watched them drive away, her father quiet and bald, hunched around so that he could back the car out, her mother with a look that was still angry and not at all softened through the windshield, and in the back seat poor old June, all dressed up as if she didn't know what a barbecue was, with all the running yelling kids and the flies. Connie sat with her eyes closed in the sun, dreaming and dazed with the warmth about her as if this were a kind of love, the caresses of love, and her mind slipped over onto thoughts of the boy she had been with the night before and how nice he had been, how sweet it always was, not the way someone like June would suppose but sweet, gentle, the way it was in movies and promised in songs; and when she opened her eyes she hardly knew where she was, the back yard ran off into weeds and a fence-like line of trees and behind it the sky was perfectly blue and still. The asbestos ranch house that was now three years old startled her—it looked small. She shook her head as if to get awake.

It was too hot. She went inside the house and turned on the radio to drown out the quiet. She sat on the edge of her bed, barefoot, and listened for an hour and a half to a program called XYZ Sunday Jamboree, record after record of hard, fast, shrieking songs she sang along with, interspersed by exclamations from "Bobby King": "An' look here, you girls at Napoleon's—Son and Charley want you to pay real close attention to this song coming up!"

And Connie paid close attention herself, bathed in a glow of slow-pulsed joy that seemed to rise mysteriously out of the music itself and lay languidly about the airless little room, breathed in and breathed out with each gentle rise and fall of her chest.

After a while she heard a car coming up the drive. She sat up at once, startled, because it couldn't be her father so soon. The gravel kept crunching all the way in from the road—the driveway was long—and Connie ran to the window. It was a car she didn't know. It was an open jalopy, painted a bright gold that caught the sunlight opaquely. Her heart began to pound and her fingers snatched at her hair, checking it, and she whispered, "Christ. Christ," wondering how bad she looked. The car came to a stop at the side door and the horn sounded four short taps, as if this were a signal Connie knew.

She went into the kitchen and approached the door slowly, then hung out the screen door, her bare toes curling down off the step. There were two boys in the car and now she recognized the driver: he had shaggy, shabby black hair that looked crazy as a wig and he was grinning at her.

"I ain't late, am I?" he said.

"Who the hell do you think you are?" Connie said.

"Toldja I'd be out, didn't I?"

"I don't even know who you are."

She spoke sullenly, careful to show no interest or pleasure, and he spoke in a fast, bright monotone. Connie looked past him to the other boy, taking her time. He had fair brown hair, with a lock that fell onto his forehead. His sideburns gave him a fierce, embarrassed look, but so far he hadn't even bothered to glance at her. Both boys wore sunglasses. The driver's glasses were metallic and mirrored everything in miniature.

"You wanta come for a ride?" he said.

Connie smirked and let her hair fall loose over one shoulder.

"Don'tcha like my car? New paint job," he said. "Hey."

"What?"

"You're cute."

She pretended to fidget, chasing flies away from the door.

"Don'tcha believe me, or what?" he said.

"Look, I don't even know who you are," Connie said in disgust.

"Hey, Ellie's got a radio, see. Mine broke down." He lifted his friend's arm and showed her the little transistor radio the boy was holding, and now Connie began to hear the music. It was the same program that was playing inside the house.

"Bobby King?" she said.

"I listen to him all the time. I think he's great."

"He's kind of great," Connie said reluctantly.

"Listen, that guy's *great*. He knows where the action is."

Connie blushed a little, because the glasses made it impossible for her to see just what this boy was looking at. She couldn't decide if she liked him or if he was just a jerk, and so she dawdled in the doorway and wouldn't come down or go back inside. She said, "What's all that stuff painted on your car?"

"Can'tcha read it?" He opened the door very carefully, as if he were afraid it might fall off. He slid out just as carefully, planting his feet firmly on the ground, the tiny metallic world in his glasses slowing down like gelatine hardening, and in the midst of it Connie's bright green blouse. "This here is my name, to begin with, he said. ARNOLD FRIEND was written in tarlike black letters on the side, with a drawing of a round, grinning face that reminded Connie of a pumpkin, except it wore sunglasses. "I wanta introduce myself, I'm Arnold Friend and that's my real name and I'm gonna be your friend, honey, and inside the car's Ellie Oscar, he's kinda shy." Ellie brought his transistor radio up to his shoulder and balanced it there. "Now, these numbers are a secret code, honey," Arnold Friend explained. He read off the numbers 33, 19, 17 and raised his eyebrows at her to see what she thought of that, but she didn't think much of it. The left rear fender had been smashed and around it was written, on the gleaming gold background: DONE BY CRAZY WOMAN DRIVER. Connie had to laugh at that. Arnold Friend was pleased at her laughter and looked up at her. "Around the other side's a lot more—you wanta come and see them?"

"No."

"Why not?"

"Why should I?"

"Don'tcha wanta see what's on the car? Don'tcha wanta go for a ride?"

"I don't know."

"Why not?"

"I got things to do."

"Like what?"

"Things."

He laughed as if she had said something funny. He slapped his thighs. He was standing in a strange way, leaning back against the car as if he were balancing himself. He wasn't tall, only an inch or so taller than she would be if she came down to him. Connie liked the way he was dressed, which was the way all of them dressed: tight faded jeans stuffed into black, scuffed boots, a belt that pulled his waist in and showed how lean he was, and a white pull-over shirt that was a little soiled and showed the hard small muscles of his arms and shoulders. He looked as if he probably did hard work, lifting and carrying things. Even his neck looked muscular. And his face was a familiar face, somehow: the jaw and chin and cheeks slightly darkened because he hadn't shaved for a day or two, and the nose long and hawklike, sniffing as if she were a treat he was going to gobble up and it was all a joke.

"Connie, you ain't telling the truth. This is your day set aside for a ride with me and you know it," he said, still laughing. The way he straightened and recovered from his fit of laughing showed that it had been all fake.

"How do you know what my name is?" she said suspiciously.

"It's Connie."

"Maybe and maybe not."

"I know my Connie," he said, wagging his finger. Now she remembered him even better, back at the restaurant, and her cheeks warmed at the thought of how she had sucked in her breath just at the moment she passed him—how she must have looked to him. And he had remembered her. "Ellie and I come out here especially for you," he said. "Ellie can sit in back. How about it?"

"Where?"

"Where what?"

"Where're we going?"

He looked at her. He took off the sunglasses and she saw how pale the skin around his eyes was, like holes that were not in shadow but instead in light. His eyes were like chips of broken glass that catch the light in an amiable way. He smiled. It was as if the idea of going for a ride somewhere, to someplace, was a new idea to him.

"Just for a ride, Connie sweetheart."

"I never said my name was Connie," she said.

"But I know what it is. I know your name and all about you, lots of things," Arnold Friend said. He had not moved yet but stood still leaning back against the side of his jalopy. "I took a special interest in you, such a pretty girl, and found out all about you—like I know your parents and sister are gone somewheres and I know where and how long they're going to be gone, and I know who you were with last night, and your best girl friend's name is Betty. Right?"

He spoke in a simple lilting voice, exactly as if he were reciting the words to a song. His smile assured her that everything was fine. In the car Ellie turned up the volume on his radio and did not bother to look around at them.

"Ellie can sit in the back seat," Arnold Friend said. He indicated his friend with a casual jerk of his chin, as if Ellie did not count and she should not bother with him.

"How'd you find out all that stuff?" Connie said.

"Listen: Betty Schultz and Tony Fitch and Jimmy Pettinger and Nancy Pettinger," he said in a chant. "Raymond Stanley and Bob Hutter—"

"Do you know all those kids?"

"I know everybody."

"Look, you're kidding. You're not from around here."

"Sure."

"But—how come we never saw you before?"

"Sure you saw me before," he said. He looked down at his boots, as if he were a little offended. "You just don't remember."

"I guess I'd remember you," Connie said.

"Yeah?" He looked up at this, beaming. He was pleased. He began to mark time with the music from Ellie's radio, tapping his fists lightly together. Connie looked away from his smile to the car, which was painted so bright it almost hurt her eyes to look at it. She looked at that name, ARNOLD FRIEND. And up at the front fender was an expression that was familiar— MAN THE FLYING SAUCERS. It was an expression kids had used the year before but didn't use this year. She looked at it for a while as if the words meant something to her that she did not yet know.

"What're you thinking about? Huh?" Arnold Friend demanded. "Not worried about your hair blowing around in the car, are you?"

"No."

"Think I maybe can't drive good?"

"How do I know?"

"You're a hard girl to handle. How come?" he said. "Don't you know I'm your friend? Didn't you see me put my sign in the air when you walked by?"

"What sign?"

"My sign." And he drew an X in the air, leaning out toward her. They were maybe ten feet apart. After his hand fell back to his side the X was still in the air, almost visible. Connie let the screen door close and stood perfectly still inside it, listening to the music from her radio and the boy's blend together. She stared at Arnold Friend. He stood there so stiffly relaxed, pretending to be relaxed, with one hand idly on the door handle as if he were keeping himself up that way and had no intention of ever moving again. She recognized most things about him, the tight jeans that showed his thighs and buttocks and the greasy leather boots and the tight shirt, and even that slippery friendly smile of his, that sleepy dreamy smile that all the boys used to get across ideas they didn't want to put into words. She recognized all this and also the singsong way he talked, slightly mocking, kidding, but serious and a little melancholy, and she recognized the way he tapped one fist against the other in homage to the perpetual music behind him. But all these things did not come together.

She said suddenly, "Hey, how old are you?"

His smiled faded. She could see then that he wasn't a kid, he was much older—thirty, maybe more. At this knowledge her heart began to pound faster.

"That's a crazy thing to ask. Can'tcha see I'm your own age?"

"Like hell you are."

"Or maybe a couple years older. I'm eighteen."

"Eighteen?" she said doubtfully.

He grinned to reassure her and lines appeared at the corners of his mouth. His teeth were big and white. He grinned so broadly his eyes became slits and she saw how thick the lashes were, thick and black as if painted with a black tarlike material. Then, abruptly, he seemed to become embarrassed and looked over his shoulder at Ellie. "*Him*, he's crazy," he said. "Ain't he a riot? He's a nut, a real character." Ellie was still listening to the music. His sunglasses told nothing about what he was thinking. He wore a bright orange shirt unbuttoned halfway to show his chest, which was a pale, bluish chest and not muscular like Arnold Friend's. His shirt collar was turned up all around and the very tips of the collar pointed out past his chin as if they were protecting him. He was pressing the transistor radio up against his ear and sat there in a kind of daze, right in the sun.

"He's kinda strange," Connie said.

"Hey, she says you're kinda strange! Kinda strange!" Arnold Friend cried. He pounded on the car to get Ellie's attention. Ellie turned for the first time and Connie saw with shock that he wasn't a kid either—he had a fair, hairless face, cheeks reddened slightly as if the veins grew too close to the surface of his skin, the face of a forty-year-old baby. Connie felt a wave of dizziness rise in her at this sight and she stared at him as if waiting for something to change the shock of the moment, make it all right again. Ellie's lips kept shaping words, mumbling along with the words blasting in his ear.

"Maybe you two better go away," Connie said faintly.

"What? How come?" Arnold Friend cried. "We come out here to take you for a ride. It's Sunday." He had the voice of the man on the radio now. It was the same voice, Connie thought. "Don'tcha know it's Sunday all day? And honey, no matter who you were with last night, today you're with Arnold Friend and don't you forget it! Maybe you better step out here," he said, and this last was in a different voice. It was a little flatter, as if the heat was finally getting to him.

"No. I got things to do."

"Hey."

"You two better leave."

"We ain't leaving until you come with us."

"Like hell I am——"

"Connie, don't fool around with me. I mean——I mean, don't fool *around*," he said, shaking his head. He laughed incredulously. He placed his sunglasses on top of his head, carefully, as if he were indeed wearing a wig, and brought the stems down behind his ears. Connie stared at him, another wave of dizziness and fear rising in her so that for a moment he wasn't even in focus but was just a blur standing there against his gold car, and she had the idea that he had driven up the driveway all right but had come from nowhere before that and belonged nowhere and that everything about him and even about the music that was so familiar to her was only half real.

"If my father comes and sees you——"

"He ain't coming. He's at a barbecue."

"How do you know that?"

"Aunt Tillie's. Right now they're uh——they're drinking. Sitting around," he said vaguely, squinting as if he were staring all the way to town and over to Aunt Tillie's back yard. Then the vision seemed to get clear and he nodded energetically. "Yeah. Sitting around. There's your sister in a blue dress, huh? And high heels, the poor sad bitch——nothing like you, sweetheart! And your mother's helping some fat woman with the corn, they're cleaning the corn—— husking the corn——"

"What fat woman?" Connie cried.

"How do I know what fat woman, I don't know every goddamn fat woman in the world!" Arnold Friend laughed.

"Oh, that's Mrs. Hornsby . . . . Who invited her?" Connie said. She felt a little lightheaded. Her breath was coming quickly.

"She's too fat. I don't like them fat. I like them the way you are, honey," he said, smiling sleepily at her. They stared at each other for a while through the screen door. He said softly, "Now, what you're going to do is this: you're going to come out that door. You're going to sit up front with me and Ellie's going to sit in the back, the hell with Ellie, right? This isn't Ellie's date. You're my date. I'm your lover, honey."

"What? You're crazy——"

"Yes, I'm your lover. You don't know what that is but you will," he said. "I know that too. I know all about you. But look: it's real nice and you couldn't ask for nobody better than me, or more polite. I always keep my word. I'll tell you how it is, I'm always nice at first, the first time. I'll hold you so tight you won't think you have to try to get away or pretend anything because you'll know you can't. And I'll come inside you where it's all secret and you'll give in to me and you'll love me."

"Shut up! You're crazy!" Connie said. She backed away from the door. She put her hands up against her ears as if she'd heard something terrible, something not meant for her. "People don't talk like that, you're crazy," she muttered. Her heart was almost too big now for her chest and its pumping made sweat break out all over her. She looked out to see Arnold Friend pause and then take a step toward the porch, lurching. He almost fell. But, like a clever drunken man, he managed to catch his balance. He wobbled in his high boots and grabbed hold of one of the porch posts.

"Honey?" he said. "You still listening?"

"Get the hell out of here!"

"Be nice, honey. Listen."

"I'm going to call the police—"

He wobbled again and out of the side of his mouth came a fast spat curse, an aside not meant for her to hear. But even this "Christ!" sounded forced. Then he began to smile again. She watched this smile come, awkward as if he were smiling from inside a mask. His whole face was a mask, she thought wildly, tanned down to his throat but then running out as if he had plastered make-up on his face but had forgotten about his throat.

"Honey—? Listen, here's how it is. I always tell the truth and I promise you this: I ain't coming in that house after you."

"You better not! I'm going to call the police if you—if you don't—"

"Honey," he said, talking right through her voice, "honey, I'm not coming in there but you are coming out here. You know why?"

She was panting. The kitchen looked like a place she had never seen before, some room she had run inside but that wasn't good enough, wasn't going to help her. The kitchen window had never had a curtain, after three years, and there were dishes in the sink for her to do—probably—and if you ran your hand across the table you'd probably feel something sticky there.

"You listening, honey? Hey?" "—going to call the police—"

"Soon as you touch the phone I don't need to keep my promise and can come inside. You won't want that."

She rushed forward and tried to lock the door. Her fingers were shaking. "But why lock it," Arnold Friend said gently, talking right into her face. "It's just a screen door. It's just nothing." One of his boots was at a strange angle, as if his foot wasn't in it. It pointed out to the left, bent at the ankle. "I mean, anybody can break through a screen door and glass and wood and iron or anything else if he needs to, anybody at all, and specially Arnold Friend. If the place got lit up with a fire, honey, you'd come runnin' out into my arms, right into my arms an' safe at home—like you knew I was your lover and I'd stopped fooling around. I don't mind a nice shy girl but I don't like no fooling around." Part of those words were spoken with a slight rhythmic lilt, and Connie somehow recognized them—the echo of a song from last year, about a girl rushing into her boy friend's arms and coming home again—

Connie stood barefoot on the linoleum floor, staring at him. "What do you want?" she whispered.

"I want you," he said.

"What?"

"Seen you that night and thought, that's the one, yes sir. I never needed to look anymore."

"But my father's coming back. He's coming to get me. I had to wash my hair first—" She spoke in a dry, rapid voice, hardly raising it for him to hear.

"No, your daddy is not coming and yes, you had to wash your hair and you washed it for me. It's nice and shining and all for me. I thank you sweetheart," he said with a mock bow, but again he almost lost his balance. He had to bend and adjust his boots. Evidently his feet did not go all the way down; the boots must have been stuffed with something so that he would seem taller. Connie stared out at him and behind him at Ellie in the car, who seemed to be looking off toward Connie's right, into nothing. This Ellie said, pulling the words out of the air one after another as if he were just discovering them, "You want me to pull out the phone?"

"Shut your mouth and keep it shut," Arnold Friend said, his face red from bending over or maybe from embarrassment because Connie had seen his boots. "This ain't none of your business."

"What—what are you doing? What do you want?" Connie said. "If I call the police they'll get you, they'll arrest you—"

"Promise was not to come in unless you touch that phone, and I'll keep that promise," he said. He resumed his erect position and tried to force his shoulders back. He sounded like a hero in a movie, declaring something important. But he spoke too loudly and it was as if he were speaking to someone behind Connie. "I ain't made plans for coming in that house where I don't belong but just for you to come out to me, the way you should. Don't you know who I am?"

"You're crazy," she whispered. She backed away from the door but did not want to go into another part of the house, as if this would give him permission to come through the door. "What do you . . . you're crazy, you. . . ."

"Huh? What're you saying, honey?"

Her eyes darted everywhere in the kitchen. She could not remember what it was, this room.

"This is how it is, honey: you come out and we'll drive away, have a nice ride. But if you don't come out we're gonna wait till your people come home and then they're all going to get it."

"You want that telephone pulled out?" Ellie said. He held the radio away from his ear and grimaced, as if without the radio the air was too much for him.

"I toldja shut up, Ellie," Arnold Friend said, "you're deaf, get a hearing aid, right? Fix yourself up. This little girl's no trouble and's gonna be nice to me, so Ellie keep to yourself, this ain't your date right? Don't hem in on me, don't hog, don't crush, don't bird dog, don't trail me," he said in a rapid, meaningless voice, as if he were running through all the expressions he'd learned but was no longer sure which of them was in style, then rushing on to new ones, making them up with his eyes closed. "Don't crawl under my fence, don't squeeze in my chipmonk hole, don't sniff my glue, suck my popsicle, keep you own greasy fingers on yourself!" He shaded his eyes and peered in at Connie, who was backed against the kitchen table. "Don't mind him, honey, he's just a creep. He's a dope. Right? I'm the boy for you, and like I said, you come out here nice like a lady and give me your hand, and nobody else gets hurt, I mean, your nice old bald-headed daddy and your mummy and your sister in her high heels. Because listen: why bring them in this?"

"Leave me alone," Connie whispered.

"Hey, you know that old woman down the road, the one with the chickens and stuff—you know her?"

"She's dead!"

"Dead? What? You know her?" Arnold Friend said.

"She's dead—"

"Don't you like her?"

"She's dead—she's—she isn't here any more—"

"But don't you like her, I mean, you got something against her? Some grudge or something?" Then his voice dipped as if he were conscious of a rudeness. He touched the sunglasses perched up on top of his head as if to make sure they were still there. "Now, you be a good girl."

"What are you going to do?"

"Just two things, or maybe three," Arnold Friend said. "But I promise it won't last long and you'll like me the way you get to like people you're close to. You will. It's all over for you here, so come on out. You don't want your people in any trouble, do you?"

She turned and bumped against a chair or something, hurting her leg, but she ran into the back room and picked up the telephone. Something roared in her ear, a tiny roaring, and she was so sick with fear that she could do nothing but listen to it—the telephone was clammy and very heavy and her fingers groped down to the dial but were too weak to touch it. She began to scream into the phone, into the roaring. She cried out, she cried for her mother, she felt her breath start jerking back and forth in her lungs as if it were something Arnold Friend was stabbing her with again and again with no tenderness. A noisy sorrowful wailing rose all about her and she was locked inside it the way she was locked inside this house.

After a while she could hear again. She was sitting on the floor with her wet back against the wall.

Arnold Friend was saying from the door, "That's a good girl. Put the phone back."

She kicked the phone away from her.

"No, honey. Pick it up. Put it back right."

She picked it up and put it back. The dial tone stopped.

"That's a good girl. Now, you come outside."

She was hollow with what had been fear but what was now just an emptiness. All that screaming had blasted it out of her. She sat, one leg cramped under her, and deep inside her brain was something like a pinpoint of light that kept going and would not let her relax. She thought, I'm not going to see my mother again. She thought, I'm not going to sleep in my bed again. Her bright green blouse was all wet.

Arnold Friend said, in a gentle-loud voice that was like a stage voice, "The place where you came from ain't there any more, and where you had in mind to go is cancelled out. This place you are now—inside your daddy's house—is nothing but a cardboard box I can knock down any time. You know that and always did know it. You hear me?"

She thought, I have got to think. I have got to know what to do.

"We'll go out to a nice field, out in the country here where it smells so nice and it's sunny," Arnold Friend said. "I'll have my arms tight around you so you won't need to try to get away and I'll show you what love is like, what it does. The hell with this house! It looks solid all right," he said. He ran a fingernail down the screen and the noise did not make Connie shiver, as it would have the day before. "Now, put your hand on your heart, honey. Feel that? That feels solid too but we know better. Be nice to me, be sweet like you can because what else is there for a girl like you but to be sweet and pretty and give in?—and get away before her people come back?"

She felt her pounding heart. Her hand seemed to enclose it. She thought for the first time in her life that it was nothing that was hers, that belonged to her, but just a pounding, living thing inside this body that wasn't really hers either.

"You don't want them to get hurt," Arnold Friend went on. "Now, get up, honey. Get up all by yourself."

She stood.

"Now, turn this way. That's right. Come over here to me.—Ellie, put that away, didn't I tell you? You dope. You miserable creepy dope," Arnold Friend said. His words were not angry but only part of an incantation. The incantation was kindly. "Now come out through the kitchen to me, honey, and let's see a smile, try it, you're a brave, sweet little girl and now they're eating corn and hot dogs cooked to bursting over an outdoor fire, and they don't know one thing about you and never did and honey, you're better than them because not a one of them would have done this for you."

Connie felt the linoleum under her feet; it was cool. She brushed her hair back out of her eyes. Arnold Friend let go of the post tentatively and opened his arms for her, his elbows pointing in toward each other and his wrists limp, to show that this was an embarrassed embrace and a little mocking, he didn't want to make her self-conscious.

She put out her hand against the screen. She watched herself push the door slowly open as if she were back safe somewhere in the other doorway, watching this body and this head of long hair moving out into the sunlight where Arnold Friend waited.

"My sweet little blue-eyed girl," he said in a half-sung sigh that had nothing to do with her brown eyes but was taken up just the same by the vast sunlit reaches of the land behind him and on all sides of him—so much land that Connie had never seen before and did not recognize except to know that she was going to it.

How to Tell a True War Story

Tim O'Brien

Tim O'Brien was born in Austin, Minnesota on October 1, 1946. He graduated from Macalester College in 1968 with a BA in political science.

Despite being against the war in Vietnam, O'Brien joined the Infantry almost immediately after his graduation. He was assigned to 3rd Platoon, A Co., 5th Battalion. 46th Infantry, a unit scarred by association with the infamous My Lai massacre in 1968. O'Brien's tour of duty as a grunt in Vietnam was from 1969-70.

After his service during Vietnam, he attended the graduate program at Harvard. He left the school to do an internship at The Washington Post, *where he became a reporter. O'Brien's stint as a reporter led to his fiction-writing career after his memoir* If I Die in a Combat Zone, Box Me Up and Send Me Home *was published in 1973.*

O'Brien writes about his experiences in the Vietnam War and the physical and emotional ramifications on his fellow "grunts" with whom he served. His meta-fictional masterpiece "How to Tell a True War Story" is in The Things They Carried, *a collection of related Vietnam War stories originally published in hardcover by Houghton Mifflin in 1990. Even though the stories are obviously based O'Brien's own experiences in the war, he still claims the book as "a work of fiction." Tim O'Brien received the National Book Award in 1979 for his book* Going After Cacciato. *He is now a professor and endowed chair at Texas State University-San Marcos. He teaches in the Creative Writing Program.*

This is true.

I had a buddy in Vietnam. His name was Bob Kiley, but everybody called him Rat.

A friend of his gets killed, so about a week later Rat sits down and writes a letter to the guy's sister. Rat tells her what a great brother she had, how together the guy was, a number one pal and comrade. A real soldier's soldier, Rat says. Then he tells a few stories to make the point, how her brother would always volunteer for stuff nobody else would volunteer for in a million years, dangerous stuff, like doing recon or going out on these really badass night patrols. Stainless steel balls, Rat tells her. The guy was a little crazy, for sure, but crazy in a good way, a real daredevil, because he liked the challenge of it, he liked testing himself, just man against gook. A great, great guy, Rat says.

Anyway, it's a terrific letter, very personal and touching. Rat almost bawls writing it. He gets all teary telling about the good times they had together, how her brother made the war seem almost fun, always raising hell and lighting up villes and bringing smoke to bear every which way. A great sense of humor, too. Like the time at this river when he went fishing with a whole damn crate of hand grenades. Probably the funniest thing in world history, Rat says, all that gore, about twenty zillion dead gook fish. Her brother, he had the right attitude. He knew how to have a good time. On Halloween, this real hot spooky night, the dude paints up his body all different colors and puts on this weird mask and hikes over to a ville and goes trick-or-treating almost stark naked, just boots and balls and an M-16. A tremendous human being, Rat says. Pretty nutso sometimes, but you could trust him with your life.

And then the letter gets very sad and serious. Rat pours his heart out. He says he loved the guy. He says the guy was his best friend in the world. They were like soul mates, he says, like twins or something, they had a whole lot in common. He tells the guy's sister he'll look her up when the war's over.

So what happens?

Rat mails the letter. He waits two months. The dumb cooze never writes back.

A true war story is never moral. It does not instruct, nor encourage virtue, nor suggest models of proper human behavior, nor restrain men from doing the things men have always done. If a story seems moral, do not believe it. If at the end of a war story you feel uplifted, or if you feel that some small bit of rectitude has been salvaged from the larger waste, then you have been made the victim of a very old and terrible lie. There is no rectitude whatsoever. There is no virtue. As a first rule of thumb, therefore, you can tell a true war story by its absolute and uncompromising allegiance to obscenity and evil. Listen to

Rat Kiley. Cooze, he says. He does not say bitch. He certainly does not say woman, or girl. He says cooze. Then he spits and stares. He's nineteen years old—it's too much for him—so he looks at you with those big sad gentle killer eyes and says cooze, because his friend is dead, and because it's so incredibly sad and true: she never wrote back.

You can tell a true war story if it embarrasses you. If you don't care for obscenity, you don't care for the truth; if you don't care for the truth, watch how you vote. Send guys to war, they come home talking dirty.

Listen to Rat: "Jesus Christ, man, I write this beautiful fuckin' letter, I slave over it, and what happens? The dumb cooze never writes back."

The dead guy's name was Curt Lemon. What happened was, we crossed a muddy river and marched west into the mountains, and on the third day we took a break along a trail junction in deep jungle. Right away, Lemon and Rat Kiley started goofing. They didn't understand about the spookiness. They were kids; they just didn't know. A nature hike, they thought, not even a war, so they went off into the shade of some giant trees—quadruple canopy, no sunlight at all—and they were giggling and calling each other yellow mother and playing a silly game they'd invented. The game involved smoke grenades, which were harmless unless you did stupid things, and what they did was pull out the pin and stand a few feet apart and play catch under the shade of those huge trees. Whoever chickened out was a yellow mother. And if nobody chickened out, the grenade would make a light popping sound and they'd be covered with smoke and they'd laugh and dance around and then do it again.

It's all exactly true.

It happened, to *me*, nearly twenty years ago, and I still remember that trail junction and those giant trees and a soft dripping sound somewhere beyond the trees. I remember the smell of moss. Up in the canopy there were tiny white blossoms, but no sunlight at all, and I remember the shadows spreading out under the trees where Curt Lemon and Rat Kiley were playing catch with smoke grenades. Mitchell Sanders sat flipping his yo-yo. Norman Bowker and Kiowa and Dave Jensen were dozing, or half dozing, and all around us were those ragged green mountains.

Except for the laughter things were quiet.

At one point, I remember, Mitchell Sanders turned and looked at me, not quite nodding, as if to warn me about something, as if he already *knew*, then after a while he rolled up his yo-yo and moved away.

It's hard to tell you what happened next.

They were just goofing. There was a noise, I suppose, which must've been the detonator, so I glanced behind me and watched Lemon step from the shade into bright sunlight. His face was suddenly brown and shining. A handsome kid, really. Sharp gray eyes, lean and narrow-waisted, and when he died it was almost beautiful, the way the sunlight came around him and lifted him up and sucked him high into a tree full of moss and vines and white blossoms.

In any war story, but especially a true one, it's difficult to separate what happened from what seemed to happen. What seems to happen becomes its own happening and has to be told that way. The angles of vision are skewed. When a booby trap explodes, you close your eyes and duck and float outside yourself. When a guy dies, like Curt Lemon, you look away and then look back for a moment and then look away again. The pictures get jumbled; you tend to miss a lot. And then afterward, when you go to tell about it, there is always that surreal seemingness, which makes the story seem untrue, but which in fact represents the hard and exact truth as it *seemed*.

In many cases a true war story cannot be believed. If you believe it, be skeptical. It's a question of credibility. Often the crazy stuff is true and the normal stuff isn't, because the normal stuff is necessary to make you believe the truly incredible craziness.

In other cases you can't even tell a true war story. Sometimes it's just beyond telling.

I heard this one, for example, from Mitchell Sanders. It was near dusk and we were sitting at my foxhole along a wide muddy river north of Quang Ngai. I remember how peaceful the twilight was. A deep pinkish red spilled out on the river, which moved without sound, and in the morning we would cross the river and march west into the mountains. The occasion was right for a good story.

"God's truth," Mitchell Sanders said. "A six-man patrol goes up into the mountains on a basic listening-post operation. The idea's to spend a week up there, just lie low and listen for enemy movement. They've got a radio along, so if they hear anything suspicious—anything—they're supposed to call in artillery or gunships, whatever it takes. Otherwise they keep strict field discipline. Absolute silence. They just listen."

Sanders glanced at me to make sure I had the scenario. He was playing with his yo-yo, dancing it with short, tight little strokes of the wrist.

His face was blank in the dusk.

"We're talking regulation, by-the-book LP. These six guys, they don't say boo for a solid week. They don't got tongues. *All* ears."

"Right," I said.

"Understand me?"

"Invisible."

Sanders nodded.

"Affirm," he said. "Invisible. So what happens is, these guys get themselves deep in the bush, all camouflaged up, and they lie down and wait and that's all they do, nothing else, they lie there for seven straight days and just listen. And man, I'll tell you—it's spooky. This is mountains. You don't *know* spooky till you been there. Jungle, sort of, except it's way up in the clouds and there's always this fog—like rain, except it's not raining—everything's all wet and swirly and tangled up and you can't see jack, you can't find your own pecker to piss with. Like you don't even have a body. Serious spooky. You just go with the vapors—the fog sort of takes you in . . . And the sounds, man. The sounds carry forever. You hear stuff nobody should overhear."

Sanders was quiet for a second, just working the yo-yo, then he smiled at me.

"So after a couple days the guys start hearing this real soft, kind of wacked-out music. Weird echoes and stuff. Like a radio or something, but it's not a radio, it's this strange gook music that comes right out of the rocks. Faraway, sort of, but right up close, too. They try to ignore it. But it's a listening post, right? So they listen. And every night they keep hearing that crazyass gook concert. All kinds of chimes and xylophones. I mean, this is wilderness—no way, it can't be real—but there it *is*, like the mountains are tuned in to Radio fucking Hanoi. Naturally they get nervous. One guy sticks Juicy Fruit in his ears. Another guy almost flips. Thing is, though, they can't report music. They can't get on the horn and call back to base and say, 'Hey, listen, we need some firepower, we got to blow away this weirdo gook rock band.' They can't do that. It wouldn't go down. So they lie there in the fog and keep their mouths shut. And what makes it extra bad, see, is the poor dudes can't horse around like normal. Can't joke it away. Can't even talk to each other except maybe in whispers, all hush-hush, and that just revs up the willies. All they do is listen."

Again there was some silence as Mitchell Sanders looked out on the river. The dark was coming on hard now, and off to the west I could see the mountains rising in silhouette, all the mysteries and unknowns.

"This next part," Sanders said quietly, "you won't believe."

"Probably not," I said.

"You won't. And you know why?" He gave me a long, tired smile. "Because it happened. Because every word is absolutely dead-on true."

Sanders made a sound in his throat, like a sigh, as if to say he didn't care if I believed him or not. But he did care. He wanted me to feel the truth, to believe by the raw force of feeling. He seemed sad, in a way.

"These six guys," he said, "they're pretty fried out by now, and one night they start hearing voices. Like at a cocktail party. That's what it sounds like, this big swank gook cocktail party somewhere out there in the fog. Music and chitchat and stuff. It's crazy, I know, but they hear the champagne corks. They hear the actual martini glasses. Real hoity-toity, all very civilized, except this isn't civilization. This is Nam.

"Anyway, the guys try to be cool. They just lie there and groove, but after a while they start hearing—you won't believe this—they hear chamber music. They hear violins and cellos. They hear this terrific mama-san soprano. Then after a while they hear gook opera and a glee club and the Haiphong Boys Choir and a barbershop quartet and all kinds of weird chanting and Buddha-Buddha stuff. And the whole time, in the background, there's still that cock-tail party going on. All these different voices. Not human voices, though. Because it's the mountains. Follow me? The rock—it's *talking*. And the fog, too, and the grass and the goddamn mongooses. Everything talks. The trees talk politics, the monkeys talk religion. The whole country. Vietnam. The place talks. It talks. Understand? Nam—it truly *talks*.

"The guys can't cope. They lose it. They get on the radio and report enemy movement—a whole army, they say—and they order up the firepower. They get arty and gunships. They call in air strikes. And I'll tell you, they fuckin' crash that cocktail party. All night long, they just smoke those moun-tains. They make jungle juice. They blow away trees and glee clubs and what-ever else there is to blow away. Scorch time. They walk napalm up and down the ridges. They bring in the Cobras and F-4s, they use Willie Peter and HE and incendiaries. It's all fire. They make those mountains burn.

"Around dawn things finally get quiet. Like you never even *heard* quiet before. One of those real thick, real misty days—just clouds and fog, they're off in this special zone—and the mountains are absolutely dead-flat silent. Like *Brigadoon*—pure vapor, you know? Everything's all sucked up inside the fog. Not a single sound, except they still *hear* it.

"So they pack up and start humping. They head down the mountain, back to base camp, and when they get there they don't say diddly. They don't talk. Not a word, like they're deaf and dumb. Later on this fat bird colonel comes up and asks what the hell happened out there. What'd they hear? Why all the ordnance? The man's ragged out, he gets down tight on their case. I mean, they spent six trillion dollars on firepower, and this fatass colonel wants answers, he wants to know what the fuckin' story is.

"But the guys don't say zip. They just look at him for a while, sort of funny like, sort of amazed, and the whole war is right there in that stare. It says everything you can't ever say. It says, man, you got wax in your ears. It says, poor bastard, you'll never know—wrong frequency—you don't *even* want to hear this. Then they salute the fucker and walk away, because certain stories you don't ever tell."

You can tell a true war story by the way it never seems to end. Not then, not ever. Not when Mitchell Sanders stood up and moved off into the dark.

It all happened.

Even now, at this instant, I remember that yo-yo. In a way, I suppose, you had to be there, you had to hear it, but I could tell how desperately Sanders wanted me to believe him, his frustration at not quite getting the details right, not quite pinning down the final and definitive truth.

And I remember sitting at my foxhole that night, watching the shadows of Quang Ngai, thinking about the coming day and how we would cross the river and march west into the mountains, all the ways I might die, all the things I did not understand.

Late in the night Mitchell Sanders touched my shoulder. "Just came to me," he whispered. "The moral, I mean. Nobody listens. Nobody hears nothin'. Like that fatass colonel. The politicians, all the civilian types. Your girlfriend. My girlfriend. Everybody's sweet little virgin girlfriend. What they need is to go out on LP. The vapors, man. Trees and rocks—you got to *listen* to your enemy."

And then again, in the morning, Sanders came up to me. The platoon was preparing to move out, checking weapons, going through all the little rituals that preceded a day's march. Already the lead squad had crossed the river and was filing off toward the west.

"I got a confession to make," Sanders said. "Last night, man, I had to make up a few things."

"I know that."

"The glee club. There wasn't any glee club."

"Right."

"No opera."

"Forget it, I understand."

"Yeah, but listen, it's still true. Those six guys, they heard wicked sound out there. They heard sound you just plain won't believe."

Sanders pulled on his rucksack, closed his eyes for a moment, then almost smiled at me. I knew what was coming.

"All right," I said, "what's the moral?"

"Forget it."

"No, go ahead."

For a long while he was quiet, looking away, and the silence kept stretching out until it was almost embarrassing. Then he shrugged and gave me a stare that lasted all day.

"Hear that quiet, man?" he said. "That quiet—just listen. There's your moral."

In a true war story, if there's a moral at all, it's like the thread that makes the cloth. You can't tease it out. You can't extract the meaning without unraveling the deeper meaning. And in the end, really, there's nothing much to say about a true war story, except maybe "Oh."

True war stories do not generalize. They do not indulge in abstraction or analysis.

For example: War is hell. As a moral declaration the old truism seems perfectly true, and yet because it abstracts, because it generalizes, I can't believe it with my stomach. Nothing turns inside.

It comes down to gut instinct. A true war story, if truly told, makes the stomach believe.

This one does it for me. I've told it before—many times, many versions—but here's what actually happened.

We crossed that river and marched west into the mountains. On the third day, Curt Lemon stepped on a booby-trapped 105 round. He was playing catch with Rat Kiley, laughing, and then he was dead. The trees were thick; it took nearly an hour to cut an LZ for the dustoff.

Later, higher in the mountains, we came across a baby VC water buffalo. What it was doing there I don't know—no farms or paddies—but we chased it down and got a rope around it and led it along to a deserted village where we set up for the night. After supper Rat Kiley went over and stroked its nose.

He opened up a can of C rations, pork and beans, but the baby buffalo wasn't interested.

Rat shrugged.

He stepped back and shot it through the right front knee. The animal did not make a sound. It went down hard, then got up again, and Rat took careful aim and shot off an ear. He shot it in the hindquarters and in the little hump at its back. He shot it twice in the flanks. It wasn't to kill; it was to hurt. He put the rifle muzzle up against the mouth and shot the mouth away. Nobody said much. The whole platoon stood there watching, feeling all kinds of things, but there wasn't a great deal of pity for the baby water buffalo. Curt Lemon was dead. Rat Kiley had lost his best friend in the world. Later in the week he would write a long personal letter to the guy's sister, who would not write back, but for now it was a question of pain. He shot off the tail. He shot away chunks of meat below the ribs. All around us there was the smell of smoke and filth and deep greenery, and the evening was humid and very hot. Rat went to automatic. He shot randomly, almost casually, quick little spurts in the belly and butt. Then he reloaded, squatted down, and shot it in the left front knee. Again the animal fell hard and tried to get up, but this time it couldn't quite make it. It wobbled and went down sideways. Rat shot it in the nose. He bent forward and whispered something, as if talking to a pet, then he shot it in the throat. All the while the baby buffalo was silent, or almost silent, just a light bubbling sound where the nose had been. It lay very still. Nothing moved except the eyes, which were enormous, the pupils shiny black and dumb.

Rat Kiley was crying. He tried to say something, but then cradled his rifle and went off by himself.

The rest of us stood in a ragged circle around the baby buffalo. For a time no one spoke. We had witnessed something essential, something brand-new and profound, a piece of the world so startling there was not yet a name for it.

Somebody kicked the baby buffalo.

It was still alive, though just barely, just in the eyes.

"Amazing," Dave Jensen said. "My whole life, I never seen anything like it."

"Never?"

"Not hardly. Not once."

Kiowa and Mitchell Sanders picked up the baby buffalo. They hauled it across the open square, hoisted it up, and dumped it in the village well.

Afterward, we sat waiting for Rat to get himself together.

"Amazing," Dave Jensen kept saying. "A new wrinkle. I never seen it before."

Mitchell Sanders took out his yo-yo. "Well, that's Nam," he said. "Garden of Evil. Over here, man, every sin's real fresh and original."

How do you generalize?

War is hell, but that's not the half of it, because war is also mystery and terror and adventure and courage and discovery and holiness and pity and despair and longing and love. War is nasty; war is fun. War is thrilling; war is drudgery. War makes you a man; war makes you dead.

The truths are contradictory. It can be argued, for instance, that war is grotesque. But in truth war is also beauty. For all its horror, you can't help but gape at the awful majesty of combat. You stare out at tracer rounds unwinding through the dark like brilliant red ribbons. You crouch in ambush as a cool, impassive moon rises over the nighttime paddies. You admire the fluid symmetries of troops on the move, the harmonies of sound and shape and proportion, the great sheets of metal-fire streaming down from a gunship, the illumination rounds, the white phosphorus, the purply orange glow of napalm, the rocket's red glare. It's not pretty, exactly. It's astonishing. It fills the eye. It commands you. You hate it, yes, but your eyes do not. Like a killer forest fire, like cancer under a microscope, any battle or bombing raid or artillery barrage has the aesthetic purity of absolute moral indifference—a powerful, implacable beauty—and a true war story will tell the truth about this, though the truth is ugly.

To generalize about war is like generalizing about peace. Almost everything is true. Almost nothing is true. At its core, perhaps, war is just another name for death, and yet any soldier will tell you, if he tells the truth, that proximity to death brings with it a corresponding proximity to life. After a firefight, there is always the immense pleasure of aliveness. The trees are alive. The grass, the soil—everything. All around you things are purely living, and you among them, and the aliveness makes you tremble. You feel an intense, out-of-the-skin awareness of your living self—your truest self, the human being you want to be and then become by the force of wanting it. In the midst of evil you want to be a good man. You want decency. You want justice and courtesy and human concord, things you never knew you wanted. There is a kind of largeness to it, a kind of godliness. Though it's odd, you're never more alive than when you're almost dead. You recognize what's valuable. Freshly, as if for the first time, you love what's best in yourself and in the world, all that might be lost. At the hour of dusk you sit at your foxhole and look out on a wide river turning pinkish red, and at the mountains beyond, and although in the morning you must cross the river and go into the mountains and do terrible things and maybe die, even so, you find yourself studying the fine colors on the river, you feel wonder and awe at the setting of the sun, and you are filled with a hard, aching love for how the world could be and always should be, but now is not.

Mitchell Sanders was right. For the common soldier, at least, war has the feel—the spiritual texture—of a great ghostly fog, thick and permanent. There is no clarity. Everything swirls. The old rules are no longer binding, the old truths no longer true. Right spills over into wrong. Order blends into chaos, love into hate, ugliness into beauty, law into anarchy, civility into savagery. The vapors suck you in. You can't tell where you are, or why you're there, and the only certainty is overwhelming ambiguity.

In war you lose your sense of the definite, hence your sense of truth itself, and therefore it's safe to say that in a true war story nothing is ever absolutely true.

Often in a true war story there is not even a point, or else the point doesn't hit you until twenty years later, in your sleep, and you wake up and shake your wife and start telling the story to her, except when you get to the end you've forgotten the point again. And then for a long time you lie there watching the story happen in your head. You listen to your wife's breathing. The war's over. You close your eyes. You smile and think, Christ, what's the *point*?

This one wakes me up.

In the mountains that day, I watched Lemon turn sideways. He laughed and said something to Rat Kiley. Then he took a peculiar half step, moving from shade into bright sunlight, and the booby-trapped 105 round blew him into a tree. The parts were just hanging there, so Dave Jensen and I were ordered to shinny up and peel him off. I remember the white bone of an arm. I remember pieces of skin and something wet and yellow that must've been the intestines. The gore was horrible, and stays with me. But what wakes me up twenty years later is Dave Jensen singing "Lemon Tree" as we threw down the parts.

You can tell a true war story by the questions you ask. Somebody tells a story, let's say, and afterward you ask, "Is it true?" and if the answer matters, you've got your answer.

For example, we've all heard this one. Four guys go down a trail. A grenade sails out. One guy jumps on it and takes the blast and saves his three buddies.

Is it true?

The answer matters.

You'd feel cheated if it never happened. Without the grounding reality, it's just a trite bit of puffery, pure Hollywood, untrue in the way all such stories are untrue. Yet even if it did happen—and maybe it did, anything's possible—even then you know it can't be true, because a true war story does not depend upon that kind of truth. Absolute occurrence is irrelevant. A thing may happen and be a total lie; another thing may not happen and be truer than the truth. For example: Four guys go down a trail. A grenade sails out. One guy jumps on it and takes the blast, but it's a killer grenade and everybody dies anyway. Before they die, though, one of the dead guys says, "The fuck you do *that* for?" and the jumper says, "Story of my life, man," and the other guy starts to smile but he's dead. That's a true story that never happened.

Twenty years later, I can still see the sunlight on Lemon's face. I can see him turning, looking back at Rat Kiley, then he laughed and took that curious half step from shade into sunlight, his face suddenly brown and shining, and when his foot touched down, in that instant, he must've thought it was the sunlight that was killing him. It was not the sunlight. It was a rigged 105 round. But if I could ever get the story right, how the sun seemed to gather around him and pick him up and lift him high into a tree, if I could somehow re-create the fatal whiteness of that light, the quick glare, the obvious cause and effect, then you would believe the last thing Curt Lemon believed, which for him must've been the final truth.

Now and then, when I tell this story, someone will come up to me afterward and say she liked it. It's always a woman. Usually it's an older woman of kindly temperament and humane politics. She'll explain that as a rule she hates war stories; she can't understand why people want to wallow in all the blood and gore. But this one she liked. The poor baby buffalo, it made her sad. Sometimes, even, there are little tears. What I should do, she'll say, is put it all behind me. Find new stories to tell.

I won't say it but I'll think it.

I'll picture Rat Kiley's face, his grief, and I'll think, *You dumb cooze.*

Because she wasn't listening.

It wasn't a *war* story. It was a *love* story.

But you can't say that. All you can do is tell it one more time, patiently, adding and subtracting, making up a few things to get at the real truth. No Mitchell Sanders, you tell her. No Lemon, no Rat Kiley. No trail junction. No baby buffalo. No vines or moss or white blossoms. Beginning to end, you tell her, it's all made up. Every goddamn detail—the mountains and the river and especially that poor dumb baby buffalo. None of it happened. *None* of it. And even if it did happen, it didn't happen in the mountains, it happened in this little village on the Batangan Peninsula, and it was raining like crazy, and one night a guy named Stink Harris woke up screaming with a leech on his tongue. You can tell a true war story if you just keep on telling it.

And in the end, of course, a true war story is never about war. It's about sunlight. It's about the special way that dawn spreads out on a river when you know you must cross the river and march into the mountains and do things you are afraid to do. It's about love and memory. It's about sorrow. It's about sisters who never write back and people who never listen.

The Artificial Nigger

Flannery O'Connor

Flannery O'Connor (1925–1964) was born in Savannah and lived most of her life in Georgia. She is a regional writer, setting most of her stories in the American South. She is best known for her short stories, though she wrote two fine novels, Wise Blood *(1952) and* The Violent Bear It Away *(1960). She died at the relatively young age of thirty-nine of lupus. She was a devout Catholic, and her Christianity clearly informs her writing; however, O'Connor's stories do not fit easily alongside mainstream writing of any sort, Christian or otherwise.*

O'Connor's body of work is quite thematically consistent. Redemption is her central theme, but it is redemption characterized by violence. This violence, her dark humor, and her extreme characterizations have caused some of her readers to call her writing "Gothic" and her characters "grotesque." O'Connor once responded to this in her trenchantly funny way, by saying, "Anything that comes out of the South is going to be called 'grotesque' by the Northern reader, unless it is grotesque, in which case it is going to be called 'realistic.'"

Her protagonists are deeply flawed and blind to their own faults. One of the chief faults from which they suffer is self-righteousness, which often takes the form, as it does in the following tale, of racism. The title "The Artificial Nigger" offends us, but it reflects the language and one of the many flaws of the story's central characters. (The reader should note how the narrator always uses the terms "Negro" or "colored," terms of respect in 1955, when the story was published.) Largely unfamiliar with an entire race of people, this story's main characters must suffer the consequences of their ignorance for a single day in the city, which becomes a figurative descent into hell for them both. Neither of them experiences actual, physical violence, but they must suffer the pain of facing some ugly truths about themselves.

At the story's climax, the main characters, Mr. Head and his grandson Nelson, come across an object that seems to hold almost mystical significance for them. The object, from which the story gets its title, is a badly weathered, plaster figure in the yard of an upper class home. This "epiphany" is pregnant with rich, interpretive potential, but remains finally ambiguous. O'Connor said, "What I had in mind to suggest with the artificial nigger was the redemptive quality of the Negro's suffering for us all." O'Connor's themes in this story include race-relations, the relationships of city to country, of youth to age, of knowledge to ignorance, and of suffering to redemption, what Mr. Head calls "that action of mercy" for which there "were no words in the world that could name it."

Mr. Head awakened to discover that the room was full of moonlight. He sat up and stared at the floor boards—the color of silver—and then at the ticking on his pillow, which might have been brocade, and after a second, he saw half of the moon five feet away in his shaving mirror, paused as if it were waiting for his permission to enter. It rolled forward and cast a dignifying light on everything. The straight chair against the wall looked stiff and attentive as if it were awaiting an order and Mr. Head's trousers, hanging to the back of it, had an almost noble air, like the garment some great man had just flung to his servant; but the face on the moon was a grave one. It gazed across the room and out the window where it floated over the horse stall and appeared to contemplate itself with the look of a young man who sees his old age before him.

Mr. Head could have said to it that age was a choice blessing and that only with years does a man enter into that calm understanding of life that makes him a suitable guide for the young. This, at least, had been his own experience.

He sat up and grasped the iron posts at the foot of his bed and raised himself until he could see the face on the alarm clock which sat on an over-turned bucket beside the chair. The hour was two in the morning. The alarm on the clock did not work but he was not dependent on any mechanical means to awaken him. Sixty years had not dulled his responses; his physical reactions, like his moral ones, were guided by his will and strong character, and these could be seen plainly in his features. He had a long tube-like face with a long rounded open jaw and a long depressed nose. His eyes were alert but quiet, and in the miraculous moonlight they had a look of composure and of ancient wisdom as if they belonged to one of the great guides of men. He might have been Vergil summoned in the middle of the night to go to Dante, or better, Raphael, awakened by a blast of God's light to fly to the side of

Tobias. The only dark spot in the room was Nelson's pallet, underneath the shadow of the window.

Nelson was hunched over on his side, his knees under his chin and his heels under his bottom. His new suit and hat were in the boxes that they had been sent in and these were on the floor at the foot of the pallet where he could get his hands on them as soon as he woke up. The slop jar, out of the shadow and made snow-white in the moonlight, appeared to stand guard over him like a small personal angel. Mr. Head lay back down, feeling entirely confident that he could carry out the moral mission of the coming day. He meant to be up before Nelson and to have the breakfast cooking by the time he awakened. The boy was always irked when Mr. Head was the first up. They would have to leave the house at four to get to the railroad junction by five-thirty. The train was to stop for them at five forty-five and they had to be there on time for this train was stopping merely to accommodate them.

This would be the boy's first trip to the city though he claimed it would be his second because he had been born there. Mr. Head had tried to point out to him that when he was born he didn't have the intelligence to determine his whereabouts but this had made no impression on the child at all and he continued to insist that this was to be his second trip. It would be Mr. Head's third trip. Nelson had said, "I will've already been there twict and I ain't but ten."

Mr. Head had contradicted him.

"If you ain't been there in fifteen years, how you know you'll be able to find your way about?" Nelson had asked. "How you know it hasn't changed some?"

"Have you ever," Mr. Head had asked, "seen me lost?"

Nelson certainly had not but he was a child who was never satisfied until he had given an impudent answer and he replied, "It's nowhere around here to get lost at."

"The day is going to come," Mr. Head prophesied, "when you'll find you ain't as smart as you think you are." He had been thinking about this trip for several months but it was for the most part in moral terms that he conceived it. It was to be a lesson that the boy would never forget. He was to find out from it that he had no cause for pride merely because he had been born in a city. He was to find out that the city is not a great place. Mr. Head meant him to see everything there is to see in a city so that he would be content to stay at home for the rest of his life. He fell asleep thinking how the boy would at last find out that he was not as smart as he thought he was.

He was awakened at three-thirty by the smell of fatback frying and he leaped off his cot. The pallet was empty and the clothes boxes had been thrown open. He put on his trousers and ran into the other room. The boy had a corn pone on cooking and had fried the meat. He was sitting in the half-dark at the table, drinking cold coffee out of a can. He had on his new suit and his new gray hat pulled low over his eyes. It was too big for him but they had ordered it a size large because they expected his head to grow. He didn't say anything but his entire figure suggested satisfaction at having arisen before Mr. Head.

Mr. Head went to the stove and brought the meat to the table in the skillet. "It's no hurry," he said. "You'll get there soon enough and it's no guarantee you'll like it when you do neither," and he sat down across from the boy whose hat teetered back slowly to reveal a fiercely expressionless face, very much the same shape as the old man's. They were grandfather and grandson but they looked enough alike to be brothers and brothers not too far apart in age, for Mr. Head had a youthful expression by daylight, while the boy's look was ancient, as if he knew everything already and would be pleased to forget it.

Mr. Head had once had a wife and daughter and when the wife died, the daughter ran away and returned after an interval with Nelson. Then one morning, without getting out of bed, she died and left Mr. Head with sole care of the year-old child. He had made the mistake of telling Nelson that he had been born in Atlanta. If he hadn't told him that, Nelson couldn't have insisted that this was going to be his second trip.

"You may not like it a bit," Mr. Head continued. "It'll be full of niggers."

The boy made a face as if he could handle a nigger.

"All right," Mr. Head said. "You ain't ever seen a nigger."

"You wasn't up very early," Nelson said.

"You ain't ever seen a nigger," Mr. Head repeated. "There hasn't been a nigger in this county since we run that one out twelve years ago and that was before you were born." He looked at the boy as if he were daring him to say he had ever seen a Negro.

"How you know I never saw a nigger when I lived there before?" Nelson asked. "I probably saw a lot of niggers."

"If you seen one you didn't know what he was," Mr. Head said, completely exasperated. "A six-month-old child don't know a nigger from anybody else."

"I reckon I'll know a nigger if I see one," the boy said and got up and straightened his slick sharply creased gray hat and went outside to the privy.

They reached the junction some time before the train was due to arrive and stood about two feet from the first set of tracks. Mr. Head carried a paper sack with some biscuits and a can of sardines in it for their lunch. A coarse-looking orange-colored sun coming up behind the east range of mountains was making the sky a dull red behind them, but in front of them it was still gray and they faced a gray transparent moon, hardly stronger than a thumbprint and completely without light. A small tin switch box and a black fuel tank were all there was to mark the place as a junction; the tracks were double and did not converge again until they were hidden behind the bends at either end of the clearing. Trains passing appeared to emerge from a tunnel of trees and, hit for a second by the cold sky, vanish terrified into the woods again. Mr. Head had had to make special arrangements with the ticket agent to have this train stop and he was secretly afraid it would not, in which case, he knew Nelson would say, "I never thought no train was going to stop for you." Under the useless morning moon the tracks looked white and fragile. Both the old man and the child stared ahead as if they were awaiting an apparition.

Then suddenly, before Mr. Head could make up his mind to turn back, there was a deep warning bleat and the train appeared, gliding very slowly, almost silently around the bend of trees about two hundred yards down the track, with one yellow front light shining. Mr. Head was still not certain it would stop and he felt it would make an even bigger idiot of him if it went by slowly. Both he and Nelson, however, were prepared to ignore the train if it passed them.

The engine charged by, filling their noses with the smell of hot metal and then the second coach came to a stop exactly where they were standing. A conductor with the face of an ancient bloated bulldog was on the step as if he expected them, though he did not look as if it mattered one way or the other to him if they got on or not. "To the right," he said.

Their entry took only a fraction of a second and the train was already speeding on as they entered the quiet car. Most of the travelers were still sleeping, some with their heads hanging off the chair arms, some stretched across two seats, and some sprawled out with their feet in the aisle. Mr. Head saw two unoccupied seats and pushed Nelson toward them. "Get in there by the winder," he said in his normal voice which was very loud at this hour of the morning. "Nobody cares if you sit there because it's nobody in it. Sit right there."

"I heard you," the boy muttered. "It's no use in you yelling," and he sat down and turned his head to the glass. There he saw a pale ghost-like face scowling at him beneath the brim of a pale ghost-like hat. His grandfather, looking quickly too, saw a different ghost, pale but grinning, under a black hat.

Mr. Head sat down and settled himself and took out his ticket and started reading aloud everything that was printed on it. People began to stir. Several woke up and stared at him. "Take off your hat," he said to Nelson and took off his own and put it on his knee. He had a small amount of white hair that had turned tobacco-colored over the years and this lay flat across the back of his head. The front of his head was bald and creased. Nelson took off his hat and put it on his knee and they waited for the conductor to come ask for their tickets.

The man across the aisle from them was spread out over two seats, his feet propped on the window and his head jutting into the aisle. He had on a light blue suit and a yellow shirt unbuttoned at the neck. His eyes had just opened and Mr. Head was ready to introduce himself when the conductor came up from behind and growled, "Tickets."

When the conductor had gone, Mr. Head gave Nelson the return half of his ticket and said, "Now put that in your pocket and don't lose it or you'll have to stay in the city."

"Maybe I will," Nelson said as if this were a reasonable suggestion.

Mr. Head ignored him. "First time this boy has ever been on a train," he explained to the man across the aisle, who was sitting up now on the edge of his seat with both feet on the floor.

Nelson jerked his hat on again and turned angrily to the window.

"He's never seen anything before," Mr. Head continued. "Ignorant as the day he was born, but I mean for him to get his fill once and for all."

The boy leaned forward, across his grandfather and toward the stranger. "I was born in the city," he said. "I was born there. This is my second trip." He said it in a high positive voice but the man across the aisle didn't look as if he understood. There were heavy purple circles under his eyes.

Mr. Head reached across the aisle and tapped him on the arm. "The thing to do with a boy," he said sagely, "is to show him all it is to show. Don't hold nothing back."

"Yeah," the man said. He gazed down at his swollen feet and lifted the left one about ten inches from the floor. After a minute he put it down and lifted the other. All through the car people began to get up and move about and yawn and stretch. Separate voices could be heard here and there and then a general hum. Suddenly Mr. Head's serene expression changed. His mouth almost closed and a light, fierce and cautious both, came into his eyes. He was looking down the length of the car. Without turning, he caught Nelson by the arm and pulled him forward. "Look," he said.

A huge coffee-colored man was coming slowly forward. He had on a light suit and a yellow satin tie with a ruby pin in it. One of his hands rested on his stomach which rode majestically under his buttoned coat, and in the other he held the head of a black walking stick that he picked up and set down with a deliberate outward motion each time he took a step. He was proceeding very slowly, his large brown eyes gazing over the heads of the passengers. He had a small white mustache and white crinkly hair. Behind him there were two young women, both coffee-colored, one in a yellow dress and one in a green. Their progress was kept at the rate of his and they chatted in low throaty voices as they followed him.

Mr. Head's grip was tightening insistently on Nelson's arm. As the procession passed them, the light from a sapphire ring on the brown hand that picked up the cane reflected in Mr. Head's eye, but he did not look up nor did the tremendous man look at him. The group proceeded up the rest of the aisle and out of the car. Mr. Head's grip on Nelson's arm loosened. "What was that?" he asked.

"A man," the boy said and gave him an indignant look as if he were tired of having his intelligence insulted.

"What kind of a man?" Mr. Head persisted, his voice expressionless.

"A fat man," Nelson said. He was beginning to feel that he had better be cautious.

"You don't know what kind?" Mr. Head said in a final tone.

"An old man," the boy said and had a sudden foreboding that he was not going to enjoy the day.

"That was a nigger," Mr. Head said and sat back.

Nelson jumped up on the seat and stood looking backward to the end of the car but the Negro had gone.

"I'd of thought you'd know a nigger since you seen so many when you was in the city on your first visit," Mr. Head continued. "That's his first nigger," he said to the man across the aisle.

The boy slid down into the seat. "You said they were black," he said in an angry voice. "You never said they were tan. How do you expect me to know anything when you don't tell me right?"

"You're just ignorant is all," Mr. Head said and he got up and moved over in the vacant seat by the man across the aisle.

Nelson turned backward again and looked where the Negro had disappeared. He felt that the Negro had deliberately walked down the aisle in order to make a fool of him and he hated him with a fierce raw fresh hate; and also, he understood now why his grandfather disliked them. He looked toward the window and the face there seemed to suggest that he might be inadequate to the day's exactions. He wondered if he would even recognize the city when they came to it.

After he had told several stories, Mr. Head realized that the man he was talking to was asleep and he got up and suggested to Nelson that they walk over the train and see the parts of it. He particularly wanted the boy to see the toilet so they went first to the men's room and examined the plumbing. Mr. Head demonstrated the ice-water cooler as if he had invented it and showed Nelson the bowl with the single spigot where the travelers brushed their teeth. They went through several cars and came to the diner.

This was the most elegant car in the train. It was painted a rich egg-yellow and had a wine-colored carpet on the floor. There were wide windows over the tables and great spaces of the rolling view were caught in miniature in the sides of the coffee pots and in the glasses. Three very black Negroes in white suits and aprons were running up and down the aisle, swinging trays and bowing and bending over the travelers eating breakfast. One of them rushed up to Mr. Head and Nelson and said, holding up two fingers, "Space for two!" but Mr. Head replied in a loud voice, "We eaten before we left!"

The waiter wore large brown spectacles that increased the size of his eye whites. "Stan' aside then please," he said with an airy wave of the arm as if he were brushing aside flies.

Neither Nelson nor Mr. Head moved a fraction of an inch. "Look," Mr. Head said.

The near corner of the diner, containing two tables, was set off from the rest by a saffron-colored curtain. One table was set but empty but at the other, facing them, his back to the drape, sat the tremendous Negro. He was speaking in a soft voice to the two women while he buttered a muffin. He had a heavy sad face and his neck bulged over his white collar on either side. "They rope them off," Mr. Head explained. Then he said, "Let's go see the kitchen," and they walked the length of the diner but the black waiter was coming fast behind them.

"Passengers are not allowed in the kitchen!" he said in a haughty voice. "Passengers are NOT allowed in the kitchen!"

Mr. Head stopped where he was and turned. "And there's good reason for that," he shouted into the Negro's chest, "because the cockroaches would run the passengers out!"

All the travelers laughed and Mr. Head and Nelson walked out, grinning. Mr. Head was known at home for his quick wit and Nelson felt a sudden keen pride in him. He realized the old man would be his only support in the strange place they were approaching. He would be entirely alone in the world if he were ever lost from his grandfather. A terrible excitement shook him and he wanted to take hold of Mr. Head's coat and hold on like a child.

As they went back to their seats they could see through the passing windows that the countryside was becoming speckled with small houses and shacks and that a highway ran alongside the train. Cars sped by on it, very small and fast. Nelson felt that there was less breath in the air than there had been thirty minutes ago. The man across the aisle had left and there was no one near for Mr. Head to hold a conversation with so he looked out the window, through his own reflection, and read aloud the names of the buildings they were passing. "The Dixie Chemical Corp!" he announced. "Southern Maid Flour! Dixie Doors! Southern Belle Cotton Products! Patty's Peanut Butter! Southern Mammy Cane Syrup!"

"Hush up!" Nelson hissed.

All over the car people were beginning to get up and take their luggage off the overhead racks. Women were putting on their coats and hats. The conductor stuck his head in the car and snarled, "Firstoppppppmry," and Nelson lunged out of his sitting position, trembling. Mr. Head pushed him down by the shoulder.

"Keep your seat," he said in dignified tones. "The first stop is on the edge of town. The second stop is at the main railroad station." He had come by this knowledge on his first trip when he had got off at the first stop and had had to pay a man fifteen cents to take him into the heart of town. Nelson sat back down, very pale. For the first time in his life, he understood that his grandfather was indispensable to him.

The train stopped and let off a few passengers and glided on as if it had never ceased moving. Outside, behind rows of brown rickety houses, a line of blue buildings stood up, and beyond them a pale rose-gray sky faded away to nothing. The train moved into the railroad yard. Looking down, Nelson saw lines and lines of silver tracks multiplying and criss-crossing. Then before he could start counting them, the face in the window started out at him, gray but distinct, and he looked the other way. The train was in the station. Both he and Mr. Head jumped up and ran to the door. Neither noticed that they had left the paper sack with the lunch in it on the seat.

They walked stiffly through the small station and came out of a heavy door into the squall of traffic. Crowds were hurrying to work. Nelson didn't know where to look. Mr. Head leaned against the side of the building and glared in front of him.

Finally Nelson said, "Well, how do you see what all it is to see?"

Mr. Head didn't answer. Then as if the sight of people passing had given him the clue, he said, "You walk," and started off down the street. Nelson followed, steadying his hat. So many sights and sounds were flooding in on him that for the first block he hardly knew what he was seeing. At the second corner, Mr. Head turned and looked behind him at the station they had left, a putty-colored terminal with a concrete dome on top. He thought that if he could keep the dome always in sight, he would be able to get back in the afternoon to catch the train again.

As they walked along, Nelson began to distinguish details and take note of the store windows, jammed with every kind of equipment—hardware, dry-goods, chicken feed, liquor. They passed one that Mr. Head called his particular attention to where you walked in and sat on a chair with your feet upon two rests and let a Negro polish your shoes. They walked slowly and stopped and stood at the entrances so he could see what went on in each place but they did not go into any of them. Mr. Head was determined not to go into any city store because on his first trip here, he had got lost in a large one and had found his way out only after many people had insulted him.

They came in the middle of the next block to a store that had a weighing machine in front of it and they both in turn stepped up on it and put in a penny and received a ticket. Mr. Head's ticket said, "You weigh 120 pounds. You are upright and brave and all your friends admire you." He put the ticket in his pocket, surprised that the machine should have got his character correct but his weight wrong, for he had weighed on a grain scale not long before and knew he weighed 110. Nelson's ticket said, "You weigh 98 pounds. You have a great destiny ahead of you but beware of dark women." Nelson did not know any women and he weighed only 68 pounds but Mr. Head pointed out that the machine had probably printed the number upside down, meaning the 9 for a 6.

They walked on and at the end of five blocks the dome of the terminal sank out of sight and Mr. Head turned to the left. Nelson could have stood in front of every store window for an hour if there had not been another more interesting one next to it. Suddenly he said, "I was born here!" Mr. Head turned and looked at him with horror. There was a sweaty brightness about his face. "This is where I come from!" he said.

Mr. Head was appalled. He saw the moment had come for drastic action. "Lemme show you one thing you ain't seen yet," he said and took him to the corner where there was a sewer entrance. "Squat down," he said, "and stick you head in there," and he held the back of the boy's coat while he got down and put his head in the sewer. He drew it back quickly, hearing a gurgling in the depths under the sidewalk. Then Mr. Head explained the sewer system, how the entire city was underlined with it, how it contained all the drainage and was full of rats and how a man could slide into it and be sucked along down endless pitchblack tunnels. At any minute any man in the city might be sucked into the sewer and never heard from again. He described it so well that Nelson was for some seconds shaken. He connected the sewer passages with the entrance to hell and understood for the first time how the world was put together in its lower parts. He drew away from the curb.

Then he said, "Yes, but you can stay away from the holes," and his face took on that stubborn look that was so exasperating to his grandfather. "This is where I come from!" he said.

Mr. Head was dismayed but he only muttered, "You'll get your fill," and they walked on. At the end of two more blocks he turned to the left, feeling that he was circling the dome; and he was correct for in a half-hour they passed in front of the railroad station again. At first Nelson did not notice that he was seeing the same stores twice but when they passed the one where you put your feet on the rests while the Negro polished your shoes, he perceived that they were walking in a circle.

"We done been here!" he shouted. "I don't believe you know where you're at!"

"The direction just slipped my mind for a minute," Mr. Head said and they turned down a different street. He still did not intend to let the dome get too far away and after two blocks in their new direction, he turned to the left. This street contained two- and three-story wooden dwellings. Anyone passing on the sidewalk could see into the rooms and Mr. Head, glancing through one window, saw a woman lying on an iron bed, looking out, with a sheet pulled over her. Her knowing expression shook him. A fierce-looking boy on a bicycle came driving down out of nowhere and he had to jump to the side to keep from being hit. "It's nothing to them if they knock you down," he said. "You better keep closer to me."

They walked on for some time on streets like this before he remembered to turn again. The houses they were passing now were all unpainted and the wood in them looked rotten; the street between was narrower. Nelson saw a colored man. Then another. Then another. "Niggers live in these houses," he observed.

"Well come on and we'll go somewheres else," Mr. Head said. "We didn't come to look at niggers," and they turned down another street but they continued to see Negroes everywhere. Nelson's skin began to prickle and they stepped along at a faster pace in order to leave the neighborhood as soon as possible. There were colored men in their undershirts standing in the doors and colored women rocking on the sagging porches. Colored children played in the gutters and stopped what they were doing to look at them. Before long they began to pass rows of stores with colored customers in them but they didn't pause at the entrances of these. Black eyes in black faces were watching them from every direction. "Yes," Mr. Head said, "this is where you were born—right here with all these niggers."

Nelson scowled. "I think you done got us lost," he said.

Mr. Head swung around sharply and looked for the dome. It was nowhere in sight. "I ain't got us lost either," he said. "You're just tired of walking."

"I ain't tired, I'm hungry," Nelson said. "Give me a biscuit."

They discovered then that they had lost the lunch.

"You were the one holding the sack," Nelson said. "I would have kepaholt of it."

"If you want to direct this trip, I'll go on by myself and leave you right here," Mr. Head said and was pleased to see the boy turn white. However, he realized they were lost and drifting farther every minute from the station. He was hungry himself and beginning to be thirsty and since they had been in the colored neighborhood, they had both begun to sweat. Nelson had on his shoes and he was unaccustomed to them. The concrete sidewalks were very hard. They both wanted to find a place to sit down but this was impossible and they kept on walking, the boy muttering under his breath, "First you lost the sack and then you lost the way," and Mr. Head growling from time to time, "Anybody wants to be from this nigger heaven can be from it!"

By now the sun was well forward in the sky. The odor of dinners cooking drifted out to them. The Negroes were all at their doors to see them pass. "Why'n't you ast one of these niggers the way?" Nelson said. "You got us lost."

"This is where you were born," Mr. Head said. "You can ast one yourself if you want to."

Nelson was afraid of the colored men and he didn't want to be laughed at by the colored children. Up ahead he saw a large colored woman leaning in a doorway that opened onto the sidewalk. Her hair stood straight out from her head for about four inches all around and she was resting on bare brown feet that turned pink at the sides. She had on a pink dress that showed her exact shape. As they came abreast of her, she lazily lifted one hand to her head and her fingers disappeared into her hair.

Nelson stopped. He felt his breath drawn up by the woman's dark eyes. "How do you get back to town?" he said in a voice that did not sound like his own.

After a minute she said, "You in town now," in a rich low tone that made Nelson feel as if a cool spray had been turned on him.

"How do you get back to the train?" he said in the same reed-like voice.

"You can catch you a car," she said.

He understood she was making fun of him but he was too paralyzed even to scowl. He stood drinking in every detail of her. His eyes traveled up from her great knees to her forehead and then made a triangular path from the glistening sweat on her neck down and across her tremendous bosom and over her bare arm back to where her fingers lay hidden in her hair. He suddenly wanted her to reach down and pick him up and draw him against her and then he wanted to feel her breath on his face. He wanted to look down and down into her eyes while she held him tighter and tighter. He had never had such a feeling before. He felt as if he were reeling down through a pitchblack tunnel.

"You can go a block down yonder and catch you a car take you to the railroad station, Sugarpie," she said.

Nelson would have collapsed at her feet if Mr. Head had not pulled him roughly away. "You act like you don't have any sense!" the old man growled.

They hurried down the street and Nelson did not look back at the woman. He pushed his hat sharply forward over his face which was already burning with shame. The sneering ghost he had seen in the train window and all the foreboding feelings he had on the way returned to him and he remembered that his ticket from the scale had said to beware of dark women and that his grandfather's had said he was upright and brave. He took hold of the old man's hand, a sign of dependence that he seldom showed.

They headed down the street toward the car tracks where a long yellow rattling trolley was coming. Mr. Head had never boarded a streetcar and he let that one pass. Nelson was silent. From time to time his mouth trembled slightly but his grandfather, occupied with his own problems, paid him no attention. They stood on the corner and neither looked at the Negroes who were passing, going about their business just as if they had been white, except that most of them stopped and eyed Mr. Head and Nelson. It occurred to Mr. Head that since the streetcar ran on tracks, they could simply follow the tracks. He gave Nelson a slight push and explained that they would follow the tracks on into the railroad station, walking, and they set off.

Presently to their great relief they began to see white people again and Nelson sat down on the sidewalk against the wall of a building. "I got to rest myself some," he said. "You lost the sack and the direction. You can just wait on me to rest myself."

"There's the tracks in front of us," Mr. Head said. "All we got to do is keep them in sight and you could have remembered the sack as good as me. This is where you were born. This is your old home town. This is your second trip. You ought to know how to do," and he squatted down and continued in this vein but the boy, easing his burning feet out of his shoes, did not answer.

"And standing there grinning like a chim-pan-zee while a nigger woman gives you direction. Great Gawd!" Mr. Head said.

"I never said I was nothing but born here," the boy said in a shaky voice. "I never said I would or wouldn't like it. I never said I wanted to come. I only said I was born here and I never had nothing to do with that. I want to go home. I never wanted to come in the first place. It was all your big idea. How you know you ain't following the tracks in the wrong direction?"

This last had occurred to Mr. Head too. "All these people are white," he said.

"We ain't passed here before," Nelson said. This was a neighborhood of brick buildings that might have been lived in or might not. A few empty automobiles were parked along the curb and there was an occasional passerby. The heat of the pavement came up through Nelson's thin suit. His eyelids began to droop, and after a few minutes his head tilted forward. His shoulders twitched once or twice and then he fell over on his side and lay sprawled in an exhausted fit of sleep.

Mr. Head watched him silently. He was very tired himself but they could not both sleep at the same time and he could not have slept anyway because he did not know where he was. In a few minutes Nelson would wake up, refreshed by his sleep and very cocky, and would begin complaining that he had lost the sack and the way. You'd have a mighty sorry time if I wasn't here, Mr. Head thought; and then another idea occurred to him. He looked at the sprawled figure for several minutes; presently he stood up. He justified what he was going to do on the grounds that it is sometimes necessary to teach a child a lesson he won't forget, particularly when the child is always reasserting his position with some new impudence. He walked without a sound to the corner about twenty feet away and sat down on a covered garbage can in the alley where he could look out and watch Nelson wake up alone.

The boy was dozing fitfully, half conscious of vague noises and black forms moving up from some dark part of him into the light. His face worked in his sleep and he had pulled his knees up under his chin. The sun shed a dull dry light on the narrow street; everything looked like exactly what it was. After a while Mr. Head, hunched like an old monkey on the garbage can lid, decided that if Nelson didn't wake up soon, he would make a loud noise by bamming his foot against the can. He looked at his watch and discovered that it was two o'clock. Their train left at six and the possibility of missing it was too awful for him to think of. He kicked his foot backwards on the can and a hollow boom reverberated in the alley.

Nelson shot up onto his feet with a shout. He looked where his grandfather should have been and stared. He seemed to whirl several times and then, picking up his feet and throwing his head back, he dashed down the street like a wild maddened pony. Mr. Head jumped off the can and galloped after but the child was almost out of sight. He saw a streak of gray disappearing diagonally a block ahead. He ran as fast as he could, looking both ways down every intersection, but without sight of him again. Then as he passed the third intersection, completely winded, he saw about half a block down the street a scene that stopped him altogether. He crouched behind a trash box to watch and get his bearings.

Nelson was sitting with both legs spread out and by his side lay an elderly woman, screaming. Groceries were scattered about the sidewalk. A crowd of women had already gathered to see justice done and Mr. Head distinctly heard the old woman on the pavement shout, "You've broken my ankle and your daddy'll pay for it! Every nickel! Police! Police!" Several of the women were plucking at Nelson's shoulder but the boy seemed too dazed to get up.

Something forced Mr. Head from behind the trash box and forward, but only at a creeping pace. He had never in his life been accosted by a policeman. The women were milling around Nelson as if they might suddenly all dive on him at once and tear him to pieces, and the old woman continued to scream that her ankle was broken and to call for an officer. Mr. Head came on so slowly that he could have been taking a backward step after each forward one, but when he was about ten feet away, Nelson saw him and sprang. The child caught him around the hips and clung panting against him.

The women all turned on Mr. Head. The injured one sat up and shouted, "You sir! You'll pay every penny of my doctor's bill that your boy has caused. He's a juve-nile deliquent! Where is an officer? Somebody take this man's name and address!"

Mr. Head was trying to detach Nelson's fingers from the flesh in the back of his legs. The old man's head had lowered itself into his collar like a turtle's; his eyes were glazed with fear and caution.

"Your boy has broken my ankle!" the old woman shouted. "Police!"

Mr. Head sensed the approach of the policeman from behind. He stared straight ahead at the women who were massed in their fury like a solid wall to block his escape, "This is not my boy," he said. "I never seen him before."

He felt Nelson's fingers fall out of his flesh.

The women dropped back, staring at him with horror, as if they were so repulsed by a man who would deny his own image and likeness that they could not bear to lay hands on him. Mr. Head walked on, through a space they silently cleared, and left Nelson behind. Ahead of him he saw nothing but a hollow tunnel that had once been the street.

The boy remained standing where he was, his neck craned forward and his hands hanging by his sides. His hat was jammed on his head so that there were no longer any creases in it. The injured woman got up and shook her fist at him and the others gave him pitying looks, but he didn't notice any of them. There was no policeman in sight.

In a minute he began to move mechanically, making no effort to catch up with his grandfather but merely following at about twenty paces. They walked on for five blocks in this way. Mr. Head's shoulders were sagging and his neck hung forward at such an angle that it was not visible from behind. He was afraid to turn his head. Finally he cut a short hopeful glance over his shoulder. Twenty feet behind him, he saw two small eyes piercing into his back like pitchfork prongs.

The boy was not of a forgiving nature but this was the first time he had ever had anything to forgive. Mr. Head had never disgraced himself before. After two more blocks, he turned and called over his shoulder in a high desperately gay voice, "Let's us go get us a Co' Cola somewhere!"

Nelson, with a dignity he had never shown before, turned and stood with his back to his grandfather.

Mr. Head began to feel the depth of his denial. His face as they walked on became all hollows and bare ridges. He saw nothing they were passing but he perceived that they had lost the car tracks. There was no dome to be seen anywhere and the afternoon was advancing. He knew that if dark overtook them in the city, they would be beaten and robbed. The speed of God's justice was only what he expected for himself, but he could not stand to think that his sins would be visited upon Nelson and that even now, he was leading the boy to his doom.

They continued to walk on block after block through an endless section of small brick houses until Mr. Head almost fell over a water spigot sticking up about six inches off the edge of a grass plot. He had not had a drink of water since early morning but he felt he did not deserve it now. Then he thought that Nelson would be thirsty and they would both drink and be brought together. He squatted down and put his mouth to the nozzle and turned a cold stream of water into his throat. Then he called out in the high desperate voice, "Come on and getcher some water!"

This time the child stared through him for nearly sixty seconds. Mr. Head got up and walked on as if he had drunk poison. Nelson, though he had not had water since some he had drunk out of a paper cup on the train, passed by the spigot, disdaining to drink where his grandfather had. When Mr. Head realized this, he lost all hope. His face in the waning afternoon light looked ravaged and abandoned. He could feel the boy's steady hate, traveling at an even pace behind him and he knew that (if by some miracle they escaped being murdered in the city) it would continue just that way for the rest of his life. He knew that now he was wandering into a black strange place where nothing was like it had ever been before, a long old age without respect and an end that would be welcome because it would be the end.

As for Nelson, his mind had frozen around his grandfather's treachery as if he were trying to preserve it intact to present at the final judgment. He walked without looking to one side or the other, but every now and then his mouth would twitch and this was when he felt, from some remote place inside himself, a black mysterious form reach up as if it would melt his frozen vision in one hot grasp.

The sun dropped down behind a row of houses and hardly noticing, they passed into an elegant suburban section where mansions were set back from the road by lawns with birdbaths on them. Here everything was entirely deserted. For blocks they didn't pass even a dog. The big white houses were like partially submerged icebergs in the distance. There were no sidewalks, only drives, and these wound around and around in endless ridiculous circles. Nelson made no move to come nearer to Mr. Head. The old man felt that if he saw a sewer entrance he would drop down into it and let himself be carried away; and he could imagine the boy standing by, watching with only a slight interest, while he disappeared.

A loud bark jarred him to attention and he looked up to see a fat man approaching with two bulldogs. He waved both arms like someone ship-wrecked on a desert island. "I'm lost!" he called. "I'm lost and can't find my way and me and this boy have got to catch this train and I can't find the station. Oh Gawd I'm lost! Oh hep me Gawd I'm lost!"

The man, who was bald-headed and had on golf knickers, asked him what train he was trying to catch and Mr. Head began to get out his tickets, trembling so violently he could hardly hold them. Nelson had come up to within fifteen feet and stood watching.

"Well," the fat man said, giving him back the tickets, "you won't have time to get back to town to make this but you can catch it at the suburb stop. That's three blocks from here," and he began explaining how to get there.

Mr. Head stared as if he were slowly returning from the dead and when the man had finished and gone off with the dogs jumping at his heels, he turned to Nelson and said breathlessly, "We're going to get home!"

The child was standing about ten feet away, his face bloodless under the gray hat. His eyes were triumphantly cold. There was no light in them, no feeling, no interest. He was merely there, a small figure, waiting. Home was nothing to him.

Mr. Head turned slowly. He felt he knew now what time would be like without seasons and what heat would be like without light and what man would be like without salvation. He didn't care if he never made the train and if it had not been for what suddenly caught his attention, like a cry out of the gathering dusk, he might have forgotten there was a station to go to.

He had not walked five hundred yards down the road when he saw, within reach of him, the plaster figure of a Negro sitting bent over on a low yellow brick fence that curved around a wide lawn. The Negro was about Nelson's size and he was pitched forward at an unsteady angle because the putty that held him to the wall had cracked. One of his eyes was entirely white and he held a piece of brown watermelon.

Mr. Head stood looking at him silently until Nelson stopped at a little distance. Then as the two of them stood there, Mr. Head breathed, "An artificial nigger!"

It was not possible to tell if the artificial Negro were meant to be young or old; he looked too miserable to be either. He was meant to look happy because his mouth was stretched up at the corners but the chipped eye and the angle he was cocked at gave him a wild look of misery instead.

"An artificial nigger!" Nelson repeated in Mr. Head's exact tone.

The two of them stood there with their necks forward at almost the same angle and their shoulders curved in almost exactly the same way and their hands trembling identically in their pockets. Mr. Head looked like an ancient child and Nelson like a miniature old man. They stood gazing at the artificial Negro as if they were faced with some great mystery, some monument to another's victory that brought them together in their common defeat. They could both feel it dissolving their differences like an action of mercy. Mr. Head had never known before what mercy felt like because he had been too good to deserve any, but he felt he knew now. He looked at Nelson and understood that he must say something to the child to show that he was still wise and in the look the boy returned he saw a hungry need for that assurance. Nelson's eyes seemed to implore him to explain once and for all the mystery of existence.

Mr. Head opened his lips to make a lofty statement and heard himself say, "They ain't got enough real ones here. They got to have an artificial one."

After a second, the boy nodded with a strange shivering about his mouth, and said, "Let's go home before we get ourselves lost again."

Their train glided into the suburb stop just as they reached the station and they boarded it together, and ten minutes before it was due to arrive at the junction, they went to the door and stood ready to jump off if it did not stop; but it did, just as the moon, restored to its full splendor, sprang from a cloud and flooded the clearing with light. As they stepped off, the sage grass was shivering gently in shades of silver and the clinkers under their feet glittered with a fresh black light. The treetops, fencing the junction like the protecting walls of a garden, were darker than the sky which was hung with gigantic white clouds illuminated like lanterns.

Mr. Head stood very still and felt the action of mercy touch him again but this time he knew that there were no words in the world that could name it. He understood that it grew out of agony, which is not denied to any man and which is given in strange ways to children. He understood it was all a man could carry into death to give his Maker and he suddenly burned with shame that he had so little of it to take with him. He stood appalled, judging himself with the thoroughness of God, while the action of mercy covered his pride like a flame and consumed it. He had never thought himself a great sinner before but he saw now that his true depravity had been hidden from him lest it cause him despair. He realized that he was forgiven for sins from the beginning of time, when he had conceived in his own heart the sin of Adam, until the present, when he had denied poor Nelson. He saw that no sin was too monstrous for him to claim as his own, and since God loved in proportion as He forgave, he felt ready at that instant to enter Paradise.

Nelson, composing his expression under the shadow of his hat brim, watched him with a mixture of fatigue and suspicion, but as the train glided past them and disappeared like a frightened serpent into the woods, even his face lightened and he muttered, "I'm glad I've went once, but I'll never go back again!"

Blackberries in June

Ron Rash

Ron Rash was born in 1953 in Chester, South Carolina, to textile worker parents. When he was eight years old, his family moved to Boiling Springs, North Carolina. Rash's ancestors had lived in the Appalachians since the mid-eighteenth century. Rash's father worked as a college professor at Gardner-Webb University, where Rash earned his B.A. in English. Rash earned an M.A. in English from Clemson University and taught at Tri-County Technical College in Pendleton, SC. He is currently the Parris Distinguished Professor in Appalachian Cultural Studies at Western Carolina University. Rash's numerous poems, short stories, and novels depict the lives of south-ern people in rural or mill-working settings and often seethe with religious imagery. Thematically, poverty, suffering, death, and survival in the lives of his Appalachian characters unify most of his works, such as "Blackberries in June" from his 2007 short story collection Chemistry and Other Stories, *which was a finalist for the PEN/Faulkner Award for Fiction.*

On those August nights when no late-after-noon thunderstorm rinsed the heat and humidity from the air, no breeze stirred the cattails and willow oak leaves, Jamie and Matt sometimes made love surrounded by water. Tonight might be such a night, Jamie thought. She rolled down the window and let air blast away some of the cigarette smoke that clung to her uniform and hair. She was exhausted from eight hours of navigating tables with hardly a pause to stand still, much less sit down, from the effort it took to lift the sides of her mouth into an unwavering smile. Exhausted too from the work she'd done at the house before her shift at the restaurant. The radio in the decade-old Ford Escort didn't work, so she hummed a Dixie Chicks song about chains being loosened. That's what she wanted, to be unchained in the weightlessness of water. She wanted to feel Matt lift and hold her so close their hearts were only inches apart.

In a few minutes the road fell sharply. At the bottom of the hill she turned off the blacktop onto what was, at least for now, more red-clay washout than road. The Escort bumped and jarred as it made its way down to the lake house. *Their* house, hers and Matt's. Barely a year married, hardly out of their teens, and they had a place they owned, not rented. It was a miracle Jamie still had trouble believing. And this night, like every night as she turned in to the drive, a part of her felt surprise the house was really there.

But it was, and already looking so much better than in June when she and Matt had signed the papers at the bank. What had been a tangle of kudzu and briars a yard and garden. Broken windows, rotted boards, and rust-rotten screens replaced. Now Jamie spent her mornings washing years of grime off walls and blinds. When that was done she could start caulking the cracks and gashes on the walls and ceilings. Matt reshingled the roof evenings after he got off, working until he could no longer see to nail. As he must have this night, because the ladder lay against the side of the house. In another month, when the shingles had been paid for, they would drive down to Seneca and buy paint. If things went well, in a year they'd have enough saved to replace the plumbing and wiring.

Matt waited on the screened-in porch. The light wasn't on but Jamie knew he was there. As she came up the steps his form emerged from the dark like something summoned out of air. He sat in the porch swing, stripped to his jeans. His work boots, shirt, and socks lay in a heap near the door. The swing creaked and swayed as she curled into his lap, her head against his chest. Her lips tasted the salty sweat on his skin as his arms pulled her closer. She felt the hardness of Matt's arms, muscled by two months of ten- to twelve-hour days cutting pulpwood. She wished of those hard muscles a kind of armor to protect him while he logged with her brother, Charlton, on the ridges where the Chauga River ran through Big Laurel Valley.

You best get a good look at your husband's pretty face right now, Charlton had said the first morning he came to pick up Matt. Feel the smooth of his skin too, little sister, because a man who cuts pulpwood don't stay pretty long.

Charlton had spoken in a joking manner, but she'd seen the certain truth of it in her brother's face, the broken nose and gapped smile, the raised, purple ridges on his arms and legs where flesh had been knitted back together. Jamie had watched Charlton as he and Matt walked to the log truck with its busted headlights and crumpled fender and cracked windshield. A truck no more beat-up and battered than its owner, Jamie had realized in that moment. Charlton was thirty years old, but he moved with the stiffness of an old man. Dr. Wesley in Seneca said he needed back surgery, but Charlton would hear nothing of it. Her sister-in-law, Linda, had told Jamie of nights Charlton drank half a bottle of whiskey to kill the pain. And sometimes, as Matt had witnessed, Charlton didn't wait until night.

The porch swing creaked as Jamie pressed her head closer to Matt's chest, close enough so she could not just hear but feel the strong, sure beat of his heart. First get the house fixed up, Jamie thought. Then when that was done she and Matt would start taking night classes again at the technical college. In a year they'd have their degrees. Then good jobs and children. It was a mantra she recited every night before falling asleep.

"Want to get in the lake?" Matt asked, softly kissing the top of her head.

"Yes," Jamie said, though she felt, to use her mother's words, tired to the bone. In some ways that was what made their lovemaking so good, especially on Saturday nights—finding in each other's bodies that last ounce of strength left from their long day, their long week, and sharing it.

They walked down the grassy slope to where a half-sunk pier leaned into the lake. On the bank they took off their clothes and stepped onto the pier, the boards trembling beneath them. At the pier's end the boards became slick with algae and water rose to their ankles. They felt for the drop-off with their feet, entered the water with a splash.

Then Jamie was weightless, the water up to her breasts, her feet lifting from the silt as she wrapped her arms around Matt. The sway of water eased away the weariness of eight hours of standing, eased as well the dim ache behind her eyes caused by hurry and noise and cigarette smoke. Water sloshed softly against the pier legs. The moon mirrored itself in the water, and Matt's head and shoulders shimmered in a yellow glow as Jamie raised her mouth to his.

They slept late the next morning, then worked on the house two hours before driving up the mountain to her grandmother's for Sunday lunch. Behind the farmhouse a barn Jamie's grandfather had built in the 1950s crumbled into a rotting pile of tin and wood. In a white oak out by the boarded-up well, a cicada called for rain.

"Let's not stay more than an hour," Matt said as they stepped onto the front porch. "That's as long as I can stand Linda."

Inside, Jamie's parents, Charlton, Linda, and their children already sat at the table. Food was on the table and the drinks poured.

"About to start without you," Linda said sharply as they sat down. "When young ones get hungry they get contrary. If you had kids you'd know that."

"Them kids don't seem to be acting contrary to me," Matt said, nodding at the three children. "The only person acting contrary is their momma."

"I'm sorry," Jamie said. "We were working on the house and lost track of time."

"I know you all are trying to save money, but I still wish you had a phone," her mother said.

Grandma Chastain came in from the kitchen with a basket of rolls. She sat down at the table beside the youngest child.

"Say us a prayer, Luther," she said to her son.

For a few minutes they ate in silence. Then Charlton turned to his father.

"You ought to have seen the satinback me and Matt killed Wednesday morning. Eight rattles and long as my leg," Charlton said. "Them chain saws have made me so deaf I didn't even hear it. I'm just glad Matt did or I'd of sure stepped right on it."

"Don't tell such a thing, Charlton," Grandma Chastain said. "I worry enough about you out in them woods all day as it is."

"How's your back, Son?" Jamie's mother asked.

It was Linda who answered.

"Bothers him all the time. He turns all night in bed trying to get comfortable. Ain't neither of us had a good night's sleep in months."

"You don't think the surgery would do you good?" Grandma Chastain asked.

Charlton shook his head.

"It didn't help Bobby Hemphill's back none. Just cost him a bunch of money and a month not being able to work."

When they'd finished dessert, Jamie's mother turned to her.

"You want to go with me and Linda to that flower show in Seneca?"

"I better not," Jamie said. "I need to work on the house."

"You and Matt are going to work yourselves clear to the bone fixing that house if you're not careful," her mother said.

Jamie's father winked at Jamie.

"Your momma's always looking for the dark cloud in a blue sky."

"I do no such thing, Luther Alexander," her mother said. "It's just the most wonderful kind of thing that Jamie and Matt have that place young as they are. It's like getting blackberries in June. I just don't want them wearing themselves out."

"They're young and healthy, Momma. They can handle it," Charlton said. "Just be happy for them."

Linda sighed loudly and Charlton's lips tightened. The smile vanished from his face. He stared at his wife but did not speak. Instead, it was Grandma Chastain who spoke.

"You two need to be in church on Sunday morning," she said to Jamie, "not working on that house. You've been blessed, and you best let the Lord know you appreciate it."

"Look at you," Linda said angrily to Christy, the youngest child. "You got that pudding all over your Sunday dress." She yanked the child from her chair. "Come on, we're going to the bathroom and clean that stain, for what little good it'll do."

Linda walked a few steps, then turned back to the table, her hand gripping Christy's arm so hard the child whimpered.

"I reckon we all don't get lucky with lake houses and such," Linda said, looking not at Matt but at Jamie, "but that don't mean we don't deserve just as much. You just make sure your husband saves enough of his strength to do the job Charlton's overpaying him to do."

"I reckon if Charlton's got any complaints about me earning my pay he can tell me his own self," Matt said.

Linda swatted Christy's backside with her free hand.

"You hush now," she said to the child and dragged her into the bathroom.

For a few moments the only sound was the ticking of the mantel clock.

"You don't pay Linda no mind," Charlton said to Matt. "The smartest thing I done in a long while is let go that no-account Talley boy and hire you. You never slack up and you don't call in sick on Mondays. You ain't got a dime from me you ain't earned."

"And I wouldn't expect otherwise," Matt said.

"Still, it's a good thing Charlton's done," Jamie's mother said as she got up, "especially letting you work percentage." She laid her hand on her son's shoulder as she reached around him to pick up his plate. "You've always been good to look after your sister, and I know she'll always be grateful, won't you, girl?"

"Yes, ma'am," Jamie said.

The bathroom door opened and Christy came out trailing her mother, her eyes swollen from crying.

"We ought to be going," Matt said, pushing back his chair. "I need to get some more shingles on that roof."

"You shouldn't to be in such a rush," Grandma Chastain said, but Matt was already walking toward the door.

Jamie pushed back her chair.

"We do need to be going."

"At least let me wrap you up something for supper," Grandma Chastain said.

Jamie thought about how much work they had to do and how good it would be not to have to cook.

"Okay, Grandma," she said.

❧

Matt was in the car when she came out, the engine running and his hands gripping the steering wheel. Jamie placed the leftovers in the backseat and got in beside Matt.

"You could have waited for me," she said.

"If I'd stayed any longer I'd of said some things you wouldn't want me to," Matt said, "and not just to Linda. Your mother and grandma need to keep their advice to themselves."

"They just care about me," Jamie said, "about us."

They drove back to the house in silence and worked until dusk. As Jamie cleaned the blinds she heard Matt's hammer tapping above as if he was nailing her shut inside the house. She thought about the rattlesnake, how it could easily have bitten Matt, and remembered twelve years earlier, when her mother and Mr. Jenkins, the elementary school principal, appeared at the classroom door.

"Your daddy's been hurt," her mother said. Charlton was outside waiting in the logging truck, and they drove the fifteen miles to the county hospital. Her father had been driving a skid loader that morning. It had rained the night before and the machine had turned over on a ridge. His hand was shattered in two places, and there was nerve damage as well. Jamie remembered stepping into the white room with her mother and seeing her father in the bed, a morphine drip jabbed into his arm like a fang. If that skidder had turned over one more time you'd be looking at a dead man, her father had told them. Charlton had quit high school and worked full-time cutting pulpwood to make sure food was on the table that winter. Her father eventually got a job as a night watchman, a job, unlike cutting pulp-wood, a man needed only one good hand to do.

"I get scared for you, for us," Jamie said that night as they lay in bed. "Sometimes I wish we'd never had the chance to buy this place."

"You don't mean that," Matt said. "This place is the best thing that might ever happen to us. How many chances do young folks get to own a house on a lake? If we hadn't seen Old Man Watson's sign before the real-estate agents did, they'd have razed the house and sold the lot alone to some Floridian at twice what we paid."

"I know that," Jamie said, "but I can't help being scared for you. It's just like things have been too easy for us. Look at Charlton. Him and Linda have been married ten years and they're still in a trailer. Linda says good luck follows us around like a dog that needs petting all the time. She thinks you and me getting this house is just one more piece of luck."

"Well, the next time she says that you tell her anybody with no better sense than to have three kids the first five years she's married can't expect to have much money left for a down payment on a house, especially with a skidder to pay off as well."

Matt turned his head toward her. She could feel the stir of his breath.

"Linda's just jealous," he said, "that and she's still pissed off Charlton's paying me percentage. Linda best be worrying about her own self. She's got troubles enough at home without stirring up troubles for other people."

"You mean Charlton's drinking?"

"Yeah. Every morning this week he's reeked of alcohol, and it ain't his aftershave. The money they waste on whiskey and her on makeup and fancy hairdos could help make a down payment, not to mention that Bronco when they already had a perfectly good car. Damn, Jamie, they got three vehicles and only two people to drive them."

Matt placed his hand on the back of Jamie's head, letting his fingers run through her cropped hair, hair shorter than his. His voice softened.

"You make your own luck," Matt said. "Some will say we're lucky when you're working in a dentist's office and I'm a shift supervisor in a plant, like we hadn't been planning that very life since we were juniors in high school. They'll forget they stayed at home nights and watched TV instead of taking classes at Tech. They'll forget how we worked near full-time jobs in high school and saved that money when they wasted theirs on new trucks and fancy clothes."

"I know that," Jamie said. "But I get so tired of people acting resentful because we're doing well. It even happens at the café. Why can't they all be like Charlton, just happy for us?"

"Because it reminds them they're too lazy and undisciplined to do it themselves," Matt said. "People like that will pull you down with them if you give them the chance, but we're not going to let them do that to us."

Matt moved his hand slowly down her spine, letting it rest in the small of the back.

"It's time to sleep, baby," he said.

Soon Matt's breathing became slow and regular. He shifted in the bed and his hand slipped free from her back. First, get the house fixed up, she told herself as she let her weariness and the sound of tree frogs and crickets carry her toward sleep.

Two more weeks passed, and it was almost time for Jamie to turn the calendar nailed by the kitchen door. She knew soon the leaves would start to turn. Frost would whiten the grass and she and Matt would sleep under piles of quilts Grandma Alexander had sewn. They'd sleep under a roof that no longer leaked. After Charlton picked up Matt, Jamie caulked the back room, the room that would someday be a nursery. As she filled in cracks she envisioned the lake house when it was completely renovated—the walls bright with fresh paint, all the leaks plugged, a porcelain tub and toilet, master bedroom built onto the back. Jamie imagined summer nights when children slept as she and Matt walked hand in hand down to the pier, undressing each other to share again the unburdening of water.

Everything but the back room's ceiling had been caulked when she stopped at one-thirty to eat lunch and change into her waitress's uniform. She was closing the front door when she heard a vehicle bumping down through the woods to the house. In a few moments she saw her father's truck, behind the windshield his distraught face. At that moment something gave inside her, as if her bones had succumbed to the weight of the flesh they carried. The sky and woods and lake seemed suddenly farther away, as if a space had been cleared that held only her. She closed her hand around the key in her palm and held it so tight her knuckles whitened. Her father kicked the cab door open with his boot.

"It's bad," he said, "real bad." He didn't cut off the engine or get out from behind the wheel. "Linda and Matt and your momma are already at the hospital."

She didn't understand, not at first. She tried to picture a situation where her mother and Linda and Matt could have been hurt together—a car wreck, or fire—something she could frame and make sense of.

"Momma and Linda are hurt too?" Jamie finally asked.

"No," her father said, "just Charlton." His voice cracked. "They're going to have to take your brother's leg off, baby."

Jamie understood then, and at that moment she felt many things, including relief that it wasn't Matt.

When they entered the waiting room, her mother and Linda sat on a long green couch. Matt sat opposite them in a blue plastic chair. Dried blood stained his work shirt and jeans. He stood up, his face pale and haggard as he embraced her. Jamie smelled the blood as she rested her head against his chest.

"We were cleaning limbs," Matt said, "and the saw jumped back and dug into his leg till it got to bone. I made a tourniquet with my belt, but he still like to have bled to death." Matt paused. "Charlton shouldn't have been running that saw. He'd been drinking."

Matt held her close a few more moments, then stepped back. He nodded toward the corner where Linda and her mother sat.

"You better say something to your momma and Linda," he said and released her arms. Jamie let go too. It was only then that she realized the key was still in her closed right hand. She slipped it into her uniform pocket.

Her mother stood when Jamie approached, but Linda stayed on the couch, her head bowed.

"Pray hard, girl," her mother said as she embraced Jamie. "Your brother is going to need every prayer he can get."

"You seen him yet, Momma?" she asked. Jamie smelled the Camay soap her mother used every night. She breathed deep, let the smell of the soap replace the smell of blood.

"No, he's still in surgery, will be for at least another hour."

Her mother released her and stepped back.

"I can't stand myself just sitting here," she said and nodded at Jamie's father standing beside the door marked SURGERY. "Come on, Luther. I'm going to get us all some doughnuts and coffee and I need you to help carry it." She turned to Jamie. "You stay here and look after Linda."

Jamie sat in the place her mother had left. Linda's head remained bowed, but her eyes were open. Jamie looked up at the wall clock. Two-twenty-three. The red minute hand went around seven more times before Jamie spoke.

"It's going to be all right, Linda," she said. It was the only thing she could think to say.

Linda lifted her head, looked right at Jamie. "You sound pretty sure of that. Maybe if it was your husband getting his leg took off you'd think different."

Linda wasn't thirty yet, but Jamie saw something she recognized in every older woman in her family. It was how they looked out at the world, their eyes resigned to bad times and trouble. I don't ever remember being young, Grandma Alexander had once told her. All I remember is something always needing to be done, whether it was hoeing a field or the washing or feeding hungry children or cows or chickens.

The elevator door opened and Jamie's parents stepped out, their hands filled with paper bags.

"You think this couldn't have happened to Matt," Linda said, raising her voice enough that Jamie's parents came no closer. "You think it happened because Charlton had been drinking."

"I don't think any such thing," Jamie said.

Linda looked at her in-laws.

"I got three young ones to feed and buy school clothes for, and a disability check ain't going to be enough to do that."

"We'll do everything we can to help you," Jamie's father said and offered Linda a cup of coffee. "Here. This will give you some strength."

"I don't need strength," Linda said, her voice wild and angry. "I need the money Charlton overpaid Matt. Money that should be ours. Money we need worse than they do."

Linda looked at her father-in-law.

"You know Charlton paid hourly wages to everybody else who worked for him."

"I earned every cent he paid me," Matt said. He had left his seat and stepped closer, standing next to Jamie now. "I been there every day and I've cut plenty of days dawn to dark. It's bad what's happened to Charlton, and I'm sorry it happened. But me and Jamie don't owe you anything." Jamie placed her hand on Matt's arm, but he jerked it away. "I ain't listening to this anymore."

"You owe us everything," Linda shouted as Matt walked toward the elevator. "If Charlton hadn't taken you on you'd never have been able to make a down payment on that lake house." Linda looked at Jamie's parents now, tears streaming down her face. "A lake house, and the five of us in a beat-up double-wide."

The surgery room door opened, and a nurse glared at them all briefly before the door closed again.

Jamie's mother sat down on the couch and pressed Linda's head to her bosom. "We're all going to do everything possible to get you all through this, and that includes Matt and Jamie," she said.

Linda sobbed now, her face smeared with mascara. Minutes passed before she raised her head. She tried to smile as she brushed tears from her cheeks and slowly lifted herself from the couch. Jamie's father gripped Linda's upper arm when her knees buckled.

"I know I look a sight," Linda said. "I best go to the bathroom and tidy up so Charlton won't see me like this." She looked at Jamie. "I'm sorry," she said.

Jamie's father walked Linda to the restroom and waited by the door.

"Come here, girl," her mother said to Jamie.

Jamie didn't move. She was afraid, almost as afraid as when she'd seen her father's face through the windshield.

"I need to call the restaurant, let them know what's going on."

"That can wait a few minutes," her mother said. "We need to talk, and right now."

Jamie remained where she was.

"I know you're put out with Linda," her mother said, "and I don't blame you. Grieving don't give her no excuse to talk that way to you and Matt." She paused, waited for Jamie to meet her eyes. "But you know you got to help them."

Jamie turned and stared at the wall clock. She thought how only two hours earlier she had been caulking the back room of the lake house.

"Me and your daddy will do what we can, but that won't be near enough. Your daddy says even if the skidder's sold, it'll bring no more than two thousand dollars. We're not talking about just Linda here. We're talking about your niece and nephews."

"Why are you saying this to me, Momma?" Jamie asked. "Matt's going to have to find another job now, and there's no way he'll make the kind of money Charlton paid him. We need all the money we got just to make the payments on the lake house, much less fix it up. We'll have tuition to pay as well come spring."

The elevator door opened. Jamie hoped it was Matt, but a chaplain got off and walked past them toward the intensive care unit.

"You've been blessed, Jamie," her mother said. "Linda's right. Charlton never let anyone but Matt work percentage. You could give Charlton the difference between what Matt got paid and the six dollars an hour anybody else would have got."

"But we'd have to sell the lake house," Jamie said. "How can you ask me and Matt to do that?"

"The same way I'd have asked your brother to quit high school. Only I never had to ask. He knew what had to be done and did it without me saying a word to him. Seventeen years old and he knew what had to be done." Her mother laid her hand on Jamie's. "That lake house, you had no right to expect such a place so young. You know it was a miracle you got it in the first place. You can't expect miracles in this life, girl."

The bathroom door opened and Linda came out. She and Jamie's father walked toward them.

"Maybe not, Momma," Jamie said, her voice low but sharp, "but when they come a person's got a right to take them."

"You got to do what's best for the whole family," her mother said, speaking quietly as well. "You got to accept that life is full of disappointments. That's something you learn as you grow older."

There had been complications during the surgery, and Jamie was unable to see Charlton until after seven-thirty. His eyes opened when she placed her hand on his, but he was too drugged to say anything coherent. Jamie wondered if he even understood what had happened to him. She hoped that for a little while longer he didn't.

When Jamie and Matt got back to the lake house it was dark, and by then things had been decided, but not before harsh words had been exchanged.

"Come on," Matt said, reaching for her hand after they got out of the Escort. "Let's go down to the lake, baby. I need one good thing to happen in my life today."

"Not tonight," Jamie said. "I'm going on in."

She changed into her nightgown. Matt came in soon afterward naked and dripping, work clothes and boots cradled in his arms. Jamie stepped out of the bathroom, a toothbrush in her hand.

"Put those clothes out on the porch," she said. "I don't want to smell that blood anymore."

Jamie was in bed when he came back, and soon Matt cut out the light and joined her. For a minute the only sounds were the crickets and tree frogs. The mattress's worn-out springs creaked as Matt turned to face her.

"I'll go see Harold Wilkinson in the morning," he said. "He knows I did good work for Charlton. I figure I can get eight dollars an hour to work on his crew, especially since I know how to run a skidder."

He reached out and laid his arm on Jamie's shoulder.

"Come here," he said, pulling her closer.

She smelled the thick, fishy odor of the lake, felt the lake's coldness on his skin.

"They'll be needing help a long time," Matt said. "In two, three years at most we'll have jobs that pay three times what we're making now. Keeping this house is going to save us a lot of money, money we can help them with later."

Matt paused.

"You listening to me?"

"Yes," Jamie said.

"Linda's parents can help too. I didn't hear your momma say a word about them helping out." Matt kissed her softly on the cheek. "They'll be all right. We'll all be all right. Go to sleep, babe. You got another long day coming."

But she did not fall asleep, not for a while, and she woke at first light. She left the bed and went to the bathroom. Jamie turned on the faucet and soaked a washcloth, wrung it out and pressed it to her face. She set it on the basin and looked at the mirror. A crack jagged across the glass like a lightning bolt, a crack caulk couldn't fill. Something else to be replaced.

Han's Crime

Naoya Shiga

Translated by Ivan Morris

Naoya Shiga (1883–1971) was one of the early masters of modern Japanese fiction and a profound influence on 20th century Japanese fiction. While still in his twenties, Shiga, the offspring of wealthy parents, became involved with the so-called Shirakaba ("White Birch") literary movement, an aristocratic reaction against the predominant influence of Western naturalism. While the White Birch writers looked initially to Western models in their efforts to break free of the naturalistic mold, they increasingly sought to assert their Japanese identity. Out of this ferment came a form of literature called shishosetsu, or the "I-Novel," a mode of fiction that drew heavily upon autobiographical experience and which has sometimes been compared to the "confessional" mode in the West. While Shiga is best known for his short stories, he did write an "I-Novel" entitled A Dark Night's Passing *(1937), which tells the story of his long estrangement from his father. In his short fiction, Shiga often turned to crime stories, but, as in the present selection (first published in 1913), his interest was not in detection so much as psychological motivation.*

Much to everyone's astonishment, the young Chinese juggler, Han, severed his wife's carotid artery with one of his heavy knives in the course of a performance. The young woman died on the spot. Han was immediately arrested.

At the scene of the event were the director of the theatre, Han's Chinese assistant, the announcer and more than three hundred spectators. There was also a policeman who had been stationed behind the audience. Despite the presence of all these witnesses, it was a complete mystery whether the killing had been intentional or accidental.

Han's act was as follows: his wife would stand in front of a wooden board about the size of a door and, from a distance of approximately four yards, he would throw his large knives at her so that they stuck in the board about two inches apart, forming a contour around her body. As each knife left his hand, he would let out a staccato exclamation as if to punctuate his performance.

The examining judge first questioned the director of the theatre.

"Would you say that this was a very difficult act?"

"No, Your Honour, it's not as difficult as all that for an experienced performer. But to do it properly, you want steady nerves and complete concentration."

"I see. Then assuming that what happened was an accident, it was an extremely unlikely type of accident?"

"Yes, indeed, Your Honour. If accidents were not so very unlikely, I should never have allowed the act in my theatre."

"Well then, do you consider that this was done on purpose?"

"No, Your Honour, I do not. And for this reason: an act of this kind performed at a distance of twelve feet requires not only skill but at the same time a certain—well, intuitive sense. It is true that we all thought a mistake virtually out of the question, but after what has happened, I think we must admit that there was always the possibility of a mistake."

"Well then, which do you think it was—a mistake or on purpose?"

"That I simply cannot say, Your Honour."

The judge felt puzzled. Here was a clear case of homicide, but whether it was manslaughter or premeditated murder it was impossible to tell. If murder, it was indeed a clever one, thought the judge.

Next, the judge decided to question the Chinese assistant who had worked with Han for many years past.

"What was Han's normal behaviour?" he asked.

"He was always very correct, Your Honour; he didn't gamble or drink or run after women. Besides, last year he took up Christianity. He studied English and in his free time always seemed to be reading collections of sermons—the Bible and that sort of thing."

"And what about his wife's behaviour?"

"Also very correct, Your Honour. Strolling players aren't always the most moral people, as you know. Mrs. Han was a pretty little woman and quite a few men used to make propositions to her, but she never paid the slightest attention to that kind of thing."

"And what sort of temperaments did they have?"

"Always very kind and gentle, Sir. They were extremely good to all their friends and acquaintances and never quarrelled with anyone. But . . ." He broke off and reflected a moment before continuing. "Your Honour, I'm afraid that if I tell you this, it may go badly for Han. But to be quite truthful, these two people, who were so gentle and unselfish to others, were amazingly cruel in their relations to each other."

"Why was that?"

"I don't know, Your Honour."

"Was that the case ever since you first knew them?"

"No, Your Honour. About two years ago Mrs. Han was pregnant. The child was born prematurely and died after about three days. That marked a change in their relations. They began having terrible rows over the most trivial things, and Han's face used to turn white as a sheet. He always ended by suddenly growing silent. He never once raised his hand against her or anything like that—I suppose it would have gone against his principles. But when you looked at him, Your Honour, you could see the terrible anger in his eyes! It was quite frightening at times.

"One day I asked Han why he didn't separate from his wife, seeing that things were so bad between them. Well, he told me that he had no real grounds for divorce, even though his love for her had died. Of course, she felt this and gradually stopped loving him too. He told me all this himself. I think the reason he began reading the Bible and all those sermons was to calm the violence in his heart and stop himself from hating his wife, whom he had no real cause to hate. Mrs. Han was really a pathetic woman. She had been with Han nearly three years and had travelled all over the country with him as a strolling player. If she'd ever left Han and gone back home, I don't think she'd have found it easy to get married. How many men would trust a woman who'd spent all that time travelling about? I suppose that's why she stayed with Han, even though they got on so badly."

"And what do you really think about this killing?"

"You mean, Your Honour, do I think it was an accident or done on purpose?"

"That's right."

"Well, Sir, I've been thinking about it from every angle since the day it happened. The more I think, the less I know what to make of it. I've talked about it with the announcer, and he also says he can't understand what happened."

"Very well. But tell me this: at the actual moment it did happen, did it occur to you to wonder whether it was accidental or on purpose?"

"Yes, Sir, it did. I thought, 'He's gone and killed her.' "

"On purpose you mean?"

"Yes, Sir. However, the announcer says that he thought, 'His hands slipped.' "

"Yes, but he didn't know about their everyday relations as you did."

"That may be, Your Honour. But afterwards I wondered if it wasn't just because I did know about those relations that I thought, 'He's killed her.' "

"What were Han's reactions at the moment?"

"He cried out, 'Ha.' As soon as I heard that, I looked up and saw blood gushing from his wife's throat. For a few seconds she kept standing there, then her knees seemed to fold up under her and her body swayed forward. When the knife fell out, she collapsed on the floor, all crumpled in a heap. Of course there was nothing any of us could do—we just sat there petrified, staring at her . . . As to Han, I really can't describe his reactions, for I wasn't looking at him. It was only when the thought struck me, 'He's finally gone and killed her' that I glanced at him. His face was dead white and his eyes closed. The stage manager lowered the curtain. When they picked up Mrs. Han's body she was already dead. Han dropped to his knees then, and for a long time he kept praying in silence."

"Did he appear very upset?"

"Yes, Sir, he was quite upset."

"Very well. If I have anything further to ask you, I shall call for you again."

The judge dismissed the Chinese assistant and now summoned Han himself to the stand. The juggler's intelligent face was drawn and pale; one could tell right away that he was in a state of nervous exhaustion.

"I have already questioned the director of the theatre and your assistant," said the judge when Han had taken his place in the witness-box. "I now propose to examine you."

Han bowed his head.

"Tell me," said the judge, "did you at any time love your wife?"

"From the day of our marriage until the child was born I loved her with all my heart."

"And why did the birth of the child change things?"

"Because I knew it was not mine."

"Did you know who the other man was?"

"I had a very good idea. I think it was my wife's cousin."

"Did you know him personally?"

"He was a close friend. It was he who first suggested that we get married. It was he who urged me to marry her."

"I presume that his relations with her occurred prior to your marriage."

"Yes, Sir. The child was born eight months after we were married."

"According to your assistant, it was a premature birth."

"That is what I told everyone."

"The child died very soon after birth, did it not? What was the cause of death?"

"He was smothered by his mother's breasts."

"Did your wife do that on purpose?"

"She said it was an accident."

The judge was silent and looked fixedly at Han's face. Han raised his head but kept his eyes lowered as he awaited the next question. The judge continued:

"Did your wife confess these relations to you?"

"She did not confess, nor did I ever ask her about them. The child's death seemed like retribution for everything and I decided that I should be as magnanimous as possible, but . . ."

"But in the end you were unable to be magnanimous?"

"That's right. I could not help thinking that the death of the child was insufficient retribution. When apart from my wife, I was able to reason calmly, but as soon as I saw her, something happened inside me. When I saw her body, my temper would begin to rise."

"Didn't divorce occur to you?"

"I often thought that I should like to have a divorce, but I never mentioned it to my wife. My wife used to say that if I left her she could no longer exist."

"Did she love you?"

"She did not love me."

"Then why did she say such things?"

"I think she was referring to the material means of existence. Her home had been ruined by her elder brother and she knew that no serious man would want to marry a woman who had been the wife of a strolling player. Also, her feet were too small for her to do any ordinary work."

"What were your physical relations?"

"I imagine about the same as with most couples."

"Did your wife have any real liking for you?"

"I do not think she really liked me. In fact, I think it must have been very painful for her to live with me as my wife. Still, she endured it. She endured it with a degree of patience almost unthinkable for a man. She used to observe me with a cold, cruel look in her eyes as my life gradually went to pieces. She never showed a flicker of sympathy as she saw me struggling in agony to escape into a better, truer sort of existence."

"Why could you not take some decisive action—have it out with her, or even leave her if necessary?"

"Because my mind was full of all sorts of ideals."

"What ideals?"

"I wanted to behave towards my wife in such a way that there would be no wrong on my side . . . But in the end it didn't work."

"Did you never think of killing your wife?"

Han did not answer and the judge repeated his question. After a long pause, Han replied:

"Before the idea of killing her occurred to me, I often used to think it would be a good thing if she died."

"Well, in that case, if it had not been against the law, don't you think you might have killed her?"

"I wasn't thinking in terms of the law, Sir. That's not what stopped me. It was just that I was weak. At the same time I had this over-mastering desire to enter into a truer sort of life."

"Nevertheless you did think of killing your wife, did you not—later on, I mean?"

"I never made up my mind to do it. But, yes, it is correct to say that I did think about it once."

"How long was that before the event?"

"The previous night . . . Or perhaps even the same morning?"

"Had you been quarrelling?"

"Yes, Sir."

"What about?"

"About something so petty that it's hardly worth mentioning."

"Try telling me about it."

"It was a question of food. I get rather short-tempered when I haven't eaten for some time. Well, that evening my wife had been dawdling and our supper wasn't ready when it should have been. I got very angry."

"Were you more violent than usual?"

"No, but afterwards I still felt worked up, which was unusual. I suppose it was because I'd been worrying so much during those past weeks about making a better existence for myself, and realising there was nothing I could do about it. I went to bed but couldn't get to sleep. All sorts of upsetting thoughts went through my mind. I began to feel that whatever I did, I should never be able to achieve the things I really wanted—that however hard I tried, I should never be able to escape from all the hateful aspects of my present life. This sad, hopeless state of affairs all seemed connected with my marriage. I desperately wanted to find a chink of light to lead me out of my darkness, but even this desire was gradually being extinguished. The hope of escape still flickered and sputtered within me, and I knew that if ever it should go out I would to all intents and purposes be a dead person.

"And then the ugly thought began flitting through my mind, 'If only she would die! If only she would die! If only she would die! Why should I not kill her?' The practical consequences of such a crime meant nothing to me any longer. No doubt I would go to prison, but life in prison could not be worse—could only be better—than this present existence. And yet somehow I had the feeling that killing my wife would solve nothing. It would have been shirking the issue, in the same way as suicide. I must go through each day's suffering as it came, I told myself; there was no way to circumvent that. That had become my true life now: to suffer.

"As my mind raced along these tracks, I almost forgot that the cause of my suffering lay beside me. Utterly exhausted, I lay there unable to sleep. I fell into a blank state of stupefaction, and as my tortured mind turned numb, the idea of killing my wife gradually faded. Then I was overcome by the sad empty feeling that follows a nightmare. I thought of all my fine resolutions for a better life, and realised that I was too weak-hearted to attain it. When dawn finally broke I saw that my wife, also, had not been sleeping . . ."

"When you got up, did you behave normally towards each other?"

"We did not say a single word to each other."

"But why didn't you think of leaving her, when things had come to this?"

"Do you mean, Your Honour, that that would have been a solution of my problem? No, no, that too would have been a shirking of the issue! As I told you, I was determined to behave towards my wife so that there would be no wrong on my side."

Han gazed earnestly at the judge, who nodded his head as a sign for him to continue.

"Next day I was physically exhausted and of course my nerves were ragged. It was agony for me to remain still, and as soon as I had got dressed I left the house and wandered aimlessly about the deserted part of the town. Constantly the thought kept returning that I must do something to solve my life, but the idea of killing no longer occurred to me. The truth is that there was a chasm between my thoughts of murder the night before and any actual decision to commit a crime! Indeed, I never even thought about that evening's performance. If I had, I certainly would have decided to leave out the knife-throwing act. There were dozens of other acts that could have been substituted.

"Well, the evening came and finally it was our turn to appear on the stage. I did not have the slightest premonition that anything out of the ordinary was to happen. As usual, I demonstrated to the audience the sharpness of my knives by slicing pieces of paper and throwing some of the knives at the floorboards. Presently my wife appeared, heavily made up and wearing an elaborate Chinese costume; after greeting the audience with her charming smile, she took up her position in front of the board. I picked up one of the knives and placed myself at the usual distance from her.

"That's when our eyes met for the first time since the previous evening. At once I understood the risk of having chosen this particular act for that night's performance! Obviously I would have to master my nerves, yet the exhaustion which had penetrated to the very marrow of my bones prevented me. I sensed that I could no longer trust my own arm. To calm myself I closed my eyes for a moment, and I sensed that my whole body was trembling.

"Now the time had come! I aimed my first knife above her head; it struck one inch higher than usual. My wife raised her arms and I prepared to throw my next two knives under each of her arms. As the first one left the ends of my fingers, I felt as if something were holding it back; I no longer had the sense of being able to determine the exact destination of my knives. It was now really a matter of luck if the knife struck at the point intended; each of my movements had become deliberate and self-conscious.

"I threw one knife to the left of my wife's neck and was about to throw another to the right when I saw a strange expression in her eyes. She seemed to be seized by a paroxysm of fear! Did she have a presentiment that this knife, that in a matter of seconds would come hurtling towards her, was going to lodge in her throat? I do not know. All I knew was that her terrible expression of fear was reflected in my own heart. I felt dizzy as if about to faint. Forcing the knife deliberately out of my hand, I as good as aimed it into space . . ."

The judge was silent, peering intently at Han.

"All at once the thought came to me, 'I've killed her,'" said Han abruptly.

"On purpose, you mean?"

"Yes. Suddenly I felt that I had done it on purpose."

"After that I understand you knelt down beside your wife's body and prayed in silence."

"Yes, Sir. That was a rather cunning device that occurred to me on the spur of the moment. I realized that everyone knew me as a believer in Christianity. But while I was making a pretence of praying, I was in fact carefully calculating what attitude to adopt."

"So you were absolutely convinced that what you had done was on purpose?"

"I was. But I realized at once that I should be able to pretend it had been an accident."

"And why did you think it had been on purpose?"

"I had lost all sense of judgement."

"Did you think you'd succeeded in giving the impression it was an accident?"

"Yes, though when I thought about it afterwards it made my flesh creep. I pretended as convincingly as I could to be grief-stricken, but if there'd been just one really sharp-witted person about, he'd have realized right away that I was only acting. Well, that evening I decided that there was no good reason why I should not be acquitted; I told myself very calmly that there wasn't a shred of material evidence against me. To be sure, everyone knew how badly I got on with my wife, but if I persisted in saying that it was an accident, no one could prove the contrary. Going over in my mind everything that had happened, I saw that my wife's death could be explained very plausibly as an accident.

"And then a strange question came to my mind: why did I myself believe that it had not been an accident? To be sure, the previous night I had thought about killing her, but might it not be that very fact which now caused me to think of my act as deliberate? Gradually I came to the point that I myself did not know what actually had happened! At that I became very happy—almost unbearably happy. I wanted to shout at the top of my lungs."

"Because you had come to consider it an accident?"

"No, that I can't say: because I no longer had the slightest idea whether it had been intentional or not. So I decided that my best way of being acquitted would be to make a clean breast of everything. Rather than deceive myself and everyone else by saying it was an accident, why not be completely honest and say I did not know what happened? I cannot declare it was a mistake; on the other hand I can't admit it was intentional. In fact, I can plead neither 'guilty' nor 'not guilty'."

Han was silent. The judge, too, remained silent for a long moment before saying softly, reflectively:

"I believe that what you have told me is true. Just one more question; do you not feel the slightest sorrow for your wife's death?"

"None at all! Even when I hated my wife most bitterly in the past, I never could have imagined I would feel such happiness in talking about her death."

"Very well," said the judge. "You may stand down."

Han silently lowered his head and left the room. Feeling strangely moved, the judge reached for his pen. On the document which lay on the table he wrote down the words, "Not Guilty."

Yellow Woman

Leslie Marmon Silko

Leslie Marmon Silko was born in 1948 in Albuquerque, New Mexico. She is a Native American writer, poet and essayist of the Laguna Pueblo tribe. She received her B.A. (with honors) from the University of New Mexico in 1969. Literary critic Kenneth Lincoln has called Silko one of the key figures in the First Wave of the Native American Renaissance.

Silko's most well-known work is Yellow Woman and a Beauty of the Spirit: Essays on Native American Life Today, *published by Simon & Schuster in March 1997. The work focuses on the Laguna People's society before Christian missionaries arrived. It is also a political statement against racist policies towards Native Americans, especially those from the Clinton Administration. It emphasizes the strong connections Silko has to the oral tradition of her past.* Yellow Woman *also contains recollections from Silko's own racial mistreatment as a mixed race person. In the introduction to* Yellow Woman, *editor Melody Graulich states: "Silko emphasizes the need to return to rituals and oral traditions of the past in order to rediscover the basis for one's cultural identity."*

Silko's other works include her first novel, Ceremony *about the importance of storytelling to the Pueblo culture and how White culture has attempted to destroy these stories as well as their ceremonies. Silko's second major novel,* Storyteller (1981), *is based on tales passed on in the Pueblo tradition to recreate stories about her own upbringing.* Delicacy and the Strength of Lace: Letters (1986) *is an edited version of her correspondence with fellow poet James Wright. She also wrote* Almanac of the Dead, *published in 1991.*

Silko was one of the original recipients of the MacArthur Foundation Grant in 1981. She received the Native Writers' Circle of the Americans Lifetime Achievement Award in 1994.

She currently resides in Tucson, Arizona, where she is professor of English at the University of Arizona.

One

My thigh clung to his with dampness, and I watched the sun rising up through the tamaracks and willows. The small brown water birds came to the river and hopped across the mud, leaving brown scratches in the alkali-white crust. They bathed in the river silently. I could hear the water, almost at our feet where the narrow fast channel bubbled and washed green ragged moss and fern leaves. I looked at him beside me, rolled in the red blanket on the white river sand. I cleaned the sand out of the cracks between my toes, squinting because the sun was above the willow trees. I looked at him for the last time, sleeping on the white river sand.

I felt hungry and followed the river south the way we had come the afternoon before, following our footprints that were already blurred by lizard tracks and bug trails. The horses were still lying down, and the black one whinnied when he saw me but he did not get up—maybe it was because the corral was made out of thick cedar branches and the horses had not yet felt the sun like I had. I tried to look beyond the pale red mesas to the pueblo. I knew it was there, even if I could not see it, on the sandrock hill above the river, the same river that moved past me now and had reflected the moon last night.

The horse felt warm underneath me. He shook his head and pawed the sand. The bay whinnied and leaned against the gate trying to follow, and I remembered him asleep in the red blanket beside the river. I slid off the horse and tied him close to the other horse. I walked north with the river again, and the white sand broke loose in footprints over footprints.

"Wake up."

He moved in the blanket and turned his face to me with his eyes still closed. I knelt down to touch him.

"I'm leaving."

He smiled now, eyes still closed. "You are coming with me, remember?" He sat up now with his bare dark chest and belly in the sun.

"Where?"

"To my place."

"And will I come back?"

He pulled his pants on. I walked away from him, feeling him behind me and smelling the willows.

"Yellow Woman," he said.

I turned to face him. "Who are you?" I asked.

He laughed and knelt on the low, sandy bank, washing his face in the river. "Last night you guessed my name, and you knew why I had come."

I stared past him at the shallow moving water and tried to remember the night, but I could only see the moon in the water and remember his warmth around me.

"But I only said that you were him and that I was Yellow Woman—I'm not really her—I have my own name and I come from the pueblo on the other side of the mesa. Your name is Silva and you are a stranger I met by the river yesterday afternoon."

He laughed softly. "What happened yesterday has nothing to do with what you will do today, Yellow Woman."

"I know—that's what I'm saying—the old stories about the ka'tsina spirit and Yellow Woman can't mean us."

My old grandpa liked to tell those stories best. There is one about Badger and Coyote who went hunting and were gone all day, and when the sun was going down they found a house. There was a girl living there alone, and she had light hair and eyes and she told them that they could sleep with her. Coyote wanted to be with her all night so he sent Badger into a prairie-dog hole, telling him he thought he saw something in it. As soon as Badger crawled in, Coyote blocked up the entrance with rocks and hurried back to Yellow Woman.

"Come here," he said gently.

He touched my neck and I moved close to him to feel his breathing and to hear his heart. I was wondering if Yellow Woman had known who she was—if she knew that she would become part of the stories. Maybe she'd had another name that her husband and relatives called her so that only the ka'tsina from the north and the storytellers would know her as Yellow Woman. But I didn't go on; I felt him all around me, pushing me down into the white river sand.

Yellow Woman went away with the spirit from the north and lived with him and his relatives. She was gone for a long time, but then one day she came back and she brought twin boys.

"Do you know the story?"

"What story?" He smiled and pulled me close to him as he said this. I was afraid lying there on the red blanket. All I could know was the way he felt, warm, damp, his body beside me. This is the way it happens in the stories, I was thinking, with no thought beyond the moment she meets the ka'tsina spirit and they go.

"I don't have to go. What they tell in stories was real only then, back in time immemorial, like they say."

He stood up and pointed at my clothes tangled in the blanket. "Let's go," he said.

I walked beside him, breathing hard because he walked fast, his hand around my wrist. I had stopped trying to pull away from him, because his hand felt cool and the sun was high, drying the river bed into alkali. I will see someone, eventually I will see someone, and then I will be certain that he is only a man—some man from nearby—and I will be sure that I am not Yellow Woman. Because she is from out of time past and I live now and I've been to school and there are highways and pickup trucks that Yellow Woman never saw.

It was an easy ride north on horseback. I watched the change from the cottonwood trees along the river to the junipers that brushed past us in the foothills, and finally there were only pinons, and when I looked up at the rim of the mountain plateau I could see pine trees growing on the edge. Once I stopped to look down, but the pale sandstone had disappeared and the river was gone and the dark lava hills were all around. He touched my hand, not speaking, but always singing softly a mountain song and looking into my eyes.

I felt hungry and wondered what they were doing at home now—my mother, my grandmother, my husband, and the baby. Cooking breakfast, saying, "Where did she go?—maybe kidnaped," and Al going to the tribal police with the details: "She went walking along the river."

The house was made with black lava rock and red mud. It was high above the spreading miles of arroyos and long mesas. I smelled a mountain smell of pitch and buck brush. I stood there beside the black horse, looking down on the small, dim country we had passed, and I shivered.

"Yellow Woman, come inside where it's warm."

Two

He lit a fire in the stove. It was an old stove with a round belly and an enamel coffeepot on top. There was only the stove, some faded Navajo blankets, and a bedroll and cardboard box. The floor was made of smooth adobe plaster, and there was one small window facing east. He pointed at the box.

"There's some potatoes and the frying pan." He sat on the floor with his arms around his knees pulling them close to his chest and he watched me fry the potatoes. I didn't mind him watching me because he was always watching me—he had been watching me since I came upon him sitting on the river bank trimming leaves from a willow twig with his knife. We ate from the pan and he wiped the grease from his fingers on his Levis.

"Have you brought women here before?" He smiled and kept chewing, so I said, "Do you always use the same tricks?"

"What tricks?" He looked at me like he didn't understand.

"The story about being a ka'tsina from the mountains. The story about Yellow Woman."

Silva was silent; his face was calm.

"I don't believe it. Those stories couldn't happen now," I said.

He shook his head and said softly, "But someday they will talk about us, and they will say, 'Those two lived long ago when things like that happened.'"

He stood up and went out. I ate the rest of the potatoes and thought about things—about the noise the stove was making and the sound of the mountain wind outside. I remembered yesterday and the day before, and then I went outside.

I walked past the corral to the edge where the narrow trail cut through the black rim rock. I was standing in the sky with nothing around me but the wind that came down from the blue mountain peak behind me. I could see faint mountain images in the distance miles across the vast spread of mesas and valleys and plains. I wondered who was over there to feel the mountain wind on those sheer blue edges—who walks on the pine needles in those blue mountains.

"Can you see the pueblo?" Silva was standing behind me.

I shook my head. "We're too far away."

"From here I can see the world." He stepped out on the edge. "The Navajo reservation begins over there." He pointed to the east. "The Pueblo boundaries are over here." He looked below us to the south, where the narrow trail seemed to come from. "The Texans have their ranches over there, starting with that valley, the Concho Valley. The Mexicans run some cattle over there too."

"Do you ever work for them?"

"I steal from them," Silva answered. The sun was dropping behind us and shadows were filling the land below. I turned away from the edge that dropped forever into the valleys below.

"I'm cold," I said; "I'm going inside." I started wondering about this man who could speak the Pueblo language so well but who lived on a mountain and rustled cattle. I decided that this man Silva must be Navajo, because Pueblo men didn't do things like that.

"You must be a Navajo."

Silva shook his head gently. "Little Yellow Woman," he said, "you never give up, do you? I have told you who I am. The Navajo people know me, too." He knelt down and unrolled the bedroll and spread the extra blankets out on a piece of canvas. The sun was down, and the only light in the house came from outside—the dim orange light from sundown.

I stood there and waited for him to crawl under the blankets.

"What are you waiting for?" he said, and I lay down beside him. He undressed me slowly like the night before beside the river—kissing my face gently and running his hands up and down my belly and legs. He took off my pants and then he laughed.

"Why are you laughing?"

"You are breathing so hard."

I pulled away from him and turned my back to him.

He pulled me around and pinned me down with his arms and chest. "You don't understand, do you, little Yellow Woman? You will do what I want."

And again he was all around me with his skin slippery against mine, and I was afraid because I understood that his strength could hurt me. I lay underneath him and I knew that he could destroy me. But later, while he slept beside me, I touched his face and I had a feeling—the kind of feeling for him that overcame me that morning along the river. I kissed him on the forehead and he reached out for me.

When I woke up in the morning he was gone. It gave me a strange feeling because for a long time I sat there on the blankets and looked around the little house for some object of his—some proof that he had been there or maybe that he was coming back. Only the blankets and the cardboard box remained. The 30-30 that had been leaning in the corner was gone, and so was the knife I had used the night before. He was gone, and I had my chance to go now. But first I had to eat, because I knew it would be a long walk home.

I found some dried apricots in the cardboard box, and I sat down on a rock at the edge of the plateau rim. There was no wind and the sun warmed me. I was surrounded by silence. I drowsed with apricots in my mouth, and I didn't believe that there were highways or railroads or cattle to steal.

When I woke up, I stared down at my feet in the black mountain dirt. Little black ants were swarming over the pine needles around my foot. They must have smelled the apricots. I thought about my family far below me. They would be wondering about me, because this had never happened to me before. The tribal police would file a report. But if old Grandpa weren't dead he would tell them what happened—he would laugh and say, "Stolen by a ka'tsina, a mountain spirit. She'll come home—they usually do." There are enough of them to handle things. My mother and grandmother will raise the baby like they raised me. Al will find someone else, and they will go on like before, except that there will be a story about the day I disappeared while I was walking along the river. Silva had come for me; he said he had. I did not decide to go. I just went. Moonflowers blossom in the sand hills before dawn, just as I followed him. That's what I was thinking as I wandered along the trail through the pine trees.

It was noon when I got back. When I saw the stone house I remembered that I had meant to go home. But that didn't seem important any more, maybe because there were little blue flowers growing in the meadow behind the stone house and the gray squirrels were playing in the pines next to the house. The horses were standing in the corral, and there was a beef carcass hanging on the shady side of a big pine in front of the house. Flies buzzed around the clotted blood that hung from the carcass. Silva was washing his hands in a bucket full of water. He must have heard me coming because he spoke to me without turning to face me.

"I've been waiting for you."

"I went walking in the big pine trees."

I looked into the bucket full of bloody water with brown-and-white animal hairs floating in it. Silva stood there letting his hand drip, examining me intently.

"Are you coming with me?"

"Where?" I asked him.

"To sell the meat in Marquez."

"If you're sure it's O.K."

"I wouldn't ask you if it wasn't," he answered.

He sloshed the water around in the bucket before he dumped it out and set the bucket upside down near the door. I followed him to the corral and watched him saddle the horses. Even beside the horses he looked tall, and I asked him again if he wasn't Navajo. He didn't say anything; he just shook his head and kept cinching up the saddle.

"But Navajos are tall."

"Get on the horse," he said, "and let's go."

The last thing he did before we started down the steep trail was to grab the .30-30 from the corner. He slid the rifle into the scabbard that hung from his saddle.

"Do they ever try to catch you?" I asked.

"They don't know who I am."

"Then why did you bring the rifle?"

"Because we are going to Marquez where the Mexicans live."

Three

The trail leveled out on a narrow ridge that was steep on both sides like an animal spine. On one side I could see where the trail went around the rocky gray hills and disappeared into the southeast where the pale sandrock mesas stood in the distance near my home. On the other side was a trail that went west, and as I looked far into the distance I thought I saw the little town. But Silva said no, that I was looking in the wrong place, that I just thought I saw houses. After that I quit looking off into the distance; it was hot and the wild-flowers were closing up their deep-yellow petals. Only the waxy cactus flowers bloomed in the bright sun, and I saw every color that a cactus blossom can be; the white ones and the red ones were still buds, but the purple and the yellow were blossoms, open full and the most beautiful of all.

Silva saw him before I did. The white man was riding a big gray horse, coming up the trail toward us. He was traveling fast and the gray horse's feet sent rocks rolling off the trail into the dry tumbleweeds. Silva motioned for me to stop and we watched the white man. He didn't see us right away, but finally his horse whinnied at our horses and he stopped. He looked at us briefly before he loped the gray horse across the three hundred yards that sep-arated us. He stopped his horse in front of Silva, and his young fat face was shadowed by the brim of his hat. He didn't look mad, but his small, pale eyes moved from the blood-soaked gunny sacks hanging from my saddle to Silva's face and then back to my face.

"Where did you get the fresh meat?" the white man asked.

"I've been hunting," Silva said, and when he shifted his weight in the saddle the leather creaked.

"The hell you have, Indian. You've been rustling cattle. We've been looking for the thief for a long time."

The rancher was fat, and sweat began to soak through his white cowboy shirt and the wet cloth stuck to the thick rolls of belly fat. He almost seemed to be panting from the exertion of talking, and he smelled rancid, maybe because Silva scared him.

Silva turned to me and smiled. "Go back up the mountain, Yellow Woman."

The white man got angry when he heard Silva speak in a language he couldn't understand. "Don't try anything, Indian. Just keep riding to Marquez. We'll call the state police from there."

The rancher must have been unarmed because he was very frightened and if he had a gun he would have pulled it out then. I turned my horse around and the rancher yelled, "Stop!" I looked at Silva for an instant and there was something ancient and dark—something I could feel in my stomach—in his eyes, and when I glanced at his hand I saw his finger on the trigger of the .30-30 that was still in the saddle scabbard. I slapped my horse across the flank and the sacks of raw meat swung against my knees as the horse leaped up the trail. It was hard to keep my balance, and once I thought I felt the saddle slipping backward; it was because of this that I could not look back.

I didn't stop until I reached the ridge where the trail forked. The horse was breathing deep gasps and there was a dark film of sweat on its neck. I looked down in the direction I had come from, but I couldn't see the place. I waited. The wind came up and pushed warm air past me. I looked up at the sky, pale blue and full of thin clouds and fading vapor trails left by jets.

I think four shots were fired—I remember hearing four hollow explosions that reminded me of deer hunting. There could have been more shots after that, but I couldn't have heard them because my horse was running again and the loose rocks were making too much noise as they scattered around his feet.

Horses have a hard time running downhill, but I went that way instead of uphill to the mountain because I thought it was safer. I felt better with the horse running southeast past the round gray hills that were covered with cedar trees and black lava rock. When I got to the plain in the distance I could see the dark green patches of tamaracks that grew along the river; and beyond the river I could see the beginning of the pale sandrock mesas. I stopped the horse and looked back to see if anyone was coming; then I got off the horse and turned the horse around, wondering if it would go back to its corral under the pines on the mountain. It looked back at me for a moment and then plucked a mouthful of green tumbleweeds before it trotted back up the trail with its ears pointed forward, carrying its head daintily to one side to avoid stepping on the dragging reins. When the horse disappeared over the last hill, the gunny sacks full of meat were still swinging and bouncing.

Four

I walked toward the river on a wood-hauler's road that I knew would eventually lead to the paved road. I was thinking about waiting beside the road for someone to drive by, but by the time I got to the pavement I had decided it wasn't very far to walk if I followed the river back the way Silva and I had come.

The river water tasted good, and I sat in the shade under a cluster of silvery willows. I thought about Silva, and I felt sad at leaving him; still, there was something strange about him, and I tried to figure it out all the way back home.

I came back to the place on the river bank where he had been sitting the first time I saw him. The green willow leaves that he had trimmed from the branch were still lying there, wilted in the sand. I saw the leaves and I wanted to go back to him—to kiss him and to touch him—but the mountains were too far away now. And I told myself, because I believe it, he will come back sometime and be waiting again by the river.

I followed the path up from the river into the village. The sun was getting low, and I could smell supper cooking when I got to the screen door of my

house. I could hear their voices inside—my mother was telling my grandmother how to fix the Jell-o and my husband, Al, was playing with the baby.
I decided to tell them that some Navajo had kidnaped me, but I was sorry that
old Grandpa wasn't alive to hear my story because it was the Yellow Woman
stories he liked to tell best.

"Works Cited" Entry:

Silko, Leslie Marmon. "Yellow Woman." 1974. Rpt. in *Nothing But the Truth:*
An Anthology of Native American Literature. Edited by John L. Purdy and James Ruppert. Upper
Saddle River, NJ: Prentice Hall, 2001. 367–74.

Harrison Bergeron

Kurt Vonnegut

Kurt Vonnegut was born on November 11, 1922, in Indianapolis, Indiana, from German-American stock. He is one of the most influential and iconic American novelists of the twentieth century, fusing irony with science fiction, absurdity, and vicious social commentary. Vonnegut attended Cornell University from 1940 to 1942. He then served in the U.S. Army during World War II. He fought in the European Theater and was captured after the Battle of the Bulge. He became a prisoner of war and was in Dresden, Germany, when allied forces firebombed the city. He witnessed this apocalyptic annihilation of Dresden, influencing his famous novel Slaughterhouse-Five *(1969). Vonnegut's penchant for satire and memories of wartime inhumanity forged the themes of many of his novels, including* The Sirens of Titan *(1959),* Mother Night *(1961), and* Cat's Cradle *(1963). Vonnegut's inimitable writing style, consisting of long sentences and minimal punctuation, is evident in his later short stories and novels, including* Breakfast of Champions *(1973),* Jailbird *(1979), and* Deadeye Dick *(1982). "Harrison Bergeron," a dystopian satire about the desire for a manufactured equality, was first published in October 1961 in* The Magazine of Fantasy and Science Fiction *and was re-published in the Vonnegut's* Welcome to the Monkey House *in 1968. Vonnegut's success and critical acclaim did little to soothe his personal demons and depression. He attempted suicide in 1984. Kurt Vonnegut died on April 11, 2007 in New York from a brain injury caused by a fall.*

The year was 2081, and everybody was finally equal. They weren't only equal before God and the law. They were equal every which way. Nobody was smarter than anybody else. Nobody was better looking than anybody else. Nobody was stronger or quicker than anybody else. All this equality was due to the 211th, 212th, and 213th Amendments to the Constitution, and to the unceasing vigilance of agents of the United States Handicapper General.

Some things about living still weren't quite right, though. April, for instance, still drove people crazy by not being spring-time. And it was in that clammy month that the H-G men took George and Hazel Bergeron's fourteen-year-old son, Harrison, away.

It was tragic, all right, but George and Hazel couldn't think about it very hard. Hazel had a perfectly average intelligence, which meant she couldn't think about anything except in short bursts. And George, while his intelligence was way above normal, had a little mental handicap radio in his ear. He was required by law to wear it at all times. It was tuned to a government transmitter. Every twenty seconds or so, the transmitter would send out some sharp noise to keep people like George from taking unfair advantage of their brains.

George and Hazel were watching television. There were tears on Hazel's cheeks, but she'd forgotten for the moment what they were about.

On the television screen were ballerinas.

A buzzer sounded in George's head. His thoughts fled in panic, like bandits from a burglar alarm.

"That was a real pretty dance, that dance they just did," said Hazel.

"Huh?" said George.

"That dance—it was nice," said Hazel.

"Yup," said George. He tried to think a little about the ballerinas. They weren't really very good—no better than anybody else would have been, anyway. They were burdened with sash-weights and bags of birdshot, and their faces were masked, so that no one, seeing a free and graceful gesture or a pretty face, would feel like something the cat drug in. George was toying with the vague notion that maybe dancers shouldn't be handicapped. But he didn't get very far with it before another noise in his ear radio scattered his thoughts.

George winced. So did two out of the eight ballerinas.

Hazel saw him wince. Having no mental handicap herself, she had to ask George what the latest sound had been.

"Sounded like somebody hitting a milk bottle with a ball peen hammer," said George.

"I'd think it would be real interesting, hearing all the different sounds," said Hazel, a little envious. "All the things they think up."

"Um," said George.

"Only, if I was Handicapper General, you know what I would do?" said Hazel. Hazel, as a matter of fact, bore a strong resemblance to the Handicapper General, a woman named Diana Moon Glampers. "If I was Diana Moon Glampers," said Hazel, "I'd have chimes on Sunday—just chimes. Kind of in honor of religion."

"I could think, if it was just chimes," said George.

"Well—maybe make 'em real loud," said Hazel. "I think I'd make a good Handicapper General."

"Good as anybody else," said George.

"Who knows better'n I do what normal is?" said Hazel.

"Right," said George. He began to think glimmeringly about his abnormal son who was now in jail, about Harrison, but a twenty-one-gun salute in his head stopped that.

"Boy!" said Hazel, "that was a doozy, wasn't it?"

It was such a doozy that George was white and trembling, and tears stood on the rims of his red eyes. Two of the eight ballerinas had collapsed to the studio floor, were holding their temples.

"All of a sudden you look so tired," said Hazel. "Why don't you stretch out on the sofa, so's you can rest your handicap bag on the pillows, honey-bunch." She was referring to the forty-seven pounds of birdshot in a canvas bag, which was padlocked around George's neck. "Go on and rest the bag for a little while," she said. "I don't care if you're not equal to me for a while."

George weighed the bag with his hands. "I don't mind it," he said. "I don't notice it any more. It's just a part of me."

"You been so tired lately—kind of wore out," said Hazel. "If there was just some way we could make a little hole in the bottom of the bag, and just take out a few of them lead balls. Just a few."

"Two years in prison and two thousand dollars fine for every ball I took out," said George. "I don't call that a bargain."

"If you could just take a few out when you came home from work," said Hazel. "I mean—you don't compete with anybody around here. You just set around."

"If I tried to get away with it," said George, "then other people'd get away with it—and pretty soon we'd be right back to the dark ages again, with everybody competing against everybody else. You wouldn't like that, would you?"

"I'd hate it," said Hazel.

"There you are," said George. "The minute people start cheating on laws, what do you think happens to society?"

If Hazel hadn't been able to come up with an answer to this question, George couldn't have supplied one. A siren was going off in his head.

"Reckon it'd fall all apart," said Hazel.

"What would?" said George blankly.

"Society," said Hazel uncertainly. "Wasn't that what you just said?"

"Who knows?" said George.

The television program was suddenly interrupted for a news bulletin. It wasn't clear at first as to what the bulletin was about, since the announcer, like all announcers, had a serious speech impediment. For about half a minute, and in a state of high excitement, the announcer tried to say, "Ladies and gentlemen—"

He finally gave up, handed the bulletin to a ballerina to read.

"That's all right——" Hazel said of the announcer, "he tried. That's the big thing. He tried to do the best he could with what God gave him. He should get a nice raise for trying so hard."

"Ladies and gentlemen——" said the ballerina, reading the bulletin. She must have been extraordinarily beautiful, because the mask she wore was hideous. And it was easy to see that she was the strongest and most graceful of all the dancers, for her handicap bags were as big as those worn by two-hundred-pound men.

And she had to apologize at once for her voice, which was a very unfair voice for a woman to use. Her voice was a warm, luminous, timeless melody. "Excuse me——" she said, and she began again, making her voice absolutely uncompetitive.

"Harrison Bergeron, age fourteen," she said in a grackle squawk, "has just escaped from jail, where he was held on suspicion of plotting to overthrow the government. He is a genius and an athlete, is under-handicapped, and should be regarded as extremely dangerous."

A police photograph of Harrison Bergeron was flashed on the screen—upside down, then sideways, upside down again, then right side up. The picture showed the full length of Harrison against a background calibrated in feet and inches. He was exactly seven feet tall.

The rest of Harrison's appearance was Halloween and hardware. Nobody had ever borne heavier handicaps. He had outgrown hindrances faster than the H-G men could think them up. Instead of a little ear radio for a mental handicap, he wore a tremendous pair of earphones, and spectacles with thick wavy lenses. The spectacles were intended to make him not only half blind, but to give him whanging headaches besides.

Scrap metal was hung all over him. Ordinarily, there was a certain symmetry, a military neatness to the handicaps issued to strong people, but Harrison looked like a walking junkyard. In the race of life, Harrison carried three hundred pounds.

And to offset his good looks, the H-G men required that he wear at all times a red rubber ball for a nose, keep his eyebrows shaved off, and cover his even white teeth with black caps at snaggle-tooth random.

"If you see this boy," said the ballerina, "do not—I repeat, do not—try to reason with him."

There was the shriek of a door being torn from its hinges.

Screams and barking cries of consternation came from the television set. The photograph of Harrison Bergeron on the screen jumped again and again, as though dancing to the tune of an earthquake.

George Bergeron correctly identified the earthquake, and well he might have—for many was the time his own home had danced to the same crashing tune. "My God——" said George, "that must be Harrison!"

The realization was blasted from his mind instantly by the sound of an automobile collision in his head.

When George could open his eyes again, the photograph of Harrison was gone. A living, breathing Harrison filled the screen.

Clanking, clownish, and huge, Harrison stood in the center of the studio. The knob of the uprooted studio door was still in his hand. Ballerinas, technicians, musicians, and announcers cowered on their knees before him, expecting to die.

"I am the Emperor!" cried Harrison. "Do you hear? I am the Emperor! Everybody must do what I say at once!" He stamped his foot and the studio shook.

"Even as I stand here—" he bellowed, "crippled, hobbled, sickened—I am a greater ruler than any man who ever lived! Now watch me become what I *can* become!"

Harrison tore the straps of his handicap harness like wet tissue paper, tore straps guaranteed to support five thousand pounds.

Harrison's scrap-iron handicaps crashed to the floor.

Harrison thrust his thumbs under the bar of the padlock that secured his head harness. The bar snapped like celery. Harrison smashed his headphones and spectacles against the wall.

He flung away his rubber-ball nose, revealed a man that would have awed Thor, the god of thunder.

"I shall now select my Empress!" he said, looking down on the cowering people. "Let the first woman who dares rise to her feet claim her mate and her throne!"

A moment passed, and then a ballerina arose, swaying like a willow.

Harrison plucked the mental handicap from her ear, snapped off her physical handicaps with marvellous delicacy. Last of all, he removed her mask.

She was blindingly beautiful.

"Now—" said Harrison, taking her heand, "shall we show the people the meaning of the word dance? Music!" he commanded.

The musicians scrambled back into their chairs, and Harrison stripped them of their handicaps, too. "Play your best," he told them, "and I'll make you barons and dukes and earls."

The music began. It was normal at first—cheap, silly, false. But Harrison snatched two musicians from their chairs, waved them like batons as he sang the music as he wanted it played. He slammed them back into their chairs.

The music began again and was much improved.

Harrison and his Empress merely listened to the music for a while—listened gravely, as though synchronizing their heartbeats with it.

They shifted their weights to their toes.

Harrison placed his big hands on the girl's tiny waist, letting her sense the weightlessness that would soon be hers.

And then, in an explosion of joy and grace, into the air they sprang!

Not only were the laws of the land abandoned, but the law of gravity and the laws of motion as well.

They reeled, whirled, swiveled, flounced, capered, gamboled, and spun.

They leaped like deer on the moon.

The studio ceiling was thirty feet high, but each leap brought the dancers nearer to it.

It became their obvious intention to kiss the ceiling.

They kissed it.

And then, neutralizing gravity with love and pure will, they remained suspended in air inches below the ceiling, and they kissed each other for a long, long time.

It was then that Diana Moon Glampers, the Handicapper General, came into the studio with a double-barreled ten-gauge shotgun. She fired twice, and the Emperor and the Empress were dead before they hit the floor.

Diana Moon Glampers loaded the gun again. She aimed it at the musicians and told them they had ten seconds to get their handicaps back on.

It was then that the Bergerons' television tube burned out.

Hazel turned to comment about the blackout to George. But George had gone out into the kitchen for a can of beer.

George came back in with the beer, paused while a handicap signal shook him up. And then he sat down again. "You been crying?" he said to Hazel.

"Yup," she said.

"What about?" he said.

"I forget," she said. "Something real sad on television."

"What was it?" he said.

"It's all kind of mixed up in my mind," said Hazel.

"Forget sad things," said George.

"I always do," said Hazel.

"That's my girl," said George. He winced. There was the sound of a rivetting gun in his head.

"Gee—I could tell that one was a doozy," said Hazel.

"You can say that again," said George.

"Gee—" said Hazel, "I could tell that one was a doozy."

Non-Fiction

Female Circumcision: Rite of Passage or Violation of Rights?

Frances A. Althaus

Frances A. Althaus has spent her career researching and writing about women's reproductive rights and reproductive health. She is currently the editor of International Perspectives on Sexual and Reproductive Health, *a journal published by The Guttmacher Institute, an organization devoted to advancing sexual and reproductive health for men and women worldwide.*

Her essay on female circumcision first appeared in International Family Planning Perspectives *in 1997. In it, she discusses the health issues associated with the practice as well as the reasons for its continued practice in many equatorial African cultures. Althaus also outlines the efforts to eliminate this female initiation ceremonial practice through education and relief efforts.*

*Frances A. Althaus is senior editor of *International Family Planning Perspectives*. The author is grateful to Nahid Toubia and Rogaia Abusharaf for their generous help in preparation of the report and to Dara Carr, Jacqueline E. Darroch, Jeannie Rosoff, Renee Samara and Susheela Singh for helpful comments on an earlier version.

❦ ⎸F⎹emale circumcision, the partial or total cutting away of the external female genitalia, has been practiced for centuries in parts of Africa, generally as one element of a rite of passage preparing young girls for womanhood and marriage. Often performed without anesthetic under septic conditions by lay practitioners with little or no knowledge of human anatomy or medicine, female circumcision can cause death or permanent health problems as well as severe pain. Despite these grave risks, its practitioners look on it as an integral part of their cultural and ethnic identity, and some perceive it as a religious obligation.

Opponents of female genital cutting, however, emphasize that the practice is detrimental to women's health and well-being. Some consider female circumcision a ritualized form of child abuse and violence against women, a violation of human rights.

The debate over female circumcision is relatively recent. The practice was rarely spoken of in Africa and little known in the West until the second half of this century. In the 1950s and 1960s, however, African activists and medical practitioners brought the health consequences of female circumcision to the attention of international organizations such as the United Nations and the World Health Organization (WHO). Still, it was not until 1979 that any formal policy statement was made: A seminar organized by WHO in Khartoum to address traditional practices affecting the health of women and children issued recommendations that governments work to eliminate the practice.[1]

During the following decade, the widespread silence surrounding female circumcision was broken. After African women's organizations met in Dakar, Senegal, in 1984 to discuss female circumcision and other detrimental cultural practices, the Inter African Committee Against Harmful Traditional Practices (IAC) was formed. With national committees in more than 20 countries, the IAC has been important in bringing the harmful effects of female circumcision to the attention of African governments. In addition, other African women's networks and organizations that had focused primarily on such issues as reproductive health, women's rights and legal justice became involved in working against the practice. Such groups as Mandalaeo Ya Wanawake in Kenya, NOW in Nigeria and New Woman in Egypt now include the elimination of female circumcision among their goals.

In part because these groups brought fresh perspectives to the issue, the emphasis in discussions of female circumcision shifted to encompass women's human and reproductive rights as well as their health. International consensus statements and treaties such as the Convention to Eliminate All Forms of Discrimination Against Women, the Convention on the Rights of the Child and the African Charter on the Rights and Welfare of the Child began to include language applicable to female circumcision. These documents, however, did not directly mention the practice, focusing instead on broad categories such as detrimental practices, violence and rights violations.[2]

With shifts in emphasis came new language: Although activists and clinicians continued to refer to female circumcision when working directly with women in the community, policy statements and other documents began to use the term "female genital mutilation." That term was used in the first international document to specifically address the practice, the Programme of Action adopted by the International Conference on Population and Development in Cairo in 1994.[3] The Program refers to female genital mutilation as a "basic rights violation" and urges governments to "prohibit and urgently stop the practice . . . wherever it exists."

In the Platform of the Fourth World Conference on Women, held in Beijing in 1995, female genital mutilation was cited as both a threat to women's reproductive health and a violation of their human rights.[4] In addition to making general recommendations, the Platform specifically called on governments to "enact and enforce legislation against the perpetrators of practices and acts of violence against women, such as female genital mutilation. . . . " Notably, the drive to include language specifically condemning female genital mutilation in the Platform was led by Africans.

Against this background of activity and changing emphasis, the plight of Fauziya Kassindja, a 17-year-old woman from Togo, focused public attention in the United States on female circumcision. More important, her case was instrumental in redefining the practice as gender-based violence that could be grounds for the granting of political asylum.[5] Kassindja, who fled her homeland in October 1994 to avoid an arranged marriage and the genital cutting that would be part of the marriage rites, was placed in a detention center after arriving in the United States under a false passport and asking for asylum. She was released a year and a half later and granted asylum after intensive media coverage of her situation.

Prevalence

Female circumcision is currently practiced in at least 28 countries stretching across the center of Africa north of the equator; it is not found in southern Africa or in the Arabic-speaking nations of North Africa, with the exception

---

*Although female circumcision is often thought to be associated with Islam, it predated Islam in Africa. Neither the Koran, the primary source for Islamic law, nor the "hadith," collections of the sayings of the Prophet Mohammed, include a direct call for the practice (see: reference 6). According to these oral histories, when Mohammed was asked his opinion on female circumcision, he told his followes "to circumcise, but not to destroy (the clitoris), for not destroying would be better for the man and would make the woman's face glow." Islamic clerics are divided, however, with some actively supporting the practice and others opposing it.

of Egypt.[6] Female circumcision occurs among Muslims, Christians, animists and one Jewish sect, although no religion requires it.*

The availability of reliable figures on the prevalence of female circumcision has increased greatly in recent years: National data have now been collected in the Demographic and Health Survey (DHS) program for six countries—the Central African Republic, Côte d'Ivoire, Egypt, Eritrea, Mali and Sudan. In these countries, from 43% to 97% of reproductive-age women have been circumcised.[7] Within countries, prevalence may vary across ethnic groups; in Mali, for example, where the overall proportion of women who have undergone circumcision is 94%, only 17% of women of Tamachek ethnicity have been circumcised.

Estimates for other countries are generally based on local surveys or anecdotal information. The estimated proportion of women who have undergone circumcision in these countries ranges from 5% in Uganda and the Congo (formerly Zaire) to 98% in Djibouti and Somalia.[8] Both because of wide variations in prevalence across social and demographic subgroups and because of data limitations, these figures should be interpreted with caution.

Types of Circumcision

Although circumcision may be performed during infancy, during adolescence or even during a woman's first pregnancy, the procedure is usually carried out on girls between ages four and 12. In the countries for which DHS data are available, the median age at excision ranges from less than two months in Eritrea to about six years in Mali and almost 10 years in Egypt. The operation is generally performed by a traditional birth attendant or an *exciseuse*, an elder village woman.

There are three basic types of genital excision, although practices vary widely. In the first type, clitoridectomy, part or all of the clitoris is amputated, while in the second (often referred to as excision), both the clitoris and the labia minora are removed. Infibulation, the third type, is the most severe: After excision of the clitoris and the labia minora, the labia majora are cut or scraped away to create raw surfaces, which are held in contact until they heal, either by stitching the edges of the wound or by tying the legs together. As the wounds heal, scar tissue joins the labia and covers the urethra and most of the vaginal orifice, leaving an opening that may be as small as a matchstick for the passage of urine and menstrual blood.[9]

The overall proportion of women who have undergone each type of circumcision is not known, although clitoridectomy appears to be by far the most common procedure. It is estimated that about 15% of all circumcised women have been infibulated, although an estimated 80–90% of all circumcisions in Djibouti, Somalia and the Sudan are of this type.[10]

Consequences of Excision

In the conditions under which female circumcision is generally performed in Africa, even the less extensive types of genital cutting can lead to potentially fatal complications, such as hemorrhage, infection and shock. The inability to pass urine because of pain, swelling and inflammation following the operation may lead to urinary tract infection. A woman may suffer from abscesses and pain from damaged nerve endings long after the initial wound has healed.

Infibulation is particularly likely to cause long-term health problems. Because the urethral opening is covered, repeated urinary tract infections are common, and stones may form in the urethra and bladder because of obstruction and infection. If the opening is very small, menstrual flow may be blocked, leading to reproductive tract infections and lowered fertility or sterility. One early study estimated that 20–25% of cases of sterility in northern Sudan can be linked to infibulation.[11]

Without deinfibulation before childbirth, obstructed labor may occur, causing life-threatening complications for both mother and infant. Because birthrates are high in many countries where infibulation is practiced, a woman's infibulation scar may be cut and resewn many times during her reproductive years.

In addition, the amputation of the clitoris and other sensitive tissue reduces a woman's ability to experience sexual pleasure. For infibulated women, the consummation of marriage is likely to be painful because of the small vaginal opening and the lack of elasticity in the scar tissue that forms it. Tearing and bleeding may occur, or the infibulation scar may have to be cut open to allow penetration.

Infibulation may make intercourse unsatisfying for men as well as women: In a study of 300 polygynous Sudanese men, each of whom had one wife who had been infibulated and one or more who had not, 266 expressed a definite sexual preference for the uninfibulated wife; in addition, 60 said they had married a second, uninfibulated wife because of the penetration difficulties they experienced with their first wife, whose scarred vaginal opening became progressively more inelastic after each birth.[12] Under such conditions, marital dissolution may occur, especially if a woman's fertility is affected. In Sudan, for example, one study found that infibulated women are almost twice as likely as other women to have lower fertility and more than twice as likely to be divorced.[13] Thus, a practice that is justified as making girls marriageable and safeguarding their fertility may actually increase the risk of marital dissolution and subfertility.

Given the medical complications and related consequences of female circumcision, why does the practice continue? First, it is unclear how frequently such problems occur, for few data exist and those that are available come from small studies or are based on self-reports. Second, in societies in which few women remain uncircumcised, problems arising from female circumcision are likely to be seen as a normal part of a woman's life and may not even be associated with circumcision. The most important reasons, however, probably lie in the social and economic conditions of women's lives.

Social Context

Female circumcision is an integral part of the societies that practice it, where patriarchal authority and control of female sexuality and fertility are givens. In communities where a person's place in society is determined by lineage traced through fathers, female circumcision reduces the uncertainty surrounding paternity by discouraging or preventing women's sexual activity outside of marriage. Although the societies that practice circumcision vary in many ways, most girls receive little education and are valued primarily for their future role as sources of labor and producers of children. In some communities, the prospective husband's family pays a brideprice to the family of the bride, giving his family the right to her labor and her children; she herself has no right to or control over either.

A girl's virginity may be considered essential to her family's ability to arrange her marriage and receive a brideprice, as well as to family honor. In Somalia, for example, a prospective husband's family may have the right to inspect the bride's body prior to marriage, and mothers regularly check their infibulated daughters to ensure that they are still "closed."[14] In this context, parents see both infibulation and early marriage as means of ensuring that their daughter remains "pure" and thus worthy of the brideprice.

In many cultures, considerable social pressure is brought to bear on families who resist conforming to the tradition of female circumcision. In Man, a town in the interior of Côte d'Ivoire, a Yacouba girl who has not been circumcised is not considered marriageable.[15] Among the Samburu of Kenya, who consider uncircumcised girls unclean, promiscuous and immature, girls are generally circumcised at age 14 or 15, usually just before they are married. A girl with a younger brother may undergo circumcision if she remains unmarried by her late teens, since custom dictates that a boy with an uncircumcised older sister may not be initiated into the warrior class.[16]

Girls' desires to conform to peer norms may make them eager to undergo circumcision, since those who remain uncut may be teased and looked down on by their age mates. In addition, the ritual cutting is often embedded in ceremonies in which the girls are feted and showered with presents and their families are honored. A girl's wishes, in any case, are often irrelevant; it is her family—often the father or elder female relatives—who decide whether she will undergo circumcision. According to one Yacouba father, "[My daughter] has no choice. I decide. Her viewpoint is not important."[17]

Indeed, girls have very little choice. Given their age and their lack of education and resources, they are dependent on their parents, and later on their husband, for the basic necessities of life. Those who resist may be cut by force. If they remain uncircumcised and their families are therefore unable to arrange a marriage, they may be cast out without any means of subsistence.

Because of their lack of choice and the powerful influence of tradition, many girls accept circumcision as a necessary, and even natural, part of life, and adopt the rationales given for its existence. Of the five countries for which DHS data are available on women's opinions toward excision, the Central African Republic is the only one in which the majority favor discontinuation.[18] A variety of justifications are given by DHS respondents who favor continuation of the practice, including preservation of virginity before marriage, fidelity after marriage, enhancement of the husband's sexual pleasure, enhancement of fertility, prevention of infant and child mortality, cleanliness and religious requirements, but tradition is by far the most commonly mentioned reason.

As these data show, women themselves are involved in perpetuating the practice of female genital cutting. Data on the attitudes of men have been collected only in Eritrea and Sudan. DHS data for Eritrea show that men are slightly more likely than women to favor discontinuation, and that men who believe the practice should be stopped are about twice as likely as their female counterparts to cite medical complications and lack of sexual satisfaction as reasons.[19] In Sudan, a 1981 study found that men are somewhat more likely than women to believe female genital cutting should continue, but are less than half as likely as women to prefer infibulation.[20]

Working for Change

Efforts to eliminate female circumcision have often been unsuccessful because opponents of the practice ignored its social and economic context. In some cases, external intervention has strengthened the resolve of communities to continue their genital cutting rituals as a way of resisting what they perceive as cultural imperialism.

During the era of colonial rule in Africa, some governments attempted to ban female circumcision and met with resistance. In Sudan, when a law banning infibulation was about to be proclaimed in 1946, many parents rushed to midwives to have their daughters infibulated in case it should become impossible later on. When some midwives were arrested for performing circumcision, anticolonial protests broke out. The British colonial government, fearing a massive nationalist revolt such as those that had occurred in Egypt and Kenya, eventually let the law go unenforced.[21]

More recently, calls to action by Western feminists and human rights activists have provoked similar negative reactions. African women have perceived many of these efforts as condescending and derogatory toward their culture. In the words of one infibulated Somali woman, "If Somali women change, it will be a change done by us, among us. When they order us to stop, tell us what we must do, it is offensive to the black person or the Muslim person who believes in circumcision. To advise is good, but not to order."[22]

In many Western publications dealing with female circumcision, one anthropologist observes, "African women are . . . depicted as aberrant, while intact Western women have their sexuality affirmed as the norm."[23] Yet, as Nahid Toubia points out, Western women also subject themselves to medically unnecessary, hazardous procedures, such as cosmetic surgery and the insertion of breast implants, to increase their sexual desirability.[24]

The strong reactions against depictions of cultures practicing female circumcision as savage, violent and abusive of women and children have led to new ways of approaching the issue. Some international organizations working against the practice are supporting local activist groups with funding, training and technical expertise rather than choosing direct involvement. Numerous projects have been mounted to eliminate female circumcision, although none have included rigorous evaluations to determine their success. The following approaches are typical:

- *Community education.* A nationwide study conducted in 1985–1986 by the National Association of Nigerian Nurses and Midwives found that female circumcision was practiced in all states and that in five of the then 11 states at least 90% of the women had been cut. In response to this information, the organization designed an eradication campaign with support from Population Action International and the Program for Appropriate Technology in Health. The project trained health workers to teach individuals about the harmful effects of female circumcision and to work through religious organizations, women's organizations and social clubs to mobilize communities against the practice.[25]

- *Alternative rituals.* The organization Maendeleo Ya Wanawake carried out a pilot project in the Meru district of Kenya in 1996 to develop an alternative initiation ritual. Some 25 mother-daughter pairs participated in a six-day training session that included information on the consequences of female circumcision and how to defend the decision not to be cut. The session culminated in a coming-of-age celebration planned by the community, excluding circumcision but including gifts and special T-shirts for the initiates, skits, and "books of wisdom" prepared by the parents of each girl.[26]

- *Drama.* In Burkina Faso, the director of a local theater group developed a play, based on the experience of his niece, on the consequences of female circumcision; the play is aimed particularly at men. A grant from the Research Action and Information Network for Bodily Integrity of Women (RAINBO) enabled him to videotape the play and show it throughout the region.[27]

Prospects for the Future

The available data provide little evidence that the practice of female circumcision will decline substantially in the near future. The Central African Republic, where prevalence is moderate, is the only country in which steady decline seems to be occurring. Young women in Côte d'Ivoire, Egypt, Eritrea and Mali appear to be no less likely than older women to have undergone circumcision. In Sudan, the sole country for which longitudinal comparisons can be made, prevalence appears to have declined slightly, from 96% to 89%, between the 1978–1979 Sudan Fertility Survey and the 1989–1990 Sudan DHS.[28] Nevertheless, the DHS data do not indicate any differences between younger and older women.

Despite the overall lack of change in the percentages of girls who undergo circumcision, changes in attitudes and practices seem to be occurring in some countries. In Eritrea, for example, women and men younger than 25 are much more likely than those in their 40s to believe that the tradition should be discontinued. In Sudan, where the great majority of women have traditionally been infibulated, there appears to be a small shift toward clitoridectomy.[29]

Given the lack of enforcement of most laws against female circumcision, it is unclear whether a purely legal approach is effective in itself. While legislation may be enforceable in countries where only a small minority adhere to the practice, that is unlikely to be the case when the majority follow the tradition. As Toubia points out, "Clear policy declarations by government and professional bodies are essential to send a strong message of disapproval, but if the majority of the society is still convinced that female genital mutilation serves the common good, legal sanctions that incriminate practitioners and families may be counterproductive."[30] In such countries, she suggests, public information campaigns and counseling of families about the effects of the practice on children may be more useful.

Substantial change is likely to occur only with improvements in the status of women in society. According to Rogaia Abusharaf, "To get married and have children, which on the surface fulfills gender expectations and the reproductive potential of females, is, in reality, a survival strategy in a society plagued with poverty, disease, and illiteracy. . . . The socioeconomic dependency of women on men affects their response to female circumcision."[31]

This view is born out by the DHS data: In most countries, women with higher levels of education and those who have income of their own are less likely than other women to have been circumcised and are also less likely to have had their daughters circumcised. As Toubia comments, "this one violation of women's rights cannot [be abolished] without placing it firmly within the context of efforts to address the social and economic injustice women face the world over. If women are to be considered as equal and responsible members of society, no aspect of their physical, psychological or sexual integrity can be compromised."[32]

References

1. World Health Organization (WHO), Khartoum Seminar on Traditional Practices Affecting the Health of Women and Children, Khartoum, Sudan, 1979.

2. Organization of African Unity, African Charter on the Rights and Welfare of the Child, 1990, Article 24(3).

3. United Nations (UN), *Report of the International Conference on Population and Development*, New York, 1994.

4. UN, *Report of the Fourth World Conference on Women, New York, 1995.*

5. C.W. Dugger, "A Refugee's Body Is Intact but Her Family Is Torn," *New York Times*, Sept. 11, 1996, pp. A1, B6–B7.

6. N. Toubia, *Female Genital Mutilation: A Call for Global Action*, RAINBO, New York, 1995.

7. R. Ndamobissi, G. Mboup and E. O. Nguélébé, *Enquéte Demographique et de Santé, République Centrafricaine, 1994–95*, Direction des Statistiques Démographiques et Sociales, Bangui, Central African Republic, and Macro International, Calverton, Md., USA, 1995; N'Cho Sombo et al., *Euquéte Demographique et de Santé, Côle d'Ivoire, 1994*, Institut National de la Statistique, Abidjan, Côte d'Ivoire and Macro International, Calverton, Md., USA, 1995; F. EI-Zanaty et al., *Egypt Demographic and Health Survey 1995*, National Population Council, Cairo, and Macro International, Calverton, Md., USA, 1996; *Eritrea Demographic and Health Survey*, National Statistics Office, Asmara, Eritrea, and Macro International, Calverton, Md., USA, 1997;S. Coulibaly et al., *Enquète Demographique et de Santé, Mali, 1995–1996*, Direction Nationale de la Statistique et de I'Informatique, Bamako, Mali, and Macro International, Calverton, Md., USA, 1996; and *Sudan Demographic and Health Survey, 1989/1990*, Ministry of Economic and National Planning. Khartoum, Sudan, and Macro International, Calverton, Md., USA, 1991.

8. N. Toubia, 1995, op. cit. (see reference 6).

9. WHO, *Female Genital Mutilation: Report of a WHO Technical Working Group*, Geneva, 1996.

10. Ibid.

11. A.Z. Mustafa, "Female Circumcision and Infibulation in the Sudan," *Journal of Obstetrics and Gynaccology of the British Commonwealth*, 73:302–306, 1966.

12. A.A. Shandall, "Circumcision and Infibulation of Females," *Sudan Medical Journal*, 5:178–212, 1967.

13. D. Balk, "Marriage and Fertility in Northeast Africa What Role Does Female 'Circumcision' Play?" unpublished manuscript, 1997.

14. A. Warsame, "Social and Cultural Implications of Infibulation in Somalia," in *Female Circumcision: Strategies to Bring About Change*, Proceedings of the International Seminar on Female Circumcision, Italian Association for Women in Development, Rome, 1989; and V.L. Barnes and J. Boddy, *Aman: The Story of a Somali Girl*, Knopf, Toronto, 1994.

15. C.W. Dugger, "African Ritual Pain: Genital Cutting," *New York Times*, Oct. 5, 1996, pp. AI & A6.

16. J.C. McKinley, Jr., "At a Ceremony in Kenya, a Brother and Sister Painfully Enter Adulthood," *New York Times*, Oct. 5, 1996, p. A6.

17. C.W. Dugger, 1996, op. cit. (see reference 15).

18. R. Ndamobissi, G. Mboup and E. O. Nguélébé, 1995, op. cit. (see reference 7).

19. *Eritrea Demographic and Health Survey, 1997*, op. cit. (see reference 7).

20. E.-H. Kheir, S. Kumar and A. R. Cross, "Female Circumcision: Attitudes and Practices in Sudan," in *Proceedings of the Demographic and Health Surveys World Conference, Washington, D.C., 1991*, Vol. 3, Columbia, Md., USA, 1991, pp. 1697–1717; and A. El Dareer, *Woman, Why Do You Weep?* Zed Books, London, 1982.

21. J. Boddy, personal communication, May 26, 1997.

22. V.L. Barnes and J. Boddy, 1994, op. cit. (see reference 14).

23. J. Boddy, "Violence Embodied? Female Circumcision, Gender Politics, and Cultural Aesthetics," in R. Dobash and R. Dobash, eds., *Rethinking Violence Against Women*, Sage, Thousand Oaks, Calif. (in press).

24. N. Toubia, 1995, op. cit. (see reference 6).

25. S. Babalola and C. Adebajo, "Evaluation Report of Female Circumcision Eradication Project in Nigeria," paper presented at the annual meeting of the American Public Health Association, New York, Nov. 18, 1996.

26. S. Rich and S. Joyce, "Eradicating Female Genital Mutilation: Lessons for Donors," occasional paper, Wallace Global Fund, Washington, D.C., 1997.

27. Ibid.

28. E.-H. Kheir, S. Kumar and A. R. Cross, 1991, op. cit. (see reference 20).

29. Ibid.

30. N. Toubia, 1995, op. cit. (see reference 6), p. 45.

31. R. M. Abusharaf, "Rethinking Feminist Discourses on Female Genital Mutilation: The Case of Sudan," *Canadian Woman Studies*, 15:52–54, 1995.

32. N. Toubia, 1995, op. cit. (see reference 6).

Correction

In "Knowledge and Attitudes About Emergency Contraception Among Health Workers in Ho Chi Minh City, Vietnam" [23:68–72], by Nguyen Thi Nhu Ngoc et al., the proportions of medical doctors and nurses or midwives who participated in the focus-group discussions (p. 69) were reversed: Approximately one-third of participants were doctors, and slightly fewer than two-thirds were nurses or midwives.

The Making, and Unmaking, of a Child Soldier

Ishmael Beah

One boy's tortuous entanglement in an African civil war.

Ishmael Beah (pronounced BAY-a) was born on November 23, 1980 in Mattru Jong, Sierra Leone, and, at the age of 12, was captured by and forcibly conscripted into The Republic of Sierra Leone Armed Forces as part of the Sierra Leonean government's strategy to defeat the Revolutionary United Front (RUF). A Long Way Gone: Memoirs of a Boy Soldier, from which "The Making, and Unmaking, of a Child Soldier" is adapted, recounts Beah's experiences as a child soldier in the brutal Sierra Leonean Civil War (1991-2002) when, as he says, he was turned into a mindless killer who slaughtered "too many people to count." Child soldiers on both sides of the conflict were given drugs as part of the training—or brainwashing—that led these children to the murder, rape, torture, and brutal amputation of thousands of Sierra Leoneans.

According to Beah's account, he was released to UNICEF three years after his recruitment by the government army. Beah was adopted by an uncle, with whom he briefly lived in Freetown, Sierra Leone. When, however, the capital city was overrun by competing military forces, Beah contacted Laura Simms, whom he had met the year before, and she helped bring him to the United States, where he attended Oberlin College in Oberlin, Ohio.

Some controversy, brought about by journalistic accounts that question the time frame and events found in Beah's story, surrounds A Long Way Gone. Beah stands by his account, however, and his supporters have cited his youth and drug addiction, along with the trauma he experienced while in the Sierra Leonean government army, as explanations for any inaccuracies in Beah's Memoirs. Defenders as well as critics, however, recognize the importance of Beah's work, both as a writer and a human rights advocate, in that he has drawn attention to the plight of children in war-torn countries, where forced conscription continues. Likewise, Beah's personal recovery continues, 14 years after his brief life as a child soldier ended. As he says, "If I choose to feel guilty for what I have done, I will want to be dead myself. I live knowing that I have been given a second life, and I just try to have fun, and be happy and live it the best I can." Now living in Brooklyn, New York, Beah works for the Human Rights Watch Children's Division Advisory Committee.

"Sometimes I feel that living in New York City, having a good family and friends, and just being alive" is a dream, that perhaps this second life of mine isn't really happening. Whenever I speak at the United Nations, Unicef or elsewhere to raise awareness of the continual and rampant recruitment of children in wars around the world, I come to realize that I still do not fully understand how I could have possibly survived the civil war in my country, Sierra Leone.

Most of my friends, after meeting the woman whom I think of as my new mother, a Brooklyn-born white Jewish-American, assume that I was either adopted at a very young age or that my mother married an African man. They would never imagine that I was 17 when I came to live with her and that I had been a child soldier and participated in one of the most brutal wars in recent history.

In early 1993, when I was 12, I was separated from my family as the Sierra Leone civil war, which began two years earlier, came into my life. The rebel army, known as the Revolutionary United Front (R.U.F.), attacked my town in the southern part of the country. I ran away, along paths and roads that were littered with dead bodies, some mutilated in ways so horrible that looking at them left a permanent scar on my memory. I ran for days, weeks and months, and I couldn't believe that the simple and precious world I had known, where nights were celebrated with storytelling and dancing and mornings greeted with the singing of birds and cock crows, was now a place where only guns spoke and sometimes it seemed even the sun hesitated to shine. After I discovered that my parents and two brothers had been killed, I felt even more lost and worthless in a world that had become pregnant with fear and suspicion as neighbor turned against neighbor and child against parent. Surviving each passing minute was nothing short of a miracle.

After almost a year of running, I, along with some friends I met along the way, arrived at an army base in the southeastern region. We thought we were now safe; little did we know what lay ahead.

1994: The First Battle

I have never been so afraid to go anywhere in my life as I was that first day. As we walked into the arms of the forest, tears began to form in my eyes, but I struggled to hide them and gripped my gun for comfort. We exhaled quietly, afraid that our own breathing could cause our deaths. The lieutenant led the line that I was in. He raised his fist in the air, and we stopped moving. Then he slowly brought it down, and we sat on one heel, our eyes surveying the forest. We began to move swiftly among the bushes until we came to the edge of a swamp, where we formed an ambush, aiming our guns into the bog. We lay flat on our stomachs and waited. I was lying next to my friend Josiah. At 11, he was even younger than I was. Musa, a friend my age, 13, was also nearby. I looked around to see if I could catch their eyes, but they were concentrating on the invisible target in the swamp. The tops of my eyes began to ache, and the pain slowly rose up to my head. My ears became warm, and tears were running down my cheeks, even though I wasn't crying. The veins on my arms stood out, and I could feel them pulsating as if they had begun to breathe of their own accord. We waited in the quiet, as hunters do. The silence tormented me.

The short trees in the swamp began to shake as the rebels made their way through them. They weren't yet visible, but the lieutenant had passed the word down through a whisper that was relayed like a row of falling dominos: "Fire on my command." As we watched, a group of men dressed in civilian clothes emerged from under the tiny bushes. They waved their hands, and more fighters came out. Some were boys, as young as we were. They sat together in line, waving their hands, discussing a strategy. My lieutenant ordered a rocket-propelled grenade (RPG) to be fired, but the commander of the rebels heard it as it whooshed its way out of the forest. "Retreat!" he called out to his men, and the grenade's blast got only a few rebels, whose split bodies flew in the air. The explosion was followed by an exchange of gunfire from both sides.

I lay there with my gun pointed in front of me, unable to shoot. My index finger became numb. I felt as if the forest had turned upside down and I was going to fall off, so I clutched the base of a tree with one hand. I couldn't think, but I could hear the sounds of the guns far away in the distance and the cries of people dying in pain. A splash of blood hit my face. In my reverie I had opened my mouth a bit, so I tasted some of the blood. As I spat it out and wiped it off my face, I saw the soldier it had come from. Blood poured out of the bullet holes in him like water rushing through newly opened tributaries. His eyes were wide open; he still held his gun. My eyes were fixed on him when I heard Josiah screaming for his mother in the most painfully piercing voice I had ever heard. It vibrated inside my head to the point that I felt my brain had shaken loose from its anchor.

I searched for Josiah. An RPG had tossed his tiny body off the ground, and he had landed on a tree stump. He wiggled his legs as his cry gradually came to an end. There was blood everywhere. It seemed as if bullets were falling into the forest from all angles. I crawled to Josiah and looked into his eyes. There were tears in them, and his lips were shaking, but he couldn't speak. As I watched him, the water in his eyes was replaced with blood that quickly turned his brown eyes red. He reached for my shoulder as if to pull himself up. But midway, he stopped moving. The gunshots faded in my head, and it was as if my heart had stopped and the whole world had come to a standstill. I covered his eyes with my fingers and lifted him from the tree stump. His backbone had been shattered. I placed him flat on the ground and picked up my gun. I didn't realize that I had stood up to take Josiah off the tree stump. I felt someone tugging at my foot. It was the corporal; he was saying something that I couldn't understand. His mouth moved, and he looked terrified. He pulled me down, and as I hit the ground, I felt my brain shaking in my skull again, and my deafness gave way.

"Get down," he was screaming. "Shoot," he said, as he crawled away from me to resume his position. As I looked to where he lay, my eyes caught Musa, whose head was covered with blood. His hands looked too relaxed. I turned toward the swamp, where there were gunmen running, trying to cross over. My face, my hands, my shirt and my gun were drenched in blood. I raised my gun and pulled the trigger, and I killed a man. Suddenly all the death I had seen since the day I was touched by war began flashing in my head. Every time I stopped shooting to change magazines and saw my two lifeless friends, I angrily pointed my gun into the swamp and killed more people. I shot everything that moved, until we were ordered to retreat because we needed another plan.

We took the guns and ammunition off the bodies of my friends and left them there in the forest, which had taken on a life of its own, as if it had trapped the souls that had departed from the dead. The branches of the trees seemed to be holding hands and bowing their heads in prayer. In the swamp, crabs had already begun feasting on the eyes of the dead. Limbs and frag-mented skulls lay on top of the bog, and the water in the swamp was stagnant with blood. I was not afraid of these lifeless bodies. I despised them and kicked them to flip them and take their guns. I found a G3 and some ammu-nition. I noticed that most of the dead gunmen and boys wore lots of jewelry on their necks and wrists.

We arrived in the village, our base, with nightfall and sat against the walls of houses. It was quiet, and perhaps afraid of the silence, we began cleaning the blood off our guns, oiling their chambers, and shooting them into the air to test their effectiveness. I went for supper that night but was unable to eat. I only drank water and felt nothing. I lay on my back in the tent with my AK-47 on my chest and the G3 I had taken from a dead rebel leaning on the peg of the tent. Nothing happened in my head. It was a void, and I stared at the roof of the tent until I was miraculously able to doze off. I had a dream that I was picking up Josiah from the tree stump and a gunman stood on top of me. He placed his gun against my forehead. I immediately woke up from my dream and began shooting inside the tent, until the 30 rounds in the magazine were finished. The corporal and the lieutenant came in afterward and took me outside. I was sweating, and they threw water on my face and gave me a few white capsules. They were the same capsules that we'd all been given before we had gone into battle, and to this day, I do not know what they contained. I stayed up all night and couldn't sleep for days. We went out two more times that week, and I had no problem shooting my gun.

Rebel Raids

After that first week of going out on raids to kill people we deemed our rebel enemies or sympathizers of the rebels, our initiation was complete. We stayed put at the base, and we boys took turns guarding posts around the village. We smoked marijuana and sniffed "brown brown," cocaine mixed with gunpowder, which was always spread out on a table near the ammunition hut, and of course I took more of the white capsules, as I had become addicted to them. The first time I took all these drugs at the same time, I began to perspire so much that I took off all my clothes. My body shook, my sight became blurred and I lost my hearing for several minutes. I walked around the village restlessly. But after several doses of these drugs, all I felt was numbness to everything and so much energy that I couldn't sleep for weeks. We watched war movies at night, Rambo "First Blood," "Rambo, First Blood, Part II," "Commando" and so on, with the aid of a generator or a car battery. We all wanted to be like Rambo; we couldn't wait to implement his techniques.

When we ran out of supplies, we raided rebel camps in towns, villages and forests. "We have good news from our informants" the lieutenant would announce. "We are moving out in five minutes to kill some rebels and take their supplies, which really belong to us." He often made speeches about how we were defending our country, how honorable we were. At these times, I would stand holding my gun and feeling special because I was part of something that took me seriously and I was not running from anyone anymore. The lieutenant's face evinced confidence; his smiles disappeared before they were completed. We would tie our heads with the green cloths that distinguished us from the rebels, and we boys would lead the way. There were no maps and no questions asked. We were simply told to follow the path until we received instructions on what to do next. We walked for long hours and stopped only to eat sardines and corned beef with gari, sniff brown brown and take more white capsules. The combination of these drugs made us fierce. The idea of death didn't cross my mind, and killing had become as easy as drinking water. After that first killing, my mind had stopped making remorseful records, or so it seemed.

Before we got to a rebel camp, we would deviate from the path and walk in the forest. Once the camp was in sight, we would surround it and wait for the lieutenant's command. The rebels roamed about; some sat against walls, dozing off, and others, boys as young as we, stood at guard posts passing around marijuana. Whenever I looked at rebels during raids, my entire body shook with fury; they were the people who had shot my friends and family. So when the lieutenant gave orders, I shot as many as I could, but I didn't feel better. After every gunfight, we would enter the rebel camp, killing those we had wounded. We would then search the houses and gather gallons of gasoline, enormous amounts of marijuana and cocaine, bales of clothes, watches, rice, salt, gari and many other things. We rounded up any civilians—men, women, boys and young girls—hiding in the huts and houses and made them carry our loot back to the base. We shot them if they tried to run away.

On one of these raids, we captured a few rebels after a long gunfight and a lot of civilian casualties. We undressed the prisoners and tied their arms behind their backs until their chests were tight as drums. "Where did you get all this ammunition from?" the corporal asked one of the prisoners, a man with an almost dreadlocked beard. He spat in the corporal's face, and the corporal immediately shot him in the head at close range. He fell to the ground, and blood slowly leaked out of his head. We cheered in admiration of the corporal's action and saluted him as he walked by. Suddenly, a rebel hiding in the bushes shot one of our boys. We dispersed around the village in search of the shooter. When the young muscular rebel was captured, the lieutenant slit his neck with his bayonet. The rebel ran before he fell to the ground and stopped moving. We cheered again, raising our guns in the air, shouting and whistling.

During that time, a lot of things were done with no reason or explanation. Sometimes we were asked to leave for war in the middle of a movie. We would come back hours later after killing many people and continue the movie as if we had just returned from intermission. We were always either on the front lines, watching a war movie or doing drugs. There was no time to be alone or to think. When we conversed with one another, we talked only about the movies and how impressed we were with the way either the lieutenant, the corporal or one of us had killed someone. It was as if nothing else existed.

The villages that we captured and turned into our bases as we went along and the forests that we slept in became my home. My squad was my family, my gun was my provider and protector and my rule was to kill or be killed. The extent of my thoughts didn't go much beyond that. We had been fighting for more than two years, and killing had become a daily activity. I felt no pity for anyone. My childhood had gone by without my knowing, and it seemed as if my heart had frozen. I knew that day and night came and went because of the presence of the moon and the sun, but I had no idea whether it was a Sunday or a Friday.

Taken From the Front

In my head my life was normal. But everything began to change in January 1996. I was 15.

One morning that month, a truck came to the village where we were based. Four men dressed in clean blue jeans and white T-shirts that said "Unicef" in big blue letters jumped out. They were shown to the lieutenant's house. It seemed as if he had been expecting them. As they sat talking on the veranda, we watched them from under the mango tree, where we sat cleaning our guns. Soon all the boys were told to line up for the lieutenant who selected a few of us and asked the adult soldiers to take away our guns and ammunition. A bunch of boys, including my friend Alhaji and me, were ushered to the truck. I stared back at the veranda where the lieutenant now stood, looking in the other direction, toward the forest, his hands crossed behind his back. I still didn't know exactly what was going on, but I was beginning to get angry and anxious. Why had the lieutenant decided to give us up to these civilians? We thought that we were part of the war until the end.

We were on the road for hours. I had gotten used to always moving and hadn't sat in one place idly for a long time. It was night when the truck stopped at a center, where there were other boys whose appearances, red eyes and somber faces resembled ours. Alhaji and I looked at this group, and he asked the boys who they were. A boy who was sitting on the stoop angrily said: "We fought for the R.U.F.; the army is the enemy. We fought for freedom, and the army killed my family and destroyed my village. I will kill any of those army bastards every time I get a chance to do so." The boy took off his shirt to fight, and on his arm was the R.U.F. brand. Mambu, one of the boys on our side, shouted, "They are rebels," and reached for his bayonet, which he had hidden in his army shorts; most of us had hidden either a knife or a grenade before our guns were taken from us. Before Mambu could grab his weapon, the R.U.F. boy punched him in the face. He fell, and when he got up, his nose was bleeding. The rebel boys drew out the few bayonets they had in their shorts and rushed toward us. It was war all over again. Perhaps the naïve men who had taken us to the center thought that removing us from the war would lessen our hatred for the R.U.F. It hadn't crossed their minds that a change of environment wouldn't immediately make us normal boys; we were dangerous, brainwashed to kill.

One boy grabbed my neck from behind. He was squeezing for the kill, and I couldn't use my bayonet effectively, so I elbowed him with all my might until he let go. He was holding his stomach when I turned around and stabbed him in his foot. The bayonet stuck, so I pulled it out with force. He fell, and I began kicking him in the face. As I went to deliver the final blow with my bayonet, someone came from behind me and sliced my hand with his knife. It was a rebel boy, and he was about to kick me down when he fell on his face. Alhaji had stabbed him in the back. He pulled the knife out, and we started kicking the boy until he stopped moving. I wasn't sure whether he was unconscious or dead. I didn't care. No one screamed or cried during the fight. After all, we had been doing such things for years and were all still on drugs.

We continued to stab and slice one another until a bunch of MPs came running through the gate toward the fight. The MPs fired a few rounds into the air to get us to stop, but we were still fighting, so they had to part us by force. They placed some of us at gunpoint and kicked others apart. Six people were killed: two on our side and four on the rebel side.

As MPs stood guard to make sure we didn't start another fight, we, the army boys, went to the kitchen to look for food. We ate and chatted about the fight. Mambu told us that he had plucked an eye out of the head of one of the R.U.F. boys, and that the boy ran to punch him, but he couldn't see, so he ran into the wall, banging his head hard and fainting. We laughed and picked up Mambu, raising him in the air. We needed the violence to cheer us after a whole day of boring travel and contemplation about why our superiors had let us go.

That night we were moved to a rehabilitation center called Benin Home. Benin Home was run by a local NGO called Children Associated With the War, in Kissy neighborhood, on the eastern outskirts of Freetown, the capital. This time, the MPs made sure to search us thoroughly before we entered. The blood of our victims and enemies was fresh on our arms and clothes. My lieutenant's words still echoed in my head: "From now on, we kill any rebel we see, no prisoners." I smiled a bit, happy that we had taken care of the rebel boys, but I also began to wonder again: Why had we been taken here? I walked up and down on the veranda, restless in my new environment. My head began to hurt.

Relearning Boyhood

It was infuriating to be told what to do by civilians. Their voices, even when they called us for breakfast, enraged me so much that I would punch the wall, my locker or anything nearby. A few days earlier, we could have decided whether they would live or die.

We refused to do anything that we were asked to do, except eat. At the end of every meal, the staff members and nurses came to talk to us about attending the scheduled medical checkups and the one-on-one counseling sessions that we hated at the minihospital that was part of Benin Home. As soon as the live-in staff, mostly men, started telling us what to do, we would throw bowls, spoons, food and benches at them. We would chase them out of the dining hall and beat them. One afternoon, after we had chased off several staff members, we placed a bucket over the cook's head and pushed him around the kitchen until he burned his hand on a boiling pot and agreed to put more milk in our tea. During that same week, the drugs were wearing off. I craved cocaine and marijuana so badly that I would roll a plain sheet of paper and smoke it. Sometimes I searched the pockets of my army shorts, which I still wore, for crumbs of marijuana or cocaine. We broke into the minihospital and stole some painkillers—white tablets and off-white—and red and yellow capsules. We emptied the capsules, ground the tablets and mixed them together. But the mixture didn't give us the effect we wanted. We got more upset day by day and, as a result, resorted to more violence. We began to fight one another day and night. We would fight for hours for no reason at all. At first the staff would intervene, but after a while they just let us go. They couldn't really stop us, and perhaps they thought that we would get this out of our systems. During these fights, we destroyed most of the furniture and threw the mattresses out in the yard. We would stop to wipe the blood off our lips, arms and legs only when the bell rang for mealtime.

It had been more than a month, and some of us had almost gone through the withdrawal stage, even though there were still instances of vomiting and collapsing at unexpected moments. These outbreaks ended, for most of us, at the end of the second month. But we now had time to think; the fastened mantle of our war memories slowly began to open. We resorted to more violence to avoid summoning thoughts of our recent lives.

Whenever I turned on the faucet, all I could see was blood gushing out. I would stare at it until it looked like water before drinking or taking a shower. Boys sometimes ran out of the hall screaming, "The rebels are coming." Other times, the younger ones sat weeping and telling us that nearby rocks were their dead families.

It took several months before I began to relearn how to sleep without the aid of medicine. But even when I was finally able to fall asleep, I would start awake less than an hour later. I would dream that a faceless gunman had tied me up and begun to slit my throat with the zigzag edge of his bayonet. I would feel the pain that the knife inflicted as the man sawed my neck. I'd wake up sweating and throwing punches in the air. I would run outside to the middle of the soccer field, sit on a stone and rock back and forth, my arms wrapped around my legs. I would try desperately to think about my childhood, but I couldn't. The fighting memories seemed to have formed a barrier that I had to break in order to think about any moment before the war. On those mornings, I would feel one of the staff members wrap a blanket around me, saying: "This isn't your fault, you know. It really isn't. You'll get through this." He would then pull me up and walk me back to the hall.

Past and Present

One day after I'd been in Benin Home for more than three months, I was sent to the minihospital for a checkup. The nurse on duty was named Esther. I had met her once before when I was sent to the minihospital after cutting my hand punching a window. Esther wore a white uniform and a white hat. Her white teeth contrasted with her dark, shiny skin, and when she smiled, her face glowed. She was tall and had big brown eyes that were kind and inviting. She must have been about 30, which I thought was too old.

That day, before Esther examined me, she gave me a present, a Walkman and a Run-DMC tape. I used to listen to rap music a lot before the war and loved it because of its poetic use of words. I put the headphones on and didn't mind being examined because the song had taken hold of me, and I listened closely to every word. But when she began examining my legs and saw the nasty scars on my left shin, she took my headphones off and asked, "How did you get these scars?"

"Bullet wounds," I casually replied.

Her face filled with sorrow, and her voice was shaking when she spoke: "You have to tell me what happened so I can prescribe treatment." At first I was reluctant, but she said she would be able to treat me effectively only if I told her what happened, especially about how my bullet wounds were treated. So I told her the whole story not because I really wanted to but because I thought that if I told her some of the truth of my war years, she would be afraid of me and would cease asking questions. She listened attentively when I began to talk:

During the second dry season of my war years, we were low on food and ammunition. So as usual, we decided to attack another village, which was a three-day walk away. We left our base that evening, stopping once a day to eat, drink and take drugs. Each of us had two guns, one strapped to our backs, the other held in our hands. On the evening of the third day, the village was in sight.

Surrounding it, we waited for the lieutenant's command. As we lay in ambush, we began to realize that the place was empty. We were beginning to suspect that something was amiss when a shot was fired from behind us. It was clear now: *we* were being ambushed. We ended up in a fight that lasted more than 24 hours. We lost several men and boys. When we finally seemed to have captured the village, we began to look around for anything we could find. I was filling my backpack with ammunition from a hut when bullets began to rain on the village again. I was hit three times in my left shin. The first two bullets went in and out, and the last one stayed inside. I couldn't walk, so I lay on the ground and released an entire round of the magazine into the bush where the bullets had come from. I remember feeling a tingle in my spine, but I was too drugged to really feel the pain, even though my leg had begun to swell. The sergeant doctor in my squad dragged me into one of the houses and tried to remove the bullet. Each time he raised his hands from my wound, I saw my blood all over his fingers. My eyes began to grow heavy, and I fainted.

I do not know what happened, but when I woke the next day, I felt as if I had nails hammered into the bones of my shin and my veins were being chiseled. I felt so much pain that I was unable to cry out loud; tears just fell from my eyes. The ceiling of the thatched-roof house where I was lying on a bed was blurry. My eyes struggled to become familiar with my surroundings. The gunfire had ceased and the village was quiet, so I assumed that the attackers had been successfully driven away. I felt a brief relief for that, but the pain in my leg returned. I tucked my lips in, closed my heavy eyelids and held tight to the edges of the wooden bed. I heard the footsteps of people entering the house. They stood by my bed, and as soon as they began to speak, I recognized their voices.

"The boy is suffering, and we have no medicine here to lessen his pain. Everything is at our former base." The sergeant doctor sighed and continued. "It will take six days to send someone to get the medicine and return. He will die from the pain by then."

"We have to send him to the former base, then," I heard my lieutenant saying. "We need those provisions from that base, anyway. Do all you can to make sure that the boy stays alive," he said and walked out. "Yes, sir," the sergeant doctor said. I slowly opened my eyes, and this time I could see clearly. I looked at his sweaty face and tried to smile a little. After having heard what they said, I swore to myself that I would fight hard and do anything for my squad after my leg was healed.

"We will get you some help," the sergeant doctor said gently, sitting by my bed and examining my leg. "Just be strong, young man,"

"Yes, sir," I said, and tried to raise my hand to salute him, but he tenderly brought my arm down.

Two soldiers came into the house, took me off the bed, placed me in a hammock and carried me outside. The treetops of the village began to spin around as they carried me out. The journey felt as if it took a month. I fainted and awoke many times, and each time I opened my eyes, it seemed as if the voices of those who carried me were fading into the distance.

Finally we got to the base, and the sergeant doctor, who had come along, went to work on me. I was injected with something. I was given cocaine, which I frantically demanded. The doctor started operating on me before the drugs took effect. The other soldiers held my hands and stuffed a cloth into my mouth. The doctor stuck a crooked-looking scissorslike tool inside my wound and fished for the bullet. I could feel the edge of the metal inside me. My entire body was racked with pain.

Just when I thought I had had enough, the doctor abruptly pulled the bullet out. A piercing pain rushed up my spine from my waist to the back of my neck. I fainted.

When I regained consciousness, it was the morning of the next day, and the drugs had kicked in. I reached my hands down to my leg and felt the bandage before I stood up and limped outside, where some soldiers and the sergeant were sitting. "Where is my weapon?" I asked them. The sergeant handed me my G3, and I began cleaning it. I shot a couple of rounds sitting against a wall, ignoring the bandage on my leg and everyone else. I smoked marijuana, ate and snorted cocaine and brown brown. That was all I did for a few days before we went back to the new base we had captured. When we left, we threw kerosene on the thatched-roof houses, lighted them with matches and fired a couple of RPGs into the walls. We always destroyed the bases we abandoned so that rebel squads wouldn't be able to use them. Two soldiers carried me in the hammock, but this time I had my gun, and I looked left and right as we traveled the forest path.

At the new base, I stayed put for three weeks. Then one day, we heard that a rebel group was on its way to attack our village. I tightened the bandage around my shin, picked up my gun and followed my squad to ambush them. We killed most of the attackers and captured a few whom we brought back to base. "These are the men responsible for the bullet holes in your leg. It's time to make sure they never shoot at you or your comrades." The lieutenant pointed at the prisoners. I was not sure if one of the captives was the shooter, but any captive would do at that time. They were all lined up, six of them, with their hands tied. I shot them in their shins and watched them suffer for an entire day before finally deciding to shoot them in the head so that they would stop crying. Before I shot each man, I looked at him and saw how his eyes gave up hope and steadied before I pulled the trigger. I found their somber eyes irritating.

❧

When I finished telling Esther the story, she had tears in her eyes, and she couldn't decide whether to rub my head, a traditional gesture indicating that things would be well, or hug me. In the end she did neither but said: "None of what happened was your fault. You were just a little boy, and anytime you want to tell me anything, I am here to listen." She stared at me, trying to catch my eye so she could assure me of what she had just said. I became angry and regretted that I had told someone, a civilian, about my experience. I hated the "It is not your fault" line that all the staff members said every time anyone spoke about the war.

I got up, and as I started walking out of the hospital, Esther said, "I will arrange a full checkup for you." She paused and then continued: "Let me keep the Walkman. You don't want the others to envy you and steal it. I will be here every day, so you can come and listen to it anytime." I threw the Walkman at her and left, putting my fingers in my ears so I couldn't hear her say, "It is not your fault."

After that, whenever Esther would see me around, she'd smile and ask me how I was doing. At first I detested her intrusions. But slowly I came to appreciate them, even looked forward to them. It was like this at the center; most boys found a staff member whom they eventually began to trust. Mine was Esther.

Over the next few months, I started to visit Esther occasionally at the minihospital, which was just across the dirt road from the dorm that I shared with more than 35 boys. During that time, Esther got me to tell her some of my dreams. She would just listen and sit quietly with me. If she wanted to say anything, she would first ask, "Would you like me to say something about your dream?" Mostly I would say no and ask for the Walkman.

One day Esther gave me a Bob Marley tape and a really nice notebook and pen and suggested that I use them to write the lyrics of the songs and that we could learn them together. After that I visited Esther at the minihospital every day, to show her what I had written. I would sing her the parts of songs I had memorized. Memorizing lyrics left me little time to think about what happened in the war. As I grew comfortable with Esther, I talked to her mainly about Bob Marley's lyrics and Run-DMC's too. She mostly listened.

One night, close to my fifth month at the center, I fell asleep while reading the lyrics of a song. I startled awake after having a dream that involved lots of people stabbing and shooting one another, and I felt all their pain. The room I stood in filled with their blood. In the dream, I then went outside to sit at dinner with my father, mother and two brothers. They didn't seem to notice that I was covered with blood.

It was the first time I dreamed of my family since I started running away from the war. The next afternoon I went to see Esther, and she could tell that something was bothering me. "Do you want to lie down?" she asked, almost whispering.

"I had this dream last night," I said looking away. "I don't know what to make of it."

She came and sat next to me and asked, "Would you like to tell me about it?" I didn't reply.

"Or just talk about it out loud and pretend I am not here. I won't say anything. Only if you ask me." She sat quietly beside me. The quietness lasted for a while, and for some reason I began to tell her my dream.

At first she just listened to me, and then gradually she started asking questions to make me talk about the lives I had lived before and during the war. "None of these things are your fault," she said, as she had repeated sternly at the end of every conversation. Even though I had heard that phrase from every staff member—and had always hated it—I began that day to believe it. That didn't make me immune to the guilt that I felt for what I had done. But it somehow lightened my burdensome memories and gave me strength to think about things. The more I spoke about my experiences to Esther, the more I began to cringe at the gruesome details, even though I didn't let her know that. I still didn't completely trust her. I only liked talking to her because I felt that she didn't judge me for what I had been a part of; she looked at me with the inviting eyes and welcoming smile that said I was still a child.

One day during my fifth month at Benin Home, I was sitting on a rock behind the classrooms when Esther came by. She sat next to me without uttering a word. She had my lyrics notebook in her hand. "I feel as if there is nothing left for me to be alive for," I said slowly. "I have no family, it is just me. No one will be able to tell stories about my childhood." I sniffled a bit.

Esther put her arms around me and pulled me closer to her. She shook me to get my full attention before she started. "Think of me as your family, your sister."

"But I didn't have a sister," I replied.

"Well, now you do," she said. "You see, this is the beauty of starting a new family. You can have different kinds of family members." She looked at me directly, waiting for me to say something.

"O.K., you can be my sister—temporarily." I emphasized the last word.

"That is fine with me. So will you come to see your temporary sister tomorrow, please?" She covered her face as if she would be sad if I said no.

"O.K., O.K., no need to be sad," I said, and we both laughed a bit.

Rejoining the Civilian World

Soon after, a group of visitors from the European Union, the United Nations, Unicef and several NGOs arrived at the center in a convoy of cars. At the request of the staff, we boys had prepared a talent show for them. I read a monologue from "Julius Caesar" and performed a short hip-hop play about the redemption of a former child soldier that I had written with Esther's encouragement. After that event, the head of the center asked me to be the spokesman for Benin Home and to speak about my experiences.

I was at the beginning of my seventh month at Benin Home when one of the field agents, Leslie, came to tell me that he was responsible for "repatriating" me—the term used to describe the process of reuniting ex-child soldiers with their former communities. My family was dead, but I knew that my father had a brother whom I had never met who lived somewhere in Freetown. Leslie said he would try to find him, and if he couldn't, he'd find me a foster family to live with.

One Saturday afternoon about two weeks later, as I chatted with Esther at the minihospital, Leslie walked in, smiling widely. "What is the good news?" Esther asked. Leslie examined my curious face, then walked back to the door and opened it. A tall man walked in.

"This is your uncle," Leslie proudly announced.

The man walked over to where I was sitting. He bent over and embraced me long and hard. My arms hung loose at my sides.

What if he is just some man pretending to be my uncle? I thought. The man let go of me. He was crying, which is when I began to believe that he was really my family, because men in Sierra Leone rarely cried.

He crouched on his heels next to me and began: "I am sorry I never came to see you all those years. I wish I had met you before today. But we can't go back now. We just have to start from here. I am sorry for your losses." He looked at Leslie and continued: "After you are done here, you can come and live with me and my family. You are my son. I don't have much, but I will give you a place to sleep, food and my love." He put his arms around me.

No one had called me "son" in a very long time. I didn't know what to say. Everyone, it seemed, was waiting for my response. I turned to my uncle, smiled at him and said: "Thank you for coming to see me. I really appreciate that you have offered me to stay with you. But I don't even know you." I put my head down.

"As I said, we cannot go back," he replied, rubbing my head and laughing a little. "But we can start from here. I am your family, and that is enough for us to begin liking each other."

I got up and hugged my uncle, and he embraced me harder than he had the first time and kissed me on my forehead. We briefly stood in silence before he began to speak again. "I will visit you every weekend. And if it is O.K., I would like you to come home with me at some point, to see where I live and to meet my wife and children—your family." My uncle's voice trembled; he was trying to hold back sobs. He rubbed my head with one hand and shook Leslie's hand with the other.

As my uncle promised, he came to visit every weekend. We would take long walks together, and they gave me a chance to get to know him. He told me about what my father was like when he was a child, and I told him about my childhood. I needed to talk about those good times before the war. But the more I heard and talked about my father, the more I missed my mother and brothers too.

About a month or so later at Benin Home, Leslie told me it was time for me to go live with my uncle. I was happy, but I was also worried about living with a family. I had been on my own for years and had taken care of myself without any guidance from anyone. If I distanced myself from the family, I was afraid that I might look ungrateful to my uncle, who didn't have to take me in; I was worried about what would happen when my nightmares took hold of me. How was I going to explain my sadness, which I was unable to hide when it took over my face, to my new family, especially the children?

I lay in my bed night after night staring at the ceiling and thinking, Why have I survived the war? Why was I the last person in my immediate family to be alive? I went to see Esther every day, though, and would say hello, ask how she was and then get lost in my own head thinking about what life was going to be like after the center. At night, I sat quietly on the veranda with my friends. I wouldn't notice when they left the bench that we all sat on.

When the day of my repatriation finally came, I walked to the minihospital building where I was to wait, my heart beating very fast. My friends Alhaji and Mambu and a boy named Mohamed were sitting on the front steps, and Esther emerged, smiling. Leslie sat in a nearby van waiting to take me to my new home.

"I have to go," I said to everyone, my voice shaking. I extended my hand to Mohamed, but instead of shaking it, he leapt up and hugged me. Mambu embraced me while Mohamed was still holding me. He squeezed me hard, as if he knew it was goodbye forever. (After I left the center, Mambu's family refused to take him in, and he ended up back on the front lines.) At the end of the hug, Alhaji shook hands with me. We squeezed each other's hands and stared into each other's eyes, remembering all that we had been through. I never saw him again, since he continually moved from one foster home to another. Esther stepped forward, her eyes watery. She hugged me tighter than she ever had. I didn't return her hug very well, as I was busy trying to hold back my tears. After she let go, she gave me a piece of paper. "This is my address," she said. "Come by anytime."

I went to Esther's home several weeks after that. But my timing wasn't good. She was on her way to work. She hugged me, and this time I squeezed back; this made her laugh after we stood apart. She looked me straight in the eyes. "Come and see me next weekend so we can have more time to catch up, O.K.?" she said. She was wearing her white uniform and was on her way to take on other traumatized children. It must be tough living with so many war stories. I was living with just one, mine, and it was difficult. Why does she do it? Why do they all do it? I thought as we went our separate ways. It was the last time I saw her. I loved her but never told her.

Three Victims of Terrorism

Benazir Bhutto

Benazir Bhutto, born June 21, 1953 in Karachi, Pakistan, was not only Pakistan's first female Prime Minister but also the first woman to lead a modern Islamic nation. Bhutto had no plans to be a politician, although she certainly had the bloodlines to do so. Her father, Shaheed Zulfikar Ali Bhutto, was Pakistan's first popularly elected Prime Minister, and her mother, Nusrat Bhutto, had served as a Member of Parliament and had, at one time, been Pakistan's Deputy Prime Minister. Benazir Bhutto became active in politics after her father was ousted from office in a 1977 military coup; he was later executed. After these traumatic events, Bhutto overcame strong opposition to lead the Pakistan Peoples Party to victory in two separate parliamentary elections in 1988 and 1993. In 1998, after both her regimes were dismissed illegally, Bhutto went into self-imposed exile in Dubai. She returned to Pakistan in October of 2007, when then-President Pervez Musharraf granted her amnesty. Barely two months later, on December 27, 2007, Bhutto was assassinated. She was buried alongside her father.

In "Three Victims of Terrorism," Bhutto condemns the Sept. 11, 2001 Al-Qaeda attacks in New York, Pennsylvania, and Washington, DC, asserting that the hijackings victimized innocents in the United States, the image of Islam itself, and the cause of democracy. Such outspoken criticism of both Al-Qaeda and the Taliban, along with her active pursuit of democracy in Pakistan, earned her the reputation among those terrorist groups as a pawn of the United States in the Muslim world. Likewise, it garnered her the overwhelming support of her people, the title of "the world's most popular politician," and the respect of human rights activist throughout the international community. In 2008, Bhutto was posthumously awarded the prestigious United Nations Prize in the Field of Human Rights.

Three Victims of Terrorism

October 4, 2002

I return to America one year after the terrorist assaults. The catastrophe that struck America on September 11th, 2001 continues to reverberate across the globe. Its impact ripples emotionally, morally, politically and economically.

I see three primary victims of the Al-Qaeda murders of that day. Of course and above all, the victims are the 3025 innocent people and their families in New York, Washington and Pennsylvania, and others like Danny Pearl who have been struck down directly by hate. Added to them are the hapless citizens of Afghanistan caught in a war forced on them by the forces of Al-Qaeda and the Taliban. Second, I see as a victim the image of Islam around the world, which was distorted by extremists who do not speak for one billion Muslims around the world.

And finally, I see as a victim . . . democracy, which is being sacrificed for expediency in my homeland of Pakistan, and in other areas of this planet.

The world is a very different place from what we had dreamed in those wonderful moments when the Berlin Wall fell and the Cold War ended.

The era of peace for which we prayed, became a time of war.

Civility was replaced with brutality.

Tolerance was replaced by terrorism.

Democracy in Pakistan is threatened with dictatorship.

This is a difficult, extraordinary and very dangerous time.

The war against international terrorism, triggered by the catastrophe of September 11th, 2001 is in a new, ambiguous and difficult phase. The senseless execution of Wall Street Journal Bureau Chief Daniel Pearl underscored the treacherous lack of ground rules of these terrorist warriors.

The reality of suicide bombings has struck my homeland—Christian churches, Muslim Mosques, urban hotels, foreign consulates and western journalists are all targets, and scores have been brutally murdered.

Simultaneously, the nuclear-armed nations of Pakistan and India stand perilously close to war, once again over the disputed province of Jammu and Kashmir.

And in Pakistan, a military dictatorship once again rules with an iron fist, crushing dialogue, debate and democracy.

This is not the way we had hoped and expected the new millennium to begin, but life has its own plan. It is our task to address the new realities, and find opportunity in the phase of tragedy.

At the outset, I wish once again to express my condolences to the people of this Nation on the savage attacks against you. As it has been made very clear over the last year, the vast majority of the people of Pakistan join with me in expressing our grief and sorrow to you.

Ladies and gentlemen, it is difficult to shake the haunting image of the Twin Towers and three thousand innocent victims, collapsing under the weight of hate. It is an image that shapes everything that has come after it—politically, emotionally and morally.

My commitment to freedom was nourished here in this land of hope and opportunity. Your nation—and its dream—is a beacon for all men and women denied human dignity across the world.

At this time of continuing crisis, the American people and American leaders must understand those who would use violence and terror in the name of Islam.

They are men of the bomb, not men of the Book.

According to Islamic teaching, "Whenever the Apostle of God sent forth a detachment, he said to it: 'Do not cheat or commit treachery, nor should you mutilate or kill children, women or old men." And there is a specific prohibition in Islamic law that bans "killing by stealth and targeting a defenseless victim in a way intended to cause terror in society."

Ladies and gentlemen, it thus further grieves me that included in the list of innocent victims of the perfidy of September 11th is the image of Islam across the world.

Our religion is not only committed to tolerance and equality, but it is committed by Koranic definition, to the principles of democracy. It is ironic that despite the strong commitment to democracy, most Muslims are living in dictatorships. The Muslim people want freedom, they need support in their search for empowerment. Much as the people of the Communist world were, so too the Muslim people are hostages in Authoritarian regimes that flourished during the days of the Cold War.

In the west, you often talk about the so-called "Muslim Street." But there is a Muslim street that western governments don't seem to see.

It is a silent street of women who are discriminated against in every aspect of life.

It is a silent street of students who are not educated.

It is a silent street of businessmen and women who are not allowed to compete.

It is a silent street of human rights activists who are jailed.

It is a silent street of political parties who are decimated.

It is a silent street of political leaders who are now political prisoners or exiles.

It is the street of the people, constrained by the authoritarian powers of the state.

It is the street of the future in the chains of the powers of ignorance, intolerance and dictatorship.

And it is a street far more likely to explode than the street of the marginal religious extremists.

In Islam, dictatorship is never condoned. Nor is cruelty ever condoned.

According to Islam, those who commit cruel acts are condemned to destruction.

Irrespective of the ignorance often demonstrated to our faith by some, and the political manipulation and distortion often shamefully practiced by fanatics, there are several key concepts that play a substantive role in the development of democracy in Islam. These include three principle of consultation known as *shura*, consensus known as *ijma* and independent judgment known as *ijtihaad*.

In this the twenty first century, the Muslim people search for freedoms that exist in other parts of the world. They search for a society that is representative and accountable and which they determine for themselves. Too few are the Muslim Nations where people are truly free.

While Christians and Jews have the Bible to guide them, the Muslims have the Holy Koran to seek guidance from. The Koran teaches that the principal operations of the democratic process—consultation between the elected officials and the people through ijma is are fundamental to Islam.

Islam teaches that Islamic society is contingent on—"mutual advise through mutual discussions on an equal footing."

The terrorists who attack America are not fighting for Islam, they are fighting for themselves. Their goal is to establish linked and intertwined theocracies of ignorance that they can control and manipulate for their own political ends.

Terrorism and fanaticism will fail unless we fall into the psychopaths' trap. Professor Samuel Huntington of Harvard wrote of an inevitable clash of civilization between the West and the Islamic world. Ladies and gentlemen, this clash is far from inevitable, unless we make it so.

There are many similarities between Islam and the Judeo-Christian traditions. These three great religions were born in the cradle of the Middle East. The word "Muslim" actually means those who follow the Prophets Moses, Jesus and Mohammad.

This is why the British, during their rule of Muslim countries, referred to the Muslims as Mohammadans. According to Islamic belief, all humanity is descended from Adam and Eve. Islam agrees that paradise ended when Eve tempted Adam with the forbidden fruit.

In the Holy Book, Abraham is our father. He built the holiest place of the Muslims known as the Kaaba, the House of God, in Saudi Arabia, with his son Ismail from whom the Muslims believe they are descended.

After building the Kaaba, God asked Abraham what he wanted as a reward. Abraham replied that many Prophets should be born to my family.

Muslims believe that Christians and Jews are descended from Isaac while they are descended from the brother of Isaac namely Ismail. But we are all the sons and daughters of Abraham.

Muslims accept the Prophets of Judaism and Christianity as their own Prophets. They accept the Holy Books of the Jews and the Christians as their own Holy Books believing that the messages of God were sent through generations through different Prophets to show humanity the path of redemption and that Mohammad was the last Prophet sent by God.

The Holy Koran has a chapter on Mary, the Mother of Jesus, whose Arabic name is Maryam. As in Christianity, the Koran speaks of the miraculous birth of Jesus and of his healing powers. It quotes the infant Jesus saying in his cradle, "God commanded me to pray and to give alms so long as I live, and to cherish my Mother". Muslims believe that paradise lies at the feet of the Mother.

The Christian King of Abyssinia, Negus, gave refuge to the Muslims believing that only a slim line separated them from Christians. When the Prophet Mohammad fled Mecca, he was given refuge by the Jews of Medina. So too did Muslims give refuse to the Jews when they were persecuted in Europe. Muslims believe that Jews, Christians and Muslims are one people who are *Able e Kitaab* that is who have religious books containing the message sent by God through his Prophets.

Contrary to what the fanatics preach, Islam preaches the importance of knowledge. The very first word of the Koran is "Read" while the Prophet of Islam exhorted his followers to go far and wide in search of knowledge and education.

Many of the teachings of Islam are similar to Judaism and Christianity. Islam says;

Do not commit adultery;

Do not cheat;

Do not kill your children for fear of poverty;

Do not lie;

Do not spy;

Do not speak ill of anyone;

Do not drink alcohol;

Do not gamble;

Do not hate or envy each other.

Like other great religions, Islam is a moral compass for its followers that gives faith and hope and offers a path for the redemption of the soul on the day of Judgment.

Ladies and Gentlemen,

September 11 will go down in history as a defining moment in our civilization. The attack on the World Trade Towers was a second Pearl Harbor that ended one period in time and heralded the beginning of another.

On that fateful day, the world tumbled out of a time when Communism was the threat, the fear, the bloc that was to be contained. The world tumbled into a different period when Islam and the Muslim Nations seemingly replaced

Communism as the new threat, the new fear and the new world that was to be contained.

In the one year since the world shook with the shock of America the invincible attacked, much has changed. Civil liberties suffered a set back. Many Muslims in America live in terror of being hauled up on suspicion and taken away. Muslims face hate crimes. Individual choice is now constrained. Many Muslims shaved their beards and changed their attire to avoid hate crimes. Hate breeds hate. And the hate of Osama and his men created hate in many otherwise generous hearts towards Muslims.

Now security rather than fundamental rights are the new messages of a new era. Many Americans seem willing to sacrifice constitutional civil rights and civil liberties to live in security.

The World Trade Center attacks shook the west and it also shook the Muslim world. Almost every Muslim country joined the war against terror. They sympathized with America and the American people.

Many Muslims wonder why, given their solidarity with America, and their condemnation of Osama and his men, they are viewed with suspicion. The reality is that racial profiling points the finger of suspicion at Muslims. Muslims have suffered for the actions of Osama and Al Qeda as a community.

This is the time to distinguish between those who commit crimes in the name of religion and those who belong to a community that wishes to live in peace and harmony with other religions. It would be a tragedy if suspicion towards Muslims led to a backlash that created a clash of civilizations.

Osama and his cohorts use commercial airliners as bombs against cities creating a new global chessboard.

All Nineteen of the hijackers that hit the world trade center were Arabs. That Arab countries could have produced men who could launch such an attack makes them the center of scrutiny in the twenty-first century. Whether one likes it or not, for the coming decades the Muslims in general and the Arab Nations in particular, will be watched and contained as carefully as were the Communist countries in the days of the Cold War.

This has triggered a growing siege mentality within the Muslim world and a change is clearly discernable since that fateful day one year back. Then the Muslim world rallied round the United States as it led the War Against Terror. Now many in the Muslim world are moving away from the new objectives set by the United States as part of the War Against Terror.

One year ago the Iraqi regime of President Saddam was isolated. Today it has rejoined the Arab World in a Summit held earlier this year in Lebanon. At the summit, embraces have replaced distances.

Although President Bush has repeatedly stated that his goal is to pre-empt danger to the world community through regime change in Iraq, most in the Muslim world remain unconvinced. Many see an attack on Iraq presaging a wider attack against an array of Muslim countries including Iran, Yemen, Somalia, Sudan, Saudi Arabia, Egypt and eventually Pakistan.

Today the intellectual opinion in the Muslim and Non-Muslim world may be on a collision course. Many intellectuals in the United States see the Arab/Muslim countries as failed Nations that gave birth to evil men who could plan the cold blooded murder of three thousand innocents in New York and Washington.

And although most Muslim intellectuals condemn the attacks on the World Trade Center, they believe that unaddressed political problems provided the atmosphere for evil to be born and that a more peaceful world can thrive only when the unsolved political issues are resolved.

America emerged stronger from the day of tragedy when airliners crashed into skyscrapers. It united as a Nation and rallied round the flag remembering the dead and sharing the sorrow as well as the determination never to let it happen again. Many Americans asked: "Why did they do this?" or "Why do they hate us so much".

President Bush provided the leadership that could give comfort to the American people when they were attacked and fears of fresh attacks proliferated. The huge military response as well as the domestic measures saved the American people from further attacks. Washington is determined to keep up its guard and Muslim countries everywhere pray it succeeds. Muslims know that an attack by fanatics could easily increase their own vulnerability.

Yet a military response is only part of the solution.

Some American leaders recognize this. President Carter's National Security Advisor Mr. Brezinsky is quoted to have said, "lurking behind every terrorist act is a specific political antecedent".

There is no grievance that could justify the senseless killing of innocent people. No religion permits such senseless killing. Those who planned the September 11 events were evil. The concern is that the evil of some men now threatens to taint otherwise good men and women within the Muslim world unless there is an agreement that terrorism knows no religion, no sect, no people, no culture and no civilization.

The United States is a great country that invokes great admiration in much of the Muslim world. At this time of trial, the American people could remember that the Muslim people are with them in condemning the events of September 11. A safer world can come about through greater understanding, greater freedoms, greater attention to resolving conflicts through political means.

The bombing of Afghanistan and the continuing violence in the Middle East and Kashmir impacts upon the people in the street. No one knows when the masses can become a mob. So far demonstrations in the Muslim world remained few and far between. Most Muslims recognized that America was wrongly targeted and it had a right to self defense, to pursuing the criminals that planned the bombings and trained and harbored the terrorists. The concern is that with a broader conflict within the Muslim world, mob fury could develop focusing on foreign targets.

The attack on the American Embassy in Iran during the time of Ayotullah Khomeni when American hostages were taken is an example. The burning of the American Embassy in Islamabad under General Zia is another. Fanatics would love nothings better than to provoke a clash of civilizations venting itself on western targets.

Today America is the world's sole superpower. Its military power is awesome. Frankly it has little need of any other country in planning an action or taking a measure to defend itself and the security of its people. The rest of the world must acquiesce, in practical terms, whether it agrees.

The American President Woodrow Wilson promoted the concept of collective security and the principle of self-determination. The war against terror is a righteous cause. One year later, the need to prevent it turning into a clash of cultures, civilizations and religions is as righteous.

Ladies and Gentlemen: During my tenure in office, Pakistan became one of the ten emerging capital markets of the world. Billions of dollars in investment flowed in creating trade, business, jobs and fuelling the housing sector as well as the financial markets.

It was a remarkable transformation of a society. It was a transformation that our underprivileged wanted.

It was a transformation that helped the poverty stricken people of my land giving them hope and opportunity. It was a transformation that helped women and children, government staff and labourers, traders and farmers, youth and intellectuals. It was a transformation that attacked ignorance and illiteracy and injustice. It was a transformation that was bringing Pakistan into the modern era as a model to all one billion Muslims around the world of what moderate, enlightened Islam could accomplish for its people.

And thus to the fanatics and the extremists, we became the enemy, the threat, and the obstacle. To Islam at the crossroads, a modern Pakistan was one fork in the road, fanaticism and ignorance the other.

My government was making progress in relations with India and with containing terrorism in Afghanistan and Pakistan. But moderation and progress is not what the Army hard-liners and religious extremists could tolerate. I was their threat, and I was eliminated. I am afraid, ladies and gentlemen, that the consequences continue to ripple across Asia.

Ladies and gentlemen, sometimes tragedy can lead to resurrection of hope and spirit. Sometimes disaster requires us to examine routes, policies and unheeded warnings.

In our governments' combined and admirable zeal to defeat the Soviets, we did not plan or work for a post-war Afghanistan built on democratic and Islamic principles of coalition, consensus and cooperation.

The fundamental mistake, which contributed to a long-term historical calamity, was that we were not consistently committed to the values of freedom, democracy and self-determination that ultimately undermine and belie the basic tenets of terrorism. America must not repeat that mistake again.

Just as democracies do not make war, democracies also do not sponsor international terrorism. The Party that I am proud to lead supports the decision of the government of Pakistan to join the US led alliance against the forces of terror. Each Muslim country joined the war against terror.

America need not coddle dictators to promote its own interests. America's interest is democracy, not tyranny. In Pakistan those of us who are committed to human rights and democracy abhor terrorism in all of its murderous forms. At this time of political crisis in Pakistan, with a military dictatorship strangling our Constitution, the United States could be standing with the people of Pakistan in their search for empowerment.

Let us remember that building a moderate, stable and democratic political structure in Afghanistan would have marginalized the Taliban and the Osamas of this world well before they had unleashed their war against the people of Afghanistan and the people of the United States.

The goal of US policy must always be to simultaneously promote stability and to strengthen democratic values. The military dictatorship of Pakistan was unable to prevent Al Qaeda regrouping in Pakistan. Al Qaeda poses a threat to the Pakistani people and the larger world community. The military regime has a vested interest in the continuation of the Al Qaeda threat. It believes it can continue with its dictatorship so long as the world community is searching for Osama, for Mullah Omar and for other leaders of that organization.

Osama Bin Laden's right hand man, Abu Zubayda, was arrested by the FBI from a house in Punjab. Al Jazeera television interviewed two most wanted Al Qaeda terrorists Khalid Shaikh and Bin Shibli in Karachi this August. Moreover, a farce is being expensively conducted in Pakistan in the name of elections. Forty percent of the real representatives of the people are prevented from contesting the elections. The stage is set for a dummy parliament again at the expense of the poverty stricken people of Pakistan.

Huge funds, including $100 million dollars from a pension fund, disappeared with the regime covering up the tracks. The state offers deals and does deals with the corrupt with a view to frame the innocent. In one case of corruption filed by my government against the corrupt, the persons were given safe passage in exchange for committing perjury against the PPP leadership. Such offers were made to many others.

Judicial orders are written by the regime and announced by the court. In my husband's case, a court was kept waiting until nine p.m. at night as the order was re-written against my husband.

One Judge resigned publicly saying he was not prepared to lie which is what the regime asked him to do. Other judges lack this courage. One lawyer was wrongly sentenced for six months for criticizing a judgment in my election tribunal matter. In the rest of the world, justice is guarded by the watchdog of public opinions.

In Islamabad there are no watch dogs. Only the hungry hounds that wail for the blood of the people of the country impoverishing them with their tyrannical rule.

The military regime staged an unconstitutional referendum to rubber-stamp its dictatorship for five years that opened Pakistan to ridicule throughout the world. Five percent turnout, no voting lists, no fixed polling stations, pictures of eight year olds voting.

It unilaterally and brazenly amended the constitution itself unlimited dictatorial power for the next five years. Powers that only Ayotullah Khomeni and Mullah Omar previously invested themselves with in Iran and Afghanistan.

He ruled by dictate that only college graduates can sit in the National Assembly, thereby disenfranchising 99% of the people of our great country. By such edicts, Harry S. Truman could not have become President of the United States because he did not attend college.

Retroactive decrees were issued to prohibit me from contesting the October parliamentary elections that observers and analysts universally predicted I would handily win.

Why does this military dictatorship so fear this woman?

I recall the words of Stalin when he mocked the power of ideas by asking, "how many divisions does the Pope have?"

Years later it would be a Polish priest and human rights organizations and democrats all over this planet that brought down the Soviet Union not by the strength of their arms, but by the strength of their ideals.

The Generals have a huge army.

They have nuclear tipped missiles.

They have thousands of tanks.

But ladies and gentlemen, they know that I have something far more powerful than their legions.

I have the people of Pakistan. The men and women of our rural villages. The middle-class businessmen and businesswomen in our cities. The students and faculty in our universities. The workers of organized labor. The poor farmer in the field. The honest soldier on the front line guarding his country.

The democratic forces of Pakistan which I lead are like Robert Kennedy described when he confronted the power of apartheid in South Africa in

1966 —"tiny ripples of hope" coalescing together in a huge tidal wave that will bring down oppression and tyranny.

The Generals exploit the war on terrorism to protect their dictatorship. Like their military predecessor, they use Pakistan's critical importance to the United States in Afghanistan as a smokescreen for dictatorship.

Human Rights Watch this September called upon President Bush to "make it clear that US support for Pakistan because of its role in the anti-terrorism effort does not give the military leadership a blank check to abuse human rights and undermine democratic processes." It also said that "By undermining democratic institutions and restricting channels for political activity, Musharraf only helps the extremists in Pakistan."

How many more September 11ths, how many more Danny Pearls, before we all come to realize that the greatest protection of freedom from terrorists is replacing dictatorships with governments responsible to the people, governments based on the values of democracy and liberty?

The stakes are high. The long-term implications are great. Democracies don't start wars, just as they don't promote and protect international terrorism. Dictators start wars and coddle terrorists, because they are not accountable, they do not need a popular mandate behind their policies.

Democracies, which operate under pluralistic and public constraints, must provide for the public welfare, must provide social services, and must provide education, health and housing. Dictatorships need not. They are free to divert their resources to military schemes and international destabilization.

Parliamentary elections in Pakistan are scheduled next month. The US and its allies must insure that these elections not only take place, but that they are free, fair and open to all parties and candidates.

I should not be here today, I should be free to campaign in the villages and towns of my country. But I am stopped from doing so by special laws passed by decree without sanction of the constitution of my country. The military regime's October farce must not be allowed to stand.

The Generals are putting hopes on a different course. They are betting that the White House is so distracted by the war on terror and the violence in the Middle East and South Asia that it will backburner the cause of democracy. Maybe they are right. But if Pakistan's nuclear-armed military dictatorship is allowed to exploit the war on international terror to legitimize its own domestic reign of terror and illegitimate power, the consequences of 911 will build like a tidal wave through the young century.

Let us recall John Kennedy's warning in his Inaugural Address over forty years ago: "He who rides the back of the tiger, usually winds up inside."

A democratic Pakistan is the world's best guarantee of the triumph of moderation and modernity among one billion Muslims at the crossroads of our history.

The best and only control for the excesses of extremism, is accountability to the people. It is for this we pray in Afghanistan. It is for this we pray in Pakistan. It is for this we pray all over the world.

In my father's last letter to me before he was murdered by one of Pakistan's many military tyrants, he quoted Tennyson:

"Ah, what shall I be at fifty if I find the world so bitter at 25."

Looking at the victims of the terrorist attack—those thousands murdered, the image of the Islamic people hurt, the forces of democracy set back a generation, it is tempting to be bitter. We must all resist this temptation. We must be strong but never bitter.

Life is at times difficult. But history teaches us that ultimately we shall prevail, because victory belongs to the forces of truth and justice.

Thank you ladies and gentlemen.

The Four Noble Truths

Gautama Buddha

Gautama Buddha (ca. 623 BCE–543 BCE), a spiritual teacher, was born Siddhartha Gautama in Lumbini, which is situated on modern Nepal near the borders of modern India; he is also known as Shakyamuni Buddha. Born a prince of the Sakya kingdom, he became "the Buddha" (literally Enlightened One *or* Awakened One*) after embarking on a quest for spiritual meaning. Buddhists do not consider Siddhartha Gautama to be the only buddha, since a buddha is anyone who realizes the dharma (highest truth). However, he is universally recognised by Buddhists as the Supreme Buddha of our age. The Four Noble Truths—*dukkha, samudaya, nirodha, *and* magga—*are taught in Buddhism as the fundamental insight or enlightenment of Gautama Buddha, which led to the formulation of Buddhist philosophy.*

I.   The world is full of suffering. Birth is suffering, decrepitude is suffering, so are sickness and death suffering. To face a man of hatred is suffering, to be separated from a beloved one is suffering, or to be vainly struggling to satisfy one's needs. In fact, life that is not free from desire and passion is always involved with suffering. This is called the Truth of Suffering.

The cause of human suffering is undoubtedly found in the thirsts of the physical organism and in the illusions of worldly passion. If these thirsts and illusions are traced to their source, they are found to be rooted in the intense desires of physical instincts. Thus desire, having a strong will-to-live at its basis, goes after what is sensed as being desirable. Sometimes desire even turns toward death. This is called the Truth of the Cause of Suffering.

If desire which lies at the root of all human passion can be removed, then passion will die out and all human suffering will be ended. This is called the Truth of the Ending of Suffering.

In order to enter into a condition where there is no desire and no suffering, one must follow a certain Path. The stages of this Noble Path are:— Right Ideas, Right Resolution, Right Speech, Right Behavior, Right Vocation, Right Effort, Right Mindfulness, Right Concentration. This is called the Truth of the Noble Path to the Ending of Desire.

People should keep these Truths clearly in mind, for the world is filled with suffering and if anyone wishes to escape from suffering they must cut the ties of worldly passion which is the sole cause of suffering. The way of life which is free from all worldly passion and suffering can only be known by enlightenment, and elightenment can only be gained by the discipline of the Noble Path.

2.   All those who are seeking enlightenment, must understand these Four Noble Truths. Without this understanding, they will wander about for a long time in the bewildering maze of life's illusions. Those who understand the Four Noble Truths are called: "The people who have acquired the eyes of enlightenment." Therefore, people who wish to follow the Buddha's teachings should concentrate their minds on these Four Noble Truths and seek to make their meaning clear. In all ages, a saint, if he is a true saint, is one who understands them and teaches them to others.

When the Four Noble Truths are clearly understood, then the Noble Path will lead them away from greed; and if they are free from greed they will not quarrel with the world, they will not act indecently, nor kill, nor steal, nor cheat, nor abuse, nor flatter, nor envy, nor lose their temper, nor forget the transciency of life; nor will they err in justice.

3.   Following the Noble Path is like entering a dark room with a light in the hand; the darkness will all be cleared away, and the room will be filled with light. People who understand the meaning of the Noble Truths and have learned to follow the Noble Path are in possession of a light of wisdom that will clear away the darkness of ignorance. Buddha leads the people, by only following the Four Noble Truths. Those who understand it properly will gain enlightenment; they will be able to guide and support others in the bewildering world, and they will be worthy of trust. When the Four Noble Truths are clearly understood, the sources of all worldly passion are dried up. Advancing from these Four Noble Truths, the disciples of Buddha will attain all other precious truths, will gain the wisdom and piety to understand all meanings, and will become able to preach the Dharma to all the people of all the world.

II

Causation

1.   There are causes for all human suffering, and there is a way by which they may be ended, because everything in the world is the result of a vast concurrence of causes and conditions, and everything disappears as these causes and conditions change and pass away. Rain falls, wind blows, plants bloom, leaves mature and are blown away; these phenomena are all interrelated with causes and conditions, are brought about by them, and disappear as the cuases and conditions change.

A child is born by the conditions of parentage; its body is nourished by food, its spirit is nurtured by teaching and experience. Therefore, both flesh and spirit are related to conditions and are changed as conditions change. A net is made up by a series of ties, so everything in this world is connected by a series of ties. If any one thinks that a mesh of a net is an independent, isolated thing, he is mistaken. It is called a net because it is made up of a series of connected meshes, and each mesh has its place and responsibilities in relation to other meshes.

2.   Blossoms bloom because of a series of conditions that lead up to blooming; leaves are blown away because a series of conditions lead up to it. Blossoms do not bloom unconditioned, nor does a leaf fall of itself. So everything has its appearing and passing away; nothing remains unchanged.

It is the everlasting and unchanging rule of this world that everything is created by a series of causes and conditions and everything disappears by the same rule; everything changes, nothing remains unchanged.

III

The Chain of Causation

1.   What, then, is the source of human grief, lamentation, pain and agony? Is it not to be found in the fact that people are generally ignorant and wilful? They cling obstinately to a life of wealth, honor, comfort, pleasure, excitement and egoism, ignorant of the fact that it is from the desire for these very things that human suffering starts. From its beginning, the world has been filled with a succession of calamities, besides there are the unavoidable facts of illness, decrepitude and death. But if one considers all the facts carefully, he must be convinced that at the base of all suffering lies the principle of ignorance and desire. If ignorance and desire can be removed, human suffering will come to an end.

The principle of ignorance is manifested in the obscurities and false imaginations that fill the human mind. These obscurities and false imaginations rise from the fact that people ignore the emptiness and transitoriness of life and are ignorant of the right reason for the succession of things. From these obscurities and false imaginations there spring impure desires for things that are in fact unobtainable, but for which they restlessly and blindly search. Because of these false imaginations and impure desires, people imagine discriminations where, among things themselves, there are no discriminations. Among the acts of human behavior, inherently, there are no discriminations of right and wrong, but people because of ignorance imagine they see distinctions and discriminate them as right and wrong, all because of the obscurities of false imaginations and impure desires.

Because of their ignorance, people are always thinking wrong thoughts and always losing the right view point, and then, by changing to their supposed ego-personality, they take wrong action and as a result grasp and become attached to a whole body of delusion. But, in fact, there is no such thing as an ego-personality, except as it is imagined by the mind in an effort to synthesise its sensual and instinctive desires. Making their karma the field of an ego-personality, using the activities of the mind as seed, beclouding the mind by ignorance, fertilizing it with the rain of impure desires, irrigating by the wilfulness of an ego-personality, they add the conception of evil, and bear about this incarnation of delusions.

2.   Ultimately this body of delusion is their own mind and, therefore, it is their own mind which causes the delusion of grief, lamentation, pain and agony. This whole world of delusion is nothing but the shadow caused by this mind, and for the same reason, the world of enlightenment also appears from this same mind.

3.   In this world there are three wrong view points, if one clings to these view points, then everything in the world must be denied. First, some people maintain the idea that all human experience is based on destiny; second, some hold that everything is created by God and controlled by his will; third, some say that everything happens by chance.

If all has been decided by destiny, both good deeds and evil deeds are destiny, weal and woe are destiny, and nothing exists outside destiny, then all human plans and effort for improvement and progress would be in vain and humanity would be without hope. The same is true of the other conceptions, for, if everything in the last resort is in the hands of God or of blind chance, what hope has humanity except in submission? It is no wonder that people holding these conceptions lose hope and relax their effort to act wisely and avoid evil. No, these three conceptions and viewpoints are all wrong;—everything is a succession of appearances whose source is the concurrence of causes and conditions, and these causes and conditions can, in a measure, be modified and controlled.

The Other Side of Hate

Andrew Corsello

Andrew Corsello is a senior writer at GQ *Magazine, which he joined as a correspondent in 1995. Prior to writing for* GQ, *he worked for three years as a staff writer at* Philadelphia *Magazine. Costello won the Society of Professional Journalists Sigma Delta Chi Award for Best Magazine Story for "Murky Waters." He also received National Magazine Award nominations for "My Body Stopped Speaking to Me," which chronicles Corsello's near-death experience due to liver failure; "The Vulgarian in the Choir Loft," an essay that was included in* The Best American Magazine Writing 2004 *(HarperCollins); and "The Wronged Man," an article about a man who was exonerated by DNA evidence twenty-two years after being wrongfully convicted of raping a child. "The Other Side of Hate," originally a* GQ *article, was featured in* The Best American Magazine Writing 2007 *(Columbia UP). This article and "The Wronged Man" also have been optioned for motion pictures. Since 1999, Andrew Corsello has been married to the Rev. Dana Corsello, an Episcopal minister. The couple has two sons.*

"The Other Side of Hate" tells the story of a white farmer and a fiery, young black priest who face conflict over the ownership of a plot of land in Zimbabwe. Ultimately, these men rise above the hatred surrounding them to overcome their own prejudices, thereby achieving forgiveness and starting the healing process as they learn how to share the land. As Costello states, "I realized that this was a story I'd wanted to write for a while, a story about forgiveness."

im Steele was mad as hell. His blacks were messing with the farm, with the land, and the land was *always* personal. He'd been born on this farm. Like many Rhodesians, his parents had planted his umbilical cord in the ground so the boy's life and the good earth would nourish each other forever. This land held the blood of his dead brother, his soul mate, thirteen months younger, who at age 19 had reached into the truck for the shotgun and accidentally tripped its hammers, taking both barrels in the stomach and crying "My God!" as he fell. *The blood of my brother in the ground.* Though Steele called himself a Christian, the earth itself was his real religion; and his good and proper use of it, a form of worship. Any abuse of the earth or the fruit it brought forth was an assault on his person.

The barn boys had been abusing that fruit, killing it with their neglect. A line had to be drawn. You could not show heel to the African. He'd take advantage every time. Everybody knew that. Lord, all that *work:* Two months ago, he'd patched the cavernous tobacco barn until it was airtight. A months ago, he'd begun harvesting the leaves and hanging them in the barn to dry. Now it was a matter of carefully controlling the humidity and temperature in the barn, keeping the iron furnace stoked day and night. And his blacks had gone lazy on him.

Every day at dawn, Steele drove down to the barn to check the leaves. And every day for the past two weeks, he'd walked into a cold barn.

"It's cold in this barn," he said on the first day.

"No, Oom Jim," said the barn boy on duty, using the Afrikaans word for "uncle." "Check the thermometer."

The thermometer read as it should have, 38 degrees Celsius, but Steele knew the boy had been sleeping on the job, letting the fire die—had heard the boss man's truck and stuck the thermometer atop the furnace for a few seconds before hanging it back among the leaves.

Steele looked at his barn boy. The boy looked back.

"Yes, Oom Jim?"

"Stoke the fire," he said, and left.

For two weeks the charade continued, until the morning that it didn't. Steele woke angry. It was still dark when he got into the truck, but he could see his own breath in the glow of the dashboard, and this made him angrier. As he drove the rutted dirt road to the barn, the head of his watch, worn on the inside of his wrist to preserve its life, rattled insistently against the steering wheel, and this, too, fed his anger. By the time he reached the barn he was teetering. He threw the barn door open, stepped forward, exhaled, watched the breath curl from his mouth.

"It's goddamn cold in here."

"No, Oom Jim. Look at the thermometer."

It was then, in 1964, at the age of 27, that Jim Steele—a man who, per his father's orders, hadn't shed a tear after his brother's death—lost control. Without another word he grabbed a cloth, gripped the handles to the furnace doors, and opened them. The fire had faded to embers, but it was still glowing. Then he turned, braced one of his thick, flat, dirty hands against the boy's chest while thrusting the other around and between his legs, lifted him off the ground, and shoved him face-first at the fire.

"Tell me," he roared. "Does *that* seem hot enough for you?"

The boy threw his palms against the furnace wall to prevent his face from entering. The farmer could hear the flesh burning but didn't pull the boy back until he could smell it. Patches of the boy's palms remained on the furnace wall, curling. The farmer continued to embrace the boy for a moment, one broad arm around the boy's back, the boy arching, squirming, his other forearm jammed against the boy's forehead.

"Is it hot enough?" he yelled again. "Is it?"

Something touched him then. It wasn't so much that he was throwing the boy to the ground as another force, like wind but *solid*, was casting the two of them in opposite directions. In an instant they were on the ground, facing each other. The boy held out his hands in supplication. Then, in a childlike voice, he began to weep. *Oom Jim, Oom Jim, oh, it is so hot, Oom Jim.*

An unreflective man, Jim Steele had only ever known himself by the things he had done. Now he had done this. For a few moments, he lost the feeling of his own body, of his presence in it. He had a queer sense of floating, of being given a glimpse for the first time in his life of what lay beyond the surface of himself. What he saw there was not bad. It was worse: It was nothing.

Before coming to his senses and going for help, Steele sat dumb on the floor of the barn, listening to the boy's mewling, smelling his burnt hands. He could not shake a growing conviction that he was somehow at the mercy of the boy, that the boy had in fact acquired great power over him—a power he would hold forever.

Paul Mufanebadza learned to hate women before he could speak, before he could even know what hate was. He was an ill infant, feverish and limp— poisoned by his own malice, it was later said. The poison *killed* him. Among his people, if a baby dies before it cuts its teeth, elderly women must bury it that very day, before sunset, in a wet place. When Paul stopped breathing, four village elders came, put their ears to the child's mouth to confirm it was dead, then carried it out to a riverbed. They dug a shallow grave in the mud and dropped the baby in. The instant they did, its eyes flashed and a careening blood scream issued from its mouth. When the boy was old enough to ask why people called him the Spooky Child, his mother told him he'd been hexed by women eager to steal his father from his family. So it was that Paul Mufanebadza learned to believe women were witches.

Two of these witches dwelled in his home. Paul Mufanebadza Sr. was a regimental sergeant major and one of the two highest-ranking black men in the Rhodesian army, which fought throughout the 1960s and 1970s to pre-serve the country's minority white rule. The sergeant major was a man of means, a man who could afford to live polygamously. Paul junior's mother was his first wife, the domestic queen. Paul senior brought the second and third of his five wives—and the children he sired by them—to live in the queen's home in the city of Masvingo.

The sergeant major didn't much care for his namesake. "Father," his boy would say, pointing to his tattered shoes, "the other children are laughing at me. May I have a new pair?" As was his custom when the Spooky Child asked for his help, the sergeant major would pull a thick sheaf of cash from his breast pocket and show it to the boy. "I've got the money here," he'd grin. "And I'm not giving it to you." The Spooky Child knew who was enjoying his father's money. Though he dreamed of killing them, he hated the witches too intensely to hurt them—hurting them would have meant touching them, and touching them would have compromised the purity of his hatred. In the teen years, as other boys chased girls, Paul Mufanebadza refused even to look at them. Instead he gazed inward, at the gleaming black obelisk, ever larger, ever harder, of his own spite.

At the nearly all-white British primary school to which his father sent him, the Spooky Child was compelled to take tea while the white wives of senior army officers corrected his poor manners. A bitter pill, but not enough. The white teachers unable to decipher his rural Shona accent, who yelled "Speak!" into his face, as if the sounds out of his mouth were not human language but the barking of some bush animal? Also a bitter pill, but still not enough. Even the worship they forced on him, of Jesus Christ, that meek little man who refused to stand up for himself: not enough.

No, it was the sergeant major's tears that finally caused all of the boy's hates to congeal into a single, self-defining thought.

"Father," he asked, "why are you crying?" The sergeant major convened the wives and children and announced that he had just received a great honor. A senior officer, a white man, had named his dog after him. "He loves his dog very much." Paul senior explained. "His dog is like his child. So he has named his dog Paul."

The thought young Paul had at that moment felt cool and clear and nourishing.

I hate women. I hate Christianity. And I hate white people.

Soon after this, Paul and his half brother, Paul Wonder—a hale and beau-tiful boy four months older than the Spooky Child and beloved of the sergeant major—were required to bring their birth certificates to school. The sergeant major produced the documents. Paul Wonder's read "Paul Wonder Mufanebadza," The Spooky Child's read "Paul Neshangwe."

"Who is Paul Neshangwe?" asked the Spooky Child.

"Do you want that certificate?"

After a long while, the boy said, "No."

"Go find another," said the sergeant major.

Paul Wonder's mother had decided that the Spooky Child should not share her son and husband's surname. The sergeant major had agreed; "Neshangwe" belonged to some distant ancestor. The children at school were greatly amused with their new classmate, Paul Neshanwge.

"You are nobody's son!" they sang. "Nobody's son!"

Throughout his youth, Paul Neshangwe's hate attained a kind of perfection, the way the country's roilings—the racial hatred, the war, the sense of Rhodesia as a sentient being tearing its own heart out—seemed to affirm his interior goings-on. By the time he was 17, living on liquor, tobacco, and marijuana, he had developed the habit of bashing his skull against the cinderblock wall of his house. It helped.

One night he turned to his older (full) brother and said, "I want to destroy something." His brother nodded. "I want to destroy a person."

They decided to open Paul Wonder with knives. They accosted him outside his home. Paul Wonder fled, screaming. His mother ran into the street.

"Let's kill them both!" Paul's brother said.

But Paul wasn't sure, so they gave up the chase. Still, Paul couldn't shake his urge to destroy something. Several days later, he noosed his neck, stepped onto a chair, knotted the rope around a pipe, and leapt into the air. The rope snapped. He tired and failed twice more in the next month, once again by hanging and once with antimalarial pills.

Then the Christians came to town, tacking up posters for a movie about the life of Jesus—a white guy, apparently. Paul and his friends began tearing the posters down to use as rolling paper. As a joke, they went to a screening, sat in the back smoking their Jesus joints and shouting "*Murungu!*—the Shona word for "white man"—whenever the lead actor spoke. In the lobby afterward, a young man approached.

"You have been taking down our posters."

Not an accusation. Just a statement of fact.

"That's us," said one of Paul's friends, pulling a joint from his pocket and lighting up. "That Jesus, he is your 'Lord and Savior,' *jah?*

The man nodded.

"Well, we've been smoking your Lord and Savior."

Someone cracked a joke about God forcing Himself upon the Virgin and making Joseph take the rap for knocking her up.

"We will pray for you," the Christian smiled.

Fuck them, Paul thought, walking away. *Fuck Jesus. Fuck the Holy Ghost. And fuck the Father.*

Fuck the Father most of all.

☙

Jim Steele knew what was coming. Wars of racial independence had been rippling across the continent, black Africans from Ghana to Mozambique to Angola overthrowing the European colonials who'd kept them under thumb for centuries. Now it was Rhodesia's turn. In November 1965, prime minister Ian Smith declared independence from Britain, which had begun urging Rhodesia toward democratic rule. The revolution began five months later—in the city of Chinhoyi, ten miles from Steele's farm—when government forces gunned down seven armed rebels. For some fifteen years the war raged, killing 30,000 blacks and 1,500 whites and ending in black-majority rule. On April 18, 1980, at a ceremony in a Harare soccer stadium in which Bob Marley performed freedom songs, Rhodesia became Zimbabwe, with a black militiaman named Robert Mugabe as its prime minister.

What shocked Jim Steele—and all his countrymen, black and white—was the inauguration speech by Mugabe, who'd spent ten years in a Rhodesian prison for "subversion" and risen to political prominence on a platform of black power. "If yesterday you hated me," he told his defeated white countrymen, "today you cannot avoid the love that binds you to me and me to you . . . The wrongs of the past must now stand forgiven and forgotten . . . It could never be a correct justification that because the whites oppressed us yesterday when they had power, the blacks must oppress them today because they have power. An evil remains an evil, whether practiced by white against black or by black against white."

For ten years, Mugabe lived those beautiful words. By 1990, thanks to his embrace of the country's whites, the economy was humming, and Zimbabwe was known as "Africa's breadbasket." The prime minister (and after 1987, president) vastly improved education and health care and brought blacks into the economy.

Shona blacks, that is. When members of the country's minority Ndebele tribe, which had been shut out of the new government, mounted a protest in the early '80s, Mugabe dispatched a shadowy militia known as the Fifth Brigade to slaughter some 30,000 Ndebele men, women, and children and to terrorize those they spared. The brigade forced survivors to sing Shona songs praising Mugabe's political party while dancing on the fresh graves of their families, and shot or hacked to death those who grieved openly.

Such a strange, divided man, Robert Mugabe. A charismatic Roman Catholic with seven university degrees. A reconciler and poet who raised his country from the ashes of total race war. And a man without hesitation or limits. By the time, years later, Zimbabwe's whites learned along with the rest of the world of the Fifth Brigade's obscenities—learned that Robert Mugabe was not the precursor to Nelson Mandela but a psychotic in the mold of Idi Amin—it was too late.

Jim Steele, too, was a divided man during the war. Not long before the first shots were fired in Chinhoyi, he decided to stop growing tobacco. No crop paid better, but what it exacted—the price of always having his money and his blacks on his mind—was more than he could afford. After 1964, Jim Steele used the 3,700 acres his father had begun farming in 1913 outside Chinhoyi to raise cattle and maize. This decision brought him a peace that remained and continued, quietly and slowly, to unfurl; while all around him, year after year, Rhodesia devoured itself, Steele devoted his time to his church, becoming an elder and lay preacher.

Good, but not enough: One Sunday in June 1970, as he sat in his pew at Lomagundi Presbyterian Church in Chinhoyi, Steele felt a tiny tendril take root in his chest, a pinprick of bliss that soon thickened into rapture, then shock, then terrible longing. Slain, drunk, he stumbled to the altar, collapsed, and confessed.

"I have been full of pride! I must surrender!"

Surrender and commit: At a time when the rest of Rhodesia's white farmers barricaded their homes with razor wire and slept with their shotguns, Steele and his wife, Janette, traveled the country distributing Gideon Bibles.

"Church is an appointment with God," he said whenever his son, who lived next door on the farm, begged his parents to stay home on Sundays. "Such an appointment cannot be canceled."

Even before the war's end, Jim Steele became known throughout Chinhoyi among both blacks and whites as a man who feared God and was fair with the blacks, a demanding boss but a tireless worker himself, a man capable of anger, surely, but slow to it.

And yet, throughout the war, this peace within him lived side by side with its opposite. Steele could not keep the country's fear and fury from penetrating his surfaces. He *detested* the war that left his farm fallow, detested the whites who had provoked it and the blacks who waged it. Steele read his Old Testament. Vengeance was His. But leaving vengeance to God did nothing to cool his wrath. It was a physical thing, a rock in the belly. And it was frightening—not because he couldn't abolish it but because he couldn't afford to. Unfettered, rage had once prompted him to feed a human being to a furnace. But measured, kept on a low simmer, anger brought a certain keenness and clarity, tuned him into what he could and couldn't expect from those mysterious others, his blacks, without whom he and his land would be lost.

So was Steele, at heart, the same man at the end of the war that he'd been before it began? Steele thought not; thought that the man who had put that boy in the furnace had been vanquished, replaced. Yes, he was still a hard man, still enraged at what fifteen years of war had visited upon his country. But he had changed his ways, and this change has been rewarded with a new consciousness and, after 1980, a measure of prosperity, had it not? By the mid-1990s, Jim Steele was a man who prayed and even thought that he had atoned not only for himself, but also in some small way for the trickery and theft and murder with which white men had made his land their own. Was he not entitled to such a sentiment?

Jim Steele was a fool. His land and his god hadn't even begun to test him.

✺

And then Paul Neshangwe changed. It was the strangest thing, not only because it happened but because it didn't take long—just a few months to begin altering the chemical structure of all that hate, of all those *hates*.

It was the Christians. They were Presbyterians, and they were relentless, coming for him in packs like hyenas after a blood scent. *How did they find him?*

Easily. After the movie, as Neshangwe and his friends smoked the Savior in the lobby, the Presbyterians politely asked them to write down who they were and where they lived. Paul's friends scribbled fake addresses. Paul . . . did not.

The Presbyterians gave chase for weeks on end. Whenever they rapped on his door, Neshangwe—a man temperamentally capable of murdering his own kin—was *seized with terror*, leapt out the window and ran. He eventually *moved*. And still, somehow, six months later, they found him. He was broke, three days without a meal, when they came knocking. He opened up, and there they were. Some black kids, Jesus boys, acolytes, whatever, and a *murungu* spoke a bit about the Man. Then he pulled the oldest evangelical's trick in the book.

"Salvation is a free gift. Do you know what that means?" Paul said nothing. The *murungu* fished a Zim dollar from his pocket, clasped its edges, and snapped it taut.

"Like salvation. A free gift. Take it."

The year was 1987. The Zim dollar was powerful. Paul bought bread, milk, paraffin. As he ate, an incomplete thought, thirteen words, played and replayed itself.

My own father, who has never in his life given me a dollar . . .

Not a lightning strike. He wasn't *smote*. But he started coming to church, just to see.

Still, the anger in this man, this *boy*, unnerved. After graduating high school, he interviewed for the ministry. "What Paul Neshangwe considers his calling is instead a confusion of rage," his evaluator wrote. He was ordered to complete university training in South Africa. Bitterly, he submitted.

The first time he preached at the university chapel, a commerce student named Lydia Chituku watched from her pew, trying to decide whether she believed the boy in the pulpit. She'd heard about the ministry student from Zimbabwe. Everyone had. An aspiring man of God who yelled down classmates and professors, smashed his head against walls, and didn't like women. Now here he was, preaching about . . . that very madness—his rage at women and white people and his father and Jesus and the church officials who'd questioned his call to the ministry. His voice was low and fierce. His eyes were hooded, half shut, as if to scorn the sight of the sanctuary. Yet he made himself so naked. He omitted nothing, spared himself nothing. He did not even claim to have shed his rage, though he did say that he was reborn and that he was learning to forgive those who had wronged him, to release them and himself.

"It's not that you hate the people and things you say you hate," she said a few weeks after they began dating. "It's that you just don't know what to do with them."

Though everyone who'd ever known Paul Neshangwe told him that his hate was a cancer, no one had ever suggested *this*—that what he comprehended as the core of his identity wasn't at all what he thought it was. Lydia became the first woman Paul Neshangwe ever loved physically and, after they married, the last. Later, after AIDS began to take his siblings—a brother, then another brother, then another brother, then a sister, then another sister, *five* of them— and Paul and Lydia began raising their orphaned nieces and nephews—nine through their home over the years, on a preacher's salary, including the children of yet another brother, who died of cerebral malaria—some began to ask whether Paul's refusal of all women before Lydia was part of God's plan, His mysterious way of sparing Paul the plague in order to preserve him for his work as a pastor. Paul always deflected the question. Even considering it made him feel unclean.

It was the oldest story in the world: A strongman becomes mesmerized by power for its own sake, transmogrifies, grows paranoid, intellectually unsupple, allergic to dissent; starts rigging elections, micromanaging the economy, imprisoning journalists he finds "offensive." By the mid-1990s, Robert Mugabe had began turning Zimbabwe into a police state ruled by fear, censorship, and his omniscient Central Intelligence Organization. The first real threat to his regime came in 1997, when the country's war veterans—the only group capable of mounting a coup d'état—demanded giveaways. The unbudgeted $4 billion Zim-dollar (roughly $250 million U.S.) payoff Mugabe ordered pulverized the economy, but the vets pressed for still more. With no cash reserves, Mugabe began laying the groundwork for land confiscations, dubbing all whites "imperialists" and "colonial agents." Once this rhetoric became reality, it did not matter that virtually all the war veterans who took over white lands were uninterested in farming—that government-backed land invasions *guaranteed* economic ruin, if not famine. What mattered was Mugabe's continued hold on power.

The Steeles knew their land would be taken. It was inevitable. Upon waking each morning, they took tea, then walked together to the balcony overlooking the fields to see if it had begun. They knew the invasion would be violating and psychologically violent, just as they knew it would begin in silence, with a stranger strolling onto their land and pushing stakes into the soft soil to mark his claim. *Not yours. Mine.* Yet even before the settlers came, Jim Steele pitied them. He knew, as they did not, that they were cannon fodder, dispatched by the government to intimidate him into fleeing his farm without a fight. This was the way of land invasions. Once the whites fled (if not from the settlers, then from the soldiers who followed), the settlers would be driven back into the bush so a war veteran or regime crony could claim his prize. Jim and Janette Steele therefore decided more than a year before the settlers appeared that they would accept their presence. It was the practical thing to do: If they made a stand, the army would take not only their farmland but their house and perhaps their lives. But it was also the Christian thing to do, a turning of the other cheek.

It began in March of 2000. One family at first, then two, then ten, twenty, forty, wordlessly forming their low circular mud huts and wood-stick chicken pens. The Steeles responded, as planned, with silence and peace.

Yet there was no peace. On his balcony each morning, teacup in hand, beholding the distant huts and pens and stick-figure humans etched against the dawn, Jim Steele felt all the old terror and rage he thought he'd shed two decades before, when the war ended. All he had ever wanted in his life was to work this land, be its steward, bring order to its natural state of chaos. Now the settlers were here with their primitive, piecemeal agriculture. In a year or two, the soldiers would kick them back where they came from, and Steele would have to watch his farm backslide into the sullen scrubland it had been before his father emigrated from Scotland to civilize it at the dawn of the past century. The farm had gone half feral in the war years. But Steele knew then that the war would end, that he would once again bring order to the land. This was different. This was far more *personal*. And this was forever. In a decade or two, he would go to his grave, and not a trace of what he and his father had worked for would remain to speak for him. He was old, afraid, angry, and now, he realized, trapped. Jim Steele stood each morning watching the strangers grow ever more numerous, ever closer, and said aloud to himself, "My God, what am I to do?"

By 1999, when he began substitute preaching in Chinhoyi, Paul Neshangwe, too, had a decision to make about the farm invasions and the devastation he knew they would bring upon his country. Robert Mugabe frequently linked Christian churches to the white "enemy." ("[When they] came to our land, they brought us the Bible and they taught us to pray. When we opened our eyes, we had the Bible and they had the land.") The CIO was even sending spies into churches to track sermonizing that was "slanderous" to the president. Most of the country's clergy decided it was not worth losing one's parish and perhaps even one's freedom to preach what everyone already knew to be true.

In July of that year, Neshangwe was invited to conduct a service at a local Methodist church. At the appointed time, he stepped up to the pulpit, closed his eyes, and prayed that his words would make him an instrument of his Father's will. Upon opening his eyes, he was surprised to find himself not with Jesus but with Moses: the wrathful Moses who killed an Egyptian because that man had abused a Jew; and the rueful Moses who subsequently witnessed a Jew beating another Jew and realized that oppressors could be Egyptian or Jewish. Then Neshangwe said it: "Oppressors can be white. Or oppressors can be black." The congregation gasped. The fear in the sanctuary was palpable, but so was the exhilaration.

Once Paul Neshangwe started, he could not stop. Could not stop preaching . . . the truth. Could not stop preaching that Zimbabwe's troubles were man-made and not "God's will." Word came one day that he was required to perform funeral rites for a deputy minister for justice. The service was held outside Chinhoyi on a stately farm, until recently owned by a white family, that President Mugabe had bequeathed to the deputy.

"You will speak first," an official told Neshangwe when he arrived.

"No," Neshangwe said, smiling. "I will speak last." Nobody spoke this way to regime officials. The man stared. Neshangwe continued. "God will have the last word. Not even our pompous and blustering minister of justice will be allowed to speak after God."

God, indeed, got the last word. His servant Paul began the eulogy thusly: "My mother has begged me not to say anything today that will get me killed. So I will endeavor not to say anything too inflammatory." He then gestured to the grandeur of the farm, the rolling red hills, the elegant homestead. "It is not for me to say whether this man was right to accept the free farm that came his way"—the pastor then pointed to the casket—"because this man now stands before the ultimate court, before the ultimate judge, in whose hands his case now rests."

The minister of justice stormed out. Neshangwe knew he was fortunate Robert Mugabe had been unable to attend. If he had, the president might well have rewarded the pastor with a death warrant.

Neshangwe frequently substituted at a Presbyterian church that had been without a permanent pastor for several years. Lomagundi Presbyterian was its official name, but around Chinhoyi it was known simply as the "white man's church." An elder, a white farmer in his sixties named Jim Steele, had been holding it together. A quiet man. Serious. All business. Not the most affable fellow, and yet Paul felt immediately and powerfully drawn to the old man, his ruminative, plainspoken tone, the way he did nothing with fanfare but just . . . did it. Steele in turn found himself fascinated with, even bewildered by, Neshangwe, a serious man of God who was nevertheless an *imp*, whose piety seemed to draw its power less from humility than from laughter. Moreover, despite the thirty years and color line separating them, Steele and Neshangwe each recognized the other as an increasingly rare breed of Zimbabwean: an authority figure with no patience for the politics of race allegiance. Steele saw in Neshangwe a man willing to state from the pulpit truths most white people wouldn't dare utter outside their living rooms; Neshangwe saw in Steele a man who recognized and even embraced the fact that as whites fled the Country, Lomagundi Presbyterian would become either a "black man's church" or an empty building.

Steele eventually told the other elders he wanted to offer the pastorship to Neshangwe.

"A *black* pastor?"

"This is not a white church," he snapped. "This is God's church."

But . . . Paul Neshangwe? Not just a black man but a provocateur? At a time when racial animosity was government *policy*? When Steele himself was on the brink of losing his land? Did the old man actually think the regime wouldn't take an active interest in such a church?

"So," Neshangwe smiled when Steele made the offer, "the white man's church wants a black pastor?"

Steele failed to see the humor.

"It's *God's* church!"

Neshangwe consulted his wife.

"My husband," said Lydia, tapping his forearm lightly as she always did when she needed to calm him or herself, "I do not wish to be a widow. Not just yet."

A whole year passed as Neshangwe mulled the offer. In the meantime, he worked as the church's full-time "interim" pastor. He was still mulling the offer during the first wave of the Chinhoyi farm invasions, when the settlers came to Jim Steele's land, and even during the second wave, when Mugabe's men came for Jim Steele.

Excepting Sabbaths, Jim Steele hadn't known an idle day in his life. Now, as the settlers took over more and more of his land, he had time on his hands. He found himself driving into town, to Paul Neshangwe's home. The men would eat *sadza* and beans, and talk. Neshangwe had never known a white farmer, so Steele told him about his life prior to the invasion, what running a farm took and what it gave back, what it was like to be a white African. Neshangwe in turn told Steele about his life in the ministry, what his white collar and black skin meant to him and to those he'd met.

One Sunday, hours before church was to begin, Steele appeared at his priest's door. Despite his abiding rage at the settlers, the farmer had begun to wonder: Was his acceptance of these people the Christian thing to do? Was he even *doing* anything?

Like Jesus, who saw little value in answering spiritual questions directly, Paul responded with a parable—his own. He told the old man about the place of hate he had come from, and about the people and moments of grace that had renewed him, expanded his sense of what was humanly possible. Jim didn't know what to believe about his priest's story—its alarming proposition that a man could be one thing and then, almost at once, its opposite. The men arrived at no conclusion together. They simply talked for a time and then went to the service. Jim returned early the next week, though, and the next, and so on, so the two men could reflect on the Gospels, on the color of their skin, on each other's lives, and on their country.

"Paul, what do you *want*?" Jim asked one day. With the church, in other words. Paul felt he wasn't being asked so much as dared. He told Jim he wanted to provide food, medicine, and spiritual support to AIDS victims; to procure tallow and sewing machines so jobless parishioners could make black-market soap and school uniforms; to pay the school fees of penniless children; to extend the church where the need was greatest—in other words, to become what others would surely call a "black church."

Jim knew the instant Paul began to speak that he'd expected his priest to respond the way he had. Had *wanted* him to. So that he could say yes. So he could be a part of Paul's plans. The farmer began to walk with the priest on his visits of parishioners in the city, holding hands and praying with urban Shona men, women, and children on the dirt floors of their cinder-block abodes, bringing milk to women too depleted by AIDS to breast-feed their infants, delivering the tallow and sewing machines in his truck.

The tract that no longer belonged to Jim Steele was vast. With time on his hands, he spent hours covering it by foot, just to see the cattle and the maize rows. Sometimes his workers walked with him. Sometimes his priest came out to the country to walk with him. Most of the settlers pretended not to notice the walkers. A few looked back blankly before returning to their work. Then one afternoon, because it seemed odd not to, Jim turned to Paul and said, "Come, let's talk to them."

In the weeks that followed, Jim Steele got to know the people who had come to take everything he had ever worked for. He spoke directly to those who knew English and, through his priest or his workers, to those who spoke only Shona. He learned their names, where they'd come from, how many children they had. With each, he found himself asking the same question he had asked Neshangwe. *What do you want?* Often his tone carried bitter reproach, sometimes mere curiosity, sometimes even concern. Regardless, the answer was always the same.

"To live, sir."

Steele had been around Shona from the day of his birth, worked side by side with them, learned to trust and be trusted by them. But as he spoke with the settlers, with the urban poor to whom Paul tended, with Paul himself, a realization dawned: He had never known a Shona man, woman, or child personally. It had never occurred to him to do so. Now it did. As soon as he replaced the old narrow questions ("Does he show up on time? Can he do the job?") with the single broad one ("What's he like?"), he began to see . . . every little thing. The way, for instance, a Shona's life was filled with "brothers" and "sisters" and "cousins" but no "friends," since to call someone a "friend" was to call him something less than immediate family, to denigrate him. Or the way a Shona and her "sisters" often broke into song—in four-part harmony!—not for any *reason* but because they drew no distinction between speaking and singing and breathing; understood the three as a single substance whose form, solid or liquid or ethereal, was determined by a person's spiritual temperature. Or the way a visit with a Shona never ended, because a Shona always walked out the door with him and Paul, accompanied them to the next home, sat a while and talked, somehow remained present after physically departing.

How had Steele failed to discern all this *fluidity*? Where before he had seen an impenetrable sameness, a *mood*, he now saw the many ways in which Shona's lives and thoughts and egos bled into one another. Their very speech, as they glided within a single sentence from Shona to English and back again, was edgeless, the native tongue glistening and ebulliently inefficient as it pushed and caressed but never cut the air. Even their understanding of time and distance was fluid: If Steele asked a settler on his land how far it was to Chinhoyi, the answer depended on where the sun sat in the sky at that moment. In the morning, it was "not far." If the sun was low in the west, it was "too far"—since (of course) one was on foot and had to consider what might emerge from the bush after dark.

"White men keep watches," Paul laughed when Jim asked. "Shona keep time."

A funny thing about Paul: The more time Jim spent with him and other Shona, the less incredible the priest's stories of himself—smoking Christ at 17; serving Him at 20—seemed. Steele had always thought people were what they were, the same at 60 as they'd been at 6, only *more*. Now he wondered: In a land where the concept of property, of *boundaries*, was (like Christianity) barely a hundred years old, why couldn't a person also be a flowing, shape-shifting thing, rather than a sedimentary accretion? Why couldn't a person have a *change of mind*—not just a change of opinion, but the kind of irrational, self-shattering change of mind that Paul's namesake, the great apostle, underwent on the road to Damascus?

Neither Jim not Paul knew exactly what was happening between them. Each felt God was speaking to him through the other, teaching him, raising him up, offering answers to questions he hadn't even been aware he was asking. Only later was it clear that both men had sensed what was to befall the older man, and together were preparing him for it.

One night, Jim Steele woke with a start. A whispering in the garden, then in the room, then in him. He felt as he always felt when visited in this way: blissfully repentant. Janette woke.

"*Emmanuel*," he told her. "God is with us."

They prayed. *Show us what you want us to do.* By dawn they had their answer: It was not enough merely to accept what had befallen them.

Word eventually circulated among the settlers that the *murungu*'s offer of free medicine was genuine. Not just over-the-counter remedies but inoculations, as well as sulfaguanidine for salmonella. Within a year, Jim and Janette Steele had cured more than a hundred malaria cases among the settlers, many of whom would have died without treatment.

Soon there was talk among Chinhoyi's farmers that Jim Steele was giving his settlers diesel and maize free of charge, even plowing (their? his?) fields with his tractor. Could any of it be true? White farmers either fled or shut themselves in their homes, then dreamed of retribution and reparation. They did not abet their own disenfranchisement. But once Jim Steele started, he could not stop. He and his workers began refitting some of his unused farm buildings into a school for the settlers' children. There were one hundred pupils at first. But once word reached beyond the farm that the school was actually . . . a *school*, with paid teachers and books, chalk and boards, pencils and paper, 300 children from eight surrounding farms began attending. Was *this* enough? Was it enough for Jim Steele to give medicine and farming aid and cash loans and education to the people who had taken his inheritance?

His boss told him it was not.

"My wife and I would be honored if you would come to our church with us on Sundays," he told the settlers. Most didn't. Some did, and continued to go, underwent baptism, took Communion, accepted Jim's embrace at the offering of the peace, even as other whites in the pews refused to shake their hands or even look at them. "The commandment tells me to love my neighbor," Steele shrugged when confronted. "It does not tell me that I get to choose my neighbor."

There was more. Worshipping alongside the settlers, Steele came to feel a connection to the land they had taken from him—a connection he had not felt when it was his. A connection to the *dirt*, actually. He'd always noticed the way bare feet on dirt was not just an everyday but an every-moment-of-every-day fact of life for those many Shona who survived on what they grew themselves. Now the thought of how that fact would shape a person, how physically and urgently aware that person would be of the miracles—*all of life itself*—made possible by that dirt. Such a person would accept the supernatural as a matter of course. Such a person would draw no distinction between his body and the world. His own mortality would feel dreadful to him, as ever, but also, in some small way, sweet. He would comprehend death not as an ending but as a point on an unending continuum.

So it came to be with Jim Steele. The dirt that settled on his skin when he was in the fields (making his white skin scuffed and lined and giving blue-black Shona skin, at high noon, an orange adobe glow), the fine red dust that in the hot months papered his nose and throat: With every breath he was communing with it, taking it—and a part of everyone and everything that had ever lived and died on it and in it, his mother and his father and his beloved brother and the numberless, nameless Shona—into his body. *Dust to dust.* The land was no longer personal; it was his very person. Jim Steele would always be a white farmer. He would always believe that he had rightfully owned his land and that it had been wrongfully taken. But now, when he considered the famous words supposedly spoken to Cecil Rhodes naive. The underlying notion—that people belonged to the land and not the other way around—was disturbing, but also strangely beautiful.

On August 6, 2001, some eighteen months after the first mud huts appeared on Jim Steele's land, a band of settlers laid siege to the home of a neighboring farmer—in retaliation, they claimed, for an attack by a posse of white farmers. Police immediately arrested the besieged man, along with twenty-one of Chinhoyi's other white farmers, including Jim Steele. In fact, both the siege and the "posse" tale were orchestrated; the arrests gave the regime a symbolic victory in the days preceding Heroes' Day, the annual celebration of the seven martyred freedom fighters of Chinhoyi, who'd begun the war for independence in 1966.

Crowds gathered outside the police station the morning after the arrests to jeer and throw garbage at the white women who came to ask after their husbands. The war veterans on duty encouraged the fun, though they motioned the crowd to relent for a black visitor.

Paul Neshangwe, who was still acting as the "interim" minister of Lomagundi Presbyterian, announced that he had come for Jim Steele. The veteran in charge eyed Neshangwe's collar with puzzlement.

"Are you his lawyer?"

"I am his priest."

The veteran stared.

"Are you here to preach to the black prisoners?"

"I am here for Mr. Steele."

Now the veteran understood—a joke.

"So tell me, *priest*," he said, playing along. "How much have these *varungu* [white men] paid you?"

It was exactly then, in the face of the veterans' mocking laughter, that Neshangwe realized he could no longer ask God to be good to people he did not love enough to serve; he would be saying yes to Steele's job offer.

"I am his priest," he said again.

The veteran, now aware that the man was serious, rose and stepped close. "Leave," he said.

On the third day, the police transferred the farmers to Chinhoyi's remand prison for accused criminals awaiting trial, where they were thrown in with the all-black general population. The decision not to isolate the white men during Heroes' weekend, which even in less inflammatory times was a holiday whites were wise to spend at home, spoke for itself: *The* varungu *are fair game.*

The guards stripped Steele naked, provided prison pajamas. No shoes. Within minutes his skin burned and itched—lice. Twelve-by-eighteen-foot cells, thirty-six men in each, six blankets. It was August, wintertime in Zimbabwe, bitter cold. At lights-out, the men lay, sardine-style, on the concrete floor. The first night was quiet. Steele had toiled alongside black men before, smelled their sweat, but this was different. The thirty-six bodies were pressed together, *locked* together, so that when one man turned over every other man was required to do the same. He could hear and smell the breath of the men on either side of him. Did he smell different to them? he wondered.

They woke at five, ate, went into the yard. The farmers convened. Steele was the oldest. They addressed their question to him.

Oom Jim, what will happen to us?

Steele didn't know. How could he? He told them so. Yet still they asked, again and again, in the yard, in the mess, through the walls separating the cells, as if the constant repetition carried a warding power. *Oom Jim, what will happen to us?*

On the second night, just after lights-out, Steele was praying silently, asking for guidance—*Show me what you want me to do, Lord*—when a voice from another cell, quiet, unfamiliar, Shona, repeated the question that had been ringing in the air.

"Oom Jim, what will happen to us?"

A sarcastic little barb?

"Yes, Oom Jim." Another Shona. "What will happen to us?"

These men were in earnest. Steele knew then what he was being shown to do. His first prison sermon, delivered while he was prone and pressed between the bodies of strangers, was short and simple, more a sentiment than a sermon.

"God says we must live one day at a time," he said to the dark. "Whether we are here four days, until the end of Heroes' weekend, or whether we are here four weeks or four years, we must ask every day for His protection and peace."

That was all. No one else spoke, and the men went to sleep.

He preached the next morning in the yard. He was surrounded at first only by the other white men, who clumped together as a defensive measure when not locked in their cells. He preached about Jesus in the wilderness, alone and beset. As always, his voice and his manner were quiet and convincing. He spoke without fear and without reproach, as if he and the other farmers were in no danger at all. The Spirit moved him to preach at length, almost thirty minutes, and when he was done there were as many black inmates as white gathered around him.

Afterward, two black prisoners introduced themselves.

"We would like to sing you a song," they said.

They were Malawian, a bass and a tenor. They sang beautifully, in harmony, in their own language. Jim couldn't understand the words but knew without having to ask that it was a Christian song.

No one planned what happened that night. No one said, "We will do it this way." It just happened, and every subsequent night the farmers were in prison—eleven more in all. At eight the lights were extinguished. For a time there was silence. Then the Malawians began to sing. A few of the hymns were familiar. Most were not. All were sung in their native language, and the way the rest of the prisoners knew what was being sung at the same time that they had no idea what was being sung made the music even more rich and strange. Time lost its purchase when the Malawians sang, so it was hard to know if they were singing for thirty minutes or an hour or two hours. They simply sang until they stopped, and when they stopped there was an observed silence. The first night this occurred, after the singing had come to an end, Jim Steele had no idea what to do. He felt called to preach, but he also felt the Malawians had brought the spirit of God upon them all, and that it was not his place to break such a silence. Indeed, it was not. Quietly, one at a time, the prisoners began to speak into the dark. As they did, one of the men against whom Steele's body was pressed, an accused thief named Simon, translated the words of those who spoke in Shona. Some offered prayers. Some offered testimonies—who they were, what they did for a living, what they wished for. Others offered confessions. The prison was divided into two classes of inmate, violent and nonviolent, and though the men on this ward had been accused of nonviolent or mildly violent crimes, many of the voices issuing from the dark told of terrible acts. Some of the confessions lasted ten minutes. Some lasted ten seconds. A heavy silence separated each.

I raped a young girl.

I stole from my neighbor.

I killed my wife.

I cursed God.

I hurt my child.

The men told their stories knowing they were being listened to. Most asked for forgiveness. Some claimed they were beyond it. Jim waited until every man who wanted to had spoken, then began to preach. He spoke a sentence or two at a time, then waited as Simon called out his words in Shona. When Steele finished, there was an amen, then sleep.

On the first Saturday morning, the guards announced that the farmers' heads would be shaved. The lice, they explained. The younger farmers raged: This was about ridicule, not lice; they would not submit. Steele motioned them to be still. The yelling—it was just what the guards wanted, so they could later claim the whites had "rioted" to justify whatever violence they were planning.

"What should we do, Oom Jim?"

"As a sheep before his shearers, as a lamb before the slaughter . . . ," he quoted to the farmers. Then to the guards: "I will be first."

There was a problem. Though the guards were prepared to beat the farmers, they hadn't actually prepared to shave them: There were no clippers in the prison. Clippers were delivered four hours later. Another problem: Since every inmate carried lice, and not just the white farmers, and since the shavings had been publicly announced, the guards were compelled to shave every head in the prison to save face. Most of the black inmates found this episode highly amusing.

That night, after the bald Malawians sang their songs, and anonymous bald inmates offered their confessions to the night, and bald Jim Steele preached his sermon and said his amen, a bald man from another cell whispered into the dark. A Shona accent.

"Oom Jim, do you really see the light at the end of the tunnel?"

"Yes, my friend," Steele said solemnly. "The truth will set you free."

A minute passed. Then, once more, the whisper.

"Oom Jim, do you think you could turn that light up a little?"

As the laughter of the prisoners faded, another voice.

"Very good."

Jim knew the voice was the warden's but couldn't read its tone.

The next day, as the prison's nonviolent inmates mingled in the yard, the warden, flanked by a dozen guards, appeared and ordered the men to sit. Then, in violation of prison policy, he ordered the so-called D inmates—the men charged with murder and arson and rape—into the yard.

This is it, Steele thought. The openness of it all surprised him. One would have thought the matter of doing in the whites would be a semi-discreet affair.

The warden ordered the D prisoners to sit. Then he pointed at Steele.

"You," he said. "Stand."

Steele stood.

"Preach."

Was this some form of mockery? Steele decided he didn't care. His job was to bear witness. He gestured to Simon. Simon stood. Then, with Simon translating, he began to preach.

"Some of you are guilty of the crimes you have been charged with. I have heard you confessing at night. Some of you are not guilty of the crimes you have been charged with. But whether you are guilty or not, you, me, all of us, are sinners. You have all done something you are ashamed of. I have done something I am ashamed of. We all need to be changed." He spoke about Daniel in the lions' den. "God was there, and God is *here*, in our midst. Do not be afraid," he said, smiling. "Do not be afraid. Because when you leave this place, the lions of the earth will be everywhere. *Do not be afraid!*"

Some of the D prisoners came to him when he was done, asking about his religion, offering confessions, thanking him. Two others—they happened to be nonviolents—wished to discuss something else.

"You are an old man," one said.

"Yes?"

The man pointed to Jim's eyes. "You do not see well."

"I see well enough."

"But you wear glasses?"

"They were taken when I arrived."

"No glasses," the man said, shaking his head. "Take off your tunic."

What?

"Your lice."

The men were offering to do for Jim what he, with his 64-year-old's eyes, could not do for himself: pick the lice from his prison pajamas. Then and every day thereafter, the two Shona, an accused thief and a vandal, meticulously picked the lice from Jim Steele's prison pajamas while the old man sat beside them in the cold air of the prison yard, naked and peaceful.

After seventeen days, when it became clear that the whites were not going to end up getting hurt, that their presence in the prison was in fact creating a most unpalatable racial harmony, that even the warden was developing worrisome tendencies, the order came down: Give the whites their bail.

They were freed with the stipulation that they leave their farms, and Chinhoyi altogether, for one month. On the day Jim and Janette Steele returned, they stopped in town for supplies. The tension was alive in the air—the sense of eyes, of suspended rules, of Chinhoyi having declared open season on whites.

Jim Steele and Paul Neshangwe said nothing when they spotted each other across the street. Just began walking. For several minutes, while the people of Chinhoyi looked on, the two men held one another.

"You are my pastor," Jim finally said. "You are my pastor."

"And you," Paul said, "are a father to me."

And still there is anger. At his government. At his losses. Even at the settlers he has provided for. Can it be reconciled with his forgiveness? Is he a changed man?

Jim Steele scorns such questions.

"Repent," he says early one Sunday morning. "*Repent.*" His tone is harsh, his knuckles white as he skins a broken extension cord with a knife. "The word itself means 'to turn around.' There can be no forgiveness without repentance, without a turning around. Remorse is not enough. Judas had remorse. But did he repent? Did he ask Jesus Christ for forgiveness and vow to change his ways? No, he went off and hung himself. Remorse is *not* repentance. It is just an emotion. Like anger—just an emotion. Repentance is a process. It involves asking, 'Lord, how shall I proceed?' and then *acting*. It is an act of will. It is not for the weak."

Jim Steele is filled with grace, but he will never forget what has been done to him. Forgiveness is not a forgetting. Jim Steele is quite aware that he has lost many of his friends and most of his money, that paint peels from the walls of his living room, that he and his wife often go days without electricity, that their phone hasn't worked in years. He will never believe that the presence of settlers on his land is just. Justice is another issue for another day. Such is Jim Steele's forgiveness: While it creates peace, it is not an absolution or an excusing. It is, like his dirty farmer's hands, rugged and unpretty and functional, a thing he will be working with until the day he dies.

But then, after the sharp words, Steele smiles at his wife and says, "Let us go." The ride to church, in an old station wagon packed with settlers, is upbeat and chatty. Every few minutes, though, the car goes silent as those inside look out at the country Robert Mugabe has killed. Such a sad nation, Zimbabwe. The return to ancient slash-and-burn agriculture has turned the verdant earth into a moonscape of baked-black dirt and the air into an acrid broth. Mugabe's misrule has driven inflation to quadruple digits while AIDS has lowered the national life expectancy to 39. After this morning's service, many parishioners will return to squalid boxes—sticks stabbed into the dirt and covered with rusted tin sheets—because their homes were bulldozed last summer as part of Operation Drive Out the Trash, a "civic beautification" project that serves to scatter into the rural areas those poor urban blacks most likely to coalesce into a force of opposition.

Zimbabwe, once lovely and flowing, is now frozen. No one can move; petrol is impossibly rare and expensive. No one can speak; CIO agents are everywhere. Those not demoralized to the point of paralysis leave if they can. Few dream of resistance. "Take up arms?" Zimbabweans say, time and again. "There is nothing left worth fighting for." Even the president has succumbed to some odd, whole-body petrification. At the dawn of Zimbabwe, Mugabe was a joyful and athletic orator. Now, at 82, the man appears embalmed, face locked in an inscrutable wooden stare, arms set as straight as oars down the sides, voice imprisoned in a narcoleptic two-note range.

The station wagon pulls up to the church an hour early, and as they have every Sunday for more than five years, Jim Steele and Paul Neshangwe reflect on their country, then choose which Bible lessons speak best to its plight. There is no acknowledgement of how radical this linking of the worldly and the otherworldly is. The growing number of black faces in what was once Chinhoyi's white-man's church speaks for itself. As does the occasional presence in the pews of CIO spies sent to report on Neshangwe's sermons. As does the charred hull of the church's parish office—firebombed during 2004's Heroes' weekend. ("Don't you think," one investigator coyly suggested, "that whoever destroyed your office is angry that you welcome both whites and blacks into your church?") Sometimes Steele's pragmatic nature prompts him to ask, "Is this too much?" Neshangwe's response is always the same: "Ah, Jim, the recklessness of faith!"

The service itself is joyously chaotic. There is no hymn list, and music doesn't occur, it *strikes*; seized by the Spirit, some guy in the back cries *Hi-ya! Hi-ya! Hi-ya!* in a piping high voice, and by the fourth *Hi-ya!* he's been joined in full harmony. As a white woman produces an acoustic guitar, two black men sprint, as if on fire, toward the altar and get to work on a bongo and a grotesquely out-of-tune upright piano.

In the middle of the madness is Jim Steele, with his old brown ill-fitting suit and his mussed hair. Is he a man who ever thinks to look in a mirror? It is not possible. Earlier, during the hour-long earthquake of Paul's sermon, he was fidgeting, flinty, tapping his watch, the disciplining father—prompting Paul to declare, without breaking the musical cadence of his sermonspeak, that "Brother Jim is tapping his watch, yes, yes . . . " But now, as he is enveloped in sung praise—in the voices of his brothers and sisters, whom he has loved and lifted and, in some cases, saved from death—the edginess, like the anger from earlier this morning, vanishes. Even the folds and shadows of his sun-baked farmer's face depart as he floats up on tiptoe, palms open and raised in supplication, eyes closed, a silly grin forming as he sings and prays. Is he still here?

He is not. He gave up his life years ago.

Salvation on Sand Mountain

Dennis Covington

Dennis Covington was born of Scotch-Irish stock in Birmingham, Alabama, in 1949. He spent most of his youth in Alabama, where he struggled with depression and substance abuse problems. Covington did not publish a novel until he was 42 years old. He has also worked as a journalist for The New York Times, *where he risked his life covering the El Salvadoran civil war in the mid-1980s, and as an English professor at the College of Wooster in Ohio and the University of Alabama at Birmingham. Covington's most acclaimed work is* Salvation on Sand Mountain: Snake Handling and Redemption in Southern Appalachia, *published in 1995. This book details Covington's deepening involvement with Southern snake-handling churches while covering the trial of an Alabama snake-handling minister accused of trying to kill his wife with poisonous snakes. As he portrays in the following selection, Covington became so fascinated with the snake-handling religion that he handled snakes himself and underwent an ecstatic religious experience.* Salvation on Sand Mountain *was a finalist for the National Book Award in 1995. Covington currently teaches creative writing at Texas Tech University in Lubbock, Texas.*

> And a vision appeared to Paul in the night; There stood a man of Macedonia, and prayed him, saying, Come over into Macedonia, and help us.
>
> —*Acts 16:9*

That spring, Charles McGlocklin told me that Glenn Summerford's cousins, Billy and Jimmy, had started a new church on top of Sand Mountain, near a place called Macedonia. Charles didn't worship with them, though.

"Why not?" I asked.

Brother Charles took a deep breath and surveyed the land around him, yellow and gray in the afternoon light. We were on the deck behind his and Aline's trailer in New Hope, Alabama. Beside the trailer was a doghouse for their blue tick hound named Smokey, and behind it was a corral for their horse, a buckskin mare named Dixie Honeydew.

"I know enough about some of those people to know I ought not to worship anymore with them," Charles said. As a snake handler, he had set himself apart from the world, and sometimes he even set himself apart from other snake handlers. It was part of the Southern character, I thought, to be always turning away like that toward some secret part of oneself.

"You know how much I love you," Charles said. He put one of his big hands on my shoulder and shook it. "You're my brother. But anytime you go up there on Sand Mountain, you be careful."

We could hear the sound of the wind through trees, a soughing, dry and hesitant, and then Dixie Honeydew neighed.

"You might be anointed when you take up a serpent," Charles continued, "but if there's a witchcraft spirit in the church, it could zap your anointing and you'd be left cold turkey with a serpent in your hand and the spirit of God gone off of you. That's when you'll get bit."

We walked around the corner of the trailer, where Jim Neel was waiting for me in a truck that had belonged to his brother.

"So you really watch and remember what Brother Charles tells you," Charles whispered. "Always be careful who you take a rattlesnake from."

This sounded like solid advice.

I got into Jim's truck, and Charles motioned for us to roll a window down. "Y'all come back any time," he yelled. "And, hey, it's not us that's messed up, Brother Dennis. It's the world."

My journey had come back around to the congregation on Sand Mountain, the remnant of Glenn Summerford's flock that had left the converted service station on Wood's Cove Road in Scottsboro and then met under a brush arbor in back of J.L. Dyal's house until the weather got too cold. After worshiping for a while in the basement of an old motel, they finally found a church for sale on the mountain. It was miles from nowhere, in the middle of a hay field south of Section, Alabama, home of Tammy Little, Miss Alabama 1984. The nearest dot on the map, though, was Macedonia, a crossroads consisting of a filling station, a country store, and a junk emporium. It was not the kind of place you'd visit of your own accord. You'd have to be led there. In fact, Macedonia had gotten its name from the place in the Bible that Paul had been called to go to in a dream. Paul's first European converts to Christianity had been in Macedonia. But that was, you know, a long time ago and in another place.

Glenn Summerford's cousins, Billy and Jimmy, negotiated the deal for the church. Billy was friendly and loose limbed, with a narrow red face and buck teeth. He'd worked mostly as a carpenter, but he'd also sold coon dogs. Jimmy was less amiable but more compact. Between them, they must have been persuasive. They got the church for two thousand dollars. A guy down the road had offered five thousand, Billy said, but the owner had decided to sell it to them. "God was working in that one," he concluded.

It was called the Old Rock House Holiness Church, in spite of the fact that it wasn't made of rock. But it was old in contrast to the brick veneer churches out on highway 35, the ones with green indoor-outdoor carpet in the vestibules and blinking U-Haul It signs out front.

The Old Rock House Holiness Church had been built in 1916, a few years before Dozier Edmonds first saw people take up serpents in Jackson County, at a church in Sauty Bottom, down by Saltpeter Cave. I'd met Dozier during the brush-arbor meetings. A rail-thin old man with thick glasses and overalls, he was the father-in-law of J.L. Dyal and the husband of Burma, the snake-handling twin. Dozier said he'd seen men get bit in that church in Sauty Bottom. They didn't go to a doctor, just swelled up a little bit. He also remembered a Holiness boy at the one-room school who would fall into a trance, reach into the potbellied stove, and get himself a whole handful of hot coals. The teacher would have to tell the boy to put them back. There was a Baptist church in those days called Hell's Half Acre, Dozier said. They didn't take up serpents, but they'd do just about anything else. They were called Buckeye Baptists. They'd preach and pray till midnight, then gamble and fight till dawn. One time a man rode a horse into the church, right up to the pulpit. Out of meanness, Dozier said. Everything was different then. "They used to tie the mules up to a white mulberry bush in the square," he said. Why, he remembered when Scottsboro itself was nothing but a mud hole. When the carnival came through, the elephants were up to their bellies in mud. There wasn't even a road up Sand Mountain until Dozier helped build one. And it seemed like the Civil War had just occurred.

Dozier came from a family of sharecroppers who lived on the property of a famous Confederate veteran named Mance. He had a bullet hole through his neck. He'd built his own casket. Every Easter, Colonel Mance invited the children of the families who lived on his property to come to the big house for an egg hunt. One Easter, he wanted the children to see what he'd look like when he was dead, so he lay down in the casket and made the children march around it. Some of the grown-ups had to help get him out. It was a pine casket with metal handles on it, Dozier said. Colonel Mance eventually died, but he wasn't buried in the casket he'd made. He'd taken that thing apart years before and given the handles to the families who lived on his property, to use as knockers on the doors of their shacks.

That was the kind of place Sand Mountain had been when the Old Rock House Holiness Church was in its heyday. By the time the Summerford brothers bought it in the winter of 1993, it had fallen onto hard times. Didn't even have a back door. Paper wasps had built nests in the eaves. The green shingles on the outside were cracked, and the paint on the window sills had just about peeled off. Billy Summerford and some of the other men from the congregation repaired and restored the church as best they could. It'd be another year, though, before they could get around to putting in a bathroom. In the meantime, there would be an outhouse for the women and a bunch of trees for the men. The church happened to be sited in the very center of a grove of old oak trees. Fields of hay surrounded the grove and stretched to the horizon. As you approached the church along a dirt road during summer heat, the oak grove looked like a dark island in the middle of a shimmering sea of gold and green.

That's the way it looked to me, anyway, on a bright Sunday morning in late June, six months after the Summerfords had bought the church, when Jim and I drove up from Birmingham for their first annual homecoming. Brother Carl had invited us by phone and given us directions. He was scheduled to preach at the homecoming. Other handlers were coming from all over—from East Tennessee and South Georgia, from the mountains of Kentucky and the scrublands of the Florida panhandle. If we hadn't had Carl's directions, we'd never have found the place. The right turn off the paved road from Macedonia was unmarked. It was one of several gravel roads that angled off into the distance. Where it crossed another paved road, there finally was a sign, made of cardboard and mounted at waist level on a wooden stake. After that, the gravel turned to dirt. Dust coated the jimsonweed. The passionflowers were in bloom, and the black-berries had begun to ripen in the heat. There were no houses on this road, and no sound except for cicadas, a steady din, like the sound of approaching rain.

For once, Jim and I were early. We stepped up on a cement block to get through the back doorway of the church. The door itself was off its hinges, and none of the windows in the church had screens. There were no cushions on the pews and no ornaments of any kind, except a portrait of Jesus etched into a mirror behind the pulpit and a vase of plastic flowers on the edge of the piano bench, where a boy with a withered hand sat staring at the keys. We took our places on a back pew and watched the handlers arrive. They greeted each other with the holy kiss, women with women, men with men, as prescribed by Paul in Romans 16. Among them was the legendary Punkin Brown, the evangelist who I'd been told would wipe the sweat off his brow with rattlesnakes. Jamie Coots from Kentucky and Allen Williams from Tennessee were also there. They sat beside Punkin on the deacons' bench. All three were young and heavyset, the sons of preachers, and childhood friends. Punkin and Jamie both wore scowls, as though they were waiting for somebody to cross their paths in an unhappy way. Allen Williams, though, looked serene. Allen's father had died drinking strychnine in 1973, and his brother had died of snakebite in 1991. Maybe he thought he didn't have anything more to lose. Or maybe he was just reconciled to losing everything he had. Within six months of sitting together on the deacons' bench at the Old Rock House Church, Jamie, Allen, and Punkin would all be bit.

The church continued to fill with familiar faces, many from what used to be The Church of Jesus with Signs Following in Scottsboro, and the music began without an introduction of any kind. James Hatfield of Old Straight Creek, a Trinitarian church on the mountain, was on drums. My red-haired friend Cecil Esslinder from Scottsboro was on guitar, grinning and tapping his feet. Cecil's wife, Carolyn, stood in the very middle of the congregation, facing backward, as was her habit, to see who might come in the back way. Also in the congregation were Bobbie Sue Thompson, twins Burma and Erma, J.L. Dyal and his wife and in-laws, and just about the whole Summerford clan. The only ones missing were Charles and Aline McGlocklin. Charles was still recovering from neck surgery on an old injury, but I knew from the conversation we'd had in New Hope that even if he'd been well, he wouldn't have come.

One woman I didn't recognize told me she was from Detroit, Michigan. This came as some surprise, and her story seemed equally improbable. She said her husband used to work in the casinos in Las Vegas, and when he died she moved to Alabama and started handling rattlesnakes at the same church on Lookout Mountain where the lead singer of the group Alabama used to handle. "Didn't you see the photo?" she asked. "It was in the *National Enquirer*."

I told her I'd missed that one.

Children were racing down the aisles. High foreheads. Eyes far apart. Gaps between their front teeth. They all looked like miniature Glenn Summerfords. Maybe they were. He had at least seven children by his first wife, and all of them were old enough to have children of their own. I started to wonder if there were any bad feelings among the Summer fords about the way Brother Carl Porter had refused to let them send the church offerings to Glenn in prison.

About that time, Brother Carl himself walked in with a serpent box containing the biggest rattlesnake I'd ever seen. Carl smelled of Old Spice and rattlesnake and something else underneath: a pleasant smell, like warm bread and apples. I associated it with the Holy Ghost. The handlers had told me that the Holy Ghost had a smell, a "sweet savor," and I had begun to think I could detect it on people and in churches, even in staid, respectable churches like the one I went to in Birmingham. Anyway, that was what I smelled on Brother Carl that day as he talked about the snake in the box. "I just got him today," he said. "He's never been in church before." Carl looked over his glasses at me and smiled. He held the serpent box up to my face and tapped the screen until the snake started rattling good.

"Got your name on him," he said to me.

A shiver went up my spine, but I just shook my head and grinned.

"Come on up to the front," he said. I followed him and sat on the first pew next to J.L. Dyal, but I made a mental note to avoid Carl's eyes during the service and to stay away from that snake of his.

Billy Summerford's wife, Joyce, led the singing. She was a big woman with a voice that wouldn't quit. *"Remember how it felt, when you walked out of the wilderness, walked out of the wilderness, walked out of the wilderness. Remember how it felt, when you walked out of the wilderness . . ."* It was one of my favorite songs because it had a double meaning now. There was the actual wilderness in the Old Testament that the Israelites were led out of, and the spiritual wilderness that was its referent, the condition of being lost. But there was also the wilderness that the New World became for my father's people. I don't mean the mountains. I mean the America that grew up around them, that tangled thicket of the heart.

"Remember how it felt, when you walked out of the wilderness . . ." My throat tightened as I sang. I remembered how it had felt when I'd sobered up in 1983. It's not often you get a second chance at life like that. And I remembered the births of my girls, the children Vicki and I had thought we'd never be able to have, Looking around at the familiar faces in the congregation, I figured they were thinking about their own wildernesses and how they'd been delivered out of them. I was still coming out of mine. It was a measure of how far I'd come, that I'd be moved nearly to tears in a rundown Holiness church on Sand Mountain. But my restless and stubborn intellect was still intact. It didn't like what it saw, a crowd of men dancing up to the serpent boxes, unclasping the lids, and taking out the poisonous snakes. Reason told me it was too early in the service. The snakes hadn't been prayed over enough. There hadn't even been any preaching yet, just Billy Summerford screaming into a microphone while the music swirled around us like a fog. But the boys from Tennessee and Kentucky had been hungry to get into the boxes. Soon, Punkin Brown was shouting at his snake, a big black-phase timber rattler that he had draped around his neck. Allen Williams was offering his copperhead up like a sacrifice, hands outstretched. But Brother Carl had the prize, and everyone seemed to know it. It was a yellow-phase timber, thick and melancholy, as big as timber rattlers come. Carl glanced at me, but I wouldn't make eye contact with him. I turned away. I walked to the back of the church and took a long drink of water from the bright yellow cooler propped up against a portrait of Jesus with his head on fire.

"Who knows what this snake is thinking?" Carl shouted. "God knows! God understands the mind of this snake!" And when I turned back around, Carl had laid the snake down and was treading barefoot on it from tail to head, as though he were walking a tightrope. Still, the snake didn't bite. I had heard about this, but never seen it before. The passage was from Luke: *Behold, I give unto you power to tread on serpents and scorpions, and over all the power of the enemy: and nothing shall by any means hurt you.* Then Carl picked the snake back up and draped it around his neck. The snake seemed to be looking for a way out of its predicament. Carl let it nuzzle into his shirt. Then the snake pulled back and cocked its head, as if in preparation to strike Carl's chest. Its head was as big as a child's hand.

Help him, Jesus! someone yelled above the din. Instead of striking, the snake started to climb Carl's sternum toward his collarbone. It went up the side of his neck and then lost interest and fell back against his chest.

The congregation was divided into two camps now, the men to the left, with the snakes, the women to the right, with each other. In front of Carl, one of the men suddenly began jumping straight up and down, as though he were on a pogo stick. Down the aisle he went and around the sanctuary. When he returned, he collapsed at Carl's feet. One of the Summerford brothers attended to him there by soaking his handkerchief with olive oil and dabbing it against the man's forehead until he sat up and yelled, "Thank God!"

In the meantime, in the corner where the women had gathered, Joyce Summerford's sister, Donna, an attractive young woman in a lime green dress, was laboring in the spirit with a cataleptic friend. She circled the friend, eyeing her contortions carefully, and then, as if fitting her into an imaginary dress, she clothed her in the spirit with her hands, an invisible tuck here, an invisible pin there, making sure the spirit draped well over the flailing arms. It took her a while. Both of the women were drenched in sweat and stuttering in tongues by the time they finished.

"They say we've gone crazy!" Brother Carl shouted above the chaos. He was pacing in front of the pulpit, the enormous rattlesnake balanced now across his shoulder. "Well, they're right!" he cried. "I've gone crazy! I've gone Bible crazy! I've got the papers here to prove it!" And he waved his worn Bible in the air. "Some people say we're just a bunch of fanatics!"

Amen. Thank God.

"Well, we are! *Hai-i-salemos-ah-cahn-ne-hi-yee!* Whew! That last one nearly took me out of here!"

It's not true that you become used to the noise and confusion of a snake-handling Holiness service. On the contrary, you become enmeshed in it. It is theater at its most intricate—improvisational, spiritual jazz. The more you experience it, the more attentive you are to the shifts in the surface and the dark shoals underneath. For every outward sign, there is a spiritual equivalent. When somebody falls to his knees, a specific problem presents itself, and the others know exactly what to do, whether it's oil for a healing, or a prayer cloth thrown over the shoulders, or a devil that needs to be cast out. The best, of course, the simplest and cleanest, is when someone gets the Holy Ghost for the first time. The younger the worshiper, the easier it seems to be for the Holy

Ghost to descend and speak—lips loosened, tongue flapping, eyes rolling backward in the head. It transcends the erotic when a thirteen-year-old girl gets the Holy Ghost. The older ones often take time. I once saw an old man whose wife had gotten the Holy Ghost at a previous service. He wanted it bad for himself, he said. Brother Charles McGlocklin started praying with him before the service even started, and all through it, the man was in one attitude or another at the front of the church—now lying spread-eagled on the floor, while a half dozen men prayed over him and laid on hands, now up and running from one end of the sanctuary to the other, now twirling, now swooning, now collapsing once again on the floor, his eyes like the eyes of a horse that smells smoke, the unknown tongue spewing from his mouth. He got the Holy Ghost at last! He got the Holy Ghost! you think, until you see him after the service eating a pimiento cheese sandwich down-stairs. His legs are crossed. He's brushing the crumbs from his lap. He agrees it was a good service all right, but it sure would have been better if he'd only gotten the Holy Ghost. You can never get enough of the Holy Ghost. Maybe that's what he means. You can never exhaust the power when the Spirit comes down, not even when you take up a snake, not even when you take up a dozen of them. The more faith you expend, the more power is released. It's an inexhaustible, eternally renewable resource. It's the only power some of these people have.

So the longer you witness it, unless you just don't get into the spontaneous and unexpected, the more you become a part of it. *I* did, and the handlers could tell. They knew before I did what was going to happen. They saw me angling in. They were already making room for me in front of the deacons' bench. As I said, I'd always been drawn to danger. Alcohol. Psychedelics. War. If it made me feel good, I'd do it. I was always up for a little trip. I figured if I could trust my guide, I'd be all right. I'd come back to earth in one piece. I wouldn't really lose my mind. That's what I thought, anyway. I couldn't be an astronaut, but there were other things I could do and be. So I got up there in the middle of the handlers. J.L. Dyal, dark and wiry, was standing on my right; a clean-cut boy named Steve Frazier on my left. Who was it going to be? Carl's eyes were saying, you. And yes, it was the big rattler, the one with my name on it, acrid-smelling, carnal, alive. And the look in Carl's eyes seemed to change as he approached me. He was embarrassed. The snake was all he had, his eyes seemed to say. But as low as it was, as repulsive, if I took it, I'd be possessing the sacred. Nothing was required except obedience. Nothing had to be given up except my own will. This was the moment. I didn't stop to think about it. I just gave in. I stepped forward and took the snake with both hands. Carl released it to me. I turned to face the congregation and lifted the rattlesnake up toward the light. It was moving like it wanted to get up even higher, to climb out of that church and into the air. And it was exactly as the handlers had told me. I felt no fear. The snake seemed to be an extension of myself. And suddenly there seemed to be nothing in the room but me and the snake. Everything else had disappeared. Carl, the congregation, Jim—all gone, all faded to white. And I could not hear the earsplitting music. The air was silent and still and filled with that strong, even light. And I realized that I, too, was fading into the white. I was losing myself by degrees, like the incredible shrinking man. The snake would be the last to go, and all I could see was the way its scales shimmered one last time in the light, and the way its head moved from side to side, searching for a way out. I knew then why the handlers took up serpents. There is power in the act of disappearing; there is victory in the loss of self. It must be close to our conception of paradise, what it's like before you're born or after you die.

I came back in stages, first with the recognition that the shouting I had begun to hear was coming from my own mouth. Then I realized I was holding a rattlesnake, and the church rushed back with all its clamor, heat, and smell. I remembered Carl and turned toward where I thought he might be. I lowered the snake to waist level. It was an enormous animal, heavy and firm. The scales on its side were as rough as calluses. I could feel its muscles rippling beneath the skin. I was aware it was not a part of me now and that I couldn't predict what it might do. I extended it toward Carl. He took it from me, stepped to the side, and gave it in turn to J.L.

"Jesus," J.L. said. "Oh, Jesus." His knees bent, his head went back. I knew it was happening to him too.

Then I looked around and saw that I was in a semicircle of handlers by the deacons' bench. Most had returned their snakes to the boxes, but Billy Summerford, Glenn's buck-toothed cousin, still had one, and he offered it to me, a medium-sized canebrake that was rattling violently. I took the snake in one hand without thinking. It was smaller than the first, but angrier, and I realized circumstances were different now. I couldn't seem to steer it away from my belt line. Fear had started to come back to me. I remembered with sudden clarity what Brother Charles had said about being careful who you took a snake from. I studied the canebrake as if I were seeing it for the first time and then gave it back to Billy Summerford. He passed it to Steve Frazier, the young man on my left. I watched Steve cradle it, curled and rattling furiously in his hands, and then I walked out the side door of the church and onto the steps, where Bobbie Sue Thompson was clutching her throat and leaning against the green shingles of the church.

"Jesus," she said. "Jesus, Jesus."

It was a sunny, fragrant day, with high-blown clouds. I looked into Bobbie Sue's face. Her eyes were wide and her mouth hooked at the corner. "Jesus," she said.

I thought at first she was in terrible pain, but then I realized she wasn't. "Yes. I know. Jesus," I said.

At the conclusion of the service, Brother Carl reminded everyone there would be dinner on the grounds. Most of the women had already slipped out, to arrange their casseroles and platters of ham on the butcher paper that covered the tables the men had set up under the trees. Jim and I waited silently in line for fried chicken, sweet potatoes, and black bottom pie, which we ate standing up among a knot of men who were discussing the merits of various coon dogs they'd owned. "The next time you handle a snake," Jim whispered, "try to give me a little warning. I ran out of film."

I told him I'd try, but that it was not something I'd be likely to do in the future, or be able to predict even if I did. There was more I wanted to tell him, but I didn't know how, and besides, I figured he knew. We'd lain in a ditch together thinking we were dead men. It was pretty much the same thing, I guessed. That kind of terror and joy.

"This one I had, it was a cur," said Gene Sherbert, a handler with a flattop and a scar. "He treed two coons at the same time."

"Same tree?" one of the other men asked.

"Naw," Gene said. "It was two separate trees, and that fool dog nearly run himself to death going back and forth."

The men laughed. "Was that Sport?" another man asked.

"Sport was Brother Glenn's dog," Gene said, and he turned his attention back to his plate.

I remembered then that Gene Sherbert was the man Glenn Summerford had accused Darlene of running with. I tried to imagine them in bed together—his flattop, her thick auburn hair. Gene was also Brother Carl's cousin. He'd kept the church in Kingston going while Carl did drugs and chased women on the Coast. Where was Brother Carl? I found a trash bag for my paper plate and went off to find him. I still felt like I had not come back all the way from the handling. My feet were light, my head still encased in an adrenaline cocoon. The air in the oak grove was golden. A breeze moved in the leaves and sent a stack of paper plates tumbling across the grass. On the breeze I heard snatches of a sweet and gentle melody. It was coming from a circle of handlers at the edge of the grove. Some were standing, some leaning against cars, some squatting on their heels in the dirt. As I got closer, I saw that Cecil Esslinder, the redheaded guitar player from Scottsboro, was sitting in the center of the circle. He was playing a dulcimer under the trees.

I stopped and listened. I'd never heard music more beautiful. It was filled with remorse and desire. When it ended, I asked Cecil what song he'd been playing. He shrugged. A hymn about Jesus. I asked how long he'd been playing the dulcimer.

"Never played one before in my life," he said.

His wife, Carolyn, was leaning into the fender of a battered Dodge Dart behind him. "Come on, Cecil," she said.

"I want to go. My head is killing me."

Cecil smiled up at me, but he was talking to Carolyn. "You ought to go up and get anointed with oil. Let 'em lay hands on you. Ask for a healing. God'll heal you."

"I know that," Carolyn said. "But you've got to have faith."

"You've *got* faith," Cecil said, still smiling at me.

"My faith's been a little poorly." She took a pill bottle from the pocket of her dress. "I'm putting my faith in here," she said.

Cecil just laughed, and so did the other men. He handed the dulcimer back to its owner and stood up from the grass. "There's something I forgot to tell you," he said to me, although I couldn't even remember the last time we'd talked.

"You have to be careful when you're casting out demons," he said. "An evil spirit can come right from that person into *you.*"

"That's when it washed over me, the memory of the story I'd written when I was nineteen. "Salvation on Sand Mountain." About a church like the Old Rock House Holiness Church, and two brothers, family men, who pretend to get saved, so they can fake their own rapture, caught up like Elijah in the air, when what they're really doing is running off to live with their girlfriends in Fort Payne. I'd never been on Sand Mountain when I wrote the story, but twenty-five years later, I knew that this was the place. This was the church, in a grove of oak trees, surrounded on all sides by fields of hay. I don't mean it resembled the church in my story. What I mean is that this was the church *itself.*

At the heart of the impulse to tell stories is a mystery so profound that even as I begin to speak of it, the hairs on the back of my hand are starting to stand on end. I believe that the writer has another eye, not a literal eye, but an eye on the inside of his head. It is the eye with which he sees the imaginary, three-dimensional, world where the story he is writing takes place. But it is also the eye with which the writer beholds the connectedness of things, of past, present, and future. The writer's literal eyes are like vestigial organs, useless except to record physical details. The only eye worth talking about is the eye in the middle of the writer's head, the one that casts its pale, sorrowful light backward over the past and forward into the future, taking everything in at once, the whole story, from beginning to end.

I found Brother Carl by his pickup truck. He was talking to J.L. Dyal. They'd just loaded the big yellow-phase rattler into the bed of the truck, and they were giving him one last look.

Carl hugged me when I walked up. "I sure am proud of you," he said.

I asked if he was leaving for Georgia already.

"I've got to get back to God's country," he said.

While Carl went to say goodbye to some of the others, J.L. and I stared at the snake in the back of the truck. I told J.L. I just couldn't believe that we'd taken it up.

"It's something, all right," he said.

I asked what it had been like for him.

"It's love, that's all it is," he said. "You love the Lord, you love the Word, you love your brother and sister. You're in one mind, one accord, you're all combined together. The Bible says we're each a part of the body, and when it all comes together . . . Hey!" He whistled through his teeth. "What was it like for you?" he asked.

I didn't know what to say.

It's hard for me to talk about myself. As a journalist, I've always tried to keep out of the story. But look what had happened to me. I loved Brother Carl, but sometimes I suspected he was crazy. Sometimes I thought he was intent on getting himself, and maybe the rest of us, killed. Half the time I walked around saying to myself, "This thing is real! This thing is real!" The other half of the time, I walked around thinking that nothing was real, and that if there really was a God, we must have been part of a dream he was having, and when he woke up . . . *poof!* Either way, I worried I'd gone off the edge, and nobody would be able to pull me back. One of my uncles by marriage was a Baptist minister, one of the kindest men I've ever known. I was fifteen, though, when he killed himself, and I didn't know the whole story. I just knew that he sent his family and friends a long, poignant, and some have said beautiful letter about how he was ready to go meet Abraham, Isaac, and Jacob. I believe he ran a high-voltage line from his basement to a ground-floor bedroom. He put "How Great Thou Art" on the record player. Then he lay down on the bed, reached up, and grabbed the live wire. He left a widow and two sons. My uncle's death confirmed a suspicion of mine that madness and religion were a hair's breadth away. My beliefs about the nature of God and man have changed over the years, but that one never has. Feeling after God is dangerous business. And Christianity without passion, danger, and mystery may not really be Christianity at all.

We AIM Not to Please

Mary Crow Dog

*Mary Crow Dog (1953-2013) was born Mary Brave Bird on Rosebud
Reservation, South Dakota. The dwelling she was raised in, typical of housing on the
reservation, was without electricity, running water, or a phone. Crow Dog's grandparents were her primary guardians; for many twentieth century Sioux children, being
raised by grandparents was the closest they got to being a part of a "tiyospaye", a traditional hunting band made up mostly of extended family. She never really knew her
father, claiming "He stayed around just long enough until mom got pregnant with me.
Then he split." Though she was raised primarily by Sioux grandparents, Crow Dog's
childhood did not center on Sioux culture. Because they wanted Crow Dog to assimilate into mainstream American society, her grandparents did not tell her much about
her ancestral background, nor did they speak their native tongue with her. As part of
the attempt to facilitate her assimilation into mainstream America, Crow Dog was
sent to a Catholic boarding school, where she suffered physical abuse at the hands of
the teachers. After quitting school, Crow Dog was generally aimless and spent her time
drinking, a habit she claims her stepfather taught her when she was only ten. She cred-
its her chance encounter with activists from the American Indian Movement (AIM)
with giving her life a sense of direction. Her introduction to the movement is chroni-
cled in "We AIM Not to Please", a selection from her 1990 autobiography* Lakota
Woman *which she co-wrote with Richard Erdoes. As a teenager, Crow Dog's experience with AIM also finally gave her the connection to her Native American heritage
she had longed for. Through the movement she met Leonard Crow Dog, a Sioux medicine man and AIM leader, and began learning from him and others a previously
unknown part of her heritage, the rituals of Native American spirituality. Her*

involvement in the protests also soon became personally significant for Mary Crow Dog; she would marry her mentor, Leonard Crow Dog, and take his surname. In 1973, she took part with AIM activists, in the occupation of Wounded Knee. The 71-day siege of a museum, church, and trading post (during which time 17-year-old Crow Dog, who was pregnant, went into labor) is also documented in the TNT movie Lakota Woman: Siege at Wounded Knee *(1994), which is based on Crow Dog's autobiography. The occupation was historically significant in that it commemorated the Wounded Knee Massacre (1890), which was the last major conflict between Native Americans and United States government troops and resulted in the deaths of 29 U.S. soldiers and 200 Native Americans, most of whom were women, children, and sick, wounded, or aged men. In* Lakota Woman, *Crow Dog's account of what it meant to be a Sioux woman in a white world, she is not shy to expose the darker challenges she faced. At one point she boldly insists that "If you plan to be born, make sure you are born white and male." Simultaneously, however, her straightforward discussion of Native American life and the movement documents a rising sense of tribal and ancestral pride.*

They call us the New Indians.
Hell, we are the Old Indians,
the landlords of this continent,
coming to collect the rent.
        —Dennis Banks

The American Indian Movement hit our reservation like a tornado, like a new wind blowing out of nowhere, a drumbeat from far off getting louder and louder. It was almost like the Ghost Dance fever that had hit the tribes in 1890, old uncle Dick Fool Bull said, spreading like a prairie fire. It even was like the old Ghost Dance song Uncle Dick was humming:

Maka sitomniya teca ukiye
Oyate ukiye, oyate ukiye . . .
A new world is coming,
A nation is coming,
The eagle brought the message.

I could feel this new thing, almost hear it, smell it, touch it. Meeting up with AIM for the first time loosened a sort of earthquake inside me. Old Black Elk in recounting his life often used the expression "As I look down from the high hill of my great old age . . ." Well, as I am looking from the hill of my old age—I am thirty-seven now but feel as if I have lived for a long time—I can see things in perspective, not subjectively, no, but in perspective. Old Black Elk had a good way of saying it. You really look back upon ten years gone past as from a hill—you have a sort of bird's-eye view. I recognize now that movements get used up and the leaders get burned out quickly. Some of our men and women got themselves killed and thereby avoided reaching the dangerous age of thirty and becoming "elder statesmen." Some leaders turned into college professors, founded alternative schools, or even took jobs as tribal officials. A few live on in the past, refusing to recognize that the dreams of the past must give way to the dreams of the future. I, that wild, rebellious teenager of ten years ago, am nursing a baby, changing diapers, and making breakfast for my somewhat extended family. And yet it was great while it lasted and I still feel that old excitement merely talking about it. Some people loved AIM, some hated it, but nobody ignored it.

I loved it. My first encounter with AIM was at a powwow held in 1971 at Crow Dog's place after the Sun Dance. Pointing at Leonard Crow Dog, I asked a young woman, "Who is that man?"

"That's Crow Dog," she said. I was looking at his long, shining braids. Wearing one's hair long at the time was still something of a novelty on the res. I asked, "Is that his real hair?"

"Yes, that's his real hair."

I noticed that almost all of the young men wore their hair long, some with eagle feathers tied to it. They all had on ribbon shirts. They had a new look about them, not that hangdog reservation look I was used to. They moved in a different way, too, confident and swaggering, the girls as well as the boys. Belonging to many tribes, they had come in a dilapidated truck covered with slogans and paintings. They had traveled to the Sun Dance all the way from California, where they had taken part in the occupation of Alcatraz Island.

One man, a Chippewa, stood up and made a speech. I had never heard anybody talk like that. He spoke about genocide and sovereignty, about tribal leaders selling out and kissing ass—white man's ass. He talked about giving up the necktie for the choker, the briefcase for the bedroll, the missionary's church for the sacred pipe. He talked about not celebrating Thanksgiving, because that would be celebrating one's own destruction. He said that white people, after stealing our land and massacring us for three hundred years, could not come to us now saying, "Celebrate Thanksgiving with us, drop in for a slice of turkey." He had himself wrapped up in an upside-down American flag, telling us that every star in this flag represented a state stolen from Indians.

Then Leonard Crow Dog spoke, saying that we had talked to the white man for generations with our lips, but that he had no ears to hear, no eyes to see, no heart to feel. Crow Dog said that now we must speak with our bodies and that he was not afraid to die for his people. It was a very emotional speech.

Some people wept. An old man turned to me and said, "These are the words I always wanted to speak, but had kept shut up within me."

I asked one of the young men, "What kind of Indians are you?" "We are AIM," he told me, "American Indian Movement. We're going to change things."

AIM was born in 1968. Its fathers were mostly men doing time in Minnesota prisons, Ojibways. It got its start in the slums of St. Paul taking care of Indian ghetto problems. It was an Indian woman who gave it its name. She told me, "At first we called ourselves 'Concerned Indian Americans' until somebody discovered that the initials spelled CIA. That didn't sound so good. Then I spoke up: 'You guys all aim to do this, or you aim to do that. Why don't you call yourselves AIM, American Indian Movement?' And that was that."

In the beginning AIM was mainly confined to St. Paul and Minneapolis. The early AIM people were mostly ghetto Indians, often from tribes which had lost much of their language, traditions, and ceremonies. It was when they came to us on the Sioux reservations that they began to learn about the old ways. We had to learn from them, too. We Sioux had lived very isolated behind what some people called the "Buckskin Curtain." AIM opened a window for us through which the wind of the 1960s and early '70s could blow, and it was no gentle breeze but a hurricane that whirled us around. It was after the traditional reservation Indians and the ghetto kids had gotten together that AIM became a force nationwide. It was flint striking flint, lighting a spark which grew into a flame at which we could warm ourselves after a long, long winter.

After I joined AIM I stopped drinking. Others put away their roach clips and airplane glue bottles. There were a lot of things wrong with AIM. We did not see these things, or did not want to see them. At the time these things were unimportant. What was important was getting it on. We kids became AIM's spearheads and the Sioux set the style. The AIM uniform was Sioux all the way, the black "angry hats" with the feathers stuck in the hatband, the bone chokers, the medicine pouches worn on our breasts, the Levi's jackets on which we embroidered our battle honors—Alcatraz, Trail of Broken Treaties, Wounded Knee. Some dudes wore a third, extra-thin braid as a scalp lock. We made up our own songs—forty-niners, honoring songs, songs for a warrior behind bars in the slammer. The AIM song was made up by a fourteen-year-old Sioux boy. The Ojibways say it was made up by one of their own kids, but we know better.

We all had a good mouth, were good speakers and wrote a lot of poetry, though we were all dropouts who could not spell. We took some of our rhetoric from the blacks, who had started their movements before we did. Like them we were minorities, poor and discriminated against, but there were differences. I think it significant that in many Indian languages a black is called a "black white man." The blacks want what the whites have, which is under-standable. They want *in*. We Indians want *out!* That is the main difference.

At first we hated all whites because we knew only one kind—the John Wayne kind. It took time before we met whites to whom we could relate and whose friendships we could accept. One of our young men met a pretty girl. She said she was Indian and looked it. She told him, "Sleep with me." In bed, in the middle of the night, he somehow found out that she was Puerto Rican. He got so mad that she was not a real skin that he beat up on her. He wanted to have to do only with Indian girls and felt tricked. He had run away from a real bad foster home, seeking refuge among his own kind. Later he felt ashamed for what he had done and apologized. Eventually we were joined by a number of Chicano brothers and sisters and learned to love and respect them, but it took time. We lived in a strange, narrow world of our own, sus-picious of all outsiders. Later, we found ourselves making speeches on cam-puses, in churches, and on street corners talking to prominent supporters such as Marlon Brando, Dick Gregory, Rip Torn, Jane Fonda, and Angela Davis. It was a long-drawn-out process of learning and experiencing, this widening of our horizons.

We formed relationships among ourselves and with outsiders. We had girls who would go to bed with any warrior who had done something brave. Other girls loved one boy only. Usually a boy would say to a girl, "Be my old lady," and she might answer, "Ohan, you are my old man." They would go find a medicine man to feather and cedar them, to smoke the pipe with them, to put a red blanket around their shoulders. That made them man and wife Indian style. Then they slept under the same blanket. The white law did not recognize such a marriage, but we would respect it. It might last only a few days. Either of them could have a run in with the law and wind up in jail or be blown away by the goons. We did not exactly lead stable lives, but some of these marriages lasted for years. Short or long, it was good while it lasted. The girl had somebody to protect and take care of her; the boy had a wincincala to cook his beans or sew him a ribbon shirt. They inspired each other to the point where they would put their bodies on the line together. It gave them something precious to remember all their lives. One seventeen-year-old boy had a twenty-two-year-old girl-friend. He called her "grandma." He had a T-shirt made for her with the word GRANDMA on it, and one for himself with the legend I LOVE GRANDMA. He was heartbroken when she left him for an "older man." Some of the AIM leaders attracted quite a number of "wives." We called them "wives of the month."

I got into one of these marriages myself. It lasted just long enough for me to get pregnant. Birth control went against our beliefs. We felt that there were not enough Indians left to suit us. The more future warriors we brought into the world, the better. My older sister Barbara got pregnant too. She went to the BIA hospital where the doctors told her she needed a cesarean. When she came to, the doctors informed her that they had taken her womb out. In their opinion, at that time, there were already too many little red bastards for the taxpayers to take care of. No use to mollycoddle those happy-go-lucky, irresponsible, oversexed AIM women. Barb's child lived for two hours. With better care, it might have made it. For a number of years BIA doctors performed thousands of forced sterilizations on Indian and Chicano women without their knowledge or consent. For this reason I was happy at the thought of having a baby, not only for myself but for Barbara, too. I was determined not to have my child in a white hospital.

In the meantime I had nine months to move around, still going from confrontation to confrontation. Wherever anthros were digging up human remains from Indian sites, we were there threatening to dig up white graves to display white men's skulls and bones in glass cases. Wherever there was an Indian political trial, we showed up before the court-house with our drums. Wherever we saw a bar with a sign NO INDIANS ALLOWED, we sensitized the owners, sometimes quite forcefully. Somehow we always found old jalopies to travel in, painted all over with Red Power slogans, and always found native people to take us in, treating us to meat soup, fry bread, and thick, black coffee. We existed entirely without money, yet we ate, traveled, and usually found a roof over our heads.

Something strange happened then. The traditional old, full-blood medicine men joined in with us kids. Not the middle-aged adults. They were of a lost generation which had given up all hope, necktie-wearers waiting for the Great White Father to do for them. It was the real old folks who had spirit and wisdom to give us. The grandfathers and grandmothers who still remembered a time when Indians were Indians, whose own grandparents or even parents had fought Custer gun in hand, people who for us were living links with a great past. They had a lot of strength and power, enough to give some of it to us. They still knew all the old legends and the right way to put on a ritual, and we were eager to learn from them. Soon they had us young girls making flesh offerings or piercing our wrists at the Sun Dance, while young warriors again put the skewers through their breast and found out the hard way where they came from. Even those who had grown up in cities, who had never been on a horse or heard an owl hoot, were suddenly getting it together. I am not bragging, but I am proud that we Lakotas started this.

The old grandmothers especially made a deep impression upon me. Women like Lizzy Fast Horse, a great-grandmother, who scrambled up all the way to the top of Mount Rushmore, standing right on the top of those gigantic bald pates, reclaiming the Black Hills for their rightful owners. Lizzy who was dragged down the mountain by the troopers, handcuffed to her nine-year-old great-granddaughter until their wrists were cut, their blood falling in drops on the snow. It is really true, the old Cheyenne saying: "A nation is not dead until the hearts of its women are on the ground." Well, the hearts of our old full-blood women were not on the ground. They were way up high and they could still encourage us with their trilling, spine-tingling brave-heart cry which always made the hairs on my back stand up and my flesh break out in goose pimples whenever I heard it, no matter how often.

We did freak out the honkies. We were feared throughout the Dakotas. I could never figure out why this should have been so. We were always the victims. We never maimed or killed. It was we who died or got crippled. Aside from ripping off a few trading posts, we were not really bad. We were loud-mouthed, made a lot of noise, and got on some people's nerves. We made Mr. White Man realize that there were other Indians besides the poor human wrecks who posed for him for a quarter—but that should not have made them kill us or hide from us under their beds. "The AIMs is coming, the AIMs is coming" was the cry that went up whenever a couple of fourteen-year-old skins in Uncle Joe hats showed up. The ranchers and the police spread the most fantastic rumors about us. The media said that we were about to stage bank robberies, storm prisons, set fire to the state capitol, blow up Mount Rushmore, and assassinate the governor. The least we were accused of was that we were planning to paint the noses of the giant Mount Rushmore heads red. Worst of all we were scaring the tourists away. The concessionaires at Rushmore and in all the Black Hills tourist traps were losing money. It was only right to kill us for that.

I think it was their bad conscience which made the local whites hate us so much. Bill Kunstler, the movement lawyer who defended us in a number of trials, once said: "You hate those most whom you have injured most." The whites near the reservations were all living on land stolen from us—stolen not in the distant past, but by their fathers and grand-fathers. They all made their living in some way by exploiting us, by using Indians as cheap labor, by running their cattle on reservation land for a mere pittance in lease money, by using us as colorful props to attract the Eastern tourists. They could only relate to the stereotyped song-and-dance Indian, locking their doors and cowering behind their curtains whenever we came to town, crying: "The AIMs is coming, get the police." Always a day or two after we made our appearance all the gun shops in the place were sold out. White folks took to toting guns again. They carried revolvers wherever they went, slept with loaded .38s under their pillows, drove around with high-powered rifles in racks behind the seats of their pickups. It was rumored that the then governor of South Dakota, who once vowed to put every AIM member behind bars or six feet underground, had imported a special, quick-firing, newly invented type of machine gun from West Germany and installed it in the dome of the state capitol, where he spent hours, training the gun on Indians who happened to walk by, zeroing in, moving the gun silently back and forth, back and forth. It may be only a story, but knowing the man, I am prepared to believe it. I did not mind their being afraid of us. It was better than being given a quarter and asked to pose smilingly for their cameras.

We were not angels. Some things were done by AIM, or rather by people who *called* themselves AIM, that I am not proud of. But AIM gave us a lift badly needed at the time. It defined our goals and expressed our innermost yearnings. It set a style for Indians to imitate. Even those Native Americans who maintained that they wanted to have nothing to do with AIM, that it ran counter to their tribal ways of life, began to dress and talk in the AIM manner. I have had some conflicts with the American Indian Movement at some time or another. I don't know whether it will live or die. Some people say that a movement dies the moment it becomes acceptable. In this case there should be some life left in its body, at least in the Dakotas. But whatever happens, one can't take away from AIM that it fulfilled its function and did what had to be done at a time which was decisive in the development of Indian America.

The Sun Dance at Rosebud in the late summer of 1972 will forever remain in my memory. Many of the AIM leaders came to Crow Dog's place to dance, to make flesh offerings, to endure the self-torture of this, our most sacred rite, gazing at the sun, blowing on their eagle-bone whistles, praying with the pipe. It was like a rebirth, like some of the prophesies of the Ghost Dancers coming true. The strange thing was seeing men undergoing the ordeal of the Sun Dance who came from tribes which had never practiced this ritual. I felt it was their way of saying, "I am an Indian again."

This Sun Dance was also an occasion for getting to know each other, for a lot of serious talk. I was happy watching the women taking a big part in these discussions. One of the AIM men laughingly said, "For years we couldn't get the women to speak up, and now we can't get them to shut up." I just listened. I was still too shy and too young to do anything else but stay in the background.

The people were tensed up. Everything was in ferment. The mood was bitter. News reached us after the Sun Dance that Richard Oaks, from the Mohawk tribe, a much loved and respected leader at Alcatraz, had been murdered by a white man. Not long before that a Sioux, Raymond Yellow Thunder, a humble, hard-working man, had been stripped naked and forced at gunpoint to dance in an American Legion hall at Gordon, Nebraska. Later he was beaten to death—just for the fun of it. Before that a millionaire rancher had shot and killed an unarmed Indian from Pine Ridge, Norman Little Brave, and gone unpunished. Norman had been a sober-minded church-goer, but that had not saved him. It was open season on Indians again and the people were saying, "Enough of this shit!" It was out of these feelings of anger, hope, and despair that the "Trail of Broken Treaties" was born.

I am still proud that it was born at Rosebud, among my people. That is probably bad. The feeling of pride in one's particular tribe is standing in the way of Indian unity. Still it is there and it is not all bad. The man who first thought of having caravans of Indians converging upon Washington from all directions was Bob Burnette. He had been tribal chairman at Rosebud and he was not an AIM member. Other Indian leaders of this caravan, such as Hank Adams, Reuben Snake, and Sid Mills—Sid and Hank from the Northwest, where they had been fighting for native fishing rights—were not AIM. Neither were the Six Nation people from upstate New York or the representatives of some Southwestern tribes, but though they had not started it, it was the AIM leaders who dominated this march in the end.

The Trail of Broken Treaties was the greatest action taken by Indians since the Battle of the Little Big Horn. As Eddie Benton, the Ojibway medicine man, told us: "There is a prophecy in our tribe's religion that one day we would all stand together. All tribes would hook arms in brotherhood and unite. I am elated because I lived to see this happen. Brothers and sisters from all over this continent united in a single cause. That is the greatest significance to Indian people . . . not what happened or what may yet happen as a result of our actions."

Each caravan was led by a spiritual leader or medicine man with his sacred pipe. The Oklahoma caravan followed the Cherokees' "Trail of Tears," retracing the steps of dying Indians driven from their homes by President Andrew Jackson. Our caravan started from Wounded Knee. This had a special symbolic meaning for us Sioux, making us feel as if the ghosts of all the women and children murdered there by the Seventh Cavalry were rising out of their mass grave to go with us.

I traveled among friends from Rosebud and Pine Ridge. My brother and my sister Barbara were among this group. I did not know what to expect. A huge protest march like this was new to me. When we arrived in Washington we got lost. We had been promised food and accommodation, but due to government pressure many church groups which had offered to put us up and feed us got scared and backed off. It was almost dawn and still we were stumbling around looking for a place to bed down. I could hardly keep my eyes open. One thing we did accomplish: in the predawn light we drove around the White House, honking our horns and beating our drums to let President Nixon know that we had arrived.

We were finally given a place to sleep in, an old, dilapidated, and abandoned church. I had just crawled into my bedroll when I saw what I thought to be a fair-sized cat walking over it. I put my glasses on and discovered that it was a big rat, the biggest and ugliest I had ever seen. The church was in an uproar. Women screamed. Mine was not the only rat in the place, as it turned out. An old lady who had hitchhiked two thousand miles from Cheyenne

River to get to Washington complained that the toilets were broken. It was the first week of November and there was no heat. An elderly Canadian Indian dragged himself around on crutches. His legs were crippled and he could find no soft place to rest. A young girl shouted that there were not only rats but also millions of cockroaches. A young Ojibway man said that he had not left the slums of St. Paul for this kind of facility. I told him that I had expected nothing else. Did he think Nixon would put him up at the Holiday Inn with wall-to-wall carpeting and color TV? Everywhere groups were standing huddled together in their blankets. People were saying, "They promised us decent housing. Look how they're treating us. We ain't gonna stand for this."

Somebody suggested, "Let's all go to the BIA." It seemed the natural thing to do, to go to the Bureau of Indian Affairs building on Constitution Avenue. They would have to put us up. It was "our" building after all. Besides, that was what we had come for, to complain about the treatment the bureau was dishing out to us. Everybody suddenly seemed to be possessed by the urge to hurry to the BIA. Next thing I knew we were in it. We spilled into the building like a great avalanche. Some people put up a tipi on the front lawn. Security guards were appointed. They put on red armbands or fastened rainbow-colored bits of cloth to their ribbon shirts or denim jackets. They watched the doors. Tribal groups took over this or that room, the Iroquois on one floor, the Sioux on another. The Oklahoma Indians, the Northwest Coast people, all made themselves a place to stay. Children were playing while old ladies got comfortable on couches in the foyer. A drum was roaring. I could smell kinnikinnick—Indian tobacco. Someone put up a sign over the front gate reading INDIAN COUNTRY. The building finally belonged to us and we lost no time turning it into a tribal village.

My little group settled down in one room on the second floor. It was nice—thick carpets, subdued light, soft couches, and easy chairs. The bureaucrats sure knew how to live. They had marble stairs, wrought-iron banisters, fine statues and paintings depicting the Noble Savage, valuable artifacts. I heard somebody speaking Sioux. I opened a door and there was Leonard Crow Dog talking to some young men, telling them why we were here, explaining what it all meant. Somebody motioned to me: "Quiet! Crow Dog is talking!" Young as I was, Crow Dog seemed an old man to me, old with responsibilities, but he was only thirty-two then. It did not occur to me that one day I would bear his children.

The takeover of the BIA building had not been planned. We honestly thought that arrangements for our stay had been made. When the promises turned out to be the same old buffalo shit, as one of the leaders put it, we simply occupied the BIA. It was a typical spontaneous Indian happening. Nobody had ordered us to do it. We were not very amenable to orders anyhow. It's not our style. The various tribal groups caucussed in their rooms, deciding what proposals to make. From time to time everybody would go down into the great hall and thrash out the proposals. The assembly hall had a stage, many chairs, and loudspeakers. Always discussions opened with one of the medicine men performing a ceremony. I think it was a black civil rights organization which brought in the first truckload of food. Later various church groups and other sympathizers donated food and money. The building had a kitchen and cafeteria and we quickly organized cooking, dishwashing, and garbage details. Some women were appointed to watch the children, old people were cared for, and a medical team was set up. Contrary to what some white people believe, Indians are very good at improvising this sort of self-government with no one in particular telling them what to do. They don't wait to be told. I guess there were altogether six to eight hundred people crammed into the building, but it did not feel crowded.

The original caravan leaders had planned a peaceful and dignified protest. There had even been talk of singing and dancing for the senators and inviting the lawmakers to an Indian fry bread and corn soup feast. It might have worked out that way if somebody had been willing to listen to us. But the word had been passed to ignore us. The people who mattered, from the president down, would not talk to us. We were not wanted. It was said that we were hoodlums who did not speak for the Indian people. The half-blood tribal chairmen with their salaries and expense accounts condemned us almost to man. Nixon sent some no-account underling to tell us that he had done more for the American Indian than any predecessor and that he saw no reason for our coming to Washington, that he had more important things to do than to talk with us—presumably surreptitiously taping his visitors and planning Watergate. We wondered what all these good things were that he had done for us.

We had planned to have Crow Dog conduct a ceremony at the grave of Ira Hayes, the Pima Indian who had won the Congressional Medal of Honor at Iwo Jima, and who had died drunk and forgotten in a ditch. The army, which was in charge of Arlington Cemetery, forbade this ceremony "because it would be political, not religious." Slowly our mood changed. There was less talk of dancing and singing for the senators and more talk about getting it on. Dennis Banks said that AIM was against violence, but that it might take another Watts to bring home to the public the plight of Native Americans. Russel Means remarked to some reporters that the media were ignoring us: "What do we have to do to get some attention? Scalp somebody?" It was on this occasion that I learned that as long as we "behaved nicely" nobody gave a damn about us, but as soon as we became rowdy we got all the support and media coverage we could wish for.

We obliged them. We pushed the police and guards out of the building. Some did not wait to be pushed but jumped out of the ground-floor windows like so many frogs. We had formulated twenty Indian demands. These were all rejected by the few bureaucrats sent to negotiate with us. The most we got out of these talks was one white official holding up an Indian baby for a snapshot, saying, "Isn't she sweet?" We had not come for baby-kissing nor for kissing ass. The moderate leaders lost credibility. It was not their fault. Soon we listened to other voices as the occupation turned into a siege. I heard somebody yelling, "The pigs are here." I could see from the window that it was true. The whole building was surrounded by helmeted police armed with all kinds of guns. A fight broke out between the police and our security. Some of our young men got hit over the head with police clubs and we saw the blood streaming down their faces. There was a rumor, which turned out to be true, that we had received an ultimatum: "Clear out—or else!"

I felt the tension rise within the building, felt it rising within me, an ant heap somebody was plunging a stick into, stirring it up. I heard a woman screaming, "They are coming, they are going to kill us all!" Men started shouting, "Women and children upstairs! Get upstairs!" But I went downstairs. I saw the riot squad outside. They had just beaten up two Indians and were hauling them off to jail. We barricaded all doors and the lowest windows with document boxes, Xerox machines, tables, file cabinets, anything we could lay our hands on. Some brothers piled up heavy typewriters on windowsills to hurl down on the police in case they tried to storm the building. Young men were singing and yelling, "It's a good day to die!" We started making weapons for ourselves. Two or three guys discovered some archery sets and were ready to defend themselves with bow and arrows. Others were swinging golf clubs, getting the feel of them. Still others were tying pen knives to fishing rods. A letter opener taped to a table leg became a tomahawk. Floyd Young Horse, a Sioux from Cherry Creek, was the first to put war paint on his face in the ancient manner. Soon a lot of young men did the same. Many wrapped themselves in upside-down American flags—like the Ghost Dancers of old.

I took apart a pair of scissors and taped one half to a broken-off chair leg and went outside to join the security. My brother was one of the guards. He saw me and laughed. He had been four years in the marines and had taught me to take apart, clean, and fire a .38. Seeing me with my measly weapon broke him up. "What are you going to do with that thing?" "Get them in the balls before they can hit me!"

At last the police were withdrawn and we were told that they had given us another twenty-four hours to evacuate the building. This was not the end of the confrontation. From then on, every morning we were given a court order to get out by six P.M. Came six o'clock and we would be standing there ready to join battle. I think many brothers and sisters were prepared to die right on the steps of the BIA building. When one of the AIM leaders was asked by a reporter whether the Indians were not afraid that their women and children could get hurt, he said, "Our women and children have taken this risk for four hundred years and accept it," and we all shouted "Right on!" I don't think I slept more than five or six hours during the whole week I was inside the BIA.

Every morning and evening was crisis time. In between, the negotiations went on. Groups of supporters arrived, good people as well as weirdos. The Indian commissioner Lewis Bruce stayed one night in the building to show his sympathy. So did LaDonna Harris, a Kiowa-Comanche and a senator's wife. One guy who called himself Wavy Gravy, who came from a place in California called the Hog Farm and who wore a single enormous earring, arrived in a psychedelically decorated bus and set up a loudspeaker system for us. At the same time the police cut all our telephone wires except the one connecting us with the Department of the Interior. A certain Reverend McIntire came with a bunch of followers waving signs and singing Christian hymns. He was known to us as a racist and Vietnam War hawk. Why he wanted to support us was a big mystery. Cameramen and reporters swarmed through the building; tourists took snapshots of our guards. It was as if all these white people around the BIA were hoping for some sort of Buffalo Bill Wild West show.

For me the high point came not with our men arming themselves, but with Martha Grass, a simple middle-aged Cherokee woman from Oklahoma, standing up to Interior Secretary Morton and giving him a piece of her mind, speaking from the heart, speaking for all of us. She talked about everyday things, women's things, children's problems, getting down to the nitty-gritty. She shook her fists in Morton's face, saying, "Enough of your bullshit!" It was good to see an Indian mother stand up to one of Washington's highest officials. "This is our building!" she told him. Then she gave him the finger.

In the end a compromise was reached. The government said they could not go on negotiating during Election Week, but they would appoint two high administration officials to seriously consider our twenty demands. Our expenses to get home would be paid. Nobody would be prosecuted. Of course, our twenty points were never gone into afterward. From the practical point of view, nothing had been achieved. As usual we had bickered among ourselves. But morally it had been a great victory. We had faced White America collectively, not as individual tribes. We had stood up to the government and gone through our baptism of fire. We had not run. As Russel Means put it, it had been "a helluva smoke signal!"

Television is an Evil

Theodore Dalrymple

Theodore Dalrymple is one of several pseudonyms used by Anthony M. Daniels. Born in London in 1949, he spent much of his early life following in his father's footsteps. Daniels' father was highly educated, despite having grown up amid squalor in London slums, and he passed his love of knowledge to his young son who began reading the philosophies of Hume and La Rochefoucauld by the age of 14. At his father's urgings, Daniels went to medical school, though he spent much of his time continuing his study of philosophy and devoting only enough energy to his medical studies as required to pass. Soon after qualifying as a doctor in 1974, Daniels moved to Rhodesia (now Zimbabwe) and took a position attending surgeries and assisting in a hospital emergency room. Though he spent only six months in Rhodesia, he witnessed the consequences of imperialism, racism, and poverty, and this experience would inspire his curiosity to travel and observe other cultures. He next moved to Cape Town, South Africa and worked as a doctor in a small province while he studied the county's history of racial segregation. He strongly opposed Apartheid and refused to follow the laws. He was sought by the country's police after having attended a black church service; fortunately he left the country before he could be caught.

Daniels' return to England in 1976 came with a shift in his career; he became a psychiatrist. He enjoyed studying the human mind and observing the complexities of man's behavior. Soon he would leave England again to pursue work as a psychiatrist in the Gilbert Islands. While living in the South Pacific, Daniel's began sending his writings for publication; his first piece was published in The Spectator *in 1983 under the name A. M. Daniels. In 1986 Daniel's published his first book* Coups and Cocaine: Two Journeys in South America *which details his travels across the continent. Two years later he published* Zanzibar to Timbuktu, *another book*

detailing his observations while traveling across Africa using only public transporta-
tion. He also began publishing numerous essays under the pen names Edward
Theberton and Thursday Msigwa.

In 1990, Daniels would begin working as a psychiatrist in an English prison. He
soon adopted the pseudonym Theodore Dalrymple so that he could comment anony-
mously on his experiences with the imprisoned mentally ill. As Dalrymple, he expands
his focus beyond the prison walls and comments on the worst characteristics and flaws
of modern society. His essays on the barbarity of contemporary civilization have been
compiled into the books Life at the Bottom *(2001) and* Our Culture, What's
Left of It *(2005). He uses his experiences gained traveling the world as well as*
his medical background and his extensive studies of philosophy to issue both bold obser-
vations and dark criticisms concerning western culture and man's motivations.
"Television Is an Evil", published November, 2013 in Taki Magazine, *is an*
example of Dalrymple's condemnations.

Most people read to confirm their prejudices rather than to learn something new or change their minds. Moreover, they recall what confirms their opinions much better than they remember what contradicts them. So aware was Charles Darwin of this human tendency that, at least according to his *Autobiography*, he wrote down anything he read that contradicted his views, for otherwise (he said) he was sure to forget it.

I must admit that like most of humanity, I am not as honest as Darwin and am reluctant to give up my cherished beliefs even in the face of facts that contradict them. I do on occasion change my mind about something, but slowly and usually without acknowledging that I have done so. I prefer to think that the opinion I now hold is the opinion I have held all my life, rather as Kim Il-sung emerged, according to his hagiographers, as a fully fledged Korean Marxist-Leninist revolutionary by the age of eight. To acknowledge that one has changed one's mind about something is to admit one's fallibility and the possibility that if one was wrong before, one might be wrong again. And in our hearts we know that we are always right.

"There is something about the evil little screen that would sully a saint and sanctify a monster." That is why I was overjoyed recently in Paris to find a well-documented book that confirmed one of my deepest prejudices, namely that television is, if not the root of all evil, at least the root of much evil. That is why I haven't had one for more than forty years. The book was called *TV Lobotomie*, which hardly needs translation. The man who put the first germ of the prejudice against TV in my mind was Malcolm Muggeridge, a now-forgotten British journalist who, bizarrely, emigrated to the Soviet Union in the 1930s in search of a better life. Far from finding the paradise he had expected, however, he found a kind of hell. During the Ukrainian famine he sent back truthful reports to the *Manchester Guardian* (now the *Guardian*), which published only some of them. He was particularly outraged by the Western intellectuals who took starvation for plenty and tyranny for freedom, and he satirized them mercilessly in his book *Winter in Moscow*.

Later in his life he became a fervent and somewhat unctuous Christian, by no means a popular thing to do in the 1960s. Perhaps he did so because it was his temperament to swim against the tide. Be that as it may, he also denounced television from his pulpit—which was, of course, television.

He denounced it with all the fervor of a temperance preacher denouncing gin or of a modern public health official denouncing tobacco. At first I laughed at him, but then I saw that he was quite right. Television is an evil.

There is so much to be said against it (and its televisual offshoots) that it is difficult to know where to begin. In my opinion, televisual entertainment is by far the most important cause of boredom in the world, and since the attempt to relieve boredom is a much underestimated cause of social pathology of all kinds, television is ultimately responsible for the squalor in the midst of wealth that is so remarkable a feature of our modern existence.

It may seem paradoxical to claim that entertainment is a serious cause of boredom. But as *TV Lobotomie* demonstrates, children who grow up with TV as a large part of their mental diet have difficulty concentrating for the rest of their lives, and since the ability to concentrate is essential to finding anything interesting that is not swift-moving and sensational, and since also a large part of life is necessarily not swift-moving and sensational, those brought up on TV are destined for boredom. Degradation relieves their boredom. Better a life of sordid crises than a life like a flat-line encephalograph.

Most parents believe that television is bad for their children, but they insist that they watch it nonetheless. Indeed, they train them to do so, for contrary to what many might think, television is not immediately attractive to young children, who would rather do something else than watch it. Having become accustomed to it, however, they need it as an addict needs his drug. The more they watch it, the worse their likely path through life. Before anyone objects that this is because those children who watch the most television come from bad homes, let me point out first that the relationship between television and scholastic failure (for example) is a causative one, and second that the worst effects of television are seen in the best homes not the worst, precisely because children from the best homes—by best, I mean those with educated parents and high incomes, admittedly a rather reductive definition—have the best cognitive prospects to ruin. As modern European architects have discovered, it is far easier to ruin the good than improve the bad.

To my shame, and against my principles, I have occasionally agreed to appear on television, though even less frequently than I have been asked. I have found those who work for TV broadcasting companies to be the most disagreeable people that I have ever encountered. I far preferred the criminals whom I encountered in my work as a prison doctor, who were more honest and upright than TV people.

In my experience, TV people are as lying, insincere, obsequious, unscrupulous, fickle, exploitative, shallow, cynical, untrustworthy, treacherous, dishonest, mercenary, low, and untruthful a group of people as is to be found on the face of this Earth. They make the average Western politician seem like a moral giant. By comparison with them, Mr. Madoff was a model of probity and Iago was Othello's best friend. I am prepared to admit that there may be—even are—exceptions, as there are exceptions good or bad in every human group, but there is something about the evil little screen that would sully a saint and sanctify a monster.

Turn off, tune out, drop completely.

America's True History of Religious Tolerance

Kenneth C. Davis

Kenneth C. Davis was born in Mount Vernon, New York. He attended Concordia College and Fordham University.

Davis is an American Popular historian who frequently appears on NPR's All Things Considered. *His most well-known work is his* Don't Know Much about History, *which spent 35 consecutive weeks on* The New York Times *bestseller list. This mammoth seller spawned Davis's* Don't Know Much About *series, which has a combined in-print total of 4.3-million copies. Davis has been dubbed the "King of Knowing" by Amazon.com because of his expertise in all of the subjects he writes about: the Bible, Mythology, the Civil War, or the American Presidents. Davis's book-selling success makes the case that "Americans don't hate history, just the dull version they slept through in class."*

Davis's other works include Two-Bit Culture: The Paperbacking of America *and* America's Hidden History: Untold Tales of the First Pilgrims, Fighting Women, and Forgotten Founders Who Shaped a Nation, *published in 2009.*

Davis wrote "America's True History of Religious Tolerance" for Smithsonian Magazine *in October 2010. The piece focuses on the idea that despite the United States having a reputation as a reassuring bastion of religious freedom, this is a myth completely at odds with the historical record of the country.*

Davis currently lives in New York City and Vermont with his wife. He has two grown children.

The idea that the United States has always been a bastion of religious freedom is reassuring—and utterly at odds with the historical record

Wading into the controversy surrounding an Islamic center planned for a site near New York City's Ground Zero memorial this past August, President Obama declared: "This is America. And our commitment to religious freedom must be unshakeable. The principle that people of all faiths are welcome in this country and that they will not be treated differently by their government is essential to who we are." In doing so, he paid homage to a vision that politicians and preachers have extolled for more than two centuries—that America historically has been a place of religious tolerance. It was a sentiment George Washington voiced shortly after taking the oath of office just a few blocks from Ground Zero.

But is it so?

In the storybook version most of us learned in school, the Pilgrims came to America aboard the *Mayflower* in search of religious freedom in 1620. The Puritans soon followed, for the same reason. Ever since these religious dissidents arrived at their shining "city upon a hill," as their governor John Winthrop called it, millions from around the world have done the same, coming to an America where they found a welcome melting pot in which everyone was free to practice his or her own faith.

The problem is that this tidy narrative is an American myth. The real story of religion in America's past is an often awkward, frequently embarrassing and occasionally bloody tale that most civics books and high-school texts either paper over or shunt to the side. And much of the recent conversation about America's ideal of religious freedom has paid lip service to this comforting tableau.

From the earliest arrival of Europeans on America's shores, religion has often been a cudgel, used to discriminate, suppress and even kill the foreign, the "heretic" and the "unbeliever"—including the "heathen" natives already here. Moreover, while it is true that the vast majority of early-generation Americans were Christian, the pitched battles between various Protestant sects and, more explosively, between Protestants and Catholics, present an unavoidable contradiction to the widely held notion that America is a "Christian nation."

First, a little overlooked history: the initial encounter between Europeans in the future United States came with the establishment of a Huguenot (French Protestant) colony in 1564 at Fort Caroline (near modern Jacksonville, Florida). More than half a century before the *Mayflower* set sail, French pilgrims had come to America in search of religious freedom.

The Spanish had other ideas. In 1565, they established a forward operating base at St. Augustine and proceeded to wipe out the Fort Caroline colony. The Spanish commander, Pedro Menéndez de Avilés, wrote to the Spanish King Philip II that he had "hanged all those we had found in [Fort Caroline] because . . . they were scattering the odious Lutheran doctrine in these Provinces." When hundreds of survivors of a shipwrecked French fleet washed up on the beaches of Florida, they were put to the sword, beside a river the Spanish called Matanzas ("slaughters"). In other words, the first encounter between European Christians in America ended in a blood bath.

The much-ballyhooed arrival of the Pilgrims and Puritans in New England in the early 1600s was indeed a response to persecution that these religious dissenters had experienced in England. But the Puritan fathers of the Massachusetts Bay Colony did not countenance tolerance of opposing religious views. Their "city upon a hill" was a theocracy that brooked no dissent, religious or political.

The most famous dissidents within the Puritan community, Roger Williams and Anne Hutchinson, were banished following disagreements over theology and policy. From Puritan Boston's earliest days, Catholics ("Papists") were anathema and were banned from the colonies, along with other non-Puritans. Four Quakers were hanged in Boston between 1659 and 1661 for persistently returning to the city to stand up for their beliefs.

Throughout the colonial era, Anglo-American antipathy toward Catholics—especially French and Spanish Catholics—was pronounced and often reflected in the sermons of such famous clerics as Cotton Mather and in statutes that discriminated against Catholics in matters of property and voting. Anti-Catholic feelings even contributed to the revolutionary mood in America after King George III extended an olive branch to French Catholics in Canada with the Quebec Act of 1774, which recognized their religion.

When George Washington dispatched Benedict Arnold on a mission to court French Canadians' support for the American Revolution in 1775, he cautioned Arnold not to let their religion get in the way. "Prudence, policy and a true Christian Spirit," Washington advised, "will lead us to look with compassion upon their errors, without insulting them." (After Arnold betrayed the American cause, he publicly cited America's alliance with Catholic France as one of his reasons for doing so.)

In newly independent America, there was a crazy quilt of state laws regarding religion. In Massachusetts, only Christians were allowed to hold public office, and Catholics were allowed to do so only after renouncing papal authority. In 1777, New York State's constitution banned Catholics from public office (and would do so until 1806). In Maryland, Catholics had full civil rights, but Jews did not. Delaware required an oath affirming belief in the Trinity. Several states, including Massachusetts and South Carolina, had official, state-supported churches.

In 1779, as Virginia's governor, Thomas Jefferson had drafted a bill that guaranteed legal equality for citizens of all religions—including those of no religion—in the state. It was around then that Jefferson famously wrote, "But it does me no injury for my neighbor to say there are twenty gods or no God. It neither picks my pocket nor breaks my leg." But Jefferson's plan did not advance—until after Patrick ("Give Me Liberty or Give Me Death") Henry introduced a bill in 1784 calling for state support for "teachers of the Christian religion."

Future President James Madison stepped into the breach. In a carefully argued essay titled "Memorial and Remonstrance Against Religious Assessments," the soon-to-be father of the Constitution eloquently laid out reasons why the state had no business supporting Christian instruction. Signed by some 2,000 Virginians, Madison's argument became a fundamental piece of American political philosophy, a ringing endorsement of the secular state that "should be as familiar to students of American history as the Declaration of Independence and the Constitution," as Susan Jacoby has written in *Freethinkers*, her excellent history of American secularism.

Among Madison's 15 points was his declaration that "the Religion then of every man must be left to the conviction and conscience of every . . . man to exercise it as these may dictate. This right is in its nature an inalienable right."

Madison also made a point that any believer of any religion should understand: that the government sanction of a religion was, in essence, a threat to religion. "Who does not see," he wrote, "that the same authority which can establish Christianity, in exclusion of all other Religions, may establish with the same ease any particular sect of Christians, in exclusion of all other Sects?" Madison was writing from his memory of Baptist ministers being arrested in his native Virginia.

As a Christian, Madison also noted that Christianity had spread in the face of persecution from worldly powers, not with their help. Christianity, he contended, "disavows a dependence on the powers of this world . . . for it is known that this Religion both existed and flourished, not only without the support of human laws, but in spite of every opposition from them."

Recognizing the idea of America as a refuge for the protester or rebel, Madison also argued that Henry's proposal was "a departure from that generous policy, which offering an Asylum to the persecuted and oppressed of every Nation and Religion, promised a lustre to our country."

After long debate, Patrick Henry's bill was defeated, with the opposition outnumbering supporters 12 to 1. Instead, the Virginia legislature took up Jefferson's plan for the separation of church and state. In 1786, the Virginia Act for Establishing Religious Freedom, modified somewhat from Jefferson's original draft, became law. The act is one of three accomplishments Jefferson included on his tombstone, along with writing the Declaration and founding the University of Virginia. (He omitted his presidency of the United States.) After the bill was passed, Jefferson proudly wrote that the law "meant to comprehend, within the mantle of its protection, the Jew, the Gentile, the Christian and the Mahometan, the Hindoo and Infidel of every denomination."

Madison wanted Jefferson's view to become the law of the land when he went to the Constitutional Convention in Philadelphia in 1787. And as framed in Philadelphia that year, the U.S. Constitution clearly stated in Article VI that federal elective and appointed officials "shall be bound by Oath or Affirmation, to support this Constitution, but no religious Test shall ever be required as a Qualification to any Office or public Trust under the United States."

This passage—along with the facts that the Constitution does not mention God or a deity (except for a pro forma "year of our Lord" date) and that its very first amendment forbids Congress from making laws that would infringe of the free exercise of religion—attests to the founders' resolve that America be a secular republic. The men who fought the Revolution may have thanked Providence and attended church regularly—or not. But they also fought a war against a country in which the head of state was the head of the church. Knowing well the history of religious warfare that led to America's settlement, they clearly understood both the dangers of that system and of sectarian conflict.

It was the recognition of that divisive past by the founders—notably Washington, Jefferson, Adams and Madison—that secured America as a secular republic. As president, Washington wrote in 1790: "All possess alike liberty of conscience and immunity of citizenship. . . . For happily the Government of the United States, which gives to bigotry no sanction, to persecution no assistance requires only that they who live under its protection should demean themselves as good citizens."

He was addressing the members of America's oldest synagogue, the Touro Synagogue in Newport, Rhode Island (where his letter is read aloud every August). In closing, he wrote specifically to the Jews a phrase that applies to Muslims as well: "May the children of the Stock of Abraham, who dwell in this land, continue to merit and enjoy the good will of the other inhabitants, while every one shall sit in safety under his own vine and figtree, and there shall be none to make him afraid."

As for Adams and Jefferson, they would disagree vehemently over policy, but on the question of religious freedom they were united. "In their seventies," Jacoby writes, "with a friendship that had survived serious political conflicts, Adams and Jefferson could look back with satisfaction on what they both considered their greatest achievement—their role in establishing a secular government whose legislators would never be required, or permitted, to rule on the legality of theological views."

Late in his life, James Madison wrote a letter summarizing his views: "And I have no doubt that every new example, will succeed, as every past one has done, in shewing that religion & Govt. will both exist in greater purity, the less they are mixed together."

While some of America's early leaders were models of virtuous tolerance, American attitudes were slow to change. The anti-Catholicism of America's Calvinist past found new voice in the 19th century. The belief widely held and preached by some of the most prominent ministers in America was that Catholics would, if permitted, turn America over to the pope. Anti-Catholic venom was part of the typical American school day, along with Bible readings. In Massachusetts, a convent—coincidentally near the site of the Bunker Hill Monument—was burned to the ground in 1834 by an anti-Catholic mob incited by reports that young women were being abused in the convent school. In Philadelphia, the City of Brotherly Love, anti-Catholic sentiment, combined with the country's anti-immigrant mood, fueled the Bible Riots of 1844, in which houses were torched, two Catholic churches were destroyed and at least 20 people were killed.

At about the same time, Joseph Smith founded a new American religion—and soon met with the wrath of the mainstream Protestant majority. In 1832, a mob tarred and feathered him, marking the beginning of a long battle between Christian America and Smith's Mormonism. In October 1838, after a series of conflicts over land and religious tension, Missouri Governor Lilburn Boggs ordered that all Mormons be expelled from his state. Three days later, rogue militiamen massacred 17 church members, including children, at the Mormon settlement of Haun's Mill. In 1844, a mob murdered Joseph Smith and his brother Hyrum while they were jailed in Carthage, Illinois. No one was ever convicted of the crime.

Even as late as 1960, Catholic presidential candidate John F. Kennedy felt compelled to make a major speech declaring that his loyalty was to America, not the pope. (And as recently as the 2008 Republican primary campaign, Mormon candidate Mitt Romney felt compelled to address the suspicions still directed toward the Church of Jesus Christ of Latter-day Saints.) Of course, America's anti-Semitism was practiced institutionally as well as socially for decades. With the great threat of "godless" Communism looming in the 1950s, the country's fear of atheism also reached new heights.

America can still be, as Madison perceived the nation in 1785, "an Asylum to the persecuted and oppressed of every Nation and Religion." But recognizing that deep religious discord has been part of America's social DNA is a healthy and necessary step. When we acknowledge that dark past, perhaps the nation will return to that "promised . . . lustre" of which Madison so grandiloquently wrote.

from Bait and Switch

Barbara Ehrenreich

A prolific writer of investigative journalism and a political activist, Barbara Ehrenreich was born in 1941 in Butte, Montana. She graduated from Reed College in 1963 with a degree in Physics, then obtained a PhD in Cellular Biology from Rockefeller University in 1968. Despite her early commitment to scientific research, her interests turned toward politics during the war in Vietnam, and she became involved in the anti-war movement in NYC during the late 1960s. Following the birth of her first child in 1970, Ehrenreich's political interests expanded to include advocating for increased access to health care for women. She coauthored "Witches, Midwives, and Nurses: A History of Women Healers" with Deirdre English. Several of her earliest books also focused on women and the American health industry, including Complaints and Disorders: The Sexual Politics of Sickness *(1973). During the 1980s Ehrenreich's continuing interest in women's issues shifted towards the exploitation of female factory workers in the emergent global economy, an interest that resulted in her influential book* Women in the Global Factory *(1983). Her need to explore and expose the conditions of the working-poor and the financial challenges facing the American middle-class became the driving force of much of her investigative journalism over the course of the last three decades.*

She has examined, in several works, the erosion of American economic stability. In Nickel and Dimed: On (Not) getting by in America *(2001) she discusses the prevalence of the financial injustice endured by low-wage workers. Ehrenreich admits that* Nickel and Dimed *affected her life in surprising ways and claims that it "plunged [her] into the nascent living wage movement, traveling to union rallies [and] picket lines" and leading to her arrest at a protest for better wages for women workers at Yale University. Following the success of her bestselling book, she*

began investigating the economic vulnerability and instability of many college educat-
ed middle class workers in her book Bait and Switch: the (futile) pursuit of
the American Dream *(2005), from which the following selection is adapted. She*
was also the founder, in 2005, of United Professionals, a non-profit organization
for white-collar American workers struggling to maintain a secure, middle-class way
of life. In 2011 she began the Economic Hardship Reporting Project in hopes of
offering unemployed and underemployed journalist an opportunity to write and give
voices to the growing crisis of economic instability. Throughout her career, Ehrenreich's
work has been thematically centered on issues of social injustice and inequality. While
her work as both a journalist and an activist often seems to present an ideological con-
flict, she reveals "I have never seen a conflict between journalism and activism: As a
journalist, I search for the truth. But as a moral person, I am obliged to do something
about it."

Introduction

Because I've written a lot about poverty, I'm used to hearing from people in scary circumstances. An eviction notice has arrived. A child has been diagnosed with a
serious illness and the health insurance has run out. The car has broken
down and there's no way to get to work. These are the routine emergencies
that plague the chronically poor. But it struck me, starting in about 2002,
that many such tales of hardship were coming from people who were once
members in good standing of the middle class—college graduates and
former occupants of mid-level white-collar positions. One such writer
upbraided me for what she saw as my neglect of hardworking, virtuous
people like herself.

> Try investigating people like me who didn't have babies in high school,
> who made good grades, who work hard and don't kiss a lot of ass and
> instead of getting promoted or paid fairly must regress to working for
> $7/hr., having their student loans in perpetual deferment, living at
> home with their parents, and generally exist in debt which they feel
> they may never get out of.

Stories of white-collar downward mobility cannot be brushed off as easily
as accounts of blue-collar economic woes, which the hard-hearted traditionally
blame on "bad choices": failing to get a college degree, for example, failing to
postpone childbearing until acquiring a nest egg, or failing to choose affluent
parents in the first place. But distressed white-collar people cannot be accused
of fecklessness of any kind; they are the ones who "did everything right." They
earned higher degrees, often setting aside their youthful passion for philosophy
or music to suffer through dull practical majors like management or finance.

In some cases, they were high achievers who ran into trouble precisely because they had risen far enough in the company for their salaries to look like a tempting cost cut. They were the losers, in other words, in a classic game of bait and switch. And while blue-collar poverty has become numbingly routine, white-collar unemployment—and the poverty that often results—remains a rude finger in the face of the American dream.

I realized that I knew very little about the mid-to upper levels of the corporate world, having so far encountered this world almost entirely through its low-wage, entry-level representatives. I was one of them—a server in a national chain restaurant, a cleaning person, and a Wal-Mart "associate"—in the course of researching an earlier book, *Nickel and Dimed: On (Not) Getting By in America.* Like everyone else, I've also encountered the corporate world as a consumer, dealing with people quite far down in the occupational hierarchy—retail clerks, customer service representatives, telemarketers. Of the levels where decisions are made—where the vice presidents, account executives, and regional managers dwell—my experience has been limited to seeing these sorts of people on airplanes, where they study books on "leadership," fiddle with spreadsheets on their laptops, or fall asleep over biographies of the founding fathers.[1] I'm better acquainted with the corporate functionaries of the future, many of whom I've met on my visits to college campuses, where "business" remains the most popular major, if only because it is believed to be the safest and most lucrative.[2]

But there have been growing signs of trouble—if not outright misery—within the white-collar corporate workforce. First, starting with the economic downturn of 2001, there has been a rise in unemployment among highly credentialed and experienced people. In late 2003, when I started this project, unemployment was running at about 5.9 percent, but in contrast to earlier economic downturns, a sizable portion—almost 20 percent, or about 1.6 million—of the unemployed were white-collar professionals.[3] Previous downturns had disproportionately hit blue-collar people; this time it was the relative-elite of professional, technical, and managerial employees who were being singled out for media sympathy. In April 2003, for example, the *New York Times Magazine* offered a much-discussed cover story about a former $300,000-a-year computer industry executive reduced, after two years of unemployment, to working as a sales associate at the Gap.[4] Throughout the first four years of the 2000s, there were similar stories of the mighty or the mere midlevel brought low, ejected from their office suites and forced to serve behind the counter at Star-bucks.

Today, white-collar job insecurity is no longer a function of the business cycle—rising as the stock market falls and declining again when the numbers improve.[5] Nor is it confined to a few volatile sectors like telecommunications or technology, or a few regions of the country like the rust belt or Silicon Valley. The economy may be looking up, the company may be raking in cash, and still the layoffs continue, like a perverse from of natural selection, weeding out the talented and successful as well as the mediocre. Since the mid-nineties, this perpetual winnowing process has been institutionalized under various euphemisms such as "downsizing," "right-sizing," "smart-sizing," "restructuring," and "de-layering"—to which we can now add the outsourcing of white-collar functions to cheaper labor markets overseas.

In the metaphor of the best-selling business book of the first few years of the twenty-first century, the "cheese"—meaning a stable, rewarding, job—has indeed been moved. A 2004 survey of executives found 95 percent expecting to move on, voluntarily or otherwise, from their current jobs, and 68 percent concerned about unexpected firings and layoffs.[6] You don't, in other words, have to lose a job to feel the anxiety and despair of the unemployed.

A second sign of trouble could be called "overemployment." I knew, from my reading, that mid-and high-level corporate executives and professionals today often face the same punishing demands on their time as low-paid wage earners who must work two jobs in order to make ends meet. Economist Juliet Schor, who wrote *The Overworked American*, and business journalist Jill Andresky Fraser, author of *White Collar Sweatshop*, describe stressed-out white-collar employees who put in ten-to twelve-hour-long days at the office, continue to work on their laptops in the evening at home, and remain tethered to the office by cell phone even on vacations and holidays. "On Wall Street, for example," Fraser reports, "it is common for a supervisor to instruct new hires to keep a spare set of clothes and toothbrush in the office for all those late night episodes when it just won't make sense to head home for a quick snooze."[7] She quotes an Intel employee:

> If you make the choice to have a home life, you will be ranked and rated at the bottom. I was willing to work the endless hours, come in on weekends, travel to the ends of the earth. I had no hobbies, no out-side interests. If I wasn't involved with the company, I wasn't anything.[8]

Something, evidently, is going seriously wrong within a socioeconomic group I had indeed neglected as too comfortable and too powerful to merit my concern. Where I had imagined comfort, there is now growing distress, and I determined to investigate. I chose the same strategy I had employed in *Nickel and Dimed*: to enter this new world myself, as an undercover reporter, and see what I could learn about the problems firsthand. Were people being driven out of their corporate jobs? What did it take to find a new one? And, if things were as bad as some reports suggested, why was there so little protest?

The plan was straightforward enough: to find a job, a "good" job, which I defined minimally as a white-collar position that would provide health insurance and an income of about $50,000 a year, enough to land me solidly in the middle class. The job itself would give me a rare firsthand glimpse into the midlevel corporate world, and the effort to find it would of course place me among the most hard-pressed white-collar corporate workers—the ones who don't have jobs.

Since I wanted to do this as anonymously as possible, certain areas of endeavor had to be excluded, such as higher education, publishing (magazines, newspapers, and books), and nonprofit liberal organizations. In any of these, I would have run the risk of being recognized and perhaps treated differently—more favorably, one hopes—than the average job seeker. But these restrictions did not significantly narrow the field, since of course most white-collar professionals work in other sectors of the for-profit, corporate world—from banking to business services, pharmaceuticals to finance.

The decision to enter corporate life—and an unfamiliar sector of it, at that—required that I abandon, or at least set aside, deeply embedded attitudes and views, including my longstanding critique of American corporations and the people who lead them. I had cut my teeth, as a fledgling investigative journalist in the seventies, on the corporations that were coming to dominate the health-care system: pharmaceutical companies, hospital chains, insurance companies. Then, sometime in the eighties, I shifted my attention to the treatment of blue-and pink-collar employees, blaming America's intractable level of poverty—12.5 percent by the federal government's official count, 25 percent by more up-to-date measures—on the chronically low wages offered to nonprofessional workers. In the last few years, I seized on the wave of financial scandals—from Enron through, at the time of this writing, HealthSouth and Hollingers International—as evidence of growing corruption within the corporate world, a pattern of internal looting without regard for employees, consumers, or even, in some cases, stockholders.

But for the purposes of this project, these criticisms and reservations had to be set aside or shoved as far back in my mind as possible. Like it or not, the corporation is the dominant unit of the global economy and the form of enterprise that our lives depend on in a day-to-day sense. I write this on an IBM laptop while sipping Lipton tea and wearing clothes from the Gap—all major firms or elements thereof. It's corporations that make the planes run (though not necessarily on time), bring us (and increasingly grow) our food, and generally "make it happen." I'd been on the outside of the corporate world, often complaining bitterly, and now I wanted in.

THIS WOULD NOT, I knew, be an altogether fair test of the job market, if only because I had some built-in disadvantages as a job seeker. For one thing, I am well into middle age, and since age discrimination is a recognized problem in the corporate world even at the tender age of forty, I was certainly vulnerable to it myself. This defect, however, is by no means unique to me. Many people—

from displaced homemakers to downsized executives—now find themselves searching for jobs at an age that was once associated with a restful retirement.

Furthermore, I had the disadvantage of never having held a white-collar job with a corporation. My one professional-level office job, which lasted for about seven months, was in the public sector, at the New York City Bureau of the Budget. It had involved such typical white-collar activities as attending meetings, digesting reports, and writing memos; but that was a long time ago, before cell phones, PowerPoint, and e-mail. In the corporate world I now sought to enter, everything would be new to me: the standards of performance, the methods of evaluation, the lines and even the modes of communication. But I'm a quick study, as you have to be in journalism, and counted on this to get me by.

The first step was to acquire a new identity and personal history to go with it, meaning, in this case, a résumé. It is easier to change your identity than you might think. Go to Alavarado and Seventh Street in Los Angeles, for example, and you will be approached by men whispering, "ID, ID." I, however, took the legal route, because I wanted my documents to be entirely in order when the job offers started coming in. My fear, perhaps exaggerated, was that my current name might be recognized, or would at least turn up an embarrassing abundance of Google entries. So in November 2003 I legally changed back to my maiden name, Barbara Alexander, and acquired a Social Security card to go with it.

As for the résumé: although it had to be faked, I wanted it as much as possible to represent my actual skills, which, I firmly believed, would enrich whatever company I went to work for. I am a writer—author of thousands of published articles and about twelve nonfiction books, counting the coauthored ones—and I know that "writing" translates, in the corporate world, into public relations or "communications" generally. Many journalism schools teach PR too, which may be fitting, since PR is really journalism's evil twin. Whereas a journalist seeks the truth, a PR person may be called upon to disguise it or even to advance an untruth. If your employer, a pharmaceutical company, claims its new drug cures both cancer and erectile dysfunction, your job is to promote it, not to investigate the grounds for these claims.

I could do this, on a temporary basis anyway, and have even done many of the things PR people routinely do: I've written press releases, pitched stories to editors and reporters, prepared press packets, and helped arrange press conferences. As an author, I have also worked closely with my publisher's PR people and have always found them to be intelligent and in every way congenial.

I have also been an activist in a variety of causes over the years, and this experience too must translate into something valuable to any firm willing to hire me. I have planned meetings and chaired them; I have worked in dozens of diverse groups and often played a leadership role in them; I am at ease as a public speaker, whether giving a lengthy speech or a brief presentation on a panel—all of which amounts to the "leadership" skills that should be an asset to any company. At the very least, I could claim to be an "event planner," capable of dividing gatherings into plenaries and break-out sessions, arranging the press coverage, and planning the follow-up events.

Even as a rough draft, the résumé took days of preparation. I had to line up people willing to lie for me, should they be called by a potential employer, and attest to the fine work I had done for them. Fortunately, I have friends who were willing to do this, some of them located at recognizable companies. Although I did not dare claim actual employment at these firms, since a call to their Human Resources departments would immediately expose the lie, I felt I could safely pretend to have "consulted" to them over the years. Suffice it to say that I gave Barbara Alexander an exemplary history in public relations, sometimes with a little event planning thrown in, and that the dissimulation involved in crafting my new résumé was further preparation for any morally challenging projects I should be called upon to undertake as a PR person.

I did not, however, embellish my new identity with an affect or mannerisms different from my own. I am not an actor and would not have been able to do this even if I had wanted to. "Barbara Alexander" was only a cover for Barbara Ehrenreich; her behavior would, for better or worse, always be my own. In fact, in a practical sense I was simply changing my occupational status from "self-employed/writer" to "unemployed"—a distinction that might be imperceptible to the casual observer. I would still stay home most days at my computer, only now, instead of researching and writing articles, I would be researching and contacting companies that might employ me. The new name and fake résumé were only my ticket into the ranks of the unemployed white-collar Americans who spend their days searching for a decent-paying job.

The project required some minimal structure; since I was stepping into the unknown, I needed to devise some guidelines for myself. My first rule was that I would do everything possible to land a job, which meant being open to every form of help that presented itself: utilizing whatever books, web sites, and businesses, for example, that I could find offering guidance to job seekers. I would endeavor to behave as I was expected to, insofar as I could decipher the expectations. I did not know exactly what forms of effort would be required of successful job seekers, only that I would, as humbly and diligently as possible, give it my best try.

Second, I would be prepared to go anywhere for a job or even an interview, and would advertise this geographic flexibility in my contacts with potential employers. I was based in Charlottesville, Virginia, throughout this project, but I was prepared to travel anywhere in the United States to get a job and then live there for several months if I found one. Nor would I shun any industry—other than those where I might be recognized—as unglamorous or morally repugnant. My third rule was that I would have to take the first job I was offered that met my requirements as to income and benefits.

I knew that the project would take a considerable investment of time and money, so I set aside ten months[9] and the sum of $5,000 for travel and other expenses that might arise in the course of job searching. My expectation was that I would make the money back once I got a job and probably come out far ahead. As for the time, I budgeted roughly four to six months for the search—five months being the average for unemployed people in 2004[10]—and another three to four months of employment. I would have plenty of time both to sample the life of the white-collar unemployed and to explore the corporate world they sought to reenter.

From the outset, I pictured this abstraction, *the corporate world*, as a castle on a hill—well fortified, surrounded by difficult checkpoints, with its glass walls gleaming invitingly from on high. I knew that it would be a long hard climb just to get to the door. But I've made my way into remote and lofty places before—college and graduate school, for example. I'm patient and crafty; I have stamina and resolve; and I believed that I could do this too.

In fact, the project, as I planned it, seemed less challenging than I might have liked. As an undercover reporter, I would of course be insulated from the real terrors of the white-collar work world, if only because I was independent of it for my income and self-esteem. Most of my fellow job seekers would probably have come to their status involuntarily, through layoffs or individual firings. For them, to lose a job is to enter a world of pain. Their income collapses to the size of an unemployment insurance check; their self-confidence plummets. Much has been written about the psychological damage incurred by the unemployed—their sudden susceptibility to depression, divorce, substance abuse, and even suicide.[11] No such calamities could occur in my life as an undercover job seeker and, later, jobholder. There would be no sudden descent into poverty, nor any real sting of rejection.

I also started with the expectation that this project would be far less demanding than the work I had undertaken for *Nickel and Dimed*. Physically, it would be a piece of cake—no scrubbing, no heavy lifting, no walking or running for hours on end. As for behavior, I imagined that I would be immune from the constant subservience and obedience demanded of low-wage blue-collar workers, that I would be far freer to be, and express, myself. As it turns out, I was wrong on all counts.

Endnotes

1. Even fiction—my favorite source of insight into cultures and times remote from my own—was no help. While the fifties and sixties had produced absorbing novels about

white-collar corporate life, including Richard Yates's *Revolutionary Road* and Sloan Wilson's *The Man in the Gray Flannel Suit*, more recent novels and films tend to ignore the white-collar corporate work world except as a backdrop to sexual intrigue.

2. National Center for Educational Statistics, http://nces.ed.gov/pubs2004/2004018.pdf.

3. According to the Bureau of Labor Statistics, women are only slightly more likely than men to be unemployed—6.1 percent compared to 5.7 percent—and white women, like myself, are about half as likely as black women to be unemployed (www.bls.gov).

4. Jonathan Mahler, "Commute to Nowhere," *New York Times Magazine*, April 13, 2003.

5. I was particularly enlightened by Jill Andresky Fraser's *White Collar Sweat-shop: The Deterioration of Work and Its Rewards in Corporate America* (New York: Norton, 2001) and Richard Sennett's *The Corrosion of Character: The Personal Consequences of Work in the New Capitalism* (New York: Norton, 1998).

6. Harvey Mackay, *We Got Fired! And It's the Best Thing That Ever Happened to Us* (New York: Ballantine, 2004), p.94.

7. Fraser, *White Collar Sweatshop*, p.23.

8. Fraser, *White Collar Sweatshop*, p. 158.

9. From December 2003 to October 2004, with the exception of most of July, when I had a brief real-life job writing biweekly columns for the *New York Times*.

10. John Leland, "For Unemployed, Wait for New Work Grows Longer," *New York Times*, January 9, 2005.

11. See, for example, Katherine S. Newman's *Falling from Grace: Downward Mobility in the Age of Affluence* (Berkeley: University of California Press, 1999) or, for a highly readable first-person account, G.J. Meyer's *Executive Blues* (New York: Franklin Square Press, 1995).

On Dumpster Diving

Lars Eighner

Lars Eighner was born in 1948 in Corpus Christi, Texas. He grew up in Houston and studied creative writing at the Corpus Christi Fine Arts Colony. He also attended the University of Texas at Austin, with a focus in ethnic studies.

Eighner, a self-proclaimed "homosexual pornographer," rose from the obscurity of gay oriented literature when the Threepenny Review *published two of his essays on homelessness, "Travels with Lizbeth," his 1993 memoir about his wanderings in the American Southwest in the 1980s and "On Dumpster Diving." The publication in 1993 of the book* Travels with Lizbeth, *based on his three years of homelessness with his beloved dog Lizbeth was received with enthusiastic reviews. "On Dumpster Diving" is a selection from* Travels with Lizbeth. *Concerning his style, Eighner states in "About Travels with Lizbeth," "My purpose was to draw an ironic contrast between the dignity of my language and the indignity of my circumstances."*

Eighner also authored two collections of stories, Bayou Boy and B.M.O.C. *(both 1993), and* Pawn to Queen Four: A Novel *(1995).*

Eighner was elected to the Texas Institute of Letters in 1994. Lizbeth, his faithful canine companion and most trusted friend, passed away peacefully in 1998.

Long Before I began Dumpster diving I was impressed with Dumpsters, enough so that I wrote the Merriam-Webster research service to discover what I could about the word "Dumpster." I learned from them that "Dumpster" is a proprietary word belonging to the Dempsey Dumpster company.

Since then I have dutifully capitalized the word although it was lowercased in almost all of the citations Merriam-Webster photocopied for me. Dempsey's word is too apt. I have never heard these things called anything but Dumpsters. I do not know anyone who knows the generic name for these objects. From time to time, however, I hear a wino or hobo give some corrupted credit to the original and call them Dipsy Dumpsters.

I began Dumpster diving about a year before I became homeless.

I prefer the term "scavenging" and use the word "scrounging" when I mean to be obscure. I have heard people, evidently meaning to be polite, use the word "foraging," but I prefer to reserve that word for gathering nuts and berries and such which I do also according to the season and the opportunity, "Dumpster diving" seems to me to be a little too cute and, in my case, inaccurate because I lack the athletic ability to lower myself into the Dumpsters as the true divers do, much to their increased profit.

I like the frankness of the word "scavenging," which I can hardly think of without picturing a big black snail on an aquarium wall. I live from the refuse of others. I am a scavenger. I think it a sound and honorable niche, although if I could I would naturally prefer to live the comfortable consumer life, perhaps—and only perhaps—as a slightly less wasteful consumer owing to what I have learned as a scavenger.

While my dog Lizbeth and I were still living in the house on Avenue B in Austin, as my savings ran out, I put almost all my sporadic income into rent. The necessities of daily life I began to extract from Dumpsters. Yes, we ate from Dumpsters. Except for jeans, all my clothes came from Dumpsters. Boom boxes, candies, bedding, toilet paper, medicine, books, a typewriter, a virgin male love doll, change sometimes amounting to many dollars: I acquired many things from the Dumpsters.

I have learned much as a scavenger. I mean to put some of what I have learned down here, beginning with the practical art of Dumpster diving and proceeding to the abstract.

What is safe to eat?

After all, the finding of objects is becoming something of an urban art. Even respectable employed people will sometimes find something tempting sticking out of a Dumpster or standing beside one. Quite a number of people, not all of them of the bohemian type, are willing to brag that they found this or that piece in the trash. But eating from Dumpsters is the thing that separates the dilettanti from the professionals.

Eating safely from the Dumpsters involves three principles: using the senses and common sense to evaluate the condition of the found materials, knowing the Dumpsters of a given area and checking them regularly, and seeking always to answer the question "Why was this discarded?"

Perhaps everyone who has a kitchen and a regular supply of groceries has, at one time or another, made a sandwich and eaten half of it before discovering mold on the bread or got a mouthful of milk before realizing the milk had turned. Nothing of the sort is likely to happen to a Dumpster diver because he is constantly reminded that most food is discarded for a reason. Yet a lot of perfectly good food can be found in Dumpsters.

Canned goods, for example, turn up fairly often in the Dumpsters I frequent. All except the most phobic people would be willing to eat from a can even if it came from a Dumpster. Canned goods are among the safest of foods to be found in Dumpsters, but are not utterly foolproof.

Although very rare with modern canning methods, botulism is a possibility. Most other forms of food poisoning seldom do lasting harm to a healthy person. But botulism is almost certainly fatal and often the first symptom is death. Except for carbonated beverages, all canned goods should contain a slight vacuum and suck air when first punctured. Bulging, rusty, dented cans and cans that spew when punctured should be avoided, especially when the contents are not very acidic or syrupy.

Heat can break down the botulin, but this requires much more cooking than most people do to canned goods. To the extent that botulism occurs at all, of course, it can occur in cans on pantry shelves as well as in cans from Dumpsters. Need I say that home-canned goods found in Dumpsters are simply too risky to be recommended.

From time to time one of my companions, aware of the source of my provisions, will ask, "Do you think these crackers are really safe to eat?" For some reason it is most often the crackers they ask about.

This question always makes me angry. Of course I would not offer my companion anything I had doubts about. But more than that I wonder why he cannot evaluate the condition of the crackers for himself. I have no special knowledge and I have been wrong before. Since he knows where the food comes from, it seems to me he ought to assume some of the responsibility for deciding what be will put in his mouth.

For myself I have few qualms about dry foods such as crackers, cookies, cereal, chips, and pasta if they are free of visible contaminates and still dry and crisp. Most often such things are found in the original packaging, which is not so much a positive sign as it is the absence of a negative one.

Raw fruits and vegetables with intact skins seem perfectly safe to me, excluding of course the obviously rotten. Many are discarded for minor imperfections which can be pared away. Leafy vegetables, grapes, cauliflower, broccoli, and similar things may be contaminated by liquids and may be impractical to wash.

Candy, especially hard candy, is usually safe if it has not drawn ants. Chocolate is often discarded only because it has become discolored as the cocoa butter de-emulsified. Candying after all is one method of food preservation because pathogens do not like very sugary substances.

All of these foods might be found in any Dumpster and can be evaluated with some confidence largely on the basis of appearance. Beyond these are foods which cannot be correcty evaluated with some confidence largely on the basis of appearance. Beyond these are foods which cannot be correctly evaluated without additional information.

I began scavenging by pulling pizzas out of the Dumpster behind a pizza delivery shop. In general prepared food requires caution, but in this case I knew when the shop closed and went to the Dumpster as soon as the last of the help left.

Such shops often get prank orders, called "bogus." Because help seldom stays long at these places pizzas are often made with the wrong topping, refused on delivery for being cold, or baked incorrectly. The products to be discarded are boxed up because inventory is kept by counting boxes: a boxed pizza can be written off; an unboxed pizza does not exist.

I never placed a bogus order to increase the supply of pizzas and I believe no one else was scavenging in this Dumpster. But the people in the shop became suspicious and began to retain their garbage in the shop overnight.

While it lasted I had a steady supply of fresh, sometimes warm pizza. Because I knew the Dumpster I knew the source of the pizza, and because I visited the Dumpster regularly I knew what was fresh and what was yesterday's.

The area I frequent is inhabited by many affluent college students. I am not here by chance; the Dumpsters in this area are very rich. Students throw out many good things, including food. In particular they tend to throw everything out when they tend to throw everything out when they move at the end of a semester, before and after breaks, and around midterm when many of them despair of college. So I find it advantageous to keep an eye on the academic calendar.

The students throw food away around the breaks because they do not know whether it has spoiled or will spoil before they return. A typical discard is a half jar of peanut butter. In fact non-organic peanut butter does not require refrigeration and is unlikely to spoil in any reasonable time. The student does not know that, and since it is Daddy's money, the student decides not to take a chance.

Opened containers require caution and some attention to the question "Why was this discarded?" But in the case of discards from student apartments, the answer may be that the item was discarded through carelessness, ignorance, or wastefulness. This can sometimes be deduced when the item is found with many others, including some that are obviously perfectly good.

Some students, and others, approach defrosting a freezer by chucking out the whole lot. Not only do the circumstances of such a find tell the story, but also the mass of frozen goods stays cold for a long time and items may be found still frozen or freshly thawed.

Yogurt, cheese, and sour cream are items that are often thrown out while they are still good. Occasionally I find a cheese with a spot of mold, which of course I just pare off, and because it is obvious why such a cheese was discarded, I treat it with less suspicion than an apparently perfect cheese found in similar circumstances. Yogurt is often discarded, still sealed, only because the expiration date on the carton had passed. This is one of my favorite finds because yogurt will keep for several days, even in warm weather.

Students throw out canned goods and staples at the end of semesters and when they give up college at midterm. Drugs, pornography, spirits, and the like are often discarded when parents are expected—Dad's day, for example. And spirits also turn up after big party weekends, presumably discarded by the newly reformed. Wine and spirits, of course, keep perfectly well even once opened.

My test for carbonated soft drinks is whether they still fizz vigorously. Many juices or other beverages are too acid or too syrupy to cause much concern provided they are not visibly contaminated. Liquids, however, require some care.

One hot day I found a large jug of Pat O'Brian's Hurricane mix. The jug had been opened, but it was still ice cold. I drank three large glasses before it became apparent to me that someone had added the rum to the mix, and not a little rum. I never tasted the rum and by the time I began to feel the effects I had already ingested a very large quantity of the beverage. Some divers would have considered this is a boon, but being suddenly and thoroughly intoxicated in a public place in the early afternoon is not my idea of a good time.

I have heard of people maliciously contaminating discarded food and even handouts, but mostly I have heard of this from people with vivid imaginations who have had no experience with the Dumpsters themselves. Just before the pizza shop stopped discarding its garbage at night, jalapenos began showing up on most of the discarded pizzas. If indeed this was meant to discourage me it was a wasted effort because I am native Texan.

For myself, I avoid game, poultry, pork, and egg-based foods whether I find them raw or cooked. I seldom have the means to cook what I find, but when I do I avail myself of plentiful supplies of beef which is often in very good condition. I suppose fish becomes disagreeable before it becomes dangerous. The dog is happy to have any such thing that is past its prime and, in fact, does not recognize fish as food until it is quite strong.

Home leftovers, as opposed to surpluses from restaurants, are very often bad. Evidently, especially among students, there is a common type of personality that carefully wraps up even the smallest leftover and shoves it into the back of the refrigerator for six months or so before discarding it. Characteristic of this type are the reused jars and margarine tubs which house the remains.

I avoid ethnic foods I am unfamiliar with. If I do not know what it is supposed to look like when it is good, I cannot be certain I will be able to tell if it is bad.

No matter how careful I am I still get dysentery at least once a month, oftener in warm weather. I do not want to paint too romantic a picture. Dumpster diving has serious drawbacks as a way of life.

I learned to scavenge gradually, on my own. Since then I have initiated several companions into the trade. I have learned that there is a predictable series of stages a person goes through in learning to scavenge.

At first the new scavenger is filled with disgust and self-loathing. He is ashamed of being seen and may lurk around, trying to duck behind things, or he may try to dive at night.

(In fact, most people instinctively look away from a scavenger. By skulking around, the novice calls attention to himself and arouses suspicion. Diving at night is ineffective and needlessly messy.)

Every grain of rice seems to be a maggot. Everything seems to stink. He can wipe the egg yolk off the found can, but he cannot erase the stigma of eating garbage out of his mind.

That stage passes with experience. The scavenger finds a pair of running shoes that fit and look and smell brand new. He finds a pocket calculator in perfect working order. He finds pristine ice cream, still frozen, more than he can eat or keep. He begins to understand: people do throw away perfectly good stuff, a lot of perfectly good stuff.

At this stage, Dumpster shyness begins to dissipate. The diver, after all, has the last laugh. He is finding all manner of good things which are his for the taking. Those who disparage his profession are the fools, not he.

He may begin to hang onto some perfectly good things for which he has neither a use nor a market. Then he begins to take note of the things which are not perfectly good but are nearly so. He mates a Walkman with broken earphones and one that is missing a battery cover. He picks up things which he can repair.

At this stage he may become lost and never recover. Dumpsters are full of things of some potential value to someone and also of things which never have much intrinsic value but are interesting. All the Dumpster divers I have known come to the point of trying to acquire everything they touch. Why not take it, they reason, since it is all free.

This is, of course, hopeless. Most divers come to realize that they must restrict themselves to items of relatively immediate utility. But in some cases the diver simply cannot control himself. I have met several of these pack-rat types. Their ideas of the values of various pieces of junk verge on the psychotic. Every bit of glass may be a diamond, they think, and all that glisters, gold.

I tend to gain weight when I am scavenging. Partly this is because I always find far more pizza and doughnuts than water-packed tuna, nonfat yogurt, and fresh vegetables. Also I have not developed much faith in the reliability of Dumpsters as a food source, although it has been proven to me many times. I tend to eat as if I have no idea where my next meal is coming from. But mostly I just hate to see food go to waste and so I eat much more than I should. Something like this drives the obsession to collect junk.

As for collecting objects, I usually restrict myself to collecting one kind of small object at a time, such as pocket calculators, sunglasses. or campaign buttons. To live on the street I must anticipate my needs to a certain extent: I must pick up and save warm bedding I find in August because it will not be found in Dumpsters in November. But even if I had a home with extensive storage space I could not save everything that might be valuable in some contingency.

I have proprietary feelings about my Dumpsters. As I have suggested, it is no accident that I scavenge from Dumpsters where good finds are common. But my limited experience with Dumpsters in other areas suggests to me that it is the population of competitors rather than the affluence of the dumpers that most affects the feasibility of survival by scavenging. The large number of competitors is what puts me off the idea of trying to scavenge in places like Los Angeles.

Curiously, I do not mind my direct competition, other scavengers, so much as I hate the can scroungers.

People scrounge cans because they have to have a little cash. I have tried scrounging cans with an able-bodied companion. Afoot a can scrounger simply cannot make more than a few dollars a day. One can extract the necessities of life from the Dumpsters directly with far less effort than would be required to accumulate the equivalent value in cans.

Can scroungers, then, are people who *must* have small amounts of cash. These are drug addicts and winos, mostly the latter because the amounts of cash are so small.

Spirits and drugs do, like all other commodities, turn up in Dumpsters and the scavenger will from time to time have a half bottle of a rather good wine with his dinner. But the wino cannot survive on these occasional finds; he must have his daily dose to stave off the DTs. All the cans he can carry will buy about three bottles of Wild Irish Rose.

I do not begrudge them the cans, but can scroungers tend to tear up the Dumpsters, mixing the contents and littering the area. They become so specialized that they can see only cans. They earn my contempt by passing up change, canned goods, and readily hockable items.

There are precious few courtesies among scavengers. But it is a common practice to set aside surplus items: pairs of shoes, clothing, canned goods, and such. A true scavenger hates to see good stuff go to waste and what he cannot use he leaves in good condition in plain sight.

Can scroungers lay waste to everything in their path and will stir one of a pair of good shoes to the bottom of a Dumpster, to be lost or ruined in the muck. Can scroungers will even go through individual garbage cans, something I have never seen a scavenger do.

Individual garbage cans are set out on the public casement only on garbage days. On other days going through them requires trespassing close to a dwelling. Going through individual garbage cans without scattering litter is almost impossible. Litter is likely to reduce the public's tolerance of scavenging. Individual garbage cans are simply not as productive as Dumpsters; people in house and duplexes do not move as often and for some reason do not tend to discard as much useful material. Moreover, the time required to go through one garbage can that serves one household is not much less than the time required to go through a Dumpster that contains the refuse of twenty apartments.

But my strongest reservation about going through individual garbage cans is that this seems to me a very personal kind of invasion to which I would object if I were a householder. Although many things in Dumpsters are obviously meant never to come to light, a Dumpster is somehow less personal.

I avoid trying to draw conclusions about the people who dump in the Dumpsters I frequent. I think it would be unethical to do so, although I know many people will find the idea of scavenger ethics too funny for words.

Dumpsters contain bank statements, bills, correspondence, and other documents, just as anyone might expect. But there are also less obvious sources of information. Pill bottles, for example. The labels on pill bottles contain the name of the patient, the name of the doctor, and the name of the drug. AIDS drugs and anti-psychotic medicines, to name but two groups, are specific and are seldom prescribed for any other disorders. The plastic compacts for birth control pills usually have complete label information.

Despite all of this sensitive information, I have had only one apartment resident object to my going through the Dumpster. In that case it turned out the resident was a University athlete who was taking bets and who was afraid I would turn up his wager slips.

Occasionally a find tells a story. I once found a small paper bag containing some unused condoms, several partial tubes of flavored sexual lubricant, a partially used compact of birth control pills, and the torn pieces of a picture of a young man. Clearly she was through with him and planning to give up sex altogether.

Dumpster things are often sad—abandoned teddy bears, shredded wedding books, despaired-of sales kits. I find many pets lying in state in Dumpsters. Although I hope to get off the streets so that Lizbeth can have a long and comfortable old age, I know this hope is not very realistic. So I suppose when her time comes she too will go into a Dumpster. I will have no better place for her. And after all, for most of her life her livelihood has come from the Dumpster. When she finds something I think is safe that has been spilled from the Dumpster I let her have it. She already knows the route around the best Dumpsters. I like to think that if she survives me she will have a chance of evading the dog catcher and of finding her sustenance on the route.

Silly vanities also come to rest in the Dumpsters. I am a rather accomplished needleworker. I get a lot of materials from the Dumpsters. Evidently sorority girls, hoping to impress someone, perhaps themselves, with their mastery of a womanly art, buy a lot of embroider-by-number kits, work a few stitches horribly, and eventually discard the whole mess. I pull out their stitches, turn the canvas over, and work an original design. Do not think I refrain from chuckling as I make original gifts from these kits.

I find diaries and journals. I have often thought of compiling a book of literary found objects. And perhaps I will one day. But what I find is hopelessly commonplace and bad without being, even unconsciously, camp. College students also discard their papers. I am horrified to discover the kind of paper which now merits an A in an undergraduate course. I am grateful, however, for the number of good books and magazines the students throw out.

In the area I know best I have never discovered vermin in the Dumpsters, but there are two kinds of kitty surprise. One is alley cats which I meet as they leap, claws first, out of Dumpsters. This is especially thrilling when I have Lizbeth in tow. The other kind of kitty surprise is a plastic garbage bag filled with some ponderous, amorphous mass. This always proves to be used cat litter.

City bees harvest doughnut glaze and this makes the Dumpster at the doughnut shop more interesting. My faith in the instinctive wisdom of animals is always shaken whenever I see Lizbeth attempt to catch a bee in her mouth, which she does whenever bees are present. Evidently some birds find Dumpsters profitable, for birdie surprise is almost as common as kitty surprise of the first kind. In hunting season all kinds of small game turn up in Dumpsters, some of it, sadly, not entirely dead. Curiously, summer and winter, maggots are uncommon.

The worst of the living and near-living hazards of the Dumpsters are the fire ants. The food that they claim is not much of a loss, but they are vicious and aggressive. It is very easy to brush against some surface of the Dumpster and pick up half a dozen or more fire ants, usually in some sensitive area such as the underarm. One advantage of bringing Lizbeth along as I make Dumpster rounds is that, for obvious reasons, she is very alert to ground-based fire ants. When Lizbeth recognizes the signs of fire ant infestation around our feet she does the Dance of the Zillion Fire Ants. I have learned not to ignore this warning from Lizbeth, whether I perceive the tiny ants or not, but to remove ourselves at Lizbeth's first pas de bourrée. All the more so because the ants are the worst in the months I wear flip-flops, if I have them.

(Perhaps someone will misunderstand the above. Lizbeth does the Dance of the Zillion Fire Ants when she recognizes more fire ants than she cares to eat, not when she is being bitten. Since I have learned to react promptly, she does not get bitten at all. It is the isolated patrol of fire ants that falls in Lizbeth's range that deserves pity. Lizbeth finds them quite tasty.)

By far the best way to go through a Dumpster is to lower yourself into it. Most of the good stuff tends to settle at the bottom because it is usually weighter than the rubbish. My more athletic companions have often demonstrated to me that they can extract much good material from a Dumpster I have already been over.

To those psychologically or physically unprepared to enter a Dumpster, I recommend a stout stick, preferably with some barb or book at one end. The hook can be used to grab plastic garbage bags. When I find canned goods or other objects loose at the bottom of a Dumpster I usually can roll them into a small bag that I can then hoist up. Much Dumpster diving is a matter of experience for which nothing will do except practice.

Dumpster diving is outdoor work, often surprisingly pleasant. It is not entirely predictable; things of interest turn up every day and some days there are finds of great value. I am always very pleased when I can turn up exactly the thing I most wanted to find. Yet in spite of the element of chance, scavenging more than most other pursuits tends to yield returns in some proportion to the effort and intelligence brought to bear. It is very sweet to turn up a few dollars in change from a Dumpster that has just been gone over by a wino.

The land is now covered with cities. The cities are full of Dumpsters. I think of scavenging as a modern from of self-reliance. In any event, after ten years of government service, where everything is geared to the lowest common denominator, I find work that rewards initiative and effort refreshing. Certainly I would be happy to have a sinecure again, but I am not heartbroken not to have one anymore.

I find from the experience of scavenging two rather deep lessons. The first is to take what I can use and let the rest go by. I have come to think that there is no value in the abstract. A thing I cannot use or make useful, perhaps by trading, has no value however fine or rare it may be. I mean useful in a broad sense—so, for example, some art I would think useful and valuable, but other art might be otherwise for me.

I was shocked to realize that some things are not worth acquiring, but now I think it is so. Some material things are white elephants that eat up the possessor's substance.

The second lesson is of the transience of material being. This has not quite converted me to a dualist, but it has made some headway in that direction. I do not suppose that ideas are immortal, but certainly mental things are longer-lived than other material things.

Once I was the sort of person who invests material objects with sentimental value. Now I no longer have those things, but I have the sentiments yet.

Many times in my travels I have lost everything but the clothes I was wearing and Lizbeth. The things I find in Dumpsters, the love letters and ragdolls of so many lives, remind me of this lesson. Now I hardly pick up a thing without envisioning the time I will cast it away. This I think is a healthy state of mind. Almost eveything I have now has already been cast out at least once, proving that what I own is valueless to someone.

Anyway, I find my desire to grab for the gaudy bauble has been largely sated. I think this is an attitude I share with the very wealthy—we both know there is plenty more where what we have came from. Between us are the rat-race millions who have confounded their selves with the objects they grasp and who nightly scavenge the cable channels looking for they know not what.

I am sorry for them.

Footbinding

John King Fairbank

John King Fairbank (1907–1991) is sometimes known as the founder of modern Chinese studies in the United States. He first traveled to China in 1932, where he remained for five years, mastering the Chinese language and studying its history and culture. In 1955, he established the Center for East Asian Research, later renamed the John King Fairbank Center, at Harvard University. In his numerous books and articles on Chinese history and society, Fairbank sought to ground his work in sociology, a departure from the more traditional humanistic approach. The present selection first appeared in Fairbank's The Great Chinese Revolution *(1986); it discusses the traditional Chinese practice of foot-binding, officially banned by the Republic of China in 1911.*

O f all the many unexplored facets of China's ancient history, the subjection of women has been the least studied. Women were fitted into the social and cosmic order (which were a continuum) by invoking the principles of Yang and Yin. All things bright, warm, active, male, and dominant were Yang while all things dark, cold, passive, female, and yielding were Yin. This dualism, seen in the alternation of night and day or the contrast of the sun and moon, was a ready-made matrix in which women could be confined. The subjection of women was thus a sophisticated and perfected institution like the other Chinese achievements, not a mere accident of male biceps or female childbearing as might be more obviously the case in a primitive tribe. The inequality between the sexes was buttressed with philosophical underpinnings and long-continued social practices. Symbolic of woman's secondary status was her bridal night:

she expected to be deflowered by a stranger, a husband selected by her family whom she had never seen before. Even though the facts may often have been less stark, the theory was hard-boiled.

Out of all this complex of theory and custom by which the Chinese world was given an enduring and stable order, the most neglected aspect is the institution of footbinding. This custom arose at court in the tenth century during the late T'ang and spread gradually among the upper class during the succeeding Sung period. By the Ming and Ch'ing eras after 1368 it had penetrated the mass of the Han Chinese population. It became so widespread that Western observers in the nineteenth century found it almost universal, not only among the upper class but throughout the farming population.

Footbinding spread as a mark of gentility and upper-class status. Small feet became a prestige item to such an extent that a girl without them could not achieve a good marriage arrangement and was subjected to the disrespect and taunts of the community. In short, bound feet became *de rigueur,* the only right-thinking thing to do for a daughter, an obligation on the part of a mother who cared about her daughter's eventual marriage and success in life. The bound foot was a must. Only tribal peoples and exceptional groups like the Manchu conquerors or the Hakka Chinese migrant groups in South China or finally the mean people, that lowest and rather small group who were below the social norms of civility, could avoid binding their daughters' feet.

The small foot was called a "golden lotus" or "golden lily" *(chin-lien)* and was much celebrated in poems and essays by male enthusiasts. Here is the early Sung poet Su Tung-p'o (1036–1101):

> Anointed with fragrance, she takes lotus steps;
> Though often sad, she steps with swift lightness.
> She dances like the wind, leaving no physical trace.
> Another stealthily but happily tries on the palace style,
> But feels such distress when she tries to walk!
> Look at them in the palms of your hands, so
> > wondrously small
> that they defy description.

The Sung philosophers stressed women's inferiority as a basic element of the social order. The great Chu Hsi (1130–1200) codified the cosmology of China as magistrally as his near contemporary Thomas Aquinas (d. 1274) codified that of Western Christendom. When he was a magistrate in Fukien province, Chu Hsi promoted footbinding to preserve female chastity and as "a means of spreading Chinese culture and teaching the separation of men and women."

By the Ming period the overwhelming majority of Han Chinese women all over the country had artificially small feet. The Manchu emperors many times inveighed against it in hortatory edicts, but to no avail. Male romanticizing on the subject continued unabated as in this poem of the fourteenth century:

> Lotus blossoms in shoes most tight,
> As if she could stand on autumnal waters!
> Her shoe tips do not peek beyond the skirt,
> Fearful lest the tiny embroideries be seen[1]

There can be no doubt that footbinding was powered by a sexual fetish. Chinese love manuals are very specific about the use of bound feet as erogenous areas. All the different ways of taking hold of the foot, rubbing it with the hands, and using the mouth, tongue, and lips are explicitly catalogued. Many cases are recorded with the verisimilitude of high-class pornography. Meanwhile, the aesthetic attractiveness of the small shoes with their bright embroidered colors was praised in literature, while the tottering gait of a bound-foot woman was considered very fetching as a symbol of feminine frailty, which indeed it was. In fact, of course, bound feet were a guarantee of chastity because they kept women within the household and unable to venture far abroad. Lily feet, once formed, could not be unlocked like a chastity belt. By leaving only men able-bodied, they ensured male domination in a very concrete way.

Thus the prevalence of footbinding down to the 1920s, while the movement against it began only in the 1890s, vividly index the speed and scope of China's modern social revolution. This may be less comprehensible to white American males than to white women, or especially to black Americans, for Chinese women within the present century have had an emancipation from veritable slavery.

While footbinding is mentioned in so many foreign books about China, it is usually passed by as a curious detail. I don't think it was. It was a major erotic invention, still another achievement in Chinese social engineering. Girls painfully deformed themselves throughout their adolescence in order to attract desirable husbands who, on their part, subscribed to a folklore of self-fulfilling beliefs: for example, that footbinding made a vagina more narrow and muscular and that lotus feet were major foci of erotic sensitivity, true erogenous zones, a net addition of 50 percent to the female equipment. Normal feet, we are now told by purveyors of sexual comfort, are an underdeveloped area sensually, but one must admit they are a bit hard to handle—whereas small lotus feet could be grasped, rubbed, licked, sucked, nibbled, and bitten. The garrulous Jesuit Father Ripa, who spent a decade at the court of K'ang-hsi in the early 1700s, reported that "Their taste is perverted to such an extraordinary degree that I knew a physician who lived with a woman with whom he had no other intercourse but that of viewing and fondling her feet.[2] Having compacted all their nerve endings in a smaller area, golden lilies were far more sensitive than, for example, the back of the neck that used to bewitch Japanese samurai. After all, they had been created especially for male appreciation. When every proper girl did it, what bride would say that her sacrifice, suffering, and inconvenience were not worth it? A bride without small feet in the old China was like a new house in today's America without utilities—who would want it? Consequently in the 1930s and '40s one still saw women on farms stumping about on their heels as they worked, victims of this old custom.

A girl's foot was made small, preferably only three inches long, by pressing the four smaller toes under the sole or ball of the foot (plantar) in order to make it narrower. At the same time it was made shorter by forcing the big toe and heel closer together so that the arch rose in a bowed shape. As a result the arch was broken and the foot could bear no weight except on the heel, if this process was begun at age five, the experience was less severe than if a little girl, perhaps in a peasant household, had been left with normal feet until age eight or ten so that she could be of more use in the household.

> When I was seven [said one woman to Ida Pruitt], my mother . . . washed and placed alum on my feet and cut the toenails. She then bent my toes toward the plantar with a binding cloth ten feet long and two inches wide, doing the right foot first and then the left. She . . . ordered me to walk but when I did the pain proved unbearable. That night . . . my feet felt on fire and I couldn't sleep; mother struck me for crying. On the following days, I tried to hide but was forced to walk on my feet . . . after several months all toes but the big one were pressed against the inner surface . . . mother would remove the bindings and wipe the blood and pus which dripped from my feet. She told me that only with removal of the flesh could my feet become slender . . . every two weeks I changed to new shoes. Each new pair was one-to-two-tenths of an inch smaller than the previous one. . . . In summer my feet smelled offensively because of pus and blood; in winter my feet felt cold because of lack of circulation . . . four of the toes were curled in like so many dead caterpillars . . . it took two years to achieve the three-inch model . . . my shanks were thin, my feet became humped, ugly and odoriferous.[3]

After the first two years the pain lessened. But constricting the feet to a three-inch size was only the beginning of trouble. By this time they were very private parts indeed and required daily care, washing and manicuring at the same time that they had to be kept constantly bound and shod night and day. Unmanicured nails could cut into the instep, bindings could destroy circulation, blood poisoning or gangrene could result. Massage and applications of hot and cold water were used to palliate the discomfort, but walking any distance remained difficult. It also produced corns on the bent-under toes, which had to be pared with a knife. Once deformed to taste, bound feet were of little use to stand on. Since weight was carried entirely on the heels, it had to be constantly shifted back and forth. Since the bound foot lacked the resilience of a normal foot, it was a tiring and unsteady support.

Footbinding, in short, had begun as an ostentatious luxury, which made a girl less useful in family work and more dependent on help from others. Yet, once the custom had spread among the populace, lotus feet were considered essential in order to get a good husband. Marriages, of course, were arranged between families and often by professional matchmakers, in whose trade the length of the lily foot was rated more important than beauty of face or person. When the anti-footbinding movement began at the end of the nineteenth century, many mothers and daughters, too, stubbornly clung to it to avoid the public shame of having large feet. The smallness of the foot, in short, was a source of social pride both to the family and to the victim. First and last one may guess that at least a billion Chinese girls during the thousand-year currency of this social custom suffered the agony of footbinding and reaped its rewards of pride and ecstasy, such as they were.

There are three remarkable things about footbinding. First, that it should have been invented at all—it was such a feat of physio-psychosociological engineering. Second, that once invented it should have spread so pervasively and lasted so long among a generally humane and practical-minded farming population. We are just at the beginning of understanding this phenomenon. The fact that an upper-class erotic luxury permeated the peasantry of Old China, for whom it could only lower productivity, suggests that the old society was extraordinarily homogeneous.

Finally, it was certainly ingenious how men trapped women into mutilating themselves for an ostensibly sexual purpose that had the effect of perpetuating male domination. Brides left their own homes and entered their husband's family in the lowest status, servants of their mothers-in-law. Husbands were chosen for them sight unseen, and might find romance in extramarital adventures or, if they could afford it, bring in secondary wives. But a woman once betrothed, if her husband-to-be died even as a child, was expected to remain a chaste widow thereafter. Mao remarked that "women hold up half the sky," but in the old China they were not supposed to lift their heads. The talent that one sees in Chinese women today had little chance to grow and express itself. This made a weak foundation for a modern society.

Endnotes

1. Howard Levy, *Chinese Footbinding: The History of a Curious Erotic Custom* (New York: Walton Rawls, 1900), p. 47.

2. Fortunato Prandi, ed. and trans., *Memoirs of Father Ripa* (London: John Murray, 1855), p. 58.

3. Ida Pruitt, *A Daughter of Han: The Autobiography of a Chinese Working Woman* (Yale University Press, 1945), p. 22.

Wal-Mart Values

Liza Featherstone

Liza Featherstone, born April 21, 1969, is a journalist whose work primarily seeks to expose issues concerning corporate responsibility. She has been published in Washington Post, The New York Times, Lingua Franca, *and* Rolling Stone. *Featherstone graduated from the University of Michigan in 1991. Since the late 1990's she has worked as a freelance journalist. Much of her early work focuses on youth activism, and in 2002 she co-authored* Students against Sweatshops: the Making of a Movement. *The book was instrumental in highlighting the need for student solidarity as an instrument in social change and was able to humanize the protester through personal essays while also focusing on the protest and the victims of unfair labor practices. Following the publication of the book, Featherstone continued to work on passionate pieces concerning labor conditions and workers' rights. Featherstone showed an increased interest in the specific facing Wal-Mart employees. Inspired by the landmark class action suit Dukes v. Wal-Mart, Featherstone began researching the case and issuing condemnation of the corporation's practices via published articles in several journals and magazines. Betty Dukes, 52, had worked for Wal-Mart for six years when she filed the legal complaint against the corporation. Her suit argues that she was denied promotions based on her sex. Moreover, the complaint argues that gender discrimination is widespread throughout the nation's largest private employer. Dukes v. Wal-Mart grew to include the complaints of over 1.6 million women and was, at one time, the largest class action lawsuit in US history. The case was tied up in the legal system for a decade and was finally dismissed by the Supreme Court in 2011. Liza Featherstone covers the early years of the case in her article "Wal-Mart Values". The article serves as a call-to-action against gender discrimination in the workplace, specifically suggesting that women "control both sides of the cash register". Featherstone would later adapt the article to include in her book* Selling Women Short: The Landmark Battle for Worker's Rights at Wal-Mart *(2004).*

Featherstone continues to pursue issues related to corporate greed and infringement on workers' rights. She has published several dozen articles on Wal-mart for The Nation. *Her numerous journal articles, in addition to her published books, gained her recognition, and she was named a 2007-2008 Knight-Bagehot fellow. This gave her the opportunity to earn a graduate degree in journalism from Columbia University. She works as an adjunct Professor at New York University and at the School of International and Public Affairs at Columbia University and continues to work as a freelance journalist.*

Wal-Mart is an unadorned eyesore surrounded by a parking lot, even its logo aggressively devoid of flourish. Proving that looks don't matter, however, the retail giant has a way with women: Four out of ten American women visit one of Wal-Mart's stores weekly. They like the low prices, convenience and overall ease of the shopping experience. Even snobbish elites are discovering its delights: A few months ago, *New York Times* fashion writer Cathy Horyn revealed, to the astonishment of fellow urban fashionistas, that much of her wardrobe comes from Wal-Mart ("Marc Jacobs?" "No, it's Wal-Mart"). Retail consultant Wendy Liebmann ecstatically dubs Wal-Mart the "benchmark by which American women rate all shopping."

Would that $15 runway knockoffs were Wal-Mart's primary contribution to women's lives. But Wal-Mart is not only America's favorite shopping destination; it's also the nation's largest private employer. The majority of Wal-Mart's "associates" (the company's treacly euphemism for employees) are women. Their average wage is $7.50 an hour, out of which they must pay for their own health insurance, which is so costly that only two in five workers buy it.

Yet Wal-Mart is not only a horrifyingly stingy employer: Many workers say it is also a sexist one. From the Third World factories in which its cheap products are made, to the floor of your local Wal-Mart, where they're displayed and sold, it is women who bear the brunt of the company's relentless cost-cutting. Ellen Rosen, a resident scholar in Brandeis University's Women's Studies Research Program, recently observed that around the world, Wal-Mart's business practices "may be leading to a new kind of globally sanctioned gender discrimination."

Gretchen Adams worked for Wal-Mart for ten years, in five different states. As a co-manager, she opened twenty-seven "Supercenters" (gargantuan, twenty-four-hour grocery/general merchandise hybrids). "There were so many inequities," she sighs with amazement, reflecting on her time at Wal-Mart. She saw men with little to no relevant experience earning starting salaries of $3,500 a year more than her own. "I had the title but not the pay," she says. "They take us for idiots."

Adams is now a witness in *Dukes v. Wal-Mart*, in which seven California women—current and former Wal-Mart employees—are charging the company with systematic sex discrimination in promotions, assignments, training and pay. Betty Dukes, for whom the suit is named, is a 52-year-old African-American woman who still works at Wal-Mart. First hired by the company in 1994 as a part-time cashier in Pittsburg, California, she was an eager employee with a sincere admiration for founder Sam Walton's "visionary spirit." A year later, with excellent performance reviews, she was given a merit pay raise and a full-time job. Two years later, after being promoted to the position of customer service manager, she began encountering harsh discrimination from her superiors; she says she was denied the training she needed in order to advance further, while that same training was given to male employees. She was also denied the opportunity to work in "male" departments like hardware, and was made to sell baby clothes instead. "I can mix a can of paint," she told reporters just after filling the suit. "I want the chance to do it."

When Dukes complained about the discrimination, managers got back at her by writing her up for minor offenses like returning late from breaks, offenses routinely committed by her white and male co-workers, who were never punished, she says. When she kept complaining, she was denied a promotion and finally demoted back to her cashier job. She went to the Wal-Mart district office to complain, but the company did nothing. Being demoted was not just humiliating: It deprived Dukes of other promotions, and her cashier job offered fewer hours and a lower hourly wage. When she was once again eligible for promotion, four new management positions, none of which had even been posted, were filled by men.

Along with more than seventy witnesses, the other named plaintiffs in *Dukes v. Wal-Mart* tell similar stories:

§ In August 1997, Patricia Surgeson, then a single mother of two, began working evenings as a part-time cashier in a Wal-Mart tire and lube department while attending community college. Within two weeks, while she was stocking shelves, she says, a male co-worker began grabbing and propositioning her. He was allowed to remain in his job, while she was transferred to the health and beauty aids department. Over the next four years, Surgeson held more responsible jobs at Wal-Mart, but these promotions weren't accompanied by raises. Many of her male co-workers were paid better than she was, she charges, even though they had less responsibility and were newer to the company.

§ Hired to work in the returns department in the Livermore, California, store in fall 1998, Cleo Page, who had already worked in two other Wal-Mart stores, was quickly promoted to a customer service manager position. Interviewing a little over a year later for a promotion, she charges, she was told that it was a man's world, and that men controlled management positions at Wal-Mart. She was repeatedly passed over for promotions, which were given to male employees, and to white women. (Page, who is African-American, also has a race discrimination claim against Wal-Mart, as does Betty Dukes, but these charges are not part of the class-action suit.) At one point, her store manager discouraged her from applying for the sporting-goods department manager position, she says, because "customers would feel comfortable" buying sporting goods from a man. She heard male co-workers complain that "women were taking over" the store, and she heard them ask each other if they knew other men who would be interested in working at Wal-Mart.

§ Christine Kwapnoski, who is still employed in a Concord, California, Sam's Club (a division of Wal-Mart), has worked for the company since 1986. She charges that management positions were never posted, though when she heard one was opening up she'd tell supervisors she was interested. Still, the jobs were given to men less qualified than herself, whom she then had to train. A store manager suggested that she "needed to blow the cobwebs off" her makeup and "doll up." She says she saw men getting paid at higher rates than she was, and getting raises more often; in one instance, Kwapnoski, a divorced mother of two, questioned a male co-worker's raise, and was told he had a family to support.

§ After thirty years of retail experience, Deborah Gunter began working at a Riverside, California, Wal-Mart in 1996 as a photo lab clerk. She says she applied for management positions and was passed over for less experienced men. She requested further training and never got it. When she was transferred to the Tire Lube Express department, she did the work of a support manager but never got the title or the pay. Her supervisor sexually harassed her, and when she complained, her hours were reduced, she says. After she trained a man to fill the support manager job, he got the title and salary, and her hours were reduced. When she complained about her reduced hours and requested a meeting with the district manager to protest the discriminatory treatment, she was fired.

And on and on. Women make up 72 percent of Wal-Mart's sales work force but only 33 percent of its managers. A study conducted for the *Dukes* plaintiffs by economist Marc Bendick found such discrepancies to be far less pronounced among Wal-Mart's competitors, which could boast of more than 50 percent female management. Even more striking, comparing Wal-Mart stores to competitors in the same location, Bendick's study found little geographic variation in these ratios, and little change over time. In fact, the percentage of women among Wal-Mart's 1999 management lagged behind that of its competitors in 1975. (Wal-Mart spokesman Bill Wertz says it's "too soon" to say how the company will defend itself against these charges.)

Depending on the outcome of a class-certification hearing next July before a San Francisco federal judge, *Dukes v. Wal-Mart* could be the largest civil rights class-action suit in history, affecting more than 700,000 women. Though a California judge ruled recently that the case must be limited to California plaintiffs, discovery is nationwide, as is the proposed class. If the plaintiffs have their way, any woman employed by the company from 1999 on would win damages. But even more important, says Brad Seligman, Betty Dukes's lawyer, "The idea is to change Wal-Mart. We will not have done our job unless we transform the personnel system at Wal-Mart and make sure there are additional opportunities for women."

Dukes is the culmination of a long history of individual sex-discrimination suits—including sexual harassment and pregnancy discrimination—against Wal-Mart, going back at least to 1981. Courts have often, though of course not always, ruled for the plaintiffs in these cases; in several sexual-harassment suits juries have awarded employees millions of dollars in punitive damages. Wal-Mart recently settled an EEOC sexual-harassment suit on behalf of a group of Wal-Mart employees in Mobile, Alabama, and several women unconnected to Dukes have discrimination suits under way.

Some of the lawsuits against Wal-Mart reflect common grievances cited by working women, inequities hardly unique to Wal-Mart, but that women's advocates rightly find particularly outrageous in the world's largest corporation. For example, a suit filed in Georgia by Lisa Smith Mauldin, a Wal-Mart customer service manager and a 22-year-old divorced mother of two, charges the company with sex discrimination because its health plan does not cover prescription contraceptives (it does cover other prescription drugs, but as the complaint spells out in painstaking legalese, only women get pregnant). Mauldin works thirty-two hours a week and makes $12.14 an hour, so the $30 monthly cost of the Pill is a significant burden for her (and certainly a prohibitive one for many fellow employees, who earn significantly lower wages). In September Mauldin's suit was certified as a class action, demanding reimbursement for all female Wal-Mart employees who have been paying for birth control out of pocket since March 2001, and demanding that Wal-Mart's insurance cover FDA-approved prescription contraceptives in the future.

Wal-Mart is also criticized for indifference to the workers, mostly young women, who make the products sold in its stores. While most major-clothing stores traffic in sweated labor, Wal-Mart's record on this issue is unusually bad. Much of the clothing sold at Wal-Mart is made in China, where workers have no freedom of association. Unlike many companies, Wal-Mart has adamantly refused to tell labor rights advocates where its factories are, rejecting even the pretense of transparency. Last year, Wal-Mart was removed from the Domini 400 Social Index, an influential socially responsible investment fund, for its failure to make sufficient efforts to uphold labor rights and for its "unresponsiveness to calls for change." Other than Nike, Wal-Mart is the only company that has been booted from the fund for this reason.

Last June, citing all of the above issues, the National Organization for Women named Wal-Mart its fifth "Merchant of Shame" and launched a public education campaign against the retailer. "It's part of our emphasis on economic justice. We don't think Wal-Mart is a woman-friendly workplace," says Olga Vives, NOW's vice president for action. NOW has asked Wal-Mart for a meeting to discuss its complaints, but since the company has not responded, Vives says, "we are getting their attention in other ways." On September 28, 600 NOW chapters demonstrated at Wal-Mart stores across the country, from Tallahassee to Salt Lake City.

NOW has been cooperating closely with the United Food and Commercial Workers, who have been trying for several years to organize Wal-Mart workers [see John Dicker, "Union Blues at Wal-Mart," July 8], an effort ruthlessly resisted by the company. Gretchen Adams, who quit Wal-Mart in December 2001, now works as an organizer with the UFCW. She's angry, not only about the way she was treated, but also about the plight of the hourly workers she supervised. "They were not paid enough to live on. There were a whole lot of single mothers," she says. "They would come in crying because they had hard decisions: whether to take their child to the doctor or pay their rent." Many hourly workers were on public assistance because their pay was so low, she recalls.

Not a single Wal-Mart store is unionized yet, but there's substantial evidence that many of the problems suffered by Wal-Mart's female employees would be alleviated by a union. A study on women in the retail food industry, published in February by the Institute for Women's Policy Research and funded by the UFCW, found that women workers in unions faced smaller gender and racial wage gaps, and earned 31 percent higher wages than women who were not in unions. In addition, the study showed that two-thirds of women in unionized retail jobs had health insurance, while only one-third of their nonunion counterparts did. Such advantages were even more dramatic for part-time workers, who are even more likely to be women.

At a November 18 press conference in Washington, DC, to announce a UFCW-initiated National Day of Action on November 21—rallies were held in more than 100 cities and towns, supported by a broad coalition of religious, environmental, student and labor groups—NOW president Kim Gandy said Wal-Mart should know that "continuing their greedy, abusive ways will cost them the business of thinking consumers." This seems unlikely, though it's probably important to make the threat. In any case, the UFCW is not calling for a nationwide Wal-Mart boycott. "We are calling for a boycott in Las Vegas," says Doug Dority, president of the UFCW. In Las Vegas, where a vigorous organizing campaign is under way, Wal-Mart has committed numerous violations of the right to organize. Las Vegas is also the most heavily unionized city in the United States. Elsewhere, however, the UFCW is not ready to take that step. "It's hard to boycott and organize at the same time," says Dority. "Because Wal-Mart uses that against you: 'Hey, the union is trying to take away your job.'"

Still, it makes sense for activists to appeal to the possible solidarity between Wal-Mart's female customers and its female work force. UFCW vice president Susan Phillips said in a recent speech, "As women, we have tremendous power. We control both sides of the cash register. We are the cashiers on one side and we are the customers on the other side. If we join hands across the cash register, we can change the economic future for women in America." Far from telling consumers not to shop at the "Big Box," on the November 21 Day of Action many UFCW locals dramatized consumer power through "shop-ins," urging protesters to go into the store, buy something while wearing a T-shirt with the UFCW's phone number on it, and tell employees they supported their right to join a union. In Seekonk, Massachusetts, a UFCW local even gave each November 21 protester a $20 bill to spend at Wal-Mart, donating the purchases to a nearby women's shelter.

In fact, Wal-Mart customers and workers have much in common: They are increasingly likely to be anybody in America. The working poor are even more likely than other Americans to shop at Wal-Mart, not necessarily because they find it a shopper's paradise—though of course some do—but because they need the discounts, or live in a remote area with few other options. (Many Wal-Mart workers say they began working at their local Wal-Mart because they shopped there; when they needed a job, they filled out its application, because Wal-Mart was already such a familiar part of their lives.) Through shoppers and "associates" alike, Wal-Mart is making billions from female poverty.

In addition to court mandates and worker organizing, changing Wal-Mart is going to take massive pressure from many constituencies; union locals will need an approach to coalition-building that is highly community-specific, yet networked nationwide, similar to that used by the progressive labor organization Jobs With Justice. The range of groups that turned out on November 21 was promising, and they have vowed to stay committed to a "People's Campaign for Justice at Wal-Mart."

Asked how long it will take to unionize Wal-Mart, Gretchen Adams, who is 56, answers without hesitation: "The rest of my life." But she's determined. As a manager opening a new store in Las Vegas, Adams says, "I was not allowed to hire any experienced help, because they might be union." Now, she deadpans, "I'm trying to get Wal-Mart the help it needs."

A Well-Regulated Militia

Paul Fussell

Paul Fussell was born on March 22, 1924 in Pasadena, California, into an extremely affluent family. He was attending Pomona College when he was drafted into the Army in 1943 to fight in World War II. During his time fighting in Europe, he was wounded in the back and legs and was awarded two Purple hearts and a Bronze Star. His experiences in that war also created a great disdain for those people who attempted to justify the use of war as a means to resolving political issues, especially those who had never served in the military.

After the war, Fussell returned to Pomona College to complete his degree, and he later attended Harvard, where he earned his master's and doctorate degrees in English. During his teaching career, he taught at numerous universities throughout the northeastern United States.

In addition to his teaching, Fussell also wrote academic books on the use of language; his writing then focused on social commentary about war and other issues. Among these works was The Great War *and* B.A.D: Or, the Dumbing of America.

Fussell also wrote numerous essays in which he offered his critique of various social issues. Among those essays is "A Well-Regulated Militia," in which he takes exception with the NRA and what he sees as their misreading of the Second Amendment to the Constitution.

This time of year Washington swarms with high school graduating classes. They come to the great pulsating heart of the Republic—no one has told them yet that it is Wall Street—to be impressed by the White House and the Capitol and the monuments and the Smithsonian and the space capsules. Given the state of public secondary education, I doubt if many of these students are interested in language and rhetoric, and I imagine very few are fascinated by such attendants of power and pressure as verbal misrepresentation and disingenuous quotation. But if any are, they can profit from a stroll past the new headquarters of the National Rifle Association of America, to be found at 1600 Rhode Island Avenue, NW.

There they will see an entrance flanked by two marble panels offering language. The one on the right reads, "The right of the people to keep and bear arms shall not be infringed" and that sounds familiar. So familiar that the student naturally expects the left-hand panel to honor the principle of symmetry by presenting the first half of the quotation, namely: "A well regulated Militia being necessary to the security of a free state, . . . " But looking to the left the stroller discovers not that clause but rather this rather lame list of NRA functions and specializations: "Firearms Safety Education. Marksmanship Training. Shooting for Recreation". It's as if in presenting its shiny public face the NRA doesn't want us to recall the crucial dependent clause of the Second Amendment, whose latter half it is so fond of invoking to urge its prerogatives. The less emphasis on the clause about the Militia, the better for the association. Hence its pretense here that the main clause is not crucially dependent on the now unadvertised subordinate clause, and indeed meaningless without it.

Because flying bullets rank close to cancer and heart disease as menaces to public health in this country, the firearm lobby, led by the NRA, comes under liberal attack regularly, but with special vigor immediately after an assault on some conspicuous person like John Lennon or Ronald Reagan. Thus in *The New Republic* of April 11, both TRB and the editors wrung their hands but failed to move the debate forward. The editorial went so far as to suggest that the Second Amendment is so obsolete that it should be amended out of the Constitution, thus depriving the NRA of a leg to stand on.

But here as everywhere a better solution would be not to fiddle with the Constitution but to take it seriously, the way we've done with the First Amendment, or, say, the Thirteenth, the one forbidding open and avowed slavery. And by taking it seriously I mean something close to taking it literally. We should "close read" and thus focus lots of attention on the Second Amendment, inviting the NRA to pull the dependent clause out of the closet, display it on its shiny new facade, and accept its implications. If they did give it equal space with the clause they love, a proposal like the following would seem more or less appropriate, and sensible enough to invite the initiative of anti-gun members of Congress like Millicent Fenwick and Edward Kennedy. They could introduce and fight for legislation providing:

1) that the Militia shall now, after these many years, be "well regulated," as the Constitution requires;

2) that any person who has chosen to possess at home a gun of any kind, and who is not a member of the police or the military or an appropriate federal agency, shall be considered to have enrolled automatically in the Militia of the United States. Badges will be issued identifying members of the Militia, which will be organized in units representing counties, towns, or boroughs. Bearing arms while not proceeding to, attending, or returning from scheduled exercises of the Militia will be severely punished;

3) that any gun owner who declines to join the regulated Militia may opt out by selling his firearms to the federal government for a bounty of $1,000 each and undertaking that if he again owns firearms he will be deemed to have enlisted in the Militia;

4) that because the Constitution specifically states that the Militia shall be "well regulated," a regular training program, familiar to all who have belonged to military units devoted to the orderly discharge of small arms, shall be instituted. This will require at least eight hours of drill each weekend in some convenient local field or park, rain or shine or snow; weekly supervised target practice (separation from the service for those who can't hit a barn door); practice in digging simple defensive works, like trenches and foxholes, as well as necessary sanitary installations like field latrines; and a six-week bivouac each summer—all under the close supervision of experienced officers and non-commissioned officers of the United States Army and Marine Corps. Other obligatory exercises of the sort suitable to lightly armed, well-regulated units might include: practice in first aid, map-reading, the erection of double-apron barbed-wire fences, long-distance marching, and lectures on military courtesy and the traditions of the Militia, beginning with the Minute Men. Per diem payments will be made to those participating in these exercises;

5) that since the purpose of the Militia is, as the Constitution says, to safeguard "the security of a free state," at times when invasion threatens, all units of the Militia will be trucked to the borders for duration of the emergency, there to remain in field conditions (here's where the practice in latrine-digging pays off) until Congress declares that the emergency has subsided. The Militia may also be ordered to other duties consistent with its constitutional identity as a disciplined volunteer force: for example, flood and emergency service (digging, sandbag filling, rescuing old people); patrolling angry or incinerated cities; or controlling crowds at large public events like patriotic parades, motor races, and professional football games;

6) that failure to appear for these scheduled drills, practices, bivouacs, and mobilizations shall result in the Militiaperson's dismissal from the service, requiring forfeiture of badge, pay, and firearm.

Why did the framers add the word "bear" to the phrase "keep and bear arms"? Because they conceived that keeping arms at home implied the public obligation to bear them in a regulated way for "the security of" not a private household but "a free state." If interstate bus fares can be regulated it's hard to see why the Militia can't be, especially since the Constitution says it must be. *The New Republic* has recognized that "the Second Amendment to the Constitution clearly connects the right to bear arms to the 18th-century national need to raise a militia." But it goes on: "That need is now obsolete, and so is the amendment." And it concludes: "If the only way this country can get control of firearms is to amend the Constitution, then it's time for Congress to get the process under way."

I think not. Rather, it's time not to amend Article II of the Bill of Rights (and Obligations), but to read it, publicize it, and embrace it. That the Second Amendment stems from assumptions that can be stigmatized as "18th-century" cuts little ice. The First Amendment stems precisely from those-assumptions, and no one wants to amend it except Yahoos. Also "18th-century" is that lovely bit in Section 9 of Article I forbidding any "Title of Nobility" to be granted by the United States. That's why we've been spared Lord Rockefeller and Sir André Kostelanetz, Knight. Thank God for the 18th century, I say. It understood not just what a firearm is and what a militia is. It understood what "well regulated" means. It knew how to compose a constitutional article and it knew how to read it. And it assumed that everyone, gun lobbyists and touring high school students alike, could understand and correctly quote it.

Statement in the Great Trial of 1922

Mohandas Gandhi

*Mohandas Gandhi (1869–1948), commonly known and addressed in India and across the world as Mahatma Gandhi (*Mahatma *is Sanskrit for* Great Soul) *and as* Bapu *(which, in many Indian languages, means Father), was one of the most important leaders in India's struggle for independence from the British Empire. Gandhi was the pioneer and perfector of* Satyagraha—*the resistance of tyranny through mass civil disobedience strongly founded upon* ahimsa *(total nonviolence)—which led India to independence and has inspired movements for civil rights and freedom across the world. In December of 1921, Gandhi, invested with executive authority on behalf of the Indian National Congress, organized the nonviolent strategy of non-cooperation with Britain, which included a boycott by Indians of British goods. On February 5, 1922, however, the nonviolent mass revolt erupted in violence. Gandhi suspended the campaign of mass civil disobedience and fasted for five days as penance for the sins of the people, which he took upon himself. Regardless of this atonement, Gandhi was arrested on March 10, 1922, and, on March 18, he was tried for sedition. At the Great Trial of 1922, Gandhi spoke in his own defense and pleaded guilty to the charge. He was sentenced to six years, though he only served a little less than two years of that sentence. On January 30, 1948, while on his way to a prayer meeting in New Delhi, Gandhi was shot and killed by Nathuram Godse, a Hindu radical with links to the extremist Hindu Mahasabha, who held Gandhi responsible for weakening India by sacrificing Hindu interests in an effort to appease minority groups. In India, Gandhi is recognized as the* Father of the Nation; *October 2, his birthday, is commemorated each year as* Gandhi Jayanti, *a national holiday.*

I owe it perhaps to the Indian public and to the public in England, to placate which this prosecution is mainly taken up, that I should explain why, from a staunch loyalist and co-operator, I have become an uncompromising disaffectionist and non-co-operator. To the Court, too, I should say why I plead guilty to the charge of promoting disaffection towards the Government established by law in India.

My public life began in 1893 in South Africa in troubled weather. My first contact with British authority in that country was not of a happy character. I discovered that as a man and an Indian I had no rights. More correctly, I discovered that I had no rights as a man because I was an Indian.

But I was not baffled. I thought that this treatment of Indians was an excrescence upon a system that was intrinsically and mainly good. I gave the Government my voluntary and hearty co-operation, criticizing it freely where I felt it was faulty, but never wishing its destruction. Consequently, when the existence of the Empire was threatened in 1899 by the Boer challenge, I offered my services to it, raised a volunteer ambulance corps and served at several actions that took place for the relief of Ladysmith. Similarly in 1906, at the time of the Zulu revolt, I raised a stretcher-bearer party and served till the end of the rebellion. On both these occasions I received medals and was even mentioned in despatches. For my work in South Africa. I was given by Lord Hardinge a Kaiser-i-Hind Gold Medal. When the War broke out in 1914 between England and Germany, I raised a volunteer ambulance corps in London consisting of the then resident Indians in London, chiefly students. Its work was acknowledged by the authorities to be valuable. Lastly, in India, when a special appeal was made at the War Conference in Delhi in 1918 by Lord Chelmsford for recruits, I struggled at the cost of my health to raise a corps in Kheda and the response was being made when the hostilities ceased and orders were received that no more recruits were wanted. In all these efforts at service, I was actuated by the belief that it was possible by such services to gain a status of full equality in the Empire for my countrymen.

The first shock came in the shape of the Rowlatt Act, a law designed to rob the people of all real freedom. I felt called upon to lead an intensive agitation against it. Then followed the Punjab horrors beginning with the massacre at Jallianwala Bagh and culminating in crawling orders,[1] public floggings and other indescribable humiliations. I discovered, too, that the plighted word of the Prime Minister to the Mussalmans of India regarding the integrity of Turkey and the holy places of Islam was not likely to be fulfilled. But, in spite of the forebodings and the grave warnings of friends, at the Amritsar Congress in 1919, I fought for co-operation and working the Montagu-Chelmsford reforms, hoping that the Prime Minister would redeem his promise to the Indian Mussalmans, that the Punjab wound would be healed and that the reforms, inadequate and unsatisfactory though they were, marked a new era of hope in the life of India.

But all that hope was shattered. The Khilafat promise was not to be redeemed. The Punjab crime was white-washed and most culprits went not only unpunished, but remained in service and some continued to draw pensions from the Indian revenue, and in some cases were even rewarded. I saw, too, that not only did the reforms not mark a change of heart, but they were only a method of further draining India of her wealth and of prolonging her servitude.

I came reluctantly to the conclusion that the British connection had made India more helpless than she ever was before, politically and economically. A disarmed India has no power of resistance against any aggressor if she wanted to engage in an armed conflict with him. So much is this the case that some of our best men consider that India must take generations before she can achieve the Dominion status. She has become so poor that she has little power of resisting famines. Before the British advent, India spun and wove in her millions of cottages just the supplement she needed for adding to her meagre agricultural resources. This cottage industry, so vital for India's existence, has been ruined by incredibly heartless and inhuman processes as described by English witnesses. Little do town-dwellers know how the semi-starved masses of India are slowly sinking to lifelessness. Little do they know that their miserable comfort represents the brokerage they get for the work they do for the foreign exploiter, that the profits and the brokerage are sucked from the masses. Little do they realize that the Government established by law in British India is carried on for this exploitation of the masses. No sophistry, no jugglery in figures can explain away the evidence that the skeletons in many villages present to the naked eye. I have no doubt whatsoever that both England and the town-dwellers of India will have to answer, if there is a God above, for this crime against humanity which is perhaps unequalled in history. The law itself in this country has been used to serve the foreign exploiter. My unbiased examination of the Punjab Martial Law cases has led me to believe that at least ninety-five per cent of convictions were wholly bad. My experience of political cases in India leads one to the conclusion that in nine out of every ten cases the condemned men were totally innocent. Their crime consisted in the love of their country. In ninety-nine cases out of a hundred, justice has been denied to Indians as against Europeans in the Courts of India. This is not an exaggerated picture. It is the experience of almost every Indian who has had anything to do with such cases. In my opinion, the administration of the law is thus prostituted consciously or unconsciously for the benefit of the exploiter.

The greatest misfortune is that Englishmen and their Indian associates in the administration of the country do not know that they are engaged in the crime I have attempted to describe. I am satisfied that many English and Indian officials honestly believe that they are administering one of the best systems devised in the world and that India is making steady though slow progress. They do not know that a subtle but effective system of terrorism and an organized display of force on the one hand, and the deprivation of all powers of retaliation or self-defense on the other, have emasculated the people and induced in them the habit of simulation. This awful habit has added to the ignorance and the self-deception of the administrators. Section 124 A under which I am happily charged is perhaps the prince among the political sections of the Indian Penal Code designed to suppress the liberty of the citizen. Affection cannot be manufactured or regulated by law. If one has no affection for a person or system, one should be free to give the fullest expression to his disaffection, so long as he does not contemplate, promote or incite to violence. But the section under which Mr. Banker and I are charged is one under which mere promotion of disaffection is a crime. I have studied some of the cases tried under it, and I know that some of the most loved of India's patriots have been convicted under it. I consider it a privilege, therefore, to be charged under it. I have endeavoured to give in their briefest outline the reasons for my disaffection. I have no personal ill will against any single administrator, much less can I have any disaffection towards the King's person. But I hold it to be a virtue to be disaffected towards a Government which in its totality has done more harm to India than any previous system. India is less manly under the British rule than she ever was before. Holding such a belief, I consider it to be a sin to have affection for the system. And it has been a precious privilege for me to be able to write what I have in the various articles tendered in evidence against me.

In fact, I believe that I have rendered a service to India and England by showing in non-co-operation the way out of the unnatural state in which both are living. In my humble opinion, non-co-operation with evil is as much a duty as is co-operation with good. But, in the past, non-co-operation has been deliberately expressed in violence to the evil-doer. I am endeavouring to show to my countrymen that violent non-co-operation only multiplies evil and that, as evil can only be sustained by violence, withdrawal of support of evil requires complete abstention from violence. Nonviolence implies voluntary submission to the penalty for non-co-operation with evil. I am here, therefore, to invite and submit cheerfully to the highest penalty that can be inflicted upon me for what in law is a deliberate crime and what appears to me to be the highest duty of a citizen. The only course open to you, the Judge, is either to resign your post and thus dissociate yourself from evil, if you feel that the law you are called upon to administer is an evil and that in reality I am innocent; or to inflict on me the severest penalty if you believe that the system and the law you are assisting to administer are good for the people of this country and that my activity is, therefore, injurious to the public weal.

Endnote

1. An order that Indians were to crawl on their hands and knees in the presence of Europeans.

Genesis 1-5

This Judeo-Christian account of God's creation of the universe is part of the first five books of the Old Testament and Torah, also called the Pentateuch or Books of Moses. These verses contain not only the creation story, but also the expulsion of Adam and Eve from the Garden of Eden, Cain's murder of his brother Abel, and a long list of the descendants of Adam and their ages.

The list of descendants is most interesting in how the list was used many centuries after it was compiled. An Irish religious scholar, Cardinal James Ussher, in writing his history of the world since its creation, in 1640, using the names and ages of Adam's descendants and working back through events in the Old Testament, determined that Creation began on October 23, 4004 BC. This date has worked its way into the debate between those who believe that the Earth is a little over 6000 years old and those who see evidence of the Earth as being billions of years in age.

Biblical scholars also cite the verses as being evidence that there was more than a single writer of the Pentateuch, that in theory there were at least four writers, labeled JEDP, whose work was compiled later to form the Pentateuch.

Evidence for this theory can be seen by closely examining the account of Creation in Genesis 1.1 to Genesis 2.4. Biblical scholars have noted the differences in the second account of Creation in Genesis 2.4 through Genesis 3.23.

Genesis 1-5 (New Revised Standard Version)

1

In the beginning when God created the heavens and the earth, the earth was a formless void and darkness covered the face of the deep, while a wind from God swept over the face of the waters. Then God said, "Let there be light"; and there was light. And God saw that the light was good; and God separated the light from the darkness. God called the light Day, and the darkness he called Night. And there was evening and there was morning, the first day.

And God said, "Let there be a dome in the midst of the waters, and let it separate the waters from the waters." So God made the dome and separated the waters that were under the dome from the waters that were above the dome. And it was so. God called the dome Sky. And there was evening and there was morning, the second day.

And God said, "Let the waters under the sky be gathered together into one place, and let the dry land appear." And it was so. God called the dry land Earth, and the waters that were gathered together he called Seas. And God saw that it was good. Then God said, "Let the earth put forth vegetation: plants yielding seed, and fruit trees of every kind on earth that bear fruit with the seed in it." And it was so. The earth brought forth vegetation: plants yielding seed of every kind, and trees of every kind bearing fruit with the seed in it. And God saw that it was good. And there was evening and there was morning, the third day.

And God said, "Let there be lights in the dome of the sky to separate the day from the night; and let them be for signs and for seasons and for days and years, and let them be lights in the dome of the sky to give light upon the earth." And it was so. God made the two great lights—the greater light to rule the day and the lesser light to rule the night—and the stars. God set them in the dome of the sky to give light upon the earth, to rule over the day and over the night, and to separate the light from the darkness. And God saw that it was good. And there was evening and there was morning, the fourth day.

And God said, "Let the waters bring forth swarms of living creatures, and let birds fly above the earth across the dome of the sky." So God created the great sea monsters and every living creature that moves, of every kind, with which the waters swarm, and every winged bird of every kind. And God saw that it was good. God blessed them, saying, "Be fruitful and multiply and fill the waters in the seas, and let birds multiply on the earth." And there was evening and there was morning, the fifth day.

And God said, "Let the earth bring forth living creatures of every kind: cattle and creeping things and wild animals of the earth of every kind." And it was so. God made the wild animals of the earth of every kind, and the cattle of every kind, and everything that creeps upon the ground of every kind. And God saw that it was good.

Then God said, "Let us make humankind in our image, according to our likeness; and let them have dominion over the fish of the sea, and over the birds of the air, and over the cattle, and over all the wild animals of the earth,[d] and over every creeping thing that creeps upon the earth."

So God created humankind in his image,
  in the image of God he created them;
    male and female he created them.

God blessed them, and God said to them, "Be fruitful and multiply, and fill the earth and subdue it; and have dominion over the fish of the sea and over the birds of the air and over every living thing that moves upon the earth." God said, "See, I have given you every plant yielding seed that is upon the face of all the earth, and every tree with seed in its fruit; you shall have them for food. And to every beast of the earth, and to every bird of the air, and to everything that creeps on the earth, everything that has the breath of life, I have given every green plant for food." And it was so. God saw everything that he had made, and indeed, it was very good. And there was evening and there was morning, the sixth day.

2

Thus the heavens and the earth were finished, and all their multitude. And on the seventh day God finished the work that he had done, and he rested on the seventh day from all the work that he had done. So God blessed the seventh day and hallowed it, because on it God rested from all the work that he had done in creation.

These are the generations of the heavens and the earth when they were created.

In the day that the LORD God made the earth and the heavens, when no plant of the field was yet in the earth and no herb of the field had yet sprung up—for the LORD God had not caused it to rain upon the earth, and there was no one to till the ground; but a stream would rise from the earth, and water the whole face of the ground— then the LORD God formed man from the dust of the ground, and breathed into his nostrils the breath of life; and the man became a living being. And the LORD God planted a garden in Eden, in the east; and there he put the man whom he had formed. Out of the ground the LORD God made to grow every tree that is pleasant to the sight and good for food, the tree of life also in the midst of the garden, and the tree of the knowledge of good and evil.

A river flows out of Eden to water the garden, and from there it divides and becomes four branches. The name of the first is Pishon; it is the one that flows around the whole land of Havilah, where there is gold; and the gold of that land is good; bdellium and onyx stone are there. The name of the second river is Gihon; it is the one that flows around the whole land of Cush. The name of the third river is Tigris, which flows east of Assyria. And the fourth river is the Euphrates.

The LORD God took the man and put him in the garden of Eden to till it and keep it. And the LORD God commanded the man, "You may freely eat of every tree of the garden; but of the tree of the knowledge of good and evil you shall not eat, for in the day that you eat of it you shall die."

Then the LORD God said, "It is not good that the man should be alone; I will make him a helper as his partner." So out of the ground the LORD God formed every animal of the field and every bird of the air, and brought them to the man to see what he would call them; and whatever the man called every living creature, that was its name. The man gave names to all cattle, and to the birds of the air, and to every animal of the field; but for the man there was not found a helper as his partner. So the LORD God caused a deep sleep to fall upon the man, and he slept; then he took one of his ribs and closed up its place with flesh. And the rib that the LORD God had taken from the man he made into a woman and brought her to the man. Then the man said,

> "This at last is bone of my bones
>   and flesh of my flesh;
> this one shall be called Woman,
>   for out of Man this one was taken."

Therefore a man leaves his father and his mother and clings to his wife, and they become one flesh. And the man and his wife were both naked, and were not ashamed.

The First Sin and Its Punishment

_3_

Now the serpent was more crafty than any other wild animal that the LORD God had made. He said to the woman, "Did God say, 'You shall not eat from any tree in the garden'?" The woman said to the serpent, "We may eat of the fruit of the trees in the garden; but God said, 'You shall not eat of the fruit of the tree that is in the middle of the garden, nor shall you touch it, or you shall die.'" But the serpent said to the woman, "You will not die; for God knows that when you eat of it your eyes will be opened, and you will be like God, knowing good and evil." So when the woman saw that the tree was good for food, and that it was a delight to the eyes, and that the tree was to be desired to make one wise, she took of its fruit and ate; and she also gave some to her husband, who was with her, and he ate. Then the eyes of both were opened, and they knew that they were naked; and they sewed fig leaves together and made loincloths for themselves.

They heard the sound of the LORD God walking in the garden at the time of the evening breeze, and the man and his wife hid themselves from the presence of the LORD God among the trees of the garden. But the LORD God called to the man, and said to him, "Where are you?" He said, "I heard the sound of you in the garden, and I was afraid, because I was naked; and I hid myself." He said, "Who told you that you were naked? Have you eaten from the tree of which I commanded you not to eat?" The man said, "The woman whom you gave to be with me, she gave me fruit from the tree, and I ate." Then the LORD God said to the woman, "What is this that you have done?" The woman said, "The serpent tricked me, and I ate." The LORD God said to the serpent,

> "Because you have done this,
> > cursed are you among all animals
> > and among all wild creatures;
> upon your belly you shall go,
> > and dust you shall eat
> > all the days of your life.
> I will put enmity between you and the woman,
> > and between your offspring and hers;
> he will strike your head,
> > and you will strike his heel."

To the woman he said,

> "I will greatly increase your pangs in childbearing;
> > in pain you shall bring forth children,
> yet your desire shall be for your husband,
> > and he shall rule over you."

And to the man he said,

> "Because you have listened to the voice of your wife,
> > and have eaten of the tree
> about which I commanded you,
> > 'You shall not eat of it,'
> cursed is the ground because of you;
> > in toil you shall eat of it all the days of your life;
> thorns and thistles it shall bring forth for you;
> > and you shall eat the plants of the field.
> By the sweat of your face
> > you shall eat bread
> until you return to the ground,
> > for out of it you were taken;
> you are dust,
> > and to dust you shall return."

The man named his wife Eve, because she was the mother of all living. And the LORD God made garments of skins for the man and for his wife, and clothed them.

Then the LORD God said, "See, the man has become like one of us, knowing good and evil; and now, he might reach out his hand and take also from the tree of life, and eat, and live forever"— therefore the LORD God sent him forth from the garden of Eden, to till the ground from which he was taken. He drove out the man; and at the east of the garden of Eden he placed the cherubim, and a sword flaming and turning to guard the way to the tree of life.

Cain Murders Abel

4

Now the man knew his wife Eve, and she conceived and bore Cain, saying, "I have produced a man with the help of the LORD." Next she bore his brother Abel. Now Abel was a keeper of sheep, and Cain a tiller of the ground. In the course of time Cain brought to the LORD an offering of the fruit of the ground, and Abel for his part brought of the firstlings of his flock, their fat portions. And the LORD had regard for Abel and his offering, but for Cain and his offering he had no regard. So Cain was very angry, and his countenance fell. The LORD said to Cain, "Why are you angry, and why has your countenance fallen? If you do well, will you not be accepted? And if you do not do well, sin is lurking at the door; its desire is for you, but you must master it."

Cain said to his brother Abel, "Let us go out to the field." And when they were in the field, Cain rose up against his brother Abel, and killed him. Then the LORD said to Cain, "Where is your brother Abel?" He said, "I do not know; am I my brother's keeper?" And the LORD said, "What have you done? Listen; your brother's blood is crying out to me from the ground! And now you are cursed from the ground, which has opened its mouth to receive your brother's blood from your hand. When you till the ground, it will no longer yield to you its strength; you will be a fugitive and a wanderer on the earth." Cain said to the LORD, "My punishment is greater than I can bear! Today you have driven me away from the soil, and I shall be hidden from your face; I shall be a fugitive and a wanderer on the earth, and anyone who meets me may kill me." Then the LORD said to him, "Not so! Whoever kills Cain will suffer a sevenfold vengeance." And the LORD put a mark on Cain, so that no one who came upon him would kill him. Then Cain went away from the presence of the LORD, and settled in the land of Nod, east of Eden.

Cain knew his wife, and she conceived and bore Enoch; and he built a city, and named it Enoch after his son Enoch. To Enoch was born Irad; and Irad was the father of Mehujael, and Mehujael the father of Methushael, and Methushael the father of Lamech. Lamech took two wives; the name of the one was Adah, and the name of the other Zillah. Adah bore Jabal; he was the ancestor of those who live in tents and have livestock. His brother's name was Jubal; he was the ancestor of all those who play the lyre and pipe. Zillah bore Tubal-cain, who made all kinds of bronze and iron tools. The sister of Tubal-cain, who made all kinds of bronze and iron tools. The sister of Tubal-cain was Naamah.

Lamech said to his wives:

> "Adah and Zillah, hear my voice;
>   you wives of Lamech, listen to what I say:
> I have killed a man for wounding me,
>   a young man for striking me.
> If Cain is avenged sevenfold,
>   truly Lamech seventy-sevenfold."

Adam knew his wife again, and she bore a son and named him Seth, for she said, "God has appointed for me another child instead of Abel, because Cain killed him." To Seth also a son was born, and he named him Enosh. At that time people began to invoke the name of the LORD.

Adam's Descendants to Noah and His Sons

5

This is the list of the descendants of Adam. When God created humankind, he made them in the likeness of God. Male and female he created them, and he blessed them and named them "Humankind" when they were created.

When Adam had lived one hundred thirty years, he became the father of a son in his likeness, according to his image, and named him Seth. The days of Adam after he became the father of Seth were eight hundred years; and he had other sons and daughters. Thus all the days that Adam lived were nine hundred thirty years; and he died.

When Seth had lived one hundred five years, he became the father of Enosh. Seth lived after the birth of Enosh eight hundred seven years, and had other sons and daughters. Thus all the days of Seth were nine hundred twelve years; and he died.

When Enosh had lived ninety years, he became the father of Kenan. Enosh lived after the birth of Kenan eight hundred fifteen years, and had other sons and daughters. Thus all the days of Enosh were nine hundred five years; and he died.

When Kenan had lived seventy years, he became the father of Mahalalel. Kenan lived after the birth of Mahalalel eight hundred and forty years, and had other sons and daughters. Thus all the days of Kenan were nine hundred and ten years; and he died.

When Mahalalel had lived sixty-five years, he became the father of Jared. Mahalalel lived after the birth of Jared eight hundred thirty years, and had other sons and daughters. Thus all the days of Mahalalel were eight hundred ninety-five years; and he died.

When Jared had lived one hundred sixty-two years he became the father of Enoch. Jared lived after the birth of Enoch eight hundred years, and had other sons and daughters. Thus all the days of Jared were nine hundred sixty-two years; and he died.

When Enoch had lived sixty-five years, he became the father of Methuselah. Enoch walked with God after the birth of Methuselah three hundred years, and had other sons and daughters. Thus all the days of Enoch were three hundred sixty-five years. Enoch walked with God; then he was no more, because God took him.

When Methuselah had lived one hundred eighty-seven years, he became the father of Lamech. Methuselah lived after the birth of Lamech seven hundred eighty-two years, and had other sons and daughters. Thus all the days of Methuselah were nine hundred sixty-nine years; and he died.

When Lamech had lived one hundred eighty-two years, he became the father of a son; he named him Noah, saying, "Out of the ground that the LORD has cursed this one shall bring us relief from our work and from the toil of our hands." Lamech lived after the birth of Noah five hundred ninety-five years, and had other sons and daughters. Thus all the days of Lamech were seven hundred seventy-seven years; and he died.

After Noah was five hundred years old, Noah became the father of Shem, Ham, and Japheth.

Small Change

Malcolm Gladwell

Malcolm Gladwell (1963——) is a Canadian journalist who has written for The American Spectator, The Washington Post *and, currently,* The New Yorker *magazine. He reported on business and science news in the* Post, *but has since extended his writing to include topics ranging from dog training to the story of David and Goliath. His subjects have expanded to include nearly anything, it seems, that interests him.*

Gladwell has written several popular books, including The Tipping Point: How Little Things Can Make a Big Difference *(2000),* Blink: The Power of Thinking Without Thinking *(2005),* Outliers: The Story of Success *(2008), a collection of his* New Yorker *essays called* What the Dog Saw: And Other Adventures *(2009) and most recently,* David and Goliath: Underdogs, Misfits and the Art of Battling Giants *(2013). In each of these books, Gladwell suggests a new way of looking at things. In* The Tipping Point, *he challenges our idea that it takes big things to cause big changes (he contends that the difference leading to big change is often quite small). In* Blink, *he suggests that snap-judgments are right more often than we might like to believe, but that when they* are *wrong, the consequences can be devastating. And in* Outliers, *he questions the amount of talent verses time necessary to be truly outstanding at something. He concludes that it takes at least 10,000 hours of practice, regardless of how talented you are.*

Such engaging approaches and surprising conclusions mark Gladwell's style. He again questions widely accepted ideas in a collection of pieces he wrote for The New Yorker *called* What the Dog Saw: And Other Adventures *(2009). Gladwell asks about a famous "dog whisperer," not what he sees in the dog, but what the dog sees in* him. *Most recently, he has challenged the notion that the story of David and Goliath is about underdogs overcoming great odds, claiming Goliath never even had a chance! Gladwell's challenging alternative points of view energize audiences and have made Gladwell a very popular speaker, appearing frequently as a guest on TED Talks and crisscrossing the country on lecture tours. His ideas have led institutions to change their approaches to making policies and to interpreting statistics (Gladwell says that even with numbers, you still have to think).*

The following article, titled "Small Change," is from the October 4ᵗʰ, 2010 issue of The New Yorker. *It challenges the popular notion that the internet promotes and even increases the same sort of activism that marked the Civil Rights Movement of the 1960's, before the internet. This is in the face of the current rise in the use of the internet as a part of revolutions throughout the world in the early 2000's. Gladwell argues that the sorts of activism engaged in on the internet, what he calls "weak-tie phenomena," tend to be low risk and short-lived, while protests such as the sit-ins in the early 1960s were "strong-tie phenomena," requiring higher risk and fuller engagement and, so, were more effective.*

At four-thirty in the afternoon on Monday, February 1, 1960, four college students sat down at the lunch counter at the Woolworth's in downtown Greensboro, North Carolina. They were freshmen at North Carolina A. & T., a black college a mile or so away.

"I'd like a cup of coffee, please," one of the four, Ezell Blair, said to the waitress.

"We don't serve Negroes here," she replied.

The Woolworth's lunch counter was a long L-shaped bar that could seat sixty-six people, with a standup snack bar at one end. The seats were for whites. The snack bar was for blacks. Another employee, a black woman who worked at the steam table, approached the students and tried to warn them away. "You're acting stupid, ignorant!" she said. They didn't move. Around five-thirty, the front doors to the store were locked. The four still didn't move. Finally, they left by a side door. Outside, a small crowd had gathered, including a photographer from the Greensboro *Record*. "I'll be back tomorrow with A. & T. College," one of the students said.

By next morning, the protest had grown to twenty-seven men and four women, most from the same dormitory as the original four. The men were dressed in suits and ties. The students had brought their schoolwork, and studied as they sat at the counter. On Wednesday, students from Greensboro's "Negro" secondary school, Dudley High, joined in, and the number of protesters swelled to eighty. By Thursday, the protesters numbered three hundred, including three white women, from the Greensboro campus of the University of North Carolina. By Saturday, the sit-in had reached six hundred. People spilled out onto the street. White teen-agers waved Confederate flags. Someone threw a firecracker. At noon, the A. & T. football team arrived. "Here comes the wrecking crew," one of the white students shouted.

By the following Monday, sit-ins had spread to Winston-Salem, twenty-five miles away, and Durham, fifty miles away. The day after that, students at Fayetteville State Teachers College and at Johnson C. Smith College, in Charlotte, joined in, followed on Wednesday by students at St. Augustine's College and Shaw University, in Raleigh. On Thursday and Friday, the protest crossed state lines, surfacing in Hampton and Portsmouth, Virginia, in Rock Hill, South Carolina, and in Chattanooga, Tennessee. By the end of the month, there were sit-ins throughout the South, as far west as Texas. "I asked every student I met what the first day of the sitdowns had been like on his campus," the political theorist Michael Walzer wrote in *Dissent*. "The answer was always the same: 'It was like a fever. Everyone wanted to go.' " Some seventy thousand students eventually took part. Thousands were arrested and untold thousands more radicalized. These events in the early sixties became a civil-rights war that engulfed the South for the rest of the decade—and it happened without e-mail, texting, Facebook, or Twitter.

The world, we are told, is in the midst of a revolution. The new tools of social media have reinvented social activism. With Facebook and Twitter and the like, the traditional relationship between political authority and popular will has been upended, making it easier for the powerless to collaborate, coördinate, and give voice to their concerns. When ten thousand protesters took to the streets in Moldova in the spring of 2009 to protest against their country's Communist government, the action was dubbed the Twitter Revolution, because of the means by which the demonstrators had been brought together. A few months after that, when student protests rocked Tehran, the State Department took the unusual step of asking Twitter to suspend scheduled maintenance of its Web site, because the Administration didn't want such a critical organizing tool out of service at the height of the demonstrations. "Without Twitter the people of Iran would not have felt empowered and confident to stand up for freedom and democracy," Mark Pfeifle, a former national-security adviser, later wrote, calling for Twitter to be nominated for the Nobel Peace Prize. Where activists were once defined by their causes, they are now defined by their tools. Facebook warriors go online to push for change. "You are the best hope for us all," James K. Glassman, a former senior State Department official, told a crowd of cyber activists at a recent conference sponsored by Facebook, A. T. & T., Howcast, MTV, and Google. Sites like Facebook, Glassman said, "give the U.S. a significant competitive advantage over terrorists. Some time ago, I said that Al Qaeda was 'eating our lunch on the Internet.' That is no longer the case. Al Qaeda is stuck in Web 1.0. The Internet is now about interactivity and conversation."

These are strong, and puzzling, claims. Why does it matter who is eating whose lunch on the Internet? Are people who log on to their Facebook page really the best hope for us all? As for Moldova's so-called Twitter Revolution, Evgeny Morozov, a scholar at Stanford who has been the most persistent of digital evangelism's critics, points out that Twitter had scant internal significance in Moldova, a country where very few Twitter accounts exist. Nor does it seem to have been a revolution, not least because the protests—as Anne Applebaum suggested in the Washington *Post*—may well have been a bit of stagecraft cooked up by the government. (In a country paranoid about Romanian revanchism, the protesters flew a Romanian flag over the Parliament building.) In the Iranian case, meanwhile, the people tweeting about the demonstrations were almost all in the West. "It is time to get Twitter's role in the events in Iran right," Golnaz Esfandiari wrote, this past summer, in *Foreign Policy*. "Simply put: There was no Twitter Revolution inside Iran." The cadre of prominent bloggers, like Andrew Sullivan, who championed the role of social media in Iran, Esfandiari continued, misunderstood the situation. "Western journalists who couldn't reach—or didn't bother reaching?—people on the ground in Iran simply scrolled through the English-language tweets post with tag #iranelection," she wrote. "Through it all, no one seemed to wonder why people trying to coordinate protests in Iran would be writing in any language other than Farsi."

Some of this grandiosity is to be expected. Innovators tend to be solipsists. They often want to cram every stray fact and experience into their new model. As the historian Robert Darnton has written, "The marvels of communication technology in the present have produced a false consciousness about the past— even a sense that communication has no history, or had nothing of importance to consider before the days of television and the Internet." But there is something else at work here, in the outsized enthusiasm for social media. Fifty years after one of the most extraordinary episodes of social upheaval in American history, we seem to have forgotten what activism is.

Greensboro in the early nineteen-sixties was the kind of place where racial insubordination was routinely met with violence. The four students who first sat down at the lunch counter were terrified. "I suppose if anyone had come up behind me and yelled 'Boo,' I think I would have fallen off my seat," one of them said later. On the first day, the store manager notified the police chief, who immediately sent two officers to the store. On the third day, a gang of white toughs showed up at the lunch counter and stood ostentatiously behind the protesters, ominously muttering epithets such as "burr-head nigger." A local Ku Klux Klan leader made an appearance. On Saturday, as tensions grew, someone called in a bomb threat, and the entire store had to be evacuated.

The dangers were even clearer in the Mississippi Freedom Summer Project of 1964, another of the sentinel campaigns of the civil-rights movement. The Student Nonviolent Coordinating Committee recruited hundreds of Northern, largely white unpaid volunteers to run Freedom Schools, register black voters, and raise civil-rights awareness in the Deep South. "No one should go *anywhere* alone, but certainly not in an automobile and certainly not at night," they were instructed. Within days of arriving in Mississippi, three volunteers—Michael Schwerner, James Chaney, and Andrew Goodman— were kidnapped and killed, and, during the rest of the summer, thirty-seven black churches were set on fire and dozens of safe houses were bombed; volunteers were beaten, shot at, arrested, and trailed by pickup trucks full of armed men. A quarter of those in the program dropped out. Activism that challenges the status quo—that attacks deeply rooted problems—is not for the faint of heart.

What makes people capable of this kind of activism? The Stanford sociologist Doug McAdam compared the Freedom Summer dropouts with the participants who stayed, and discovered that the key difference wasn't, as might be expected, ideological fervor. "*All* of the applicants—participants and withdrawals alike—emerge as highly committed, articulate supporters of the goals and values of the summer program," he concluded. What mattered more was an applicant's degree of personal connection to the civil-rights movement. All the volunteers were required to provide a list of personal contacts—the people they wanted kept apprised of their activities—and participants were far more likely than dropouts to have close friends who were also going to Mississippi. High-risk activism, McAdam concluded, is a "strong-tie" phenomenon.

This pattern shows up again and again. One study of the Red Brigades, the Italian terrorist group of the nineteen-seventies, found that seventy per cent of recruits had at least one good friend already in the organization. The same is true of the men who joined the mujahideen in Afghanistan. Even revolutionary actions that look spontaneous, like the demonstrations in East Germany that led to the fall of the Berlin Wall, are, at core, strong-tie phenomena. The opposition movement in East Germany consisted of several hundred groups, each with roughly a dozen members. Each group was in limited contact with the others: at the time, only thirteen per cent of East

Germans even had a phone. All they knew was that on Monday nights, outside St. Nicholas Church in downtown Leipzig, people gathered to voice their anger at the state. And the primary determinant of who showed up was "critical friends"—the more friends you had who were critical of the regime the more likely you were to join the protest.

So one crucial fact about the four freshmen at the Greensboro lunch counter—David Richmond, Franklin McCain, Ezell Blair, and Joseph McNeil—was their relationship with one another. McNeil was a roommate of Blair's in A. & T.'s Scott Hall dormitory. Richmond roomed with McCain one floor up, and Blair, Richmond, and McCain had all gone to Dudley High School. The four would smuggle beer into the dorm and talk late into the night in Blair and McNeil's room. They would all have remembered the murder of Emmett Till in 1955, the Montgomery bus boycott that same year, and the showdown in Little Rock in 1957. It was McNeil who brought up the idea of a sit-in at Woolworth's. They'd discussed it for nearly a month. Then McNeil came into the dorm room and asked the others if they were ready. There was a pause, and McCain said, in a way that works only with people who talk late into the night with one another, "Are you guys chicken or not?" Ezell Blair worked up the courage the next day to ask for a cup of coffee because he was flanked by his roommate and two good friends from high school.

The kind of activism associated with social media isn't like this at all. The platforms of social media are built around weak ties. Twitter is a way of following (or being followed by) people you may never have met. Facebook is a tool for efficiently managing your acquaintances, for keeping up with the people you would not otherwise be able to stay in touch with. That's why you can have a thousand "friends" on Facebook, as you never could in real life.

This is in many ways a wonderful thing. There is strength in weak ties, as the sociologist Mark Granovetter has observed. Our acquaintances—not our friends—are our greatest source of new ideas and information. The Internet lets us exploit the power of these kinds of distant connections with marvellous efficiency. It's terrific at the diffusion of innovation, interdisciplinary collaboration, seamlessly matching up buyers and sellers, and the logistical functions of the dating world. But weak ties seldom lead to high-risk activism.

In a new book called "The Dragonfly Effect: Quick, Effective, and Powerful Ways to Use Social Media to Drive Social Change," the business consultant Andy Smith and the Stanford Business School professor Jennifer Aaker tell the story of Sameer Bhatia, a young Silicon Valley entrepreneur who came down with acute myelogenous leukemia. It's a perfect illustration of social media's strengths. Bhatia needed a bone-marrow transplant, but he could not find a match among his relatives and friends. The odds were best with a donor of his ethnicity, and there were few South Asians in the national bone-marrow database. So Bhatia's business partner sent out an e-mail explaining Bhatia's plight to more than four hundred of their acquaintances, who forwarded the e-mail to their personal contacts; Facebook pages and YouTube videos were devoted to the Help Sameer campaign. Eventually, nearly twenty-five thousand new people were registered in the bone-marrow database, and Bhatia found a match.

But how did the campaign get so many people to sign up? By not asking too much of them. That's the only way you can get someone you don't really know to do something on your behalf. You can get thousands of people to sign up for a donor registry, because doing so is pretty easy. You have to send in a cheek swab and—in the highly unlikely event that your bone marrow is a good match for someone in need—spend a few hours at the hospital. Donating bone marrow isn't a trivial matter. But it doesn't involve financial or personal risk; it doesn't mean spending a summer being chased by armed men in pickup trucks. It doesn't require that you confront socially entrenched norms and practices. In fact, it's the kind of commitment that will bring only social acknowledgment and praise.

The evangelists of social media don't understand this distinction; they seem to believe that a Facebook friend is the same as a real friend and that signing up for a donor registry in Silicon Valley today is activism in the same sense as sitting at a segregated lunch counter in Greensboro in 1960. "Social networks are particularly effective at increasing motivation," Aaker and Smith write. But that's not true. Social networks are effective at increasing *participation*—by lessening the level of motivation that participation requires. The Facebook page of the Save Darfur Coalition has 1,282,339 members, who have donated an average of nine cents apiece. The next biggest Darfur charity on Facebook has 22,073 members, who have donated an average of thirty-five cents. Help Save Darfur has 2,797 members,who have given, on average, fifteen cents. A spokesperson for the Save Darfur Coalition told *Newsweek*, "We wouldn't necessarily gauge someone's value to the advocacy movement based on what they've given. This is a powerful mechanism to engage this critical population. They inform their community, attend events, volunteer. It's not something you can measure by looking at a ledger." In other words, Facebook activism succeeds not by motivating people to make a real sacrifice but by motivating them to do the things that people do when they are not motivated enough to make a real sacrifice. We are a long way from the lunch counters of Greensboro.

The students who joined the sit-ins across the South during the winter of 1960 described the movement as a "fever." But the civil-rights movement was more like a military campaign than like a contagion. In the late nineteen-fifties, there had been sixteen sit-ins in various cities throughout the South, fifteen of which were formally organized by civil-rights organizations like the N.A.A.C.P. and CORE. Possible locations for activism were scouted. Plans were drawn up. Movement activists held training sessions and retreats for would-be protesters. The Greensboro Four were a product of this groundwork: all were members of the N.A.A.C.P. Youth Council. They had close ties with the head of the local N.A.A.C.P. chapter. They had been briefed on the earlier wave of sit-ins in Durham, and had been part of a series of movement meetings in activist churches. When the sit-in movement spread from Greensboro throughout the South, it did not spread indiscriminately. It spread to those cities which had preëxisting "movement centers"—a core of dedicated and trained activists ready to turn the "fever" into action.

The civil-rights movement was high-risk activism. It was also, crucially, strategic activism: a challenge to the establishment mounted with precision and discipline. The N.A.A.C.P. was a centralized organization, run from New York according to highly formalized operating procedures. At the Southern Christian Leadership Conference, Martin Luther King, Jr., was the unquestioned authority. At the center of the movement was the black church, which had, as Aldon D. Morris points out in his superb 1984 study, "The Origins of the Civil Rights Movement," a carefully demarcated division of labor, with various standing committees and disciplined groups. "Each group was task-oriented and coordinated its activities through authority structures," Morris writes. "Individuals were held accountable for their assigned duties, and important conflicts were resolved by the minister, who usually exercised ultimate authority over the congregation."

This is the second crucial distinction between traditional activism and its online variant: social media are not about this kind of hierarchical organization. Facebook and the like are tools for building *networks*, which are the opposite, in structure and character, of hierarchies. Unlike hierarchies, with their rules and procedures, networks aren't controlled by a single central authority. Decisions are made through consensus, and the ties that bind people to the group are loose.

This structure makes networks enormously resilient and adaptable in low-risk situations. Wikipedia is a perfect example. It doesn't have an editor, sitting in New York, who directs and corrects each entry. The effort of putting together each entry is self-organized. If every entry in Wikipedia were to be erased tomorrow, the content would swiftly be restored, because that's what happens when a network of thousands spontaneously devote their time to a task.

There are many things, though, that networks don't do well. Car companies sensibly use a network to organize their hundreds of suppliers, but not to design their cars. No one believes that the articulation of a coherent design philosophy is best handled by a sprawling, leaderless organizational system. Because networks don't have a centralized leadership structure and clear lines of authority, they have real difficulty reaching consensus and setting goals. They can't think strategically; they are chronically prone to conflict and error. How do you make difficult choices about tactics or strategy or philosophical direction when everyone has an equal say?

The Palestine Liberation Organization originated as a network, and the international-relations scholars Mette Eilstrup-Sangiovanni and Calvert Jones argue in a recent essay in *International Security* that this is why it ran into such trouble as it grew: "Structural features typical of networks—the absence of central authority, the unchecked autonomy of rival groups, and the inability to arbitrate quarrels through formal mechanisms—made the P.L.O. excessively vulnerable to outside manipulation and internal strife."

In Germany in the nineteen-seventies, they go on, "the far more unified and successful left-wing terrorists tended to organize hierarchically, with professional management and clear divisions of labor. They were concentrated geographically in universities, where they could establish central leadership, trust, and camaraderie through regular, face-to-face meetings." They seldom betrayed their comrades in arms during police interrogations. Their counterparts on the right were organized as decentralized networks, and had no such discipline. These groups were regularly infiltrated, and members, once arrested, easily gave up their comrades. Similarly, Al Qaeda was most dangerous when it was a unified hierarchy. Now that it has dissipated into a network, it has proved far less effective.

The drawbacks of networks scarcely matter if the network isn't interested in systemic change—if it just wants to frighten or humiliate or make a splash—or if it doesn't need to think strategically. But if you're taking on a powerful and organized establishment you have to be a hierarchy. The Montgomery bus boycott required the participation of tens of thousands of people who depended on public transit to get to and from work each day. It lasted a *year*. In order to persuade those people to stay true to the cause, the boycott's organizers tasked each local black church with maintaining morale, and put together a free alternative private carpool service, with forty-eight dispatchers and forty-two pickup stations. Even the White Citizens Council, King later said, conceded that the carpool system moved with "military precision." By the time King came to Birmingham, for the climactic showdown with Police Commissioner Eugene (Bull) Connor, he had a budget of a million dollars, and a hundred full-time staff members on the ground, divided into operational units. The operation itself was divided into steadily escalating phases, mapped out in advance. Support was maintained through consecutive mass meetings rotating from church to church around the city.

Boycotts and sit-ins and nonviolent confrontations—which were the weapons of choice for the civil-rights movement—are high-risk strategies. They leave little room for conflict and error. The moment even one protester deviates from the script and responds to provocation, the moral legitimacy of the entire protest is compromised. Enthusiasts for social media would no doubt have us believe that King's task in Birmingham would have been made infinitely easier had he been able to communicate with his followers through Facebook, and contented himself with tweets from a Birmingham jail. But networks are messy: think of the ceaseless pattern of correction and revision, amendment and debate, that characterizes Wikipedia. If Martin Luther King, Jr., had tried to do a wiki-boycott in Montgomery, he would have been steam-rollered by the white power structure. And of what use would a digital communication tool be in a town where ninety-eight per cent of the black community could be reached every Sunday morning at church? The things that King needed in Birmingham—discipline and strategy—were things that online social media cannot provide.

The bible of the social-media movement is Clay Shirky's "Here Comes Everybody." Shirky, who teaches at New York University, sets out to demonstrate the organizing power of the Internet, and he begins with the story of Evan, who worked on Wall Street, and his friend Ivanna, after she left her smart phone, an expensive Sidekick, on the back seat of a New York City taxicab. The telephone company transferred the data on Ivanna's lost phone to a new phone, whereupon she and Evan discovered that the Sidekick was now in the hands of a teenager from Queens, who was using it to take photographs of herself and her friends.

When Evan e-mailed the teen-ager, Sasha, asking for the phone back, she replied that his "white ass" didn't deserve to have it back. Miffed, he set up a Web page with her picture and a description of what had happened. He forwarded the link to his friends, and they forwarded it to their friends. Someone found the MySpace page of Sasha's boyfriend, and a link to it found its way onto the site. Someone found her address online and took a video of her home while driving by; Evan posted the video on the site. The story was picked up by the news filter Digg. Evan was now up to ten e-mails a minute. He created a bulletin board for his readers to share their stories, but it crashed under the weight of responses. Evan and Ivanna went to the police, but the police filed the report under "lost," rather than "stolen," which essentially closed the case. "By this point millions of readers were watching," Shirky writes, "and dozens of mainstream news outlets had covered the story." Bowing to the pressure, the N.Y.P.D. reclassified the item as "stolen." Sasha was arrested, and Evan got his friend's Sidekick back.

Shirky's argument is that this is the kind of thing that could never have happened in the pre-Internet age—and he's right. Evan could never have tracked down Sasha. The story of the Sidekick would never have been publicized. An army of people could never have been assembled to wage this fight. The police wouldn't have bowed to the pressure of a lone person who had misplaced something as trivial as a cell phone. The story, to Shirky, illustrates "the ease and speed with which a group can be mobilized for the right kind of cause" in the Internet age.

Shirky considers this model of activism an upgrade. But it is simply a form of organizing which favors the weak-tie connections that give us access to information over the strong-tie connections that help us persevere in the face of danger. It shifts our energies from organizations that promote strategic and disciplined activity and toward those which promote resilience and adaptability. It makes it easier for activists to express themselves, and harder for that expression to have any impact. The instruments of social media are well suited to making the existing social order more efficient. They are not a natural enemy of the status quo. If you are of the opinion that all the world needs is a little buffing around the edges, this should not trouble you. But if you think that there are still lunch counters out there that need integrating it ought to give you pause.

Shirky ends the story of the lost Sidekick by asking, portentously, "What happens next?"—no doubt imagining future waves of digital protesters. But he has already answered the question. What happens next is more of the same. A networked, weak-tie world is good at things like helping Wall Streeters get phones back from teen-age girls. *Viva la revolución.*

from The Tao of Pooh

Benjamin Hoff

Benjamin Hoff was born in 1946 and was raised in Sylvan, Oregon. He attended Evergreen State College, where he earned a degree in Asian Art in 1973. While working various jobs (tree pruner, hospital orderly, musician, and investigative reporter), he began to write The Tao of Pooh *in an effort to explain the fundamentals of Taoism (Daoism). He uses Winnie the Pooh and episodes from the Winnie-the-Pooh stories, by A. A. Milne, to illustrate the basic principles and teachings of Taoism to Westerners.* The Tao of Pooh, *since its initial publication, has been translated into over 20 languages. Hoff published* The Te of Piglet *about 10 years later to further enlighten his readers about Taoism.*

The Tao (dao) is defined as the "way" or "path," which one strives to follow to achieve harmony and balance with one's surroundings. The principle text in Taoism is the Tao te Ching (Dao de Jing), *which is believed to have been written around the 6th century BC by Lao Tzu, who is credited with the development of Taoism. One of the main principles of Taoism is "wu wei," or "effortless action," which Winnie the Pooh represents in Hoff's book.*

The How of Pooh?

"Y ou see, Pooh," I said, "a lot of people don't seem to know what Taoism is . . . "

"Yes?" said Pooh, blinking his eyes.

"So that's what this chapter is for—to explain things a bit."

"Oh, I see," said Pooh.

"And the easiest way to do that would be for us to go to China for a moment."

"*What?*" said Pooh, his eyes wide open in amazement. "Right now?"

"Of course. All we need to do is lean back, relax, and there we are."

"Oh, I see," said Pooh.

Let's imagine that we have walked down a narrow street in a large Chinese city and have found a small shop that sells scrolls painted in the classic manner. We go inside and ask to be shown something allegorical—something humorous, perhaps, but with some sort of Timeless Meaning. The shopkeeper smiles. "I have just the thing," he tells us. "A copy of *The Vinegar Tasters!*" He leads us to a large table and unrolls the scroll, placing it down for us to examine. "Excuse me—I must attend to something for a moment," he says, and goes into the back of the shop, leaving us alone with the painting.

Although we can see that this is a fairly recent version, we know that the original was painted long ago; just when is uncertain. But by now, the theme of the painting is well known.

We see three men standing around a vat of vinegar. Each has dipped his finger into the vinegar and has tasted it. The expression on each man's face shows his individual reaction. Since the painting is allegorical, we are to understand that these are no ordinary vinegar tasters, but are instead representatives of the "Three Teachings" of China, and that the vinegar they are sampling represents the Essence of Life. The three masters are K'ung Fu-tse (Confucius), Buddha, and Lao-tse, author of the oldest existing book of Taoism. The first has a sour look on his face, the second wears a bitter expression, but the third man is smiling.

To K'ung Fu-tse (kung FOOdsuh), life seemed rather sour. He believed that the present was out of step with the past, and that the government of man on earth was out of harmony with the Way of Heaven, the government of the universe. Therefore, he emphasized reverence for the Ancestors, as well as for the ancient rituals and ceremonies in which the emperor, as the Son of Heaven, acted as intermediary between limitless heaven and limited earth. Under Confucianism, the use of precisely measured court music, prescribed steps, actions, and phrases all added up to an extremely complex system of rituals, each used for a particular purpose at a particular time. A saying was recorded about K'ung Fu-tse: "If the mat was not straight, the Master would not sit." This ought to give an indication of the extent to which things were carried out under Confucianism.

To Buddha, the second figure in the painting, life on earth was bitter, filled with attachments and desires that led to suffering. The world was seen as a setter of traps, a generator of illusions, a revolving wheel of pain for all creatures. In order to find peace, the Buddhist considered it necessary to transcend "the world of dust" and reach Nirvana, literally a state of "no wind." Although the essentially optimistic attitude of the Chinese altered Buddhism considerably after it was brought in from its native India, the devout Buddhist often saw the way to Nirvana interrupted all the same by the bitter wind of everyday existence.

To Lao-tse (LAOdsuh), the harmony that naturally existed between heaven and earth from the very beginning could be found by anyone at any time, but not by following the rules of the Confucianists. As he stated in his *Tao Te Ching* (DAO DEH JEENG), the "Tao Virtue Book," earth was in essence a reflection of heaven, run by the same laws—*not* by the laws of men. These laws affected not only the spinning of distant planets, but the activities of the birds in the forest and the fish in the sea. According to Lao-tse, the more man interfered with the natural balance produced and governed by the universal laws, the further away the harmony retreated into the distance. The more forcing, the more trouble. Whether heavy or light, wet or dry, fast or slow, everything had its own nature already within it, which could not be violated without causing difficulties. When abstract and arbitrary rules were imposed from the outside, struggle was inevitable. Only then did life become sour.

To Lao-tse, the world was not a setter of traps but a teacher of valuable lessons. Its lessons needed to be learned, just as its laws needed to be followed; then all would go well. Rather than turn away from "the world of dust," Lao-tse advised others to "join the dust of the world." What he saw operating behind everything in heaven and earth he called *Tao* (DAO), "the Way." A basic principle of Lao-tse's teaching was that this Way of the Universe could not be adequately described in words, and that it would be insulting both to its unlimited power and to the intelligent human mind to attempt to do so. Still, its nature could be understood, and those who cared the most about it, and the life from which it was inseparable, understood it best.

Over the centuries Lao-tse's classic teachings were developed and divided into philosophical, monastic, and folk religious forms. All of these could be included under the general heading of Taoism. But the basic Taoism that we are concerned with here is simply a particular way of appreciating, learning from, and working with whatever happens in everyday life. From the Taoist point of view, the natural result of this harmonious way of living is happiness. You might say that happy serenity is the most noticeable characteristic of the Taoist personality, and a subtle sense of humor is apparent even in the most profound Taoist writings, such as the twenty-five-hundred-year-old *Tao Te Ching*. In the writings of Taoism's second major writer, Chuang-tse (JUANGdsuh), quiet laughter seems to bubble up like water from a fountain.

"But what does that have to do with vinegar?" asked Pooh.

"I thought I had explained that," I said.

"I don't think so," said Pooh.

"Well, then, I'll explain it now."

"That's good," said Pooh.

In the painting, why is Lao-tse smiling? After all, that vinegar that represents life must certainly have an unpleasant taste, as the expressions on the faces of the other two men indicate. But, through working in harmony with life's circumstances, Taoist understanding changes what others may perceive as negative into something positive. From the Taoist point of view, sourness and bitterness come from the interfering and unappreciative mind. Life itself, when understood and utilized for what it is, is sweet. That is the message of *The Vinegar Tasters*.

"Sweet? You mean like honey?" asked Pooh.

"Well, maybe not *that* sweet," I said. "That would be overdoing it a bit."

"Are we still supposed to be in China?" Pooh asked cautiously.

"No, we're through explaining and now we're back at the writing table."

"Oh."

"Well, we're just in time for something to eat," he added, wandering over to the kitchen cupboard.

Nowhere and Nothing

"Where are we going?" said Pooh, hurrying after him, and wondering whether it was to be an Explore or a What-shall-I-do-about-you-know-what.

"Nowhere," said Christopher Robin.

So they began going there, and after they had walked a little way Christopher Robin said:

"What do you like doing best in the world, Pooh?"

(And of course, what Pooh liked doing best was going to Christopher Robin's house and eating, but since we've already quoted that, we don't think we need to quote it again.)

"I like that too," said Christopher Robin, "but what I like *doing* best is Nothing."

"How do you do Nothing?" asked Pooh, after he had wondered for a long time.

"Well, it's when people call out at you just as you're going off to do it, What are you going to do, Christopher Robin, and you say, Oh, nothing, and then you go and do it."

"Oh, I see," said Pooh.

"This is a nothing sort of thing that we're doing now."

"Oh, I see," said Pooh again.

"It means just going along, listening to all the things you can't hear, and not bothering."

Chuang-tse described it this way:

> Consciousness wandered North to the land of the Dark Waters and climbed the Unnoticeable Slope, where he met Speechless Non-Doer. "I have three questions for you," Consciousness said. "First, what thoughts and efforts will lead us to understanding the Tao? Second, where must we go and what must we do to find peace in the Tao? Third, from what point must we start and which road must we follow in order to reach the Tao?" Speechless Non-Doer gave him no answer.

Consciousness traveled South to the land of the Bright Ocean and climbed the Mountain of Certainty, where he saw Impulsive Speech-Maker. He asked him the same questions. "Here are the answers," Impulsive Speech-Maker replied. But as soon as he started to speak, he became confused and forgot what he was talking about.

Consciousness returned to the palace and asked the Yellow Emperor, who told him, "To have no thought and put forth no effort is the first step towards understanding the Tao. To go nowhere and do nothing is the first step towards finding peace in the Tao. To start from no point and follow no road is the first step towards reaching the Tao."

What Chuang-tse, Christopher Robin, and Pooh are describing is the Great Secret, the key that unlocks the doors of wisdom, happiness, and truth. What is that magic, mysterious something? Nothing. To the Taoist, Nothing is *something*, and Something—at least the sort of thing that many consider to be important—is really nothing at all. Our explanation of this will attempt to give some sort of indication of what the Taoists call *T'ai Hsü*, the "Great Nothing."

We will begin with an illustration from the writings of Chuang-tse:

On his way back from the K'un-lun Mountains, the Yellow Emperor lost the dark pearl of Tao. He sent Knowledge to find it, but Knowledge was unable to understand it. He sent Distant Vision, but Distant Vision was unable to see it. He sent Eloquence, but Eloquence was unable to describe it.

Finally, he sent Empty Mind, and Empty Mind came back with the pearl.

When Eeyore lost his tail, who found it for him? Clever Rabbit? No. He was busy doing Clever Things. Scholarly Owl? No. He didn't recognize it when he saw it. Know-It-All Eeyore? No. He didn't even realize that it was missing until Pooh told him. And even then, it took a while to convince him that the tail was definitely Not There.

Then Pooh went off to find it. First, he stopped at Owl's house, and Owl told him in twenty-five thousand monotonous words or more that the Thing To Do would be to Issue a Reward, which would involve writing out a ... (yawn) ... notice, and putting it ... (YAWN) ... all over the ... (umm). Oh, yes—where were we? All over the Forest. And then they went outside ...

And Pooh looked at the knocker and the notice below it, and he looked at the bell-rope and the notice below it, and the more he looked at the bell-rope, the more he felt that he had seen something like it, somewhere else, sometime before.

"Handsome bell-rope, isn't it?" said Owl.

Pooh nodded.

"It reminds me of something," he said, "but I can't think what. Where did you get it?"

"I just came across it in the Forest. It was hanging over a bush, and I thought at first somebody lived there, so I rang it, and nothing happened, and then I rang it again very loudly, and it came off in my hand, and as nobody seemed to want it, I took it home, and———"

Aha. So Pooh returned the tail to Eeyore, and after it had been put back in place, Eeyore felt much better.

For a while, anyway.

An Empty sort of mind is valuable for finding pearls and tails and things because it can see what's in front of it. An Overstuffed mind is unable to. While the Clear mind listens to a bird singing, the Stuffed-Full-of-Knowledge-and-Cleverness mind wonders what *kind* of bird is singing. The more Stuffed Up it is, the less it can hear through its own ears and see through its own eyes. Knowledge and Cleverness tend to concern themselves with the wrong sorts of things, and a mind confused by Knowledge, Cleverness, and Abstract Ideas tends to go chasing off after things that don't matter, or that don't even exist, instead of seeing, appreciating, and making use of what is right in front of it.

Let's consider Emptiness in general for a moment. What is it about a Taoist landscape painting that seems so refreshing to so many different kinds of people? The Emptiness, the space that's not filled in. What is it about fresh snow, clean air, pure water? Or good music? As Claude Debussy expressed it, "Music is the space between the notes."

"Wooh *Baby*! Oooaowee *BABY*! (Wanga wanga wanga.) Baby, don't *leave* me! (Wanga wanga crash bang!) Baby, don't *LEAVE* me!" (Click.) Like silence after noise, or cool, clear water on a hot, stuffy day, Emptiness cleans out the messy mind and charges up the batteries of spiritual energy.

Many people are afraid of Emptiness, however, because it reminds them of Loneliness. Everything has to be filled in, it seems—appointment books, hillsides, vacant lots—but when all the spaces are filled, the Loneliness *really* begins. Then the Groups are joined, the Classes are signed up for, and the Gift-to-Yourself items are bought. When the Loneliness starts creeping in the door, the Television vision Set is turned on to make it go away. But it doesn't go away. So some of *us* do instead, and after discarding the emptiness of the Big Congested Mess, we discover the fullness of Nothing.

One of our favorite examples of the value of Nothing is an incident in the life of the Japanese emperor Hirohito. Now, being emperor in one of the most frantically Confucianist countries in the world is not necessarily all that *relaxing*. From early morning until late at night, practically every minute of the emperor's time is filled in with meetings, audiences, tours, inspections, and who-knows-what. And through a day so tightly scheduled that it would make a stone wall seem open by comparison, the emperor must glide, like a great ship sailing in a steady breeze.

In the middle of a particularly busy day, the emperor was driven to a meeting hall for an appointment of some kind. But when he arrived, there was no one there. The emperor walked into the middle of the great hall, stood silently for a moment, then bowed to the empty space. He turned to his assistants, a large smile on his face. "We must schedule more appointments like this," he told them. "I haven't enjoyed myself so much in a long time."

In the forty-eighth chapter of the *Tao Te Ching*, Lao-tse wrote, "To attain knowledge, add things every day. To attain wisdom, remove things every day." Chuang-tse described the principle in his own humorous way:

"I am learning," Yen Hui said.

"How?" the Master asked.

"I forgot the rules of Righteousness and the levels of Benevolence," he replied.

"Good, but could be better," the Master said.

A few days later, Yen Hui remarked, "I am making progress."

"How?" the Master asked.

"I forgot the Rituals and the Music," he answered.

"Better, but not perfect," the Master said.

Some time later, Yen Hui told the Master, "Now I sit down and forget everything."

The Master looked up, startled. "What do you mean, you forget everything?" he quickly asked.

"I forget my body and senses, and leave all appearance and information behind," answered Yen Hui. "In the middle of Nothing, I join the Source of All Things."

The Master bowed. "You have transcended the limitations of time and knowledge. I am far behind you. You have found the Way!"

Gathering, analyzing, sorting, and storing information—these functions and more the mind can perform so automatically, skillfully, and effortlessly that it makes the most sophisticated computer look like a plastic toy by comparison. But it can do infinitely more. To use the mind as it's all too commonly used, on the kinds of things that it's usually used on, is about as inefficient and inappropriate as using a magic sword to open up a can of beans. The power of a clear mind is beyond description. But it can be attained by anyone who can appreciate and utilize the value of Nothing.

Let's say you get an idea—or, as Pooh would more accurately say, it gets you. Where did it come from? From this something, which came from *that* something? If you are able to trace it all the way back to its source, you will discover that it came from Nothing. And chances are, the greater the idea, the more directly it came from there. "A stroke of genius! Completely unheard of! A revolutionary new approach!" Practically everyone has gotten some sort of an idea like that sometime, most likely after a sound sleep when everything was so clear and filled with Nothing that an Idea suddenly appeared in it. But we don't have to fall asleep for a few hours for that to happen. We can be awake, instead—*completely* awake. The process is very natural.

It starts when we are children, helpless but aware of things, enjoying what is around us. Then we reach adolescence, still helpless but trying to at least *appear* independent. When we outgrow that stage, we become adults—self-sufficient individuals able and mature enough to help others as we have learned to help ourselves.

But the adult is not the highest stage of development. The end of the cycle is that of the independent, clear-minded, all-seeing Child. That is the level known as wisdom. When the *Tao Te Ching* and other wise books say things like, "Return to the beginning; become a child again," that's what they're referring to. Why do the en*light*ened seem filled with light and happiness, like children? Why do they sometimes even look and talk like children? Because they are. The wise are Children Who Know. Their minds have been emptied of the countless minute somethings of small learning, and filled with the wisdom of the Great Nothing, the Way of the Universe.

> They walked on, thinking of This and That, and by-and-by they came to an enchanted place on the very top of the Forest called Galleons Lap, which is sixty-something trees in a circle; and Christopher Robin knew that it was enchanted because nobody had ever been able to count whether it was sixty-three or sixty-four, not even when he tied a piece of string round each tree after he had counted it. Being enchanted, its floor was not like that floor of the Forest, gorse and bracken and heather, but close-set grass, quiet and smooth and green . . . . Sitting there they could see the whole world spread out until it reached the sky, and whatever there was all the world over was with them in Galleons Lap.

There the Pooh books come to an end, in the Enchanted Place at the top of the Forest. We can go there at any time. It's not far away; it's not hard to find. Just take the path to Nothing, and go Nowhere until you reach it. Because the Enchanted Place is right where you are, and if you're Friendly With Bears, you can find it.

The Declaration of Independence

Thomas Jefferson

Thomas Jefferson (1743–1826) was born in Virginia to a well-to-do, land-owning family. He graduated from the College of William and Mary and then studied law. When he was elected at age 26 to the Virginia legislature, he had already begun forming his revolutionary views. As a delegate to the Second Continental Congress in 1775, he was the principal writer of the Declaration of Independence, *which was adopted on July 4, 1776. After the Revolution, he was Governor of Virginia from 1775 to 1777. From then until 1801, when he was elected the third President of the United States, Jefferson served in various federal positions, including Secretary of State and ambassador to France. Jefferson was influential as an advocate of democracy in the early years of the United States, and his ideas were typical of eighteenth-century Enlightenment thought. Ironically, Jefferson died on July 4, 1826, within hours of his good friend and fellow patriot, John Adams. The* Declaration of Independence, *which shows Jefferson's ideas and style, is not only an important historical document but also an eloquent statement of the founding principles of the United States of America.*

In Congress, July 4, 1776
A DECLARATION by the Representatives
of the United States of America,
In General Congress Assembled.

W hen in the Course of human Events, it becomes necessary for one People to dissolve the Political Bands which have connected them with another, and to assume among the Powers of the Earth, the separate and equal Station to which the Laws of Nature and of Nature's God entitle them, a decent Respect to the Opinions of Mankind requires that they should declare the causes which impel them to the Separation.

We hold these Truths to be self-evident, that all Men are created equal, that they are endowed by their Creator with certain unalienable Rights, that among these are Life, Liberty, and the Pursuit of Happiness—That to secure these Rights, Governments are instituted among Men, deriving their just Powers from the Consent of the Governed, that whenever any Form of Government becomes destructive of these Ends, it is the Right of the People to alter or to abolish it, and to institute new Government, laying its Foundation on such Principles, and organizing its Powers in such Form, as to them shall seem most likely to effect their Safety and Happiness. Prudence, indeed, will dictate that Governments long established should not be changed for light and transient Causes; and accordingly all Experience hath shewn, that Mankind are more disposed to suffer, while Evils are sufferable, than to right themselves by abolishing the Forms to which they are accustomed. But when a long Train of Abuses and Usurpations, pursuing invariably the same Object, evinces a Design to reduce them under absolute Despotism, it is their Right, it is their Duty, to throw off such Government, and to provide new Guards for their future Security. Such has been the patient Sufferance of these Colonies; and such is now the Necessity which constrains them to alter their former Systems of Government. The History of the present king of Great-Britain is a History of repeated Injuries and Usurpations, all having in direct Object the Establishment of an absolute Tyranny over these States. To prove this, let Facts be submitted to a candid World.

He has refused his Assent to Laws, the most wholesome and necessary for the public good.

He has forbidden his Governors to pass Laws of immediate and pressing importance, unless suspended in their Operation till his Assent should be obtained; and when so suspended, he has utterly neglected to attend to them.

He has refused to pass other Laws for the Accommodation of large Districts of People, unless those People would relinquish the Right of Representation in the Legislature, a Right inestimable to them, and formidable to Tyrants only.

He has called together Legislative Bodies at Places unusual, uncomfortable, and distant from the Depository of their public Records, for the sole Purpose of fatiguing them into Compliance with his Measures.

He has dissolved Representative Houses repeatedly, for opposing with manly Firmness his Invasions on the Rights of the People.

He has refused for a long Time, after such Dissolutions, to cause others to be elected; whereby the Legislative Powers, incapable of Annihilation, have returned to the People at large for their exercise; the State remaining in the mean time exposed to all the Dangers of Invasion from without, and Convulsions within.

He has endeavoured to prevent the Population of these States; for that Purpose obstructing the Laws for Naturalization of Foreigners; refusing to pass others to encourage their Migrations hither, and raising the Conditions of new Appropriations of Lands.

He has obstructed the Administration of Justice, by refusing his Assent to Laws for establishing Judiciary Powers.

He has made judges dependent on his Will alone, for the Tenure of their Offices, and the Amount and Payment of their Salaries.

He has erected a Multitude of new Offices, and sent hither Swarms of Officers to harass our People, and eat out their Substance.

He has kept among us, in Times of Peace, Standing Armies, without the consent of our Legislatures.

He has affected to render the Military independent of and superior to the Civil Power.

He has combined with others to subject us to a jurisdiction foreign to our Constitution, and unacknowledged by our Laws; giving his Assent to their Acts of pretended Legislation:

For quartering large Bodies of Armed Troops among us:

For protecting them, by a mock Trial, from Punishment for any Murders which they should commit on the Inhabitants of these States:

For cutting off our Trade with all Parts of the World:

For imposing Taxes on us without our Consent:

For depriving us, in many Cases, of the Benefits of Trial by Jury:

For transporting us beyond Seas to be tried for pretended Offences:

For abolishing the free System of English Laws in a neighbouring Province, establishing therein an arbitrary Government, and enlarging its Boundaries, so as to render it at once an Example and fit Instrument for introducing the same absolute Rule into these Colonies:

For taking away our Charters, abolishing our most valuable Laws, and altering fundamentally the Forms of our Governments:

For suspending our own Legislatures, and declaring themselves invested with Power to legislate for us in all Cases whatsoever.

He has abdicated Government here, by declaring us out of his Protection and waging War against us.

He has plundered our Seas, ravaged our Coasts, burnt our Towns, and destroyed the Lives of our People.

He is, at this Time, transporting large Armies of foreign Mercenaries to compleat the Works of Death, Desolation, and Tyranny, already begun with circumstances of Cruelty and Perfidy, scarcely paralleled in the most barbarous Ages, and totally unworthy the Head of a civilized Nation.

He has constrained our fellow Citizens taken Captive on the high Seas to bear Arms against their Country, to become the Executioners of their Friends and Brethren, or to fall themselves by their Hands.

He has excited domestic Insurrections amongst us, and has endeavoured to bring on the Inhabitants of our Frontiers, the merciless Indian Savages, whose known Rule of Warfare, is an undistinguished Destruction, of all Ages, Sexes and Conditions.

In every stage of these Oppressions we have Petitioned for Redress in the most humble Terms: Our repeated Petitions have been answered only by repeated Injury. A Prince, whose Character is thus marked by every act which may define a Tyrant, is unfit to be the Ruler of a free People.

Nor have we been wanting in Attentions to our British Brethren. We have warned them from Time to Time of Attempts by their Legislature to extend an unwarrantable Jurisdiction over us. We have reminded them of the Circumstances of our Emigration and Settlement here. We have appealed to their native Justice and Magnanimity, and we have conjured them by the Ties of our common Kindred to disavow these Usurpations, which, would inevitably interrupt our Connections and Correspondence. They too have been deaf to the Voice of justice and of Consanguinity. We must, therefore, acquiesce in the Necessity, which denounces our Separation, and hold them, as we hold the rest of Mankind, Enemies in War, in Peace, Friends.

We, therefore, the Representatives of the UNITED STATES OF AMERICA, in GENERAL CONGRESS, Assembled, appealing to the Supreme Judge of the World for the Rectitude of our Intentions, do, in the Name, and by Authority of the good People of these Colonies, solemnly Publish and Declare, That these United Colonies, are, and of Right ought to be, FREE AND INDEPENDENT STATES; that they are absolved from all Allegiance to the British Crown, and that all political Connection between them and the State of Great-Britain, is and ought to be totally dissolved; and that as FREE AND INDEPENDENT STATES, they have full Power to levy War, conclude Peace, contract Alliances, establish Commerce, and to do all other Acts and Things which INDEPENDENT STATES may of right do. And for the support of this Declaration, with a firm Reliance on the Protection of divine Providence, we mutually pledge to each other our Lives, our Fortunes, and our sacred Honor.

Signed by ORDER and in BEHALF of the CONGRESS,
JOHN HANCOCK, PRESIDENT.
ATTEST.
CHARLES THOMSON, SECRETARY.
PHILADELPHIA: PRINTED BY JOHN DUNLAP.

Watching TV Makes You Smarter

Steven Johnson

Steven Berlin Johnson, author, lecturer, web-developer, media theorist, and pop-culture critic, was born June 6, 1968. Johnson earned a bachelor's degree in Semiotics from Brown University and went on to earn a Masters in English Literature from Columbia University. Before age 30, Johnson was named one of the "50 People Who Matter Most on the Internet" by Newsweek *for his work as co-founder and editor-in chief of* Feed, *an online magazine that was widely celebrated for publishing articles and opinion pieces that covered a mix of topics from politics to emerging technologies.* Feed *received praise from both the* Wall Street Journal *and The* New York Times *for its ability to use the new capabilities in technology to enhance the traditional field of print journalism. His work with the e-zine helped to inform and inspire Johnson's first book* Interface Culture: How New Technology Transfers the Way We Create and Communicate (1997). *Johnson has since published 7 more books, mostly dealing with technology, science, and human interaction, including the best-selling* The Ghost Map, Where Good Ideas Come From, *and* Future Perfect. *His works have been translated into dozens of languages. Steven Johnson's work goes beyond just commenting and criticizing technology's influence on society; his work actually contributes to shaping the way interactions on the web have progressed.*

The following selection is adapted from Johnson's book Everything Bad is good for you: How Today's Popular Culture Is Actually Making Us Smarter. *Published in 2005, the book offers a provocative counter-argument to the popular claims that modern media is detrimental to society. The author's argument in "Watching TV Makes You Smarter" focuses on the benefits of television for both the viewer and society at-large. While Johnson addresses the role of pop-media in disseminating popular morality, his real focus in on the cognitive demands of modern media in a theory he calls the Sleeper Curve. Johnson's praise of shows like* Lost *and* The Sopranos *work, according to* New York Times *contributor "to convince us that pop culture is not the intellectual tranquilizer that its sound-alike critics have made it out to be but a potent promoter of cerebral fitness." The controversial claims presented in Johnson's "Everything Bad is Good for you" have catapulted his philosophical explorations to pop-culture status, leading to his appearances on such popular programs as* The Colbert Report *and* The Daily Show.

The Sleeper Curve

> SCIENTIST A: Has he asked for anything special?
> SCIENTIST B: Yes, this morning for breakfast . . . he requested something called "wheat germ, organic honey and tiger's milk."
> SCIENTIST A: Oh, yes. Those were the charmed substances that some years ago were felt to contain life-preserving properties.
> SCIENTIST B: You mean there was no deep fat? No steak or cream-pies or . . . hot fudge?
> SCIENTIST A: Those were thought to be unhealthy.

From Woody Allen's "Sleeper"

On Jan. 24, the Fox network showed an episode of its hit drama "24," the real-time thriller known for its cliffhanger tension and often-gruesome violence. Over the preceding weeks, a number of public controversies had erupted around "24," mostly focused on its portrait of Muslim terrorists and its penchant for torture scenes. The episode that was shown on the 24th only fanned the flames higher: in one scene, a terrorist enlists a hit man to kill his child for not fully supporting the jihadist cause; in another scene, the secretary of defense authorizes the torture of his son to uncover evidence of a terrorist plot.

But the explicit violence and the post-9/11 terrorist anxiety are not the only elements of "24" that would have been unthinkable on prime-time network television 20 years ago. Alongside the notable change in content lies an equally notable change in form. During its 44 minutes—a real-time hour, minus 16 minutes for commercials—the episode connects the lives of 21 distinct characters, each with a clearly defined "story arc," as the Hollywood jargon has it: a defined personality with motivations and obstacles and specific relationships with other characters. Nine primary narrative threads wind their way through those 44 minutes, each drawing extensively upon events and information revealed in earlier episodes. Draw a map of all those intersecting plots and personalities, and you get structure that—where formal complexity is concerned—more closely resembles "Middlemarch" than a hit TV drama of years past like "Bonanza."

For decades, we've worked under the assumption that mass culture follows a path declining steadily toward lowest-common-denominator standards, presumably because the "masses" want dumb, simple pleasures and big media companies try to give the masses what they want. But as that "24" episode suggests, the exact opposite is happening: the culture is getting more cognitively demanding, not less. To make sense of an episode of "24," you have to integrate far more information than you would have a few decades ago watching a comparable show. Beneath the violence and the ethnic stereotypes, another trend appears: to keep up with entertainment like "24," you have to pay attention, make inferences, track shifting social relationships. This is what I call the Sleeper Curve: the most debased forms of mass diversion—video games and violent television dramas and juvenile sitcoms—turn out to be nutritional after all.

I believe that the Sleeper Curve is the single most important new force altering the mental development of young people today, and I believe it is largely a force for good: enhancing our cognitive faculties, not dumbing them down. And yet you almost never hear this story in popular accounts of today's media. Instead, you hear dire tales of addiction, violence, mindless escapism. It's assumed that shows that promote smoking or gratuitous violence are bad for us, while those that thunder against teen pregnancy or intolerance have a positive role in society. Judged by that morality-play standard, the story of popular culture over the past 50 years—if not 500—is a story of decline: the morals of the stories have grown darker and more ambiguous, and the anti-heroes have multiplied.

The usual counterargument here is that what media have lost in moral clarity, they have gained in realism. The real world doesn't come in nicely packaged public-service announcements, and we're better off with entertainment like "The Sopranos" that reflects our fallen state with all its ethical ambiguity. I happen to be sympathetic to that argument, but it's not the one I want to make here. I think there is another way to assess the social virtue of pop culture, one that looks at media as a kind of cognitive workout, not as a series of life lessons. There may indeed be more "negative messages" in the mediasphere today. But that's not the only way to evaluate whether our television shows or video games are having a positive impact. Just as important—if not more important—is the kind of thinking you have to do to make sense of a cultural experience. That is where the Sleeper Curve becomes visible.

Televised Intelligence

Consider the cognitive demands that televised narratives place on their viewers. With many shows that we associate with "quality" entertainment— "The Mary Tyler Moore Show," "Murphy Brown," "Frasier"—the intelligence arrives fully formed in the words and actions of the characters on-screen. They say witty things to one another and avoid lapsing into tired sitcom clichés, and we smile along in our living rooms, enjoying the company of these smart people. But assuming we're bright enough to understand the sentences they're saying, there's no intellectual labor involved in enjoying the show as a viewer. You no more challenge your mind by watching these intelligent shows than you challenge your body watching "Monday Night Football." The intellectual work is happening on-screen, not off.

But another kind of televised intelligence is on the rise. Think of the cognitive benefits conventionally ascribed to reading: attention, patience, retention, the parsing of narrative threads. Over the last half-century, programming on TV has increased the demands it places on precisely these mental faculties. This growing complexity involves three primary elements: multiple threading, flashing arrows and social networks.

According to television lore, the age of multiple threads began with the arrival in 1981 of "Hill Street Blues," the Steven Bochco police drama invariably praised for its "gritty realism." Watch an episode of "Hill Street Blues" side by side with any major drama from the preceding decades—"Starsky and Hutch," for instance, or "Dragnet"—and the structural transformation will jump out at you. The earlier shows follow one or two lead characters, adhere to a single dominant plot and reach a decisive conclusion at the end of the episode. Draw an outline of the narrative threads in almost every "Dragnet" episode, and it will be a single line: from the initial crime scene, through the investigation, to the eventual cracking of the case. A typical "Starsky and Hutch" episode offers only the slightest variation on this liner formula: the introduction of a comic subplot that usually appears only at the tail ends of the episode, creating a structure that looks like this graph. The vertical axis represents the number of individual threads, and the horizontal axis is time.

"STARSKY AND HUTCH" (ANY EPISODE)

A "Hill Street Blues" episode complicates the picture in a number of profound ways. The narrative weaves together a collection of distinct strands— sometimes as many as 10, though at least half of the threads involve only a few quick scenes scattered through the episode. The number of primary characters—and not just bit parts—swells significantly. And the episode has fuzzy borders: picking up one or two threads from previous episodes at the outset and leaving one or two threads from previous episodes at the outset and leaving one or two threads open at the end. Charted graphically, an average episode looks like this:

"HILL STREET BLUES" (EPISODE 85)

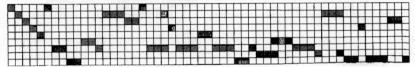

Critics generally cite "Hill Street Blues" as the beginning of "serious drama" native in the television medium—differentiating the series from the single-episode dramatic programs from the 50's, which were Broadway plays performed in front of a camera. But the "Hill Street" innovations weren't all that original; they'd long played a defining role in popular television, just not during the evening hours. The structure of a "Hill Street" episode—and indeed of all the critically acclaimed dramas that followed, from "thirtysomething" to "Six Feet Under"—is the structure of a soap opera. "Hill Street Blues" might have sparked a new golden age of television drama during its seven-year run, but it did so by using a few crucial tricks that "Guiding Light" and "General Hospital" mastered long before.

Bochco's genius with "Hill Street" was to marry complex narrative structure with complex subject matter. "Dallas" had already shown that the extended, interwoven threads of the soap-opera genre could survive the week-long interruptions of a prime-time show, but the actual content of "Dallas" was fluff. (The most probing issue it addressed was the question, now folkloric, of who shot J.R.) "All in the Family" and "Rhoda" showed that you could tackle complex social issues, but they did their tackling in the comfort of the sitcom living room. "Hill Street" had richly drawn characters confronting difficult social issues and a narrative structure to match.

Since "Hill Street" appeared, the multi-threaded drama has become the most widespread fictional genre on prime time: "St. Elsewhere," "L.A. Law," "thirtysomething," "Twin Peaks," "N.Y.P.D. Blue," "E.R.," "The West Wing," "Alias," "Lost." (The only prominent holdouts in drama are shows like "Law and Order" that have essentially updated the venerable "Dragnet" format and thus remained anchored to a single narrative line.) Since the early 80's, however, there has been a noticeable increase in narrative complexity in these dramas. The most ambitious show on TV to date, "The Sopranos," routinely follows up to a dozen distinct threads over the course of an episode, with more than 20 recurring characters. An episode from late in the first season looks like this:

"THE SOPRANOS" (EPISODE 8)

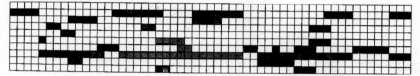

The total number of active threads equals the multiple plots of "Hill Street," but here each thread is more substantial. The show doesn't offer a clear distinction between dominant and minor plots; each story line carries its weight in the mix. The episode also displays a chordal mode of storytelling entirely absent from "Hill Street": a single scene in "The Sopranos" will often connect to three different threads at the same time, layering one plot atop another. And every single thread in this "Sopranos" episode builds on events from previous episodes and continues on through the rest of the season and beyond.

Put those charts together, and you have a portrait of the Sleeper Curve rising over the past 30 years of popular television. In a sense, this is as much a map of cognitive changes in the popular mind as it is a map of on-screen developments, as if the media titans decided to condition our brains to follow ever-larger numbers of simultaneous threads. Before "Hill Street," the conventional wisdom among television execs was that audiences wouldn't be comfortable following more than three plots in a single episode, and indeed, the "Hill Street" pilot, which was shown in January 1981, brought complaints from viewers that the show was too complicated. Fast-forward two decades, and shows like "The Sopranos" engage their audiences with narratives that make "Hill Street" look like "Three's Company." Audiences happily embrace that complexity because they've been trained by two decades of multi-threaded dramas.

Multi-threading is the most celebrated structural feature of the modern television drama, and it certainly deserves some of the honor that has been doled out to it. And yet multi-threading is only part of the story.

The Case for Confusion

Shortly after the arrival of the first-generation slasher movies—"Halloween," "Friday the 13th"—Paramount released a mock-slasher flick called "Student Bodies," parodying the genre just as the "Scream" series would do 15 years later. In one scene, the obligatory nubile teenage baby sitter hears a noise outside a suburban house; she opens the door to investigate, finds nothing and then goes back inside. As the door shuts behind her, the camera swoops in on the doorknob, and we see that she has left the door unlocked. The camera pulls back and then swoops down again for emphasis. And then a flashing arrow appears on the screen, with text that helpfully explains: "Unlocked!"

That flashing arrow is parody, of course, but it's merely an exaggerated version of a device popular stories use all the time. When a sci-fi script inserts into some advanced lab a nonscientist who keeps asking the science geeks to explain what they're doing with that particle accelerator, that's a flashing arrow that gives the audience precisely the information it needs in order to make sense of the ensuing plot. ("Whatever you do, don't spill water on it, or you'll set off a massive explosion!") These hints serve as a kind of narrative hand-holding. Implicitly, they say to the audience, "We realize you have no idea what a particle accelerator is, but here's the deal: all you need to know is that it's a big fancy thing that explodes when wet." They focus the mind on relevant details: "Don't worry about whether the baby sitter is going to break up with her boyfriend. Worry about that guy lurking in the bushes." They reduce the amount of analytic work you need to do to make sense of a story. All you have to do is follow the arrows.

By this standard, popular television has never been harder to follow. If narrative threads have experienced a population explosion over the past 20 years, flashing arrows have grown correspondingly scarce. Watching our pinnacle of early 80's TV drama, "Hill Street Blues," we find there's an informational wholeness to each scene that differs markedly from what you see on shows like "The West Wing" or "The Sopranos" or "Alias" or "E.R."

"Hill Street" has ambiguities about future events: will a convicted killer be executed? Will Furillo marry Joyce Davenport? Will Renko find it in himself to bust a favorite singer for cocaine possession? But the present-tense of each scene explains itself to the viewer with little ambiguity. There's an open question or a mystery driving each of these stories—how will it all turn out?—but there's no mystery about the immediate activity on the screen. A contemporary drama like "The West Wing," on the other hand, constantly embeds mysteries into the presenttense events: you see characters performing actions or discussing events about which crucial information has been deliberately withheld. Anyone who has watched more than a handful of "The West Wing" episodes closely will know the feeling: scene after scene refers to some clearly crucial but unexplained piece of information, and after the sixth reference, you'll find yourself wishing you could rewind the tape to figure out what they're talking about, assuming you've missed something. And then you realize that you're supposed to be confused. The open question posed by these sequences is not "How will this turn out in the end?" The question is "What's happening right now?"

The deliberate lack of hand-holding extends down to the microlevel of dialogue as well. Popular entertainment that addresses technical issues—

whether they are the intricacies of passing legislation, or of performing a heart bypass, or of operating a particle accelerator—conventionally switches between two modes of information in dialogue: texture and substance. Texture is all the arcane verbiage provided to convince the viewer that they're watching Actual Doctors at Work; substance is the material planted amid the background texture that the viewer needs make sense of the plot.

Conventionally, narratives demarcate the line between texture and substance by inserting cues that flag or translate the important data. There's an unintentionally comical moment in the 2004 block-buster "The Day After Tomorrow" in which the beleaguered climatologist (played by Dennis Quaid) announces his theory about the imminent arrival of a new ice age to a gathering of government officials. In his speech, he warns that "we have hit a critical desalinization point!" At this moment, the writer-director Roland Emmerich—a master of brazen arrow-flashing—has an official follow with the obliging remark: "It would explain what's driving this extreme weather." They might as well have had a flashing "Unlocked!" arrow on the screen.

The dialogue on shows like "The West Wing" and "E.R.," on the other hand, doesn't talk down to its audiences. It rushes by, the words accelerating in sync with the high-speed tracking shots that glide through the corridors and operating rooms. The characters talk faster in these shows, but the truly remarkable thing about the dialogue is not purely a matter of speed; it's the willingness to immerse the audience in information that most viewers won't understand. Here's a typical scene from "E.R.":

[WEAVER AND WRIGHT push a gurney containing a 16-year-old girl. Her parents, JANNA AND FRANK MIKAMI, follow close behind. CARTER AND LUCY fall in.]

> WEAVER: 16-year-old, unconscious, history of biliary atresia.
> CARTER: Hepatic coma?
> WEAVER: Looks like it.
> MR. MIKAMI: She was doing fine until six months ago.
> CARTER: What medication is she on?
> MRS. MIKAMI: Ampicillin, tobramycin, vitamins a, d and k.
> LUCY: Skin's jaundiced.
> WEAVER: Same with the sclera. Breath smells sweet.
> CARTER: Fetor hepaticus?
> WEAVER: Yep.
> LUCY: What's that?
> WEAVER: Her liver's shut down. Let's dip a urine. [To CARTER]
>   Guys, it's getting a little crowded in here, why don't you deal with
>   the parents? Start lactulose, 30 cc's per NG.
> CARTER: We're giving medicine to clean her blood.
> WEAVER: Blood in the urine, two-plus.
> CARTER: The liver failure is causing her blood not to clot.

MRS. MIKAMI: Oh, God. . . .

CARTER: Is she on the transplant list?

MR. MIKAMI: She's been Status 2a for six months, but they haven't been able to find her a match.

CARTER: Why? What's her blood type?

MR. MIKAMI: AB.

[This hits CARTER like a lightning bolt. LUCY gets it, too. They share a look.]

There are flashing arrows here, of course—"The liver failure is causing her blood not to clot"—but the ratio of medical jargon to layperson translation is remarkably high. From a purely narrative point of view, the decisive line arrives at the very end: "AB." The 16-year-old's blood type connects her to an earlier plot line, involving a cerebral-hemorrhage victim who—after being dramatically revived in one of the opening scenes—ends up brain-dead. Far earlier, before the liver-failure scene above, Carter briefly discusses harvesting the hemorrhage victim's organs for transplants, and another doctor makes a passing reference to his blood type being the rare AB (thus making him an unlikely donor). The twist here revolves around a statistically unlikely event happening at the E.R.—an otherwise perfect liver donor showing up just in time to donate his liver to a recipient with the same rare blood type. But the show reveals this twist with remarkable subtlety. To make sense of that last "AB" line—and the look of disbelief on Carter's and Lucy's faces—you have to recall a passing remark uttered earlier regarding a character who belongs to a completely different thread. Shows like "E.R." may have more blood and guts than popular TV had a generation ago, but when it comes to storytelling, they possess a quality that can only be described as subtlety and discretion.

Even Bad TV is Better

Skeptics might argue that I have stacked the deck here by focusing on relatively highbrow titles like "The Sopranos" or "The West Wing," when in fact the most significant change in the last five years of narrative entertainment involves reality TV. Does the contemporary pop cultural landscape look quite as promising if the representative show is "Joe Millionaire" instead of "The West Wing"?

I think it does, but to answer that question properly, you have to avoid the tendency to sentimentalize the past. When people talk about the golden age of television in the early 70's—invoking shows like "The Mary Tyler Moore Show" and "All in the Family"—they forget to mention how awful most television programming was during much of that decade. If you're going to look at pop-culture trends, you have to compare apples to apples, or in this case, lemons to lemons. The relevant comparison is not between "Joe Millionaire" and "MASH"; it's between "Joe Millionaire" and "The Newlywed Game," or between "Survivor" and "The Love Boat."

What you see when you make these head-to-head comparisons is that a rising tide of complexity has been lifting programming at the bottom of the quality spectrum and at the top. "The Sopranos" is several times more demanding of its audiences than "Hill Street" was, and "Joe Millionaire" has made comparable advances over "Battle of the Network Stars." This is the ultimate test of the Sleeper Curve theory: even the junk has improved.

If early television took its cues from the stage, today's reality programming is reliably structured like a video game: a series of competitive tests, growing more challenging over time. Many reality shows borrow a subtler device from gaming culture as well: the rules aren't fully established at the outset. You learn as you play.

On a show like "Survivor" or "The Apprentice," the participants—and the audience—know the general objective of the series, but each episode involves new challenges that haven't been ordained in advance. The final round of the first season of "The Apprentice," for instance, threw a monkey wrench into the strategy that governed the play up to that point, when Trump announced that the two remaining apprentices would have to assemble and manage a team of subordinates who had already been fired in earlier episodes of the show. All of a sudden the overarching objective of the game—do anything to avoid being fired—presented a potential conflict to the remaining two contenders: the structure of the final round favored the survivor who had maintained the best relationships with his comrades. Suddenly, it wasn't enough just to have clawed your way to the top; you had to have made friends while clawing. The original "Joe Millionaire" went so far as to undermine the most fundamental convention of all—that the show's creators don't openly lie to the contestants about the prizes—by inducing a construction worker to pose as man of means while 20 women competed for his attention.

Reality programming borrowed another key ingredient from games: the intellectual labor of probing the system's rules for weak spots and opportunities. As each show discloses its conventions, and each participant reveals his or her personality traits and background, the intrigue in watching comes from figuring out how the participants should best navigate the environment that has been created for them. The pleasure in these shows comes not from watching other people being humiliated on national television; it comes from depositing other people in a complex, high-pressure environment where no established strategies exist and watching them find their bearings. That's why the watercooler conversation about these shows invariably tracks in on the strategy displayed on the previous night's episode: why did Kwame pick Omarosa in that final round? What devious strategy is Richard Hatch concocting now?

When we watch these shows, the part of our brain that monitors the emotional lives of the people around us—the part that tracks subtle shifts in intonation and gesture and facial expression—scrutinizes the action on the screen, looking for clues. We trust certain characters implicitly and vote others off the island in a heartbeat. Traditional narrative shows also trigger emotional connections to the characters, but those connections don't have the same participatory effect, because traditional narratives aren't explicitly about strategy. The phrase "Monday-morning quarterbacking" describes the engaged feeling that spectators have in relation to games as opposed to stories. We absorb stories, but we second-guess games. Reality programming has brought that second-guessing to prime time, only the game in question revolves around social dexterity rather than the physical kind.

The Rewards of Smart Culture

The quickest way to appreciate the Sleeper Curve's cognitive training is to sit down and watch a few hours of hit programming from the late 70's on Nick at Nite or the SOAPnet channel or on DVD. The modern viewer who watches a show like "Dallas" today will be bored by the content—not just because the show is less salacious than today's soap operas (which it is by a small margin) but also because the show contains far less information in each scene, despite the fact that its soap-opera structure made it one of the most complicated narratives on television in its prime. With "Dallas," the modern viewer doesn't have to think to make sense of what's going on, and not having to think is boring. Many recent hit shows—"24," "Survivor," "The Sopranos," "Alias," "Lost," "The Simpsons," "E.R."—take the opposite approach, layering each scene with a thick network of affiliations. You have to focus to follow the plot, and in focusing you're exercising the parts of your brain that map social networks, that fill in missing information, that connect multiple narrative threads.

Of course, the entertainment industry isn't increasing the cognitive complexity of its products for charitable reasons. The Sleeper Curve exists because there's money to be made by making culture smarter. The economics of television syndication and DVD sales mean that there's a tremendous financial pressure to make programs that can be watched multiple times, revealing new nuances and shadings on the third viewing. Meanwhile, the Web has created a forum for annotation and commentary that allows more complicated shows to prosper, thanks to the fan sites where each episode of shows like "Lost" or "Alias" is dissected with an intensity usually reserved for Talmud scholars. Finally, interactive games have trained a new generation of media consumers to probe complex environments and to think on their feet, and that gamer audience has now come to expect the same challenges from their television shows. In the end, the Sleeper Curve tells us something about the human mind. It may be drawn toward the sensational where content is concerned—sex does sell, after all. But the mind also likes to be challenged; there's real pleasure to be found in solving puzzles, detecting patterns or unpacking a complex narrative system.

In pointing out some of the ways that popular culture has improved our minds, I am not arguing that parents should stop paying attention to the way their children amuse themselves. What I am arguing for is a change in the criteria we use to determine what really is cognitive junk food and what is genuinely nourishing. Instead of a show's violent or tawdry content, instead of wardrobe malfunctions or the F-word, the true test should be whether a given show engages or sedates the mind. Is it a single thread strung together with predictable punch lines every 30 seconds? Or does it map a complex social network? Is your on-screen character running around shooting everything in sight, or is she trying to solve problems and manage resources? If your kids want to watch reality TV, encourage them to watch "Survivor" over "Fear Factor." If they want to watch a mystery show, encourage "24" over "Law and Order." If they want to play a violent game, encourage Grand Theft Auto over Quake. Indeed, it might be just as helpful to have a rating system that used mental labor and not obscenity and violence as its classification scheme for the world of mass culture.

Kids and grown-ups each can learn from their increasingly shared obsessions. Too often we imagine the blurring of kid and grown-up cultures as a series of violations: the 9-year-olds who have to have nipple broaches explained to them thanks to Janet Jackson; the middle-aged guy who can't wait to get home to his Xbox. But this demographic blur has a commendable side that we don't acknowledge enough. The kids are forced to think like grown-ups: analyzing complex social networks, managing resources, tracking subtle narrative intertwinings, recognizing long-term patterns. The grown-ups, in turn, get to learn from the kids: decoding each new technological wave, parsing the interfaces and discovering the intellectual rewards of play. Parents should see this as an opportunity, not a crisis. Smart culture is no longer something you force your kids to ingest, like green vegetables. It's something you share.

For Group Discussion

In a small group, have one of the group members read aloud the last paragraph of the article, in which Johnson discusses how parents and children can benefit from "smart culture" on TV. Make a list of the benefits for kids and the benefits for parents. Then discuss whether you think each of the benefits can be realistically achieved by watching "smart TV." Draw on your own experiences and your own knowledge of TV programs in order to decide whether Johnson's argument is reasonable or whether he's overstating the positives of watching TV.

Writing Suggestion

Johnson provides some visual evidence to support his assertion that TV shows have become increasingly complex. The three graphs included in the article show the number of plot threads in single episodes of "Starsky and Hutch," "Hill Street Blues," and "The Sopranos." A quick visual comparison of these graphs does indeed suggest that "The Sopranos" has more plot threads and more interweaving of these threads than the two earlier shows. Your assignment is to create a similar chart for a current TV show of your choice. Choose a show to watch, and as you're watching keep note of each time a new plot thread occurs or there's a reference to another thread. After the show is over, plot these elements on a simple chart in which the vertical axis represents each plot thread and the horizontal axis represents time. To make the task easier, label each plot thread on the vertical axis (something Johnson doesn't do). After you've finished the chart, write a paragraph in which you draw conclusions about the relative complexity of the show as compared to the three examples Johnson offers.

Men, Masculinities, and the Media

Jackson Katz

Jackson Katz is an educator, filmmaker, author, lecturer, and social theorist. He has a reputation as one of the country's leading anti-sexist male activists. In 1993, he co-founded the "Mentors in Violence Prevention (MVP)" program for The Center for the Study of Sport in Society at Northeastern University. The program has enlisted the help of collegiate and professional athletes to bring awareness to and to fight against male violence against women.

MVP has provided training for players and other personnel to teams in the NFL and Major League Baseball, as well as NASCAR. Katz's organization, MVP Strategies, has also provided gender violence prevention training to colleges, law enforcement agencies, community organizations and large corporations throughout the United States. The U.S. military has also utilized the training at its bases throughout the world and at its service academies.

Katz has also made documentaries, such as "Wrestling with Manhood," and written books, such as The Macho Paradox: Why Some Men Hurt Women and How All Men Can Help, *in his campaign to eliminate violence against women.*

"Men, Masculinities, and Media: Some Introductory Notes" addresses the complexities of male identity and its social construct—or how it is defined by the media. Is society's notion of masculinity as false as that it has perpetuated for femininity?

The climactic scene in The Wizard of Oz where Toto pulls back the curtain to reveal a nervous, tragic man pretending to be the Great and Powerful Oz represents more than just a classic moment in American cinematic history. It is also a powerful metaphor for looking at masculinity in a new way: not as a fixed, inevitable, natural state of being, but rather as a projection, a performance, a mask that men often wear to shield our vulnerability and hide our humanity.

In fact, the poses we strike and the images we create can tell us a great deal about what's going on in individual men's lives, and in our culture as a whole. That's why it is important for us to pull back the curtain and take a sober look—both at the images themselves and what's behind them.

These images tell a story—actually part of a story—about what's been happening with American men over the past generation. The last quarter of the 20th century has been marked by rapid and seismic changes in gender and sexual relations. In the brave new world in which we live, at the dawn of the 21st century, these changes have created new life experiences and identities for whole generations of women and men. It has been well-documented that the enormous baby boom generation catalyzed the modern multicultural women's movement, which is one of the key transformative social movements in the history of the human species.

Young people in the U.S. who came of age in the 1970s, 80s, and 90s, including the younger boomers, Generation X, and the so-called millenium generation, are the first generations to have grown up with this movement, not simply to have reacted to it, but literally to have grown up with it. Consequently, many young men of all races and ethnicities have embraced new notions of sexual equality, and are pioneering new ways of being in egalitarian relationships with women, as friends, lovers and husbands, classmates, colleagues, and fellow workers.

Not surprisingly, however, some men have reacted very poorly to these changes. It's not just in extreme movements in foreign cultures—like the Taliban in Afghanistan—where we can see male backlash played out. Many U.S. men, of varying class and racial backgrounds, have been decentered and threatened by women's increased assertions of strength, integrity, and social and economic power. One manifestation of the backlash is the pandemic rates of violence perpetrated by men and boys against women and girls, rates that have persisted despite decades of feminist antiviolence activism.

Through all of this momentous social change, a proliferation of mass media images has helped structure the way we think and react to the shifting gender terrain. The post-sixties generations are immersed in a world of media imagery whose scope and variety is, to say the least, historically unprecedented. The bottom line: if you want to understand what's going on with contemporary American masculinities, you have to look at what's going on in the media.

Over the past few decades, cultural theorists such as Raymond Williams (Williams, 1981) have argued that while it's people who produce the images that bombard us daily on tv, on billboards, in video games and in film, it is equally true to stay that this virtual landscape of images, in some sense, produces us. This means that were not just consumers of these images; we don't simply make our way through the thousands of images we see daily and pick and choose what we like and don't like. These images have a profound impact on who we are, and on our tastes, attitudes, and the kinds of choices we make.

Feminists who have analyzed media content to date have primarily focused on images of women, and what we can learn from them about women's lives. This is crucial and important work. But until recently there has been relatively little attention paid to images of men.

Consider the pioneering feminist media literacy work of Jean Kilbourne (Kilbourne, 1979), or the work of Naomi Wolf (Wolf, 1991) on western constructions of female beauty. As these and other feminist theorists and activists have long maintained, images of women's bodies as represented in the mainstream media are thinner, more waifish, and younger than women's bodies in the real world. Showing women this way is a means of symbolically taking power away from them, because thin, waifish women literally take up less space in the world, and hence are less threatening. These images, feminists remind us, are flooding the visual landscape at a time when women are challenging traditional male power on many different fronts.

Only in the past decade, as queer theorists and profeminist men's studies scholars have taken up the subject, has there been any significant attention paid to how men's bodies are represented and what that suggests about recent developments in men's lives. It is axiomatic that for every story about women's lives, there is a corresponding story about men's. For example, while image of women have been thinner and more waifish, images of men have gotten bigger, stronger, more muscular, and more violent. What accounts for this?

Young men for the past several decades have been challenged by women in areas that our fathers and grandfathers never were—in education, the workplace, business, the professions. But one area where men as a group continue to assume they have a significant advantage over women as a group is in the area of physical size and strength. As a result, physical size and strength for many men have become increasingly important to proving manhood. This is borne out by a review of changes over the past generation in the body morphology of male action film stars, the musculature of the dolls that young boys play with, as well as the exaggerated strutting and posing of many rock and rap performers.

Tough guy posing, even though it's often just an act, also has the effect of keeping men in line. Fed by a constant stream of images informed by the Marlboro Man ethos of the "real man" as a stoic rugged individualist, millions of boys and men learn early on that acting like a man means you don't complain, you don't admit weakness, you don't ever let others see the anxious man behind the curtain. This sort of conditioning starts very young, as does the pressure on boys and young men to compete—in school, in sports, in their social milieu—to live up to their fathers' visions of them as manly men.

But the pretense of omnipotence and invulnerability that is implied by ubiquitous images of physically powerful males is not just emotionally stultifying. It also gets a lot of men—and boys—killed. Richard Majors and Janet Billson have examined one angle of this phenomenon with their concept of "cool pose" (Majors, 1992). The cool pose is a style affected by poor urban Black males who have few resources (middle-class income or the expectation of one, education, workplace authority, social status) to earn respect as men beyond their bodies, and their ability to strike a pose of "cool," "badness," or violence.

But it's not just poor Black males and other men of color who fall into a hypermasculine posture to compensate for their disadvantages in other areas of life. Poor and working-class white men are also denied opportunities available to more privileged middle-class males. White suburban, middle-class males are the leading purchasers of rap music, including misogynous gangsta rap; these young men take poses that grow out of mean city street culture and adopt them to their lives in relatively (at least superficially) nonviolent suburban communities.

Over the past 10 or 15 years, there has been an outpouring of scholarship, books, articles, and discussion about masculinities, the gendered nature of men's lives, and how men have and have not adjusted to the changes catalyzed by feminism. This work has accelerated the long-term feminist project of shining the spotlight on the intimate workings of the dominant group, men. The purpose is not to push women aside and put men back on center stage, but to understand the ways that male dominance functions in the hope that this understanding can hasten the process of breaking down sexual inequality and improving the lives of women and men.

Furthering our understanding of the ways that media imagery helps shape the construction of masculinities is a critical part of this effort. The more we can, like Toto, deflate the power of the unrealistic images that dominate our visual and psychic landscapes, the better we'll be able to face honestly the ongoing challenges of our time.

Endnotes

1. As the sociologist Bob Connell (1997) and others have argued, "masculinity" as a singular construct does not account for the differences in power among groups of men (e.g. men of different classes, races, and sexual orientations). For the purpose of

this essay I use "masculinity" to refer to individual men's sense of their own gender, and "masculinities" to refer to structures in the larger gender order.

2. One of the first educational videos to examine images of masculinity was State Roles and Tight Buns: Images of Men in Advertising (1984), by the OASIS collective in Boston. MA.

References

Connel, R.W. (1987) Gender and Power. Stanford, CA: Stanford University Press.

Kilbourne. J. (1979) Killing Us Softly: Advertising's Image of Women. Cambridge. MA: Cambridge Documentary Film.

Majors, R. and Billson. J. (1992) Cool Pose: The dilemmas of black manhood in America. New York: Lexington Books.

Williams. R. (1981) The Sociology of Culture, Chicago: University of Chicago Press.

Wolf. N. (1991) The Beauty Myth: How images of beauty are used against women. New York: William and Morrow.

Jackson katz is the founder and director of MVP Strategies, an organization that provides gender violence prevention training to colleges, high schools, professional and college sports teams, community groups, corporations, and the U.S. military. He is a regular contributor to the Centers' annual Gender Equity Conference..

Thanks to Jeremy Earp for input and assistance in this essay.

Letter from Birmingham Jail

Martin Luther King, Jr.

Martin Luther King, Jr. (1929–1968) was born in Atlanta, Georgia. The son and grandson of Baptist ministers, he attended Morehouse College, Crozer Theological Seminary, and Boston University where he received a Ph.D. (1955) and met his future wife, Coretta Scott. King's active involvement in the civil rights movement began in 1955, when he led a boycott of segregated buses in Montgomery, Alabama. Throughout his career as a civil rights leader, King organized boycotts, sit-ins, mass demonstrations, and other nonviolent protest activities. As a result of these activities, King was arrested, jailed, stoned, stabbed, and beaten; his house was bombed; and he was placed under secret surveillance by then FBI director J. Edgar Hoover. Despite these hardships, King's leadership was continually bolstered by his belief in nonviolence, and, in 1964, he was awarded the Nobel Peace Prize. On April 4, 1968, King, while supporting striking city workers in Memphis, Tennessee, was shot and killed. In the following letter, written on April 16, 1963 (four months before he delivered his "I Have a Dream" speech and five years before his assassination), King responds to eight clergymen from Alabama who wanted civil rights activists to give up public demonstrations, which the clergymen claimed were inciting violent responses, and to take their cause instead to the courts and the negotiation table. The clergymen's public statement is printed below, followed by King's response (printed here as it appeared originally).

Public Statement by Eight Alabama Clergymen

(April 12, 1963)

We the undersigned clergymen are among those who, in January, issued "An Appeal for Law and Order and Common Sense," in dealing with racial problems in Alabama. We expressed understanding that honest convictions in racial matters could properly be pursued in the courts, but urged that decisions of those courts should in the meantime be peacefully obeyed.

Since that time there has been some evidence of increased forbearance and a willingness to face facts. Responsible citizens have undertaken to work on various problems which cause racial friction and unrest. In Birmingham, recent public events have given indication that we all have opportunity for a new constructive and realistic approach to racial problems.

However, we are now confronted by a series of demonstrations by some of our Negro citizens, directed and led in part by outsiders. We recognize the natural impatience of people who feel that their hopes are slow in being realized. But we are convinced that these demonstrations are unwise and untimely.

We agree rather with certain local Negro leadership which has called for honest and open negotiation of racial issues in our area. And we believe this kind of facing of issues can best be accomplished by citizens of our own metropolitan area, white and Negro, meeting with their knowledge and experience of the local situation. All of us need to face that responsibility and find proper channels for its accomplishment.

Just as we formerly pointed out that "hatred and violence have no sanction in our religious and political traditions," we also point out that such actions as incite to hatred and violence, however technically peaceful those actions may be, have not contributed to the resolution of our local problems. We do not believe that these days of new hope are days when extreme measures are justified in Birmingham.

We commend the community as a whole, and the local news media and law enforcement officials in particular, on the calm manner in which these demonstrations have been handled. We urge the public to continue to show restraint should the demonstrations continue, and the law enforcement officials to remain calm and continue to protect our city from violence.

We further strongly urge our own Negro community to withdraw support from these demonstrations, and to unite locally in working peacefully for a better Birmingham. When rights are consistently denied, a cause should be pressed in the courts and in negotiations among local leaders, and not in the streets. We appeal to both our white and Negro citizenry to observe the principles of law and order and common sense.

Signed by:

C. C. J. CARPENTER, D.D., LL.D., *Bishop of Alabama*

JOSEPH A. DURICK, D.D., *Auxiliary Bishop, Diocese of Mobile, Birmingham*

RABBI MILTON L. GRAFMAN, *Temple Eman-El, Birmingham, Alabama*

BISHOP PAUL HARDIN, *Bishop of the Alabama-West Florida Conference of the Methodist Church*

BISHOP NOLAN B. HARMON, *Bishop of the North Alabama Conference of the Methodist Church*

GEORGE M. MURRAY, D.D., LL.D., *Bishop Coadjutor, Episcopal Diocese of Alabama*

EDWARD V. RAMAGE, *Moderator, Synod of the Alabama Presbyterian Church in the United States*

EARL STALLINGS, *Pastor, First Baptist Church, Birmingham, Alabama*

Letter from Birmingham Jail

MARTIN LUTHER KING, JR.
Birmingham City Jail
April 16, 1963

Bishop C. C. J. CARPENTER
Bishop JOSEPH A. DURICK
Rabbi MILTON L. GRAFMAN
Bishop PAUL HARDIN
Bishop NOLAN B. HARMON
The Rev. GEORGE M. MURRAY
The Rev. EDWARD V. RAMAGE
The Rev. EARL STALLINGS

My Dear Fellow Clergymen:[1]

While confined here in the Birmingham city jail, I came across your recent statement calling my present activities "unwise and untimely." Seldom do I pause to answer criticism of my work and ideas. If I sought to answer all the criticisms that cross my desk, my secretaries would have little time for anything other than such correspondence in the course of the day, and I would have no time for constructive work. But since I feel that you are men of genuine good will and that your criticisms are sincerely set forth, I want to try to answer your statement in what I hope will be patient and reasonable terms.

I think I should indicate why I am here in Birmingham, since you have been influenced by the view which argues against "outsiders coming in." I have the honor of serving as president of the Southern Christian Leadership Conference, an organization operating in every southern state, with headquarters in Atlanta, Georgia. We have some eighty-five affiliated organizations across the South, and one of them is the Alabama Christian Movement for Human Rights. Frequently we share staff, educational, and financial resources with our affiliates. Several months ago the affiliate here in Birmingham asked us to be on call to engage in a nonviolent direct-action program if such were deemed necessary. We readily consented, and when the hour came we lived up to our promise. So I, along with several members of my staff, am here because I was invited here. I am here because I have organizational ties here. . . .

But more basically, I am in Birmingham because injustice is here. Just as the prophets of the eighth century B.C. left their villages and carried their "thus saith the Lord" far beyond the boundaries of their home towns, and just as the Apostle Paul left his village of Tarsus and carried the gospel of Jesus Christ to the far corners of the Greco-Roman world, so am I compelled to carry the gospel of freedom beyond my own home town: Like Paul, I must constantly respond to the Macedonian call for aid.

Moreover, I am cognizant of the interrelatedness of all communities and states. I cannot sit idly by in Atlanta and not be concerned about what happens in Birmingham. Injustice anywhere is a threat to justice everywhere. We are caught in an inescapable network of mutuality, tied in a single garment of destiny. Whatever affects one directly, affects all indirectly. Never again can we afford to live with the narrow, provincial "outside agitator" idea. Anyone who lives inside the United States can never be considered an outsider anywhere within its bounds.

You deplore the demonstrations taking place in Birmingham. But your statement, I am sorry to say, fails to express a similar concern for the conditions that brought about the demonstrations. I am sure that none of you would want to rest content with the superficial kind of social analysis that deals merely with effects and does not grapple with underlying causes. It is unfortunate that demonstrations are taking place in Birmingham, but it is even more unfortunate that the city's white power structure left the Negro community with no alternative.

In any nonviolent campaign there are four basic steps: collection of the facts to determine whether injustices exist; negotiation; self-purification; and direct action. We have gone through all these steps in Birmingham. There can be no gainsaying the fact that racial injustice engulfs this community. Birmingham is probably the most thoroughly segregated city in the United States. Its ugly record of brutality is widely known. Negroes have experienced grossly unjust treatment in the courts. There have been more unsolved bombings of Negro homes and churches in Birmingham than in any other city in the nation. These are the hard, brutal facts of the case. On the basis of these conditions, Negro leaders sought to negotiate with the city fathers. But the latter consistently refused to engage in good-faith negotiation.

Then, last September, came the opportunity to talk with leaders of Birmingham's economic community. In the course of the negotiations, certain promises were made by the merchants—for example, to remove the stores' humiliating racial signs. On the basis of these promises, the Reverend Fred Shuttlesworth and the leaders of the Alabama Christian Movement for Human Rights agreed to a moratorium on all demonstrations. As the weeks and months went by, we realized that we were the victims of a broken promise. A few signs, briefly removed, returned; the others remained.

As in so many past experiences, our hopes had been blasted, and the shadow of deep disappointment settled upon us. We had no alternative except to prepare for direct action, whereby we would present our very bodies as a means of laying our case before the conscience of the local and the national community. Mindful of the difficulties involved, we decided to undertake a process of self-purification. We began a series of workshops on nonviolence, and we repeatedly asked ourselves: "Are you able to accept blows without retaliating?" "Are you able to endure the ordeal of jail?" We decided to schedule our direct-action program for the Easter season, realizing that except for Christmas, this is the main shopping period of the year. Knowing that a strong economic-withdrawal program would be the by-product of direct action, we felt that this would be the best time to bring pressure to bear on the merchants for the needed change.

Then it occurred to us that Birmingham's mayoral election was coming up in March, and we speedily decided to postpone action until after election day. When we discovered that the Commissioner of Public Safety, Eugene "Bull" Connor, had piled up enough votes to be in the run-off, we decided again to postpone action until the day after the run-off so that the demonstrations could not be used to cloud the issues. Like many others, we waited to see Mr. Connor defeated, and to this end we endured postponement after postponement. Having aided in this community need, we felt that our direct-action program could be delayed no longer.

You may well ask: "Why direct action? Why sit-ins, marches and so forth? Isn't negotiation a better path?" You are quite right in calling for negotiation. Indeed, this is the very purpose of direct action. Nonviolent direct action seeks to create such a crisis and foster such a tension that a community which has constantly refused to negotiate is forced to confront the issue. It seeks so to dramatize the issue that it can no longer be ignored. My citing the creation of tension as part of the work of the nonviolent-resister may sound rather shocking. But I must confess that I am not afraid of the word "tension." I have earnestly opposed violent tension, but there is a type of constructive, nonviolent tension which is necessary for growth. Just as Socrates felt that it was necessary to create a tension in the mind so that individuals could rise from the bondage of myths and half-truths to the unfettered realm of creative analysis and objective appraisal, so must we see the need for nonviolent gadflies to create the kind of tension in society that will help men rise from the dark depths of prejudice and racism to the majestic heights of understanding and brotherhood.

The purpose of our direct-action program is to create a situation so crisis-packed that it will inevitably open the door to negotiation. I therefore concur with you in your call for negotiation. Too long has our beloved Southland been bogged down in a tragic effort to live in monologue rather than dialogue.

One of the basic points in your statement is that the action that I and my associates have taken in Birmingham is untimely. Some have asked: "Why didn't you give the new city administration time to act?" The only answer that I can give to this query is that the new Birmingham administration must be prodded about as much as the outgoing one, before it will act. We are sadly mistaken if we feel that the election of Albert Boutwell as mayor will bring the millennium to Birmingham. While Mr. Boutwell is a much more gentle person than Mr. Connor, they are both segregationists, dedicated to maintenance of the status quo. I have hope that Mr. Boutwell will be reasonable enough to see the futility of massive resistance to desegregation. But he will not see this without pressure from devotees of civil rights. My friends, I must say to you that we have not made a single gain in civil rights without determined legal and nonviolent pressure. Lamentably, it is an historical fact that privileged groups seldom give up their privileges voluntarily. Individuals may see the moral light and voluntarily give up their unjust posture; but, as Reinhold Niebuhr has reminded us, groups tend to be more immoral than individuals.

We know through painful experience that freedom is never voluntarily given by the oppressor; it must be demanded by the oppressed. Frankly, I have yet to engage in a direct-action campaign that was "well timed" in the view of those who have not suffered unduly from the disease of segregation. For years now I have heard the word "Wait!" It rings in the ear of every Negro with piercing familiarity. This "Wait" has almost always meant "Never." We must come to see, with one of our distinguished jurists, that "justice too long delayed is justice denied."

We have waited for more than 340 years for our constitutional and God-given rights. The nations of Asia and Africa are moving with jetlike speed toward gaining political independence, but we still creep at horse-and-buggy pace toward gaining a cup of coffee at a lunch counter. Perhaps it is easy for those who have never felt the stinging darts of segregation to say, "Wait." But when you have seen vicious mobs lynch your mothers and fathers at will and drown your sisters and brothers at whim; when you have seen hate-filled policemen curse, kick and even kill your black brothers and sisters; when you see the vast majority of your twenty million Negro brothers smothering in an airtight cage of poverty in the midst of an affluent society; when you suddenly find your tongue twisted and your speech stammering as you seek to explain to your six-year-old daughter why she can't go to the public amusement park that has just been advertised on television, and see tears welling up in her eyes when she is told that Funtown is closed to colored children, and see ominous clouds of inferiority beginning to form in her little mental sky, and see her beginning to distort her personality by developing an unconscious bitterness toward white people; when you have to concoct an answer for a five-year-old son who is asking: "Daddy, why do white people treat colored people so mean?"; when you take a cross-country drive and find it necessary to sleep night after night in the uncomfortable corners of your automobile because no motel will accept you; when you are humiliated day in and day out by nagging signs reading "white" and "colored"; when your first name becomes "nigger," your middle name becomes "boy" (however old you are) and your last name becomes "John," and your wife and mother are never given the respected title

"Mrs."; when you are harried by day and haunted by night by the fact that you are a Negro, living constantly at tiptoe stance, never quite knowing what to expect next, and are plagued with inner fears and outer resentments; when you are forever fighting a degenerating sense of "nobodiness"—you will understand why we find it difficult to wait. There comes a time when the cup of endurance runs over, and men are no longer willing to be plunged into the abyss of despair. I hope, sirs, you can understand our legitimate and unavoidable impatience.

You express a great deal of anxiety over our willingness to break laws. This is certainly a legitimate concern. Since we so diligently urge people to obey the Supreme Court's decision of 1954 outlawing segregation in the public schools, at first glance it may seem rather paradoxical for us consciously to break laws. One may well ask: "How can you advocate breaking some laws and obeying others?" The answer lies in the fact that there are two types of laws: just and unjust. I would be the first to advocate obeying just laws. One has not only a legal but a moral responsibility to obey just laws. Conversely, one has a moral responsibility to disobey unjust laws. I would agree with St. Augustine that "an unjust law is no law at all."

Now, what is the difference between the two? How does one determine whether a law is just or unjust? A just law is a man-made code that squares with the moral law or the law of God. An unjust law is a code that is out of harmony with the moral law. To put it in the terms of St. Thomas Aquinas: An unjust law is a human law that is not rooted in eternal law and natural law. Any law that uplifts human personality is just. Any law that degrades human personality is unjust. All segregation statutes are unjust because segregation distorts the soul and damages the personality. It gives the segregator a false sense of superiority and the segregated a false sense of inferiority. Segregation, to use the terminology of the Jewish philosopher Martin Buber, substitutes an "I-it" relationship for an "I-thou" relationship and ends up relegating persons to the status of things. Hence segregation is not only politically, economically and sociologically unsound, it is morally wrong and sinful. Paul Tillich has said that sin is separation. Is not segregation an existential expression of man's tragic separation, his awful estrangement, his terrible sinfulness? Thus it is that I can urge men to obey the 1954 decision of the Supreme Court, for it is morally right; and I can urge them to disobey segregation ordinances, for they are morally wrong.

Let us consider a more concrete example of just and unjust laws. An unjust law is a code that a numerical or power majority group compels a minority group to obey but does not make binding on itself. This is *difference* made legal. By the same token, a just law is a code that a majority compels a minority to follow and that it is willing to follow itself. This is *sameness* made legal.

Let me give another explanation. A law is unjust if it is inflicted on a minority that, as a result of being denied the right to vote, had no part in enacting or devising the law. Who can say that the legislature of Alabama which set up that state's segregation laws was democratically elected? Throughout Alabama all sorts of devious methods are used to prevent Negroes from becoming registered voters, and there are some counties in which, even though Negroes constitute a majority of the population, not a single Negro is registered. Can any law enacted under such circumstances be considered democratically structured?

Sometimes a law is just on its face and unjust in its application. For instance, I have been arrested on a charge of parading without a permit. Now, there is nothing wrong in having an ordinance which requires a permit for a parade. But such an ordinance becomes unjust when it is used to maintain segregation and to deny citizens the First-Amendment privilege of peaceful assembly and protest.

I hope you are able to see the distinction I am trying to point out. In no sense do I advocate evading or defying the law, as would the rabid segregationist. That would lead to anarchy. One who breaks an unjust law must do so openly, lovingly, and with a willingness to accept the penalty. I submit that an individual who breaks a law that conscience tells him is unjust, and who willingly accepts the penalty of imprisonment in order to arouse the conscience of the community over its injustice, is in reality expressing the highest respect for law.

Of course, there is nothing new about this kind of civil disobedience. It was evidenced sublimely in the refusal of Shadrach, Meshach and Abednego to obey the laws of Nebuchadnezzar, on the ground that a higher moral law was at stake. It was practiced superbly by the Early Christians, who were willing to face hungry lions and the excruciating pain of chopping blocks rather than submit to certain unjust laws of the Roman Empire. To a degree, academic freedom is a reality today because Socrates practiced civil disobedience. In our own nation, the Boston Tea Party represented a massive act of civil disobedience.

We should never forget that everything Adolf Hitler did in Germany was "legal" and everything the Hungarian freedom fighters did in Hungary was "illegal." It was "illegal" to aid and comfort a Jew in Hitler's Germany. Even so, I am sure that, had I lived in Germany at the time, I would have aided and comforted my Jewish brothers. If today I lived in a Communist country where certain principles dear to the Christian faith are suppressed, I would openly advocate disobeying that country's antireligious laws.

I must make two honest confessions to you, my Christian and Jewish brothers. First, I must confess that over the past few years I have been gravely disappointed with the white moderate. I have almost reached the regrettable conclusion that the Negro's great stumbling block in his stride toward freedom is not the White Citizen's Counciler or the Ku Klux Klanner, but the white moderate, who is more devoted to "order" than to justice; who prefers a negative peace which is the absence of tension to a positive peace which is the presence of justice; who constantly says: "I agree with you in the goal you seek, but I cannot agree with your methods of direct action"; who paternalistically believes he can set the timetable for another man's freedom; who lives by a mythical concept of time and who constantly advises the Negro to wait for a "more convenient season." Shallow understanding from people of good will is more frustrating than absolute misunderstanding from people of ill will. Lukewarm acceptance is much more bewildering than outright rejection.

I had hoped that the white moderate would understand that law and order exist for the purpose of establishing justice and that when they fail in this purpose they become the dangerously structured dams that block the flow of social progress. I had hoped that the white moderate would understand that the present tension in the South is a necessary phase of the transition from an obnoxious negative peace, in which the Negro passively accepted his unjust plight, to a substantive and positive peace, in which all men will respect the dignity and worth of human personality. Actually, we who engage in nonviolent direct action are not the creators of tension. We merely bring to the surface the hidden tension that is already alive. We bring it out in the open, where it can be seen and dealt with. Like a boil that can never be cured so long as it is covered up but must be opened with all its ugliness to the natural medicines of air and light, injustice must be exposed, with all the tension its exposure creates, to the light of human conscience and the air of national opinion before it can be cured.

In your statement you assert that our actions, even though peaceful, must be condemned because they precipitate violence. But is this a logical assertion? Isn't this like condemning a robbed man because his possession of money precipitated the evil act of robbery? Isn't this like condemning Socrates because his unswerving commitment to truth and his philosophical inquiries precipitated the act by the misguided populace in which they made him drink hemlock? Isn't this like condemning Jesus because his unique God-consciousness and never-ceasing devotion to God's will precipitated the evil act of crucifixion? We must come to see that, as the federal courts have consistently affirmed, it is wrong to urge an individual to cease his efforts to gain his basic constitutional rights because the quest may precipitate violence. Society must protect the robbed and punish the robber.

I had also hoped that the white moderate would reject the myth concerning time in relation to the struggle for freedom. I have just received a letter from a white brother in Texas. He writes: "All Christians know that the colored people will receive equal rights eventually, but it is possible that you are in too great a religious hurry. It has taken Christianity almost two thousand years to accomplish what it has. The teachings of Christ take time to come to earth." Such an attitude stems from a tragic misconception of time, from the strangely irrational notion that there is something in the very flow of time that will inevitably cure all ills. Actually, time itself is neutral; it can be used either destructively or constructively. More and more I feel that the people of ill will have used time much more effectively than have the people of good will. We will have to repent in this generation not merely for the hateful words and actions of the bad people but for the appalling silence of the good people. Human progress never rolls in on wheels of inevitability; it comes through the tireless efforts of men willing to be coworkers with God, and without this hard work, time itself becomes an ally of the forces of social stagnation. We must use time creatively, in the knowledge that the time is always ripe to do right. Now is the time to make real the promise of democracy and transform our pending national elegy into a creative psalm of brotherhood. Now is the time to lift our national policy from the quicksand of racial injustice to the solid rock of human dignity.

You speak of our activity in Birmingham as extreme. At first I was rather disappointed that fellow clergymen would see my nonviolent efforts as those of an extremist. I began thinking about the fact that I stand in the middle of two opposing forces in the Negro community. One is a force of complacency, made up in part of Negroes who, as a result of long years of oppression, are so drained of self-respect and a sense of "somebodiness" that they have adjusted to segregation; and in part of a few middle-class Negroes who, because of a degree of academic and economic security and because in some ways they profit by segregation, have become insensitive to the problems of the masses. The other force is one of bitterness and hatred, and it comes perilously close to advocating violence. It is expressed in the various black nationalist groups that are springing up across the nation, the largest and best-known being Elijah Muhammad's Muslim movement. Nourished by the Negro's frustration over the continued existence of racial discrimination, this movement is made up of people who have lost faith in America, who have absolutely repudiated Christianity, and who have concluded that the white man is an incorrigible "devil."

I have tried to stand between these two forces, saying that we need emulate neither the "do-nothingism" of the complacent nor the hatred and despair of the black nationalist. For there is the more excellent way of love and nonviolent protest. I am grateful to God that, through the influence of the Negro church, the way of nonviolence became an integral part of our struggle.

If this philosophy had not emerged, by now many streets of the South would, I am convinced, be flowing with blood. And I am further convinced that if our white brothers dismiss as "rabble-rousers" and "outside agitators" those of us who employ nonviolent direct action, and if they refuse to support our nonviolent efforts, millions of Negroes will, out of frustration and despair, seek solace and security in black-nationalist ideologies—a development that would inevitably lead to a frightening racial nightmare.

Oppressed people cannot remain oppressed forever. The yearning for freedom eventually manifests itself, and that is what has happened to the American Negro. Something within has reminded him of his birthright of freedom, and something without has reminded him that it can be gained. Consciously or unconsciously, he has been caught up by the *Zeitgeist*,[2] and with his black brothers of Africa and his brown and yellow brothers of Asia, South America and the Caribbean, the United States Negro is moving with a sense of great urgency toward the promised land of racial justice. If one recognizes this vital urge that has engulfed the Negro community, one should readily understand why public demonstrations are taking place. The Negro has many pent-up resentments and latent frustrations, and he must release them. So let him march; let him make prayer pilgrimages to the city hall; let him go on freedom rides—and try to understand why he must do so. If his repressed emotions are not released in nonviolent ways, they will seek expression through violence; this is not a threat but a fact of history. So I have not said to my people: "Get rid of your discontent." Rather, I have tried to say that this normal and healthy discontent can be channeled into the creative outlet of nonviolent direct action. And now this approach is being termed extremist.

But though I was initially disappointed at being categorized as an extremist, as I continued to think about the matter I gradually gained a measure of satisfaction from the label. Was not Jesus an extremist for love: "Love your enemies, bless them that curse you, do good to them that hate you, and pray for them which despitefully use you, and persecute you." Was not Amos an extremist for justice: "Let justice roll down like waters and righteousness like an ever-flowing stream." Was not Paul an extremist for the Christian gospel: "I bear in my body the marks of the Lord Jesus." Was not Martin Luther an extremist: "Here I stand; I cannot do otherwise, so help me God." And John Bunyan: "I will stay in jail to the end of my days before I make a butchery of my conscience." And Abraham Lincoln: "This nation cannot survive half slave and half free." And Thomas Jefferson: "We hold these truths to be self-evident, that all men are created equal. . . ." So the question is not whether we will be extremists, but what kind of extremists we will be. Will we be extremists for hate or for love? Will we be extremists for the preservation of injustice or for the extension of justice? In that dramatic scene on Calvary's hill three men were crucified. We must never forget that all three were crucified for the same crime—the crime of extremism. Two were extremists for immorality, and thus fell below their environment. The other, Jesus Christ, was

an extremist for love, truth and goodness, and thereby rose above his environment. Perhaps the South, the nation and the world are in dire need of creative
extremists.

I had hoped that the white moderate would see this need. Perhaps I was
too optimistic; perhaps I expected too much. I suppose I should have realized
that few members of the oppressor race can understand the deep groans and
passionate yearnings of the oppressed race, and still fewer have the vision to
see that injustice must be rooted out by strong, persistent and determined
action. I am thankful, however, that some of our white brothers in the South
have grasped the meaning of this social revolution and committed themselves
to it. They are still all too few in quantity, but they are big in quality. Some—
such as Ralph McGill, Lillian Smith, Harry Golden, James McBride Dabbs,
Ann Braden and Sarah Patton Boyle—have written about our struggle in eloquent and prophetic terms. Others have marched with us down nameless
streets of the South. They have languished in filthy, roach-infested jails, suffering the abuse and brutality of policemen who view them as "dirty nigger-
lovers." Unlike so many of their moderate brothers and sisters, they have
recognized the urgency of the moment and sensed the need for powerful
"action" antidotes to combat the disease of segregation.

Let me take note of my other major disappointment. I have been so
greatly disappointed with the white church and its leadership. Of course, there
are some notable exceptions. I am not unmindful of the fact that each of you
has taken some significant stands on this issue. I commend you, Reverend
Stallings, for your Christian stand on this past Sunday, in welcoming Negroes
to your worship service on a nonsegregated basis. I commend the Catholic
leaders of this state for integrating Spring Hill College several years ago.

But despite these notable exceptions, I must honestly reiterate that I have
been disappointed with the church. I do not say this as one of those negative
critics who can always find something wrong with the church. I say this as a
minister of the gospel, who loves the church; who was nurtured in its bosom;
who has been sustained by its spiritual blessings and who will remain true to
it as long as the cord of life shall lengthen.

When I was suddenly catapulted into the leadership of the bus protest
in Montgomery, Alabama, a few years ago, I felt we would be supported by
the white church. I felt that the white ministers, priests and rabbis of the
South would be among our strongest allies. Instead, some have been outright
opponents, refusing to understand the freedom movement and misrepre-
senting its leaders; all too many others have been more cautious than coura-
geous and have remained silent behind the anesthetizing security of
stained-glass windows.

In spite of my shattered dreams, I came to Birmingham with the hope that
the white religious leadership of this community would see the justice of our

cause and, with deep moral concern, would serve as the channel through which our just grievances could reach the power structure. I had hoped that each of you would understand. But again I have been disappointed.

I have heard numerous southern religious leaders admonish their worshipers to comply with a desegregation decision because it is the law, but I have longed to hear white ministers declare: "Follow this decree because integration is morally right and because the Negro is your brother." In the midst of blatant injustices inflicted upon the Negro, I have watched white churchmen stand on the sideline and mouth pious irrelevancies and sanctimonious trivialities. In the midst of a mighty struggle to rid our nation of racial and economic injustice, I have heard many ministers say: "Those are social issues, with which the gospel has no real concern." And I have watched many churches commit themselves to a completely otherworldly religion which makes a strange, un-Biblical distinction between body and soul, between the sacred and the secular.

I have traveled the length and breadth of Alabama, Mississippi and all the other southern states. On sweltering summer days and crisp autumn mornings I have looked at the South's beautiful churches with their lofty spires pointing heavenward. I have beheld the impressive outlines of her massive religious-education buildings. Over and over I have found myself asking: "What kind of people worship here? Who is their God?" Where were their voices when the lips of Governor Barnett dripped with words of interposition and nullification? Where were they when Governor Wallace gave a clarion call for defiance and hatred? Where were their voices of support when bruised and weary Negro men and women decided to rise from the dark dungeons of complacency to the bright hills of creative protest?

Yes, these questions are still in my mind. In deep disappointment I have wept over the laxity of the church. But be assured that my tears have been tears of love. There can be no deep disappointment where there is not deep love. Yes, I love the church. How could I do otherwise? I am in the rather unique position of being the son, the grandson and the great-grandson of preachers. Yes, I see the church as the body of Christ. But, oh! How we have blemished and scarred that body through social neglect and through fear of being nonconformists.

There was a time when the church was very powerful—in the time when the early Christians rejoiced at being deemed worthy to suffer for what they believed. In those days the church was not merely a thermometer that recorded the ideas and principles of popular opinion; it was a thermostat that transformed the mores of society. Whenever the early Christians entered a town, the people in power became disturbed and immediately sought to convict the Christians for being "disturbers of the peace" and "outside agitators." But the Christians pressed on, in the conviction that they were "a colony of heaven," called to obey God rather than man. Small in number, they were big in commitment. They were too God-intoxicated to be "astronomically intimidated." By their effort and example they brought an end to such ancient evils as infanticide and gladiatorial contests.

Things are different now. So often the contemporary church is a weak, ineffectual voice with an uncertain sound. So often it is an archdefender of the status quo. Far from being disturbed by the presence of the church, the power structure of the average community is consoled by the church's silent—and often even vocal—sanction of things as they are.

But the judgment of God is upon the church as never before. If today's church does not recapture the sacrificial spirit of the early church, it will lose its authenticity, forfeit the loyalty of millions, and be dismissed as an irrelevant social club with no meaning for the twentieth century. Every day I meet young people whose disappointment with the church has turned into outright disgust.

Perhaps I have once again been too optimistic. Is organized religion too inextricably bound to the status quo to save our nation and the world? Perhaps I must turn my faith to the inner spiritual church, the church within the church, as the true *ekklesia* and the hope of the world. But again I am thankful to God that some noble souls from the ranks of organized religion have broken loose from the paralyzing chains of conformity and joined us as active partners in the struggle for freedom. They have left their secure congregations and walked the streets of Albany, Georgia, with us. They have gone down the highways of the South on tortuous rides for freedom. Yes, they have gone to jail with us. Some have been dismissed from their churches, have lost the support of their bishops and fellow ministers. But they have acted in the faith that right defeated is stronger than evil triumphant. Their witness has been the spiritual salt that has preserved the true meaning of the gospel in these troubled times. They have carved a tunnel of hope through the dark mountain of disappointment.

I hope the church as a whole will meet the challenge of this decisive hour. But even if the church does not come to the aid of justice, I have no despair about the future. I have no fear about the outcome of our struggle in Birmingham, even if our motives are at present misunderstood. We will reach the goal of freedom in Birmingham and all over the nation, because the goal of America is freedom. Abused and scorned though we may be, our destiny is tied up with America's destiny. Before the pilgrims landed at Plymouth, we were here. Before the pen of Jefferson etched the majestic words of the Declaration of Independence across the pages of history, we were here. For more than two centuries our forebears labored in this country without wages; they made cotton king; they built the homes of their masters while suffering gross injustice and shameful humiliation—and yet out of a bottomless vitality they continued to thrive and develop. If the inexpressible cruelties of slavery could not stop us, the opposition we now face will surely fail. We will win our freedom because the sacred heritage of our nation and the eternal will of God are embodied in our echoing demands.

Before closing I feel impelled to mention one other point in your statement that has troubled me profoundly. You warmly commended the Birmingham police force for keeping "order" and "preventing violence." I doubt that you would have so warmly commended the police force if you had seen its dogs sinking their teeth into unarmed, nonviolent Negroes. I doubt that you would so quickly commend the policemen if you were to observe their ugly and inhumane treatment of Negroes here in the city jail; if you were to watch them push and curse old Negro women and young Negro girls; if you were to see them slap and kick old Negro men and young boys; if you were to observe them, as they did on two occasions, refuse to give us food because we wanted to sing our grace together. I cannot join you in your praise of the Birmingham police department.

It is true that the police have exercised a degree of discipline in handling the demonstrators. In this sense they have conducted themselves rather "nonviolently" in public. But for what purpose? To preserve the evil system of segregation. Over the past few years I have consistently preached that nonviolence demands that the means we use must be as pure as the ends we seek. I have tried to make clear that it is wrong to use immoral means to attain moral ends. But now I must affirm that it is just as wrong, or perhaps even more so, to use moral means to preserve immoral ends. Perhaps Mr. Connor and his policemen have been rather nonviolent in public, as was Chief Pritchett in Albany, Georgia, but they have used the moral means of nonviolence to maintain the immoral end of racial injustice. As T. S. Eliot has said: "The last temptation is the greatest treason: To do the right deed for the wrong reason."

I wish you had commended the Negro sit-inners and demonstrators of Birmingham for their sublime courage, their willingness to suffer and their amazing discipline in the midst of great provocation. One day the South will recognize its real heroes. They will be the James Merediths, with the noble sense of purpose that enables them to face jeering and hostile mobs, and with the agonizing loneliness that characterizes the life of the pioneer. They will be old, oppressed, battered Negro women, symbolized in a seventy-two-year-old woman in Montgomery, Alabama, who rose up with a sense of dignity and with her people decided not to ride segregated buses, and who responded with ungrammatical profundity to one who inquired about her weariness: "My feets is tired, but my soul is at rest." They will be the young high school and college students, the young ministers of the gospel and a host of their elders, courageously and nonviolently sitting in at lunch counters and willingly going to jail for conscience sake. One day the South will know that when these disinherited children of God sat down at lunch counters, they were in reality standing up for what is best in the American dream and for the most sacred values in our Judaeo-Christian heritage, thereby bringing our nation back to those great wells of democracy which were dug deep by the founding fathers in their formulation of the Constitution and the Declaration of Independence.

Never before have I written so long a letter. I'm afraid it is much too long to take your precious time. I can assure you that it would have been much shorter if I had been writing from a comfortable desk, but what else can one do when he is alone in a narrow jail cell, other than write long letters, think long thoughts and pray long prayers?

If I have said anything in this letter that overstates the truth and indicates an unreasonable impatience, I beg you to forgive me. If I have said anything that understates the truth and indicates my having a patience that allows me to settle for anything less than brotherhood, I beg God to forgive me.

I hope this letter finds you strong in the faith. I also hope that circumstances will soon make it possible for me to meet each of you, not as an integrationist or a civil-rights leader but as a fellow clergyman and a Christian brother. Let us all hope that the dark clouds of racial prejudice will soon pass away and the deep fog of misunderstanding will be lifted from our fear-drenched communities, and in some not too distant tomorrow the radiant stars of love and brotherhood will shine over our great nation with all their scintillating beauty.

—Yours for the cause of Peace and Brotherhood,

MARTIN LUTHER KING, JR.

Endnotes

1. This response to a published statement by eight fellow clergymen from Alabama . . . was composed under somewhat constricting circumstances. Begun on the margins of the newspaper in which the statement appeared while I was in jail, the letter was continued on scraps of writing paper supplied by a friendly Negro trusty, and concluded on a pad my attorneys were eventually permitted to leave me. Although the text remains in substance unaltered, I have indulged in the author's prerogative of polishing it for publication.

2. **Zeitgeist** spirit of the age. [Ed. note.]

Toolbox

Stephen King

Stephen King (1947—) was born in Maine where he continues to live, and which is also the setting for a majority of his stories and novels. In this sense, he may be considered an American regional writer. He is most recognized as a writer of horror fiction, a genre he is credited for helping to make more "mainstream" in the 1970s. At the time of the writing of this introduction, he has written fifty novels, numerous short stories, and five books of non-fiction. Though his books continue to enter publication at the top of the bestseller's list, the early work that established his reputation includes novels such as Carrie, The Shining, *and* The Stand, *to name a few.*

King is one of the most successful writers in the world, having sold more than 350 million copies of his books. He was at one time considered the most successful living writer in human history, kicking off the "mega" author phenomenon which characterized the latter third of the twentieth century and which continues into this one. Nearly all of his books have been adapted for film. One of his nicknames in the industry is "Bestsellersaurus Rex."

This success has not come without some criticism. Upon King's being awarded the "Distinguished Contribution" award by the National Book Foundation in 2003, literary critic and Yale professor, Harold Bloom, wrote in The Boston Globe *that this was evidence of the "dumbing down" of literature and merely a cynical acknowledgement of King's ability to "keep the publishing world afloat." He claimed King to be "an immensely inadequate writer on a sentence-by-sentence, paragraph-by-paragraph, book-by-book basis."*

King praises writers such as J.K. Rowling (Harry Potter), for which Bloom blames him. But King has also been critical of writers such as Stephenie Meyers (Twilight), saying in a 2009 interview with USA Weekend, *"She's not very good." So, Stephen King has opinions about good and bad writing, and his "distinguishing" success at it naturally leads many people to ask him for advice. (The question he claims to be asked more than any other is, "Where do you get your ideas?" It is a question he finds hard to answer.) In one of his non-fiction books,* On Writing: A Memoir of the Craft, *first published in 2000, three years before his award and Bloom's comments, King tries explaining how he does it. He remembers his own experience of becoming a writer and describes his process of writing. One of the most practical sections of the book is called "Toolbox." Here, King shares what he believes to be the most important "tools" for writing well.*

> *Grandpa was a carpenter,*
> *he built houses, stores and banks,*
> *he chain-smoked Camel cigarettes*
> *and hammered nails in planks.*
> *He was level-on-the-level,*
> *shaved even every door,*
> *and voted for Eisenhower*
> *'cause Lincoln won the war.*

That's one of my favorite John Prine lyrics, probably because my grandpa was also a carpenter. I don't know about stores and banks, but Guy Pillsbury built his share of houses and spent a good many years making sure the Atlantic Ocean and the harsh seacoast winters didn't wash away the Winslow Homer estate in Prout's Neck. Fazza smoked cigars, though, not Camels. It was my Uncle Oren, also a carpenter, who smoked the Camels. And when Fazza retired, it was Uncle Oren who inherited the old fellow's toolbox. I don't remember its being there in the garage on the day I dropped the cinderblock on my foot, but it probably was sitting in its accustomed place just outside the nook where my cousin Donald kept his hockey sticks, ice skates, and baseball glove.

The toolbox was what we called a big 'un. It had three levels, the top two removable, all three containing little drawers as cunning as Chinese boxes. It was handmade, of course. Dark wooden slats were bound together by tiny nails and strips of brass. The lid was held down by big latches; to my child's eye they looked like the latches on a giant's lunchbox. Inside the top was a silk lining, rather odd in such a context and made more striking still by the pattern, which was pinkish-red cabbage roses fading into a smog of grease and dirt. On the sides were great big grabhandles. You never saw a toolbox like this one for sale at Wal-Mart or Western Auto, believe me. When my uncle first got it, he found a brass etching of a famous Homer painting—I believe it was

The Undertow—lying in the bottom. Some years later Uncle Oren had it authenticated by a Homer expert in New York, and a few years after that I believe he sold it for a good piece of money. Exactly how or why Fazza came by the engraving in the first place is a mystery, but there was no mystery about the origins of the toolbox—he made it himself.

One summer day I helped Uncle Oren replace a broken screen on the far side of the house. I might have been eight or nine at the time. I remember following him with the replacement screen balanced on my head, like a native bearer in a Tarzan movie. He had the toolbox by the grabhandles, horsing it along at thigh level. As always, Uncle Oren was wearing khaki pants and a clean white tee-shirt. Sweat gleamed in his graying Army crewcut. A Camel hung from his lower lip. (When I came in years later with a pack of Chesterfields in my breast pocket, Uncle Oren sneered at them and called them "stockade cigarettes.")

We finally reached the window with the broken screen and he set the toolbox down with an audible sigh of relief. When Dave and I tried to lift it from its place on the garage floor, each of us holding one of the handles, we could barely budge it. Of course we were just little kids back then, but even so I'd guess that Fazza's fully loaded toolbox weighed between eighty and a hundred and twenty pounds.

Uncle Oren let me undo the big latches. The common tools were all on the top layer of the box. There was a hammer, a saw, the pliers, a couple of sized wrenches and an adjustable; there was a level with that mystic yellow window in the middle, a drill (the various bits were neatly drawered farther down in the depths), and two screwdrivers. Uncle Oren asked me for a screwdriver.

"Which one?" I asked.

"Either-or," he replied.

The broken screen was held on by loophead screws, and it really didn't matter whether he used a regular screwdriver or the Phillips on them; with loopheads you just stuck the screwdriver's barrel through the hole at the top of the screw and then spun it the way you spin a tire iron once you've got the lugnuts loose.

Uncle Oren took the screws out—there were eight, which he handed to me for safekeeping—and then removed the old screen. He set it against the house and held up the new one. The holes in the screen's frame mated up neatly with the holes in the window-frame. Uncle Oren grunted with approval when he saw this. He took the loophead screws back from me, one after the other, got them started with his fingers, then tightened them down just as he'd loosened them, by inserting the screwdriver's barrel through the loops and turning them.

When the screen was secure, Uncle Oren gave me the screwdriver and told me to put it back in the toolbox and "latch her up." I did, but I was puzzled. I asked him why he'd lugged Fazza's toolbox all the way around the house, if all he'd needed was that one screwdriver. He could have carried a screwdriver in the back pocket of his khakis.

"Yeah, but Stevie," he said, bending to grasp the handles, "I didn't know what else I might find to do once I got out here, did I? It's best to have your tools with you. If you don't, you're apt to find something you didn't expect and get discouraged."

I want to suggest that to write to your best abilities, it behooves you to construct your own toolbox and then build up enough muscle so you can carry it with you. Then, instead of looking at a hard job and getting discouraged, you will perhaps seize the correct tool and get immediately to work.

Fazza's toolbox had three levels. I think that yours should have at least four. You could have five or six, I suppose, but there comes a point where a toolbox becomes too large to be portable and thus loses its chief virtue. You'll also want all those little drawers for your screws and nuts and bolts, but where you put those drawers and what you put in them . . . well, that's your little red wagon, isn't it? You'll find you have most of the tools you need already, but I advise you to look at each one again as you load it into your box. Try to see each one new, remind yourself of its function, and if some are rusty (as they may be if you haven't done this seriously in awhile), clean them off.

Common tools go on top. The commonest of all, the bread of writing, is vocabulary. In this case, you can happily pack what you have without the slightest bit of guilt and inferiority. As the whore said to the bashful sailor, "It ain't how much you've got, honey, it's how you use it."

Some writers have enormous vocabularies; these are folks who'd know if there really *is* such a thing as an insalubrious dithyramb or a cozening raconteur, people who haven't missed a multiple-choice answer in Wilfred Funk's *It Pays to Increase Your Word Power* in oh, thirty years or so. For example:

> The leathery, undeteriorative, and almost indestructible quality was an inherent attribute of the thing's form of organization, and pertained to some paleogean cycle of invertebrate evolution utterly beyond our powers of speculation.
>
> —H. P. Lovecraft, *As the Mountains of Madness*

Like it? Here's another:

> In some [of the cups] there was no evidence whatever that anything had been planted; in others, wilted brown stalks gave testimony to some inscrutable depredation.
>
> —T. Coraghessan Boyle, *Budding Prospects*

And yet a third—this is a good one, you'll like it:

> Someone snatched the old woman's blindfold from her and she and the juggler were clouted away and when the company turned in to sleep and the low fire was roaring in the blast like a thing alive these four yet crouched at the edge of the firelight among their strange chattels and watched how the ragged flames fled down the wind as if sucked by some maelstrom out there in the void, some vortex in that waste apposite to which man's transit and his reckonings alike lay abrogate.
>
> —Cormac McCarthy, *Blood Meridian*

Other writers use smaller, simpler vocabularies. Examples of this hardly seem necessary, but I'll offer a couple of my favorites, just the same:

> He came to the river. The river was there.
>
> —Ernest Hemingway, "Big Two-Hearted River"

> They caught the kid doing something nasty under the bleachers.
>
> —Theodore Sturgeon, *Some of Your Blood*

> This is what happened.
>
> —Douglas Fairbairn, *Shoot*

> Some of the owner men were kind because they hated what they had to do, and some of them were angry because they hated to be cruel, and some of them were cold because they had long ago found that one could not be an owner unless one were cold.
>
> —John Steinbeck, *The Grapes of Wrath*

The Steinbeck sentence is especially interesting. It's fifty words long. Of those fifty words, thirty-nine have but one syllable. That leaves eleven, but even that number is deceptive; Steinbeck uses because three times, owner twice, and hated twice. There is no word longer than two syllables in the entire sentence. The structure is complex; the vocabulary is not far removed from the old Dick and Jane primers. *The Grapes of Wrath* is, of course, a fine novel. I believe that *Blood Meridian* is another, although there are great whacks of it that I don't fully understand. What of that? I can't decipher the words to many of the popular songs I love, either.

There's also stuff you'll never find in the dictionary, but it's still vocabulary. Check out the following:

> "Egggh, whaddaya? Whaddaya want from me?"
> "Here come Hymie!"
> "Unnh! Unnnh! Unnnhh!"
> "Chew my willie, Yo' Honor."
> "Yeggghhh, fuck you, too, man!"
>
> —Tom Wolfe, *Bonfire of the Vanities*

This last is phonetically rendered street vocabulary. Few writers have Wolfe's ability to translate such stuff to the page. (Elmore Leonard is another writer who can do it.) Some street-rap gets into the dictionary eventually, but not until it's safely dead. And I don't think you'll ever find Yeggghhh in Webster's Unabridged.

Put your vocabulary on the top shelf of your toolbox, and don't make any conscious effort to improve it. (You'll be doing that as you read, of course . . . but that comes later.) One of the really bad things you can do to your writing is to dress up the vocabulary, looking for long words because you're maybe a little bit ashamed of your short ones. This is like dressing up a household pet in evening clothes. The pet is embarrassed and the person who committed this act of premeditated cuteness should be even more embarrassed. Make yourself a solemn promise right now that you'll never use "emolument" when you mean "tip" and you'll never say John stopped long enough to perform an act of excretion when you mean John stopped long enough to take a shit. If you believe "take a shit" would be considered offensive or inappropriate by your audience, feel free to say John stopped long enough to move his bowels (or perhaps John stopped long enough to "push"). I'm not trying to get you to talk dirty, only plain and direct. Remember that the basic rule of vocabulary is *use the first word that comes to your mind, if it is appropriate and colorful.* If you hesitate and cogitate, you will come up with another word—of course you will, there's always another word—but it probably won't be as good as your first one, or as close to what you really mean.

This business of meaning is a very big deal. If you doubt it, think of all the times you've heard someone say "I just can't describe it" or "That isn't what I mean." Think of all the times you've said those things yourself, usually in a tone of mild or serious frustration. The word is only a representation of the meaning; even at its best, writing almost always falls short of full meaning. Given that, why in God's name would you want to make things worse by choosing a word which is only cousin to the one you really wanted to use?

And *do* feel free to take appropriateness into account; as George Carlin once observed, in some company it's perfectly all right to prick your finger, but very bad form to finger your prick.

2

You'll also want grammar on the top shelf of your toolbox, and don't annoy me with your moans of exasperation or your cries that you *don't understand* grammar, you *never did understand* grammar, you flunked that *whole semester* in Sophomore English, writing is fun but grammar sucks the big one.

Relax. Chill. We won't spend much time here because we don't need to. One either absorbs the grammatical principles of one's native language in conversation and in reading or one does not. What Sophomore English does (or tries to do) is little more than the naming of parts.

And this isn't high school. Now that you're not worried that (a) your skirt is too short or too long and the other kids will laugh at you, (b) you're not going to make the varsity swimming team, (c) you're still going to be a pimple-studded virgin when you graduate (probably when you die, for that matter), (d) the physics teacher won't grade the final on a curve, or (e) nobody really likes you anyway AND THEY NEVER DID . . . now that all that extraneous shit is out of the way, you can study certain academic matters with a degree of concentration you could never manage while attending the local textbook loonybin. And once you start, you'll find you know almost all of the stuff anyway—it is, as I said, mostly a matter of cleaning the rust off the drillbits and sharpening the blade of your saw.

Plus . . . oh, to hell with it. If you can remember all the accessories that go with your best outfit, the contents of your purse, the starting lineup of the New York Yankees or the Houston Oilers, or what label "Hang On Sloopy" by The McCoys was on, you are capable of remembering the difference between a gerund (verb form used as a noun) and a participle (verb form used as an adjective).

I thought long and hard about whether or not to include a detailed section on grammar in this little book. Part of me would actually like to; I taught it successfully at high school (where it hid under the name Business English), and I enjoyed it as a student. American grammar doesn't have the sturdiness of British grammar (a British advertising man with a proper education can make magazine copy for ribbed condoms sound like the Magna goddam Carta), but it has its own scruffy charm.

In the end I decided against it, probably for the same reason William Strunk decided not to recap the basics when he wrote the first edition of *The Elements of Style:* if you don't know, it's too late. And those really incapable of grasping grammar—as I am incapable of playing certain guitar riffs and progressions—will have little or no use for a book like this, anyway. In that sense I am preaching to the converted. Yet allow me to go on just a little bit further—will you indulge me?

Vocabulary used in speech or writing organizes itself in seven parts of speech (eight, if you count interjections such as Oh! and Gosh! and Fuhgeddaboudit!). Communication composed of these parts of speech must be organized by rules of grammar upon which we agree. When these rules break down, confusion and misunderstanding result. Bad grammar produces bad sentences. My favorite example from Strunk and White is this one: "As a mother of five, with another one on the way, my ironing board is always up."

Nouns and verbs are the two indispensable parts of writing. Without one of each, no group of words can be a sentence, since a sentence is, by definition, a group of words containing a subject (noun) and a predicate (verb); these strings of words begin with a capital letter, end with a period, and combine to make a complete thought which starts in the writer's head and then leaps to the reader's.

Must you write complete sentences each time, every time? Perish the thought. If your work consists only of fragments and floating clauses, the Grammar Police aren't going to come and take you away. Even William Strunk, that Mussolini of rhetoric, recognized the delicious pliability of language. "It is an old observation," he writes, "that the best writers sometimes disregard the rules of rhetoric." Yet he goes on to add this thought, which I urge you to consider: "Unless he is certain of doing well, [the writer] will probably do best to follow the rules."

The telling clause here is *Unless he is certain of doing well.* If you don't have a rudimentary grasp of how the parts of speech translate into coherent sentences, how can you be certain that you *are* doing well? How will you know if you're doing ill, for that matter? The answer, of course, is that you can't, you won't. One who does grasp the rudiments of grammar finds a comforting simplicity at its heart, where there need be only nouns, the words that name, and verbs, the words that act.

Take any noun, put it with any verb, and you have a sentence. It never fails. Rocks explode. Jane transmits. Mountains float. These are all perfect sentences. Many such thoughts make little rational sense, but even the stranger ones (Plums deify!) have a kind of poetic weight that's nice. The simplicity of noun-verb construction is useful—at the very least it can provide a safety net for your writing. Strunk and White caution against too many simple sentences in a row, but simple sentences provide a path you can follow when you fear getting lost in the tangles of rhetoric—all those restrictive and nonrestrictive clauses, those modifying phrases, those appositives and compound-complex sentences. If you start to freak out at the sight of such unmapped territory (unmapped by you, at least), just remind yourself that rocks explode, Jane transmits, mountains float, and plums deify. Grammar is not just a pain in the ass; it's the pole you grab to get your thoughts up on their feet and walking. Besides, all those simple sentences worked for Hemingway, didn't they? Even when he was drunk on his ass, he was a fucking genius.

If you want to refurbish your grammar, go to your local used-book store and find a copy of *Warriner's English Grammar and Composition*—the same book most of us took home and dutifully covered with brown paper shopping-bags when we were sophomores and juniors in high school. You'll be relieved and delighted, I think, to find that almost all you need is summarized on the front and back endpapers of the book.

3

Despite the brevity of his style manual, William Strunk found room to discuss his own dislikes in matters of grammar and usage. He hated the phrase "student body," for instance, insisting that "studentry" was both clearer and without the ghoulish connotations he saw in the former term. He thought "personalize" a pretentious word. (Strunk suggests "Get up a letterhead" to replace "Personalize your stationery.") He hated phrases such as "the fact that" and "along these lines."

I have my own dislikes—I believe that anyone using the phrase "That's so cool" should have to stand in the corner and that those using the far more odious phrases "at this point in time" and "at the end of the day" should be sent to bed without supper (or writing-paper, for that matter). Two of my other pet peeves have to do with this most basic level of writing, and I want to get them off my chest before we move along.

Verbs come in two types, active and passive. With an active verb, the subject of the sentence is doing something. With a passive verb, something is being done *to* the subject of the sentence. The subject is just letting it happen. *You should avoid the passive tense.* I'm not the only one who says so; you can find the same advice in *The Elements of Style*.

Messrs. Strunk and White don't speculate as to why so many writers are attracted to passive verbs, but I'm willing to; I think timid writers like them for the same reason timid lovers like passive partners. The passive voice is safe. There is no troublesome action to contend with; the subject just has to close its eyes and think of England, to paraphrase Queen Victoria. I think unsure writers also feel the passive voice somehow lends their work authority, perhaps even a quality of majesty. If you find instruction manuals and lawyers' torts majestic, I guess it does.

The timid fellow writes The meeting will be held at seven o'clock because that somehow says to him, "Put it this way and people will believe *you really know.*" Purge this quisling thought! Don't be a muggle! Throw back your shoulders, stick out your chin, and put that meeting in charge! Write The meeting's at seven. There, by God! Don't you feel better?

I won't say there's no place for the passive tense. Suppose, for instance, a fellow dies in the kitchen but ends up somewhere else. The body was carried from the kitchen and placed on the parlor sofa is a fair way to put this, although "was carried" and "was placed" still irk the shit out of me. I accept them but I don't embrace them. What I would embrace is Freddy and Myra carried the body out of the kitchen and laid it on the parlor sofa. Why does the body have to be the subject of the sentence, anyway? It's dead, for Christ's sake! Fuhgeddaboudit!

Two pages of the passive voice—just about any business document ever written, in other words, not to mention reams of bad fiction—make me want to scream. It's weak, it's circuitous, and it's frequently tortuous, as well. How about this: My first kiss will always be recalled by me as how my romance with Shayna was begun. Oh, man—who farted, right? A simpler way to express this idea—sweeter and more forceful, as well—might be this: My romance with Shayna began with our first kiss. I'll never forget it. I'm not in love with this because it uses *with* twice in four words, but at least we're out of that awful passive voice.

You might also notice how much simpler the thought is to understand when it's broken up into *two* thoughts. This makes matters easier for the reader, and the reader must always be your main concern; without Constant Reader, you are just a voice quacking in the void. And it's no walk in the park being the guy on the receiving end. "[Will Strunk] felt the reader was in serious trouble most of the time," E.B. White writes in his introduction to *The Elements of Style*, "a man floundering in a swamp, and that it was the duty of anyone trying to write English to drain this swamp quickly and get his man up on dry ground, or at least throw him a rope." And remember: The writer threw the rope, not The rope was thrown by the writer. Please oh please.

The other piece of advice I want to give you before moving on to the next level of the toolbox is this: *The adverb is not your friend.*

Adverbs, you will remember from your own version of Business English, are words that modify verbs, adjectives, or other adverbs. They're the ones that usually end in -ly. Adverbs, like the passive voice, seem to have been created with the timid writer in mind. With the passive voice, the writer usually expresses fear of not being taken seriously; it is the voice of little boys wearing shoepolish mustaches and little girls clumping around in Mommy's high heels. With adverbs, the writer usually tells us he or she is afraid he/she isn't expressing himself/herself clearly, that he or she is not getting the point or the picture across.

Consider the sentence He closed the door firmly. It's by no means a terrible sentence (at least it's got an active verb going for it), but ask yourself if firmly really has to be there. You can argue that it expresses a degree of difference between He closed the door and He slammed the door, and you'll get no argument from me . . . but what about context? What about all the enlightening (not to say emotionally moving) prose which came *before* He closed the door firmly? Shouldn't this tell us how he closed the door? And if the foregoing prose *does* tell us, isn't firmly an extra word? Isn't it redundant?

Someone out there is now accusing me of being tiresome and anal-retentive. I deny it. I believe the road to hell is paved with adverbs, and I will shout it from the rooftops. To put it another way, they're like dandelions. If you have one on your lawn, it looks pretty and unique. If you fail to root it out, however, you find five the next day . . . fifty the day after that . . . and then, my brothers and sisters, your lawn is totally, completely, and profligately covered with dandelions. By then you see them for the weeds they really are, but by then it's—*GASP!!*—too late.

I can be a good sport about adverbs, though. Yes I can. With one exception: dialogue attribution. I insist that you use the adverb in dialogue attribution only in the rarest and most special of occasions . . . and nor even then, if you can avoid it. Just to make sure we all know what we're talking about, examine these three sentences:

> "Put it down!" she shouted.
> "Give it back," he pleaded, "it's mine."
> "Don't be such a fool, Jekyll," Utterson said.

In these sentences, shouted, pleaded, and said are verbs of dialogue attribution. Now look at these dubious revisions:

> "Put it down!" she shouted menacingly.
> "Give it back," he pleaded abjectly, "it's mine."
> "Don't be such a fool, Jekyll," Utterson said contemptuously.

The three latter sentences are all weaker than the three former ones, and most readers will see why immediately. "Don't be such a fool, Jekyll," Utterson said contemptuously is the best of the lot; it is only a cliché, while the other two are actively ludicrous. Such dialogue attributions are sometimes known as "Swifties," after Tom Swift, the brave inventor-hero in a series of boys' adventure novels written by Victor Appleton II. Appleton was fond of such sentences as "Do your worst!" Tom cried bravely and "My father helped with the equations," Tom said modestly. When I was a teenager there was a party-game based on one's ability to create witty (or half-witty) Swifties. "You got a nice butt, lady," he said cheekily is one I remember; another is "I'm the plumber," he said, with a flush. (In this case the modifier is an adverbial phrase.) When debating whether or not to make some pernicious dandelion of an adverb part of your dialogue attribution, I suggest you ask yourself if you really want to write the sort of prose that might wind up in a party-game.

Some writers try to evade the no-adverb rule by shooting the attribution verb full of steroids. The result is familiar to any reader of pulp fiction or paperback originals:

> "Put down the gun, Utterson!" Jekyll grated.
> "Never stop kissing me!" Shayna gasped.
> "You damned tease!" Bill jerked out.

Don't do these things. Please oh please.

The best form of dialogue attribution is said, as in the said, she said, Bill said, Monica said. If you want to see this put stringently into practice, I urge you to read or reread a novel by Larry McMurtry, the Shane of dialogue attribution. That looks damned snide on the page, but I'm speaking with complete sincerity. McMurtry has allowed few adverbial dandelions to grow on his lawn. He believes in he-said/she-said even in moments of emotional crisis (and in Larry McMurtry novels there are a lot of those). Go and do thou likewise.

Is this a case of "Do as I say, not as I do?" The reader has a perfect right to ask the question, and I have a duty to provide an honest answer. Yes. It is. You need only look back through some of my own fiction to know that I'm just another ordinary sinner. I've been pretty good about avoiding the passive tense, but I've spilled out my share of adverbs in my time, including some (it shames me to say it) in dialogue attribution. (I have never fallen so low as "he grated" or "Bill jerked out," though.) When I do it, it's usually for the same reason any writer does it: because I am afraid the reader won't understand me if I don't.

I'm convinced that fear is at the root of most bad writing. If one is writing for one's own pleasure, that fear may be mild—*timidity* is the word I've used here. If, however, one is working under deadline—a school paper, a newspaper article, the SAT writing sample—that fear may be intense. Dumbo got airborne with the help of a magic feather; you may feel the urge to grasp a passive verb or one of those nasty adverbs for the same reason. Just remember before you do that Dumbo didn't need the feather; the magic was in him.

You probably *do* know what you're talking about, and can safely energize your prose with active verbs. And you probably *have* told your story well enough to believe that when you use he said, the reader will know how he said it—fast or slowly, happily or sadly. Your man may be floundering in a swamp, and by all means throw him a rope if he is . . . but there's no need to knock him unconscious with ninety feet of steel cable.

Good writing is often about letting go of fear and affectation. Affectation itself, beginning with the need to define some sorts of writing as "good" and other sorts as "bad," is fearful behavior. Good writing is also about making good choices when it comes to picking the tools you plan to work with.

No writer is entirely without sin in these matters. Although William Strunk got E. B. White in his clutches when White was but a naive undergraduate at Cornell (give them to me when they're young and they're mine forever, heh-heh-heh), and although White both understood and shared Strunk's prejudice against loose writing and the loose thinking which prompts it, he admits, "I suppose I have written *the fact that* a thousand times in the heat of composition, revised it out maybe five hundred times in the cool aftermath. To be batting only .500 this late in the season, to fail half the time to connect with this fat pitch, saddens me . . ." Yet E. B. White went on to write for a good many years following his initial revisions of Strunk's "little book" in

1957. I will go on writing in spite of such stupid lapses as "You can't be serious," Bill said unbelievingly. I expect you to do the same thing. There is a core simplicity to the English language and its American variant, but it's a slippery core. All I ask is that you do as well as you can, and remember that, while to write adverbs is human, to write he said or she said is divine.

4

Lift out the top layer of your toolbox—your vocabulary and all the grammar stuff. On the layer beneath go those elements of style upon which I've already touched. Strunk and White offer the best tools (and the best rules) you could hope for, describing them simply and clearly. (They are offered with a refreshing strictness, beginning with the rule on how to form possessives: you always add 's, even when the word you're modifying ends in s—always write Thomas's bike and never Thomas' bike—and ending with ideas about where it's best to place the most important parts of a sentence. They say at the end, and everyone's entitled to his/her opinion, but I don't believe With a hammer he killed Frank will ever replace He killed Frank with a hammer.)

Before leaving the basic elements of form and style, we ought to think for a moment about the paragraph, the form of organization which comes after the sentence. To that end, grab a novel—preferably one you haven't yet read—down from your shelf (the stuff I'm telling you applies to most prose, but since I'm a fiction writer, it's fiction I usually think about when I think about writing). Open the book in the middle and look at any two pages. Observe the pattern—the lines of type, the margins, and most particularly the blocks of white space where paragraphs begin or leave off.

You can tell *without even reading* if the book you've chosen is apt to be easy or hard, right? Easy books contain lots of short paragraphs—including dialogue paragraphs which may only be a word or two long—and lots of white space. They're as airy as Dairy Queen ice cream cones. Hard books, ones full of ideas, narration, or description, have a stouter look. A *packed* look. Paragraphs are almost as important for how they look as for what they say; they are maps of intent.

In expository prose, paragraphs can (and should) be neat and utilitarian. The ideal expository graf contains a topic sentence followed by others which explain or amplify the first. Here are two paragraphs from the ever-popular "informal essay" which illustrate this simple but powerful form of writing:

> When I was ten, I feared my sister Megan. It was impossible for her to come into my room without breaking at least one of my favorite toys, usually the favorite of favorites. Her gaze had some magical tape-destroying quality; any poster she looked at seemed to fall off the wall only seconds later. Well-loved articles of clothing disappeared from

the closet. She didn't take them (at least I don't think so), only made them vanish. I'd usually find that treasured tee-shirt or my favorite Nikes deep under the bed months later, looking sad and abandoned among the dust kitties. When Megan was in my room, stereo speakers blew, window-shades flew up with a bang, and the lamp on my desk usually went dead.

She could be consciously cruel, too. On one occasion, Megan poured orange juice into my cereal. On another, she squirted toothpaste into the toes of my socks while I was taking a shower. And although she never admitted it, I am positive that whenever I fell asleep on the couch during half-time of the Sunday afternoon pro football games on TV, she rubbed boogers in my hair.

Informal essays are, by and large, silly and insubstantial things; unless you get a job as a columnist at your local newspaper, writing such fluffery is a skill you'll never use in the actual mall-and-filling-station world. Teachers assign them when they can't think of any other way to waste your time. The most notorious subject, of course, is "How I Spent My Summer Vacation." I taught writing for a year at the University of Maine in Orono and had one class loaded with athletes and cheerleaders. They liked informal essays, greeting them like the old high school friends they were. I spent one whole semester fighting the urge to ask them to write two pages of well-turned prose on the subject of "If Jesus Were My Teammate." What held me back was the sure and terrible knowledge that most of them would take to the task with enthusiasm. Some might actually weep while in the throes of composition.

Even in the informal essay, however, it's possible to see how strong the basic paragraph form can be. Topic-sentence-followed-by-support-and-description insists that the writer organize his/her thoughts, and it also provides good insurance against wandering away from the topic. Wandering isn't a big deal in an informal essay, is practically *de rigueur*, as a matter of fact— but it's a very bad habit to get into when working on more serious subjects in a more formal manner. Writing is refined thinking. If your master's thesis is no more organized than a high school essay titled "Why Shania Twain Turns Me On," you're in big trouble.

In fiction, the paragraph is less structured—it's the beat instead of the actual melody. The more fiction you read and write, the more you'll find your paragraphs forming on their own. And that's what you want. When composing it's best not to think too much about where paragraphs begin and end; the trick is to let nature take its course. If you don't like it later on, fix it then. That's what rewrite is all about. Now check out the following:

> Big Tony's room wasn't what Dale had expected. The light had an odd yellowish cast that reminded him of cheap motels he'd stayed in, the ones where he always seemed to end up with a scenic view of the

parking lot. The only picture was Miss May hanging askew on a push-pin. One shiny black shoe stuck out from under the bed.

"I dunno why you keep askin me about O'Leary," Big Tony said.

"You think my story's gonna change?"

"Is it?" Dale asked.

"When your story's true it don't change. The truth is always the same boring shit, day in and day out."

Big Tony sat down, lit a cigarette, ran a hand through his hair.

"I ain't seen that fuckin mick since last summer. I let him hang around because he made me laugh, once showed me this thing he wrote about what it woulda been like if Jesus was on his high school football team, had a picture of Christ in a helmet and kneepads and everythin, but what a troublesome little fuck he turned out to be! I wish I'd never seen him!"

We could have a fifty-minute writing class on just this brief passage. It would encompass dialogue attribution (not necessary if we know who's speaking; Rule 17, omit needless words, in action), phonetically rendered language (dunno, gonna), the use of the comma (there is none in the line When your story's true it don't change because I want you to hear it coming out all in one breath, without a pause), the decision not to use the apostrophe where the speaker has dropped a *g* . . . and all that stuff is just from the top level of the toolbox.

Let's stick with the paragraphs, though. Notice how easily they flow, with the turns and rhythms of the story dictating where each one begins and ends. The opening graf is of the classic type, beginning with a topic sentence that is supported by the sentences which follow. Others, however, exist solely to differentiate between Dale's dialogue and Big Tony's.

The most interesting paragraph is the fifth one: Big Tony sat down, lit a cigarette, ran a hand through his hair. It's only a single sentence long, and expository paragraphs almost never consist of a single sentence. It's not even a very *good* sentence, technically speaking; to make it perfect in the *Warriner's* sense, there should be a conjunction (and). Also, what exactly is the purpose of this paragraph?

First, the sentence may be flawed in a technical sense, but it's a good one in terms of the entire passage. Its brevity and telegraphic style vary the pace and keep the writing fresh. Suspense novelist Jonathan Kellerman uses this technique very successfully. In *Survival of the Fittest*, he writes: The boat was thirty feet of sleek white fiberglass with gray trim. Tall masts, the sails tied. *Satori* painted on the hull in black script edged with gold.

It is possible to overuse the well-turned fragment (and Kellerman sometimes does), but frags can also work beautifully to streamline narration, create clear images, and create tension as well as to very the proseline. A series of grammatically proper sentences can stiffen that line, make it less pliable. Purists hate to hear that and will deny it to their dying breath, but it's true. Language does not always have to wear a tie and laceup shoes. The object of fiction isn't grammatical correctness but to make the reader welcome and then tell a story . . . to make him/her forget, whenever possible, that he/she is reading a story at all. The single-sentence paragraph more closely resembles talk than writing, and that's good. Writing is seduction. Good talk is part of seduction. If not so, why do so many couples who start the evening at dinner wind up in bed?

The other uses of this paragraph include stage direction, minor but useful enhancement of character and setting, and a vital moment of transition. From protesting that his story is true, Big Tony moves on to his memories of O'Leary. Since the source of dialogue doesn't change, Tony's sitting down and lighting up could take place in the same paragraph, with the dialogue picking up again afterward, but the writer doesn't elect to do it that way. Because Big Tony takes a new tack, the writer breaks the dialogue into two paragraphs. It's a decision made instantaneously in the course of writing, one based entirely on the beat the writer hears in his/her own head. That beat is part of the genetic hardwiring (Kellerman writes a lot of frags because he *hears* a lot of frags), but it's also the result of the thousands of hours that writer has spent composing, and the *tens* of thousands of hours he/she may have spent reading the compositions of others.

I would argue that the paragraph, not the sentence, is the basic unit of writing—the place where coherence begins and words stand a chance of becoming more than mere words. If the moment of quickening is to come, it comes at the level of the paragraph. It is a marvellous and flexible instrument that can be a single word long or run on for pages (one paragraph in Don Robertson's historical novel *Paradise Falls* is sixteen pages long; there are paragraphs in Ross Lockridge's *Raintree County* which are nearly that). You must learn to use it well if you are to write well. What this means is lots of practice; you have to learn the beat.

5

Grab that book you were looking at off the shelf again, would you? The weight of it in your hands tells you other stuff that you can take in without reading a single word. The book's length, naturally, but more: the commitment the writer shouldered in order to create the work, the commitment Constant Reader must make to digest it. Not that length and weight alone indicate excellence; many epic tales are pretty much epic crap—just ask my critics, who will moan about entire Canadian forests massacred in order to print my drivel. Conversely, short doesn't always mean sweet. In some cases (*The Bridges of*

Madison County, for instance), short means far *too* sweet. But there is that matter of commitment, whether a book is good or bad, a failure or a success. Words have weight. Ask anyone who works in the shipping department of a book company warehouse, or in the storage room of a large bookstore.

Words create sentences; sentences create paragraphs; sometimes paragraphs quicken and begin to breathe. Imagine, if you like, Frankenstein's monster on its slab. Here comes lightning, not from the sky but from a humble paragraph of English words. Maybe it's the first really good paragraph you ever wrote, something so fragile and yet full of possibility that you are frightened. You feel as Victor Frankenstein must have when the dead conglomeration of sewn-together spare parts suddenly opened its watery yellow eyes. *Oh my God, it's breathing,* you realize. *Maybe it's even thinking. What in bell's name do I do next?*

You go on to the third level, of course, and begin to write real fiction. Why shouldn't you? Why should you fear? Carpenters don't build monsters, after all; they build houses, stores, and banks. They build some of wood a plank at a time and some of brick a brick at a time. You will build a paragraph at a time, constructing these of your vocabulary and your knowledge of grammar and basic style. As long as you stay level-on-the-level and shave even every door, you can build whatever you like—whole mansions, if you have the energy.

Is there any rationale for building entire mansions of words? I think there is, and that the readers of Margaret Mitchell's *Gone with the Wind* and Charles Dickens's *Bleak House* understand it: sometimes even a monster is no monster. Sometimes it's beautiful and we fall in love with all that story, more than any film or TV program could ever hope to provide. Even after a thousand pages we don't want to leave the world the writer has made for us, or the make-believe people who live there. You wouldn't leave after two thousand pages, if there were two thousand. The *Rings* trilogy of J. R. R. Tolkien is a perfect example of this. A thousand pages of hobbits hasn't been enough for three generations of post—World War II fantasy fans; even when you add in that clumsy, galumphing dirigible of an epilogue, *The Silmarillion,* it hasn't been enough. Hence Terry Brooks, Piers Anthony, Robert Jordan, the questing rabbits of *Watership Down,* and half a hundred others. The writers of these books are creating the hobbits they still love and pine for; they are trying to bring Frodo and Sam back from the Grey Havens because Tolkien is no longer around to do it for them.

At its most basic we are only discussing a learned skill, but do we not agree that sometimes the most basic skills can create things far beyond our expectations? We are talking about tools and carpentry, about words and style . . . but as we move along, you'd do well to remember that we are also talking about magic.

Shitty First Drafts

Anne Lamott

Anne Lamott was born in San Francisco in 1954. She attended Goucher College in Baltimore. In her literary life, she has worked as a food reviewer, book reviewer, single parent, non-fiction writer and novelist. She is also a sober alcoholic, a born-again Christian, and a liberal activist. Lamott includes her Northern California rearing, community and lifestyle in most of her works, almost treating it as another character, like Faulkner's Yoknapatawpha County.

One of Lamott's best-known works is Bird by Bird: Some Instructions on Writing and Life, published in 1994. This book is about the art of writing and contains the essay "Shitty First Drafts," in which she proclaims the importance of the so-called "shitty first draft," which can lead to the excellence and refinement of later drafts. It is a thesis based on overt perfectionism crushing creativity. Rather than pedantic preaching about writing, Lamott's text is a friendly, comfortable and down-to — earth guide to overcoming the psychological roadblocks for the beginning writer.

Her other fiction includes Rosie (1983), Crooked Little Heart (1997), All New People (2000), and Blue Shoes (2002). Lamott's nonfiction books include Operating Instructions: A Journal of My Son's First Year (1993) and Tender Mercies: Some Thoughts on Faith (1999).

Lamott received a Guggenheim Fellowship in 1985, and has taught at UC Davis. She also participates in writing conferences across the country. Lamott's writes an "online diary," for Salon Magazine called "Word by Word." In 1999, Academy Award —winning filmmaker Freida Mock made a documentary about Lamott, called "Bird by Bird with Annie" (1999). Lamott was inducted into the California Hall of Fame in 2010.

N ow, practically even better news than that of short assignments is the idea of shitty first drafts. All good writers write them. This is how they end up with good second drafts and terrific third drafts. People tend to look at successful writers, writers who are getting their books published and maybe even doing well financially, and think that they sit down at their desks every morning feeling like a million dollars, feeling great about who they are and how much talent they have and what a great story they have to tell; that they take in a few deep breaths, push back their sleeves, roll their necks a few times to get all the cricks out, and dive in, typing fully formed passages as fast as a court reporter. But this is just the fantasy of the uninitiated. I know some very great writers, writers you love who write beautifully and have made a great deal of money, and not *one* of them sits down routinely feeling wildly enthusiastic and confident. Not one of them writes elegant first drafts. All right, one of them does, but we do not like her very much. We do not think that she has a rich inner life or that God likes her or can even stand her. (Although when I mentioned this to my priest friend Tom, he said you can safely assume you've created God in your own image when it turns out that God hates all the same people you do.)

Very few writers really know what they are doing until they've done it. Nor do they go about their business feeling dewy and thrilled. They do not type a few stiff warm-up sentences and then find themselves bounding along like huskies across the snow. One writer I know tells me that he sits down every morning and says to himself nicely, "It's not like you don't have a choice, because you do—you can either type or kill yourself." We all often feel like we are pulling teeth, even those writers whose prose ends up being the most natural and fluid. The right words and sentences just do not come pouring out like ticker tape most of the time. Now, Muriel Spark is said to have felt that she was taking dictation from God every morning—sitting there, one supposes, plugged into a Dictaphone, typing away, humming. But this is a very hostile and aggressive position. One might hope for bad things to rain down on a person like this.

For me and most of the other writers I know, writing is not rapturous. In fact, the only way I can get anything written at all is to write really, really shitty first drafts.

The first draft is the child's draft, where you let it all pour out and then let it romp all over the place, knowing that no one is going to see it and that you can shape it later. You just let this childlike part of you channel whatever voices and visions come through and onto the page. If one of the characters wants to say, "Well, so what, Mr. Poopy Pants?," you let her. No one is going to see it. If the kid wants to get into really sentimental, weepy, emotional territory, you let him. Just get it all down on paper, because there may be something great in those six crazy pages that you would never have gotten to by more rational, grown-up means. There may be something in the very last line of the very last paragraph on page six that you just love, that is so beautiful or wild that you now know what you're supposed to be writing about, more or less, or in what direction you might go—but there was no way to get to this without first getting through the first five and a half pages.

I used to write food reviews for *California* magazine before it folded. (My writing food reviews had nothing to do with the magazine folding, although every single review did cause a couple of canceled subscriptions. Some readers took umbrage at my comparing mounds of vegetable puree with various expresidents' brains.) These reviews always took two days to write. First I'd go to a restaurant several times with a few opinionated, articulate friends in tow. I'd sit there writing down everything anyone said that was at all interesting or funny. Then on the following Monday I'd sit down at my desk with my notes, and try to write the review. Even after I'd been doing this for years, panic would set in. I'd try to write a lead, but instead I'd write a couple of dreadful sentences, xx them out, try again, xx everything out, and then feel despair and worry settle on my chest like an x-ray apron. It's over, I'd think, calmly. I'm not going to be able to get the magic to work this time. I'm ruined. I'm through. I'm toast. Maybe, I'd think, I can get my old job back as a clerk-typist. But probably not. I'd get up and study my teeth in the mirror for a while. Then I'd stop, remember to breathe, make a few phone calls, hit the kitchen and chow down. Eventually I'd go back and sit down at my desk, and sigh for the next ten minutes. Finally I would pick up my one-inch picture frame, stare into it as if for the answer, and every time the answer would come: all I had to do was to write a really shitty first draft of, say, the opening paragraph. And no one was going to see it.

So I'd start writing without reining myself in. It was almost just typing, just making my fingers move. And the writing would be *terrible*. I'd write a lead paragraph that was a whole page, even though the entire review could only be three pages long, and then I'd start writing up descriptions of the food, one dish at a time, bird by bird, and the critics would be sitting on my shoulders, commenting like cartoon characters. They'd be pretending to snore, or rolling their eyes at my overwrought descriptions, no matter how hard I tried to tone those descriptions down, no matter how conscious I was of what a friend said to me gently in my early days of restaurant reviewing. "Annie," she said, "it is just a piece of *chicken*. It is just a bit of *cake*."

But because by then I had been writing for so long, I would eventually let myself trust the process—sort of, more or less. I'd write a first draft that was maybe twice as long as it should be, with a self-indulgent and boring beginning, stupefying descriptions of the meal, lots of quotes from my black-humored friends that made them sound more like the Manson girls than food lovers, and no ending to speak of. The whole thing would be so long and incoherent and hideous that for the rest of the day I'd obsess about getting creamed by a car before I could write a decent second draft. I'd worry that people would read what I'd written and believe that the accident had really been a suicide, that I had panicked because my talent was waning and my mind was shot.

The next day, though, I'd sit down, go through it all with a colored pen, take out everything I possibly could, find a new lead somewhere on the second page, figure out a kicky place to end it, and then write a second draft. It always turned out fine, sometimes even funny and weird and helpful. I'd go over it one more time and mail it in.

Then, a month later, when it was time for another review, the whole process would start again, complete with the fears that people would find my first draft before I could rewrite it.

Almost all good writing begins with terrible first efforts. You need to start somewhere. Start by getting something—anything—down on paper. A friend of mine says that the first draft is the down draft—you just get it down. The second draft is the up draft—you fix it up. You try to say what you have to say more accurately. And the third draft is the dental draft, where you check every tooth, to see if it's loose or cramped or decayed, or even, God help us, healthy.

What I've learned to do when I sit down to work on a shitty first draft is to quiet the voices in my head. First there's the vinegar-lipped Reader Lady, who says primly, "Well, *that's* not very interesting, is it?" And there's the emaciated German male who writes these Orwellian memos detailing your thought crimes. And there are your parents, agonizing over your lack of loyalty and discretion; and there's William Burroughs, dozing off or shooting up because he finds you as bold and articulate as a houseplant; and so on. And there are also the dogs: let's not forget the dogs, the dogs in their pen who will surely hurtle and snarl their way out if you ever *stop* writing, because writing is, for some of us, the latch that keeps the door of the pen closed, keeps those crazy ravenous dogs contained.

Quieting these voices is at least half the battle I fight daily. But this is better than it used to be. It used to be 87 percent. Left to its own devices, my mind spends much of its time having conversations with people who aren't there. I walk along defending myself to people, or exchanging repartee with them, or rationalizing my behavior, or seducing them with gossip, or pretending I'm on their TV talk show or whatever. I speed or run an aging yellow light or don't come to full stop, and one nanosecond later am explaining to imaginary cops exactly why I had to do what I did, or insisting that I did not in fact do it.

I happened to mention this to a hypnotist I saw many years ago, and he looked at me very nicely. At first I thought he was feeling around on the floor for the silent alarm button, but then he gave me the following exercise, which I still use to this day.

Close your eyes and get quiet for a minute, until the chatter starts up. Then isolate one of the voices and imagine the person speaking as a mouse. Pick it up by the tail and drop it into a mason jar. Then isolate another voice, pick it up by the tail, drop it in the jar. And so on. Drop in any high-maintenance parental units, drop in any contractors, lawyers, colleagues, children, anyone who is whining in your head. Then put the lid on, and watch all these mouse people clawing at the glass, jabbering away, trying to make you feel like shit because you won't do what they want—won't give them more money, won't be more successful, won't see them more often. Then imagine that there is a volume-control button on the bottle. Turn it all the way up for a minute, and listen to the stream of angry, neglected, guilt-mongering voices. Then turn it all the way down and watch the frantic mice lunge at the glass, trying to get to you. Leave it down, and get back to your shitty first draft.

A writer friend of mine suggests opening the jar and shooting them all in the head. But I think he's a little angry, and I'm sure nothing like this would ever occur to you.

The Wild Beast

Peter Maass

Peter Maass (1960–) was born and raised in Los Angeles, California. In 1983, he graduated from the University of California at Berkeley, and, since then, he has lived and worked as a journalist throughout Eastern and Western Europe, as well as Asia, for publications such as The Wall Street Journal/Europe, The New York Times, The International Herald Tribune, *and* The Washington Post. *During most of 1992 and 1993, Maass lived in Bosnia, covering the war for the Post. Maass' first book,* Love Thy Neighbor: A Story of War *(1996), in which he records his experiences in Bosnia, won* The Los Angeles Times Book Prize *(for nonfiction) and the Overseas Press Club Book Prize.* Love Thy Neighbor *provides a vivid account of the horrors committed by "the wild beast" of human cruelty. Maass now lives in New York City, where he is a contributing writer at* The New York Times Magazine.

When you grow up in America, you don't really learn how foul humans can smell, just as you don't learn about the smell of death. Taking a crowded bus in the summer exposes you to unpleasant odors, but that is a transitory experience. If you turn your head or move a few steps away from an offending commuter, the smell is gone.

No amount of journeys on buses, however, can prepare you for the stink of refugees. When you enter a sports hall filled with women and children who have not washed for a month, or when you enter a cowshed filled with male prisoners who have not washed for two or three months, you smell something new, and it is terrible. You think that somebody has wrapped a discarded dishrag around your face, and that you must inhale air through it. Of course the smell is disgusting. It is the smell of filth, the smell of animals. We have an easy time thinking of animals as animals in part because they smell like animals. That's a difference between us and them. But what are you supposed to think when you find a group of humans who smell no better than cows, even worse? It reminds you that humans are animals, with the ability to stink like pigs, and kill like wolves.

The sports hall in Split reeked of sweat, not from athletes but from refugees. The basketball floor was jammed full of Bosnians, mostly women and children who had just straggled into town. They slept on blankets, one family per. The court was too small for all of them, so a few hundred refugees were living on the bleacher seats. It was May 1992. Many of the Bosnians had not showered since the war began a month earlier, having been trapped in basements all the time or scrambling through forests. The wait for the gym showers was so long that, days after arriving in Croatia, most had not begun the first stop of cleansing their bodies. Just six weeks before, some of them had been well-groomed doctors and lawyers, but now they smelled like livestock. It was only the smallest insult the war had bestowed on them.

Split is a city along the Adriatic Sea, the main port of Croatia's Dalmatia region and the only place in Europe that makes me feel like I am in California. It is a land of abundant food, great wines and bronzed women who look like goddesses. The people are relaxed in Dalmatia, tinged more by the carefree attitude of the Italians who face them on the other side of the Adriatic, and who ruled them intermittently in the past centuries, than the dark passions of the Balkans. Even when Croatia declared independence from Yugoslavia in 1991 and fought a six-month war, Split was left virtually untouched—just a few protest marches, a small amount of bloodshed, and then it was over, leaving no physical scars. It suited my needs perfectly, a comfortable classroom where I could learn about Bosnia before making the journey inland, over the mountains and into the real world of war.

I sat down on the gym floor with Munevera, who had just arrived with her two children, a daughter of seven, a son of five. She had come on foot from Foca, a Bosnian town that's about a six-hour drive from Split, in normal times. She had to leave Foca in the middle of the night, when attacks by bands of Serb paramilitary soldiers became too frightening, and then she had to sneak from one safe village to the next, never in a direct line, avoiding roads, walking through forests and mountains, sneaking past Serb villages, occasionally being shot at. She was on Bosnia's underground railroad, and it was a rough ride. She could rest for no more than a day at safe villages, because other refugees were arriving and food was running out. I asked how long it took to get from Foca to Split.

"Forty-five days," she said.

"Excuse me?"

"Forty-five days."

"You have been walking for forty-five days?"

"Yes. But only at night. It was too dangerous to walk during the day."

I wrote it down in my notebook but I didn't believe it. How could she have been on the run with two children for forty-five days? During World War II people wandered for that long, even longer, but Bosnia's war was a small-time affair, a few people killed, a few thousand refugees, it would be over in a couple of months, when the politicians would come to their senses again. She wasn't marching from Russia to Poland. The year was 1992, not 1942, and Bosnia had smooth roads and fast cars with antilock braking systems and double-overhead cam engines. What was going on? I looked at Munevera's feet for an answer. She was wearing a pair of blue snow boots. They had been the best thing to put over her feet when she fled into mountains still covered with snow. She had run for so long that by the time she arrived in Split, in late May, the seasons had changed. It was 72 degrees outside. I was wearing a T-shirt. And she was wearing snow boots, her only shoes.

Munevera had been "cleansed." That word, cleansed, had not yet entered the American vocabulary. It was a learning process, and I was at the start of it. Like an infant trying to speak, you had to learn the building blocks of cleansing before you could understand its meaning. First the syllables, then the word; articles of speech, then grammar. So you had to learn about mass arrests, torture, rapes and expulsions, and you needed to understand that it was a system rather than a series of random incidents. Then you could understand what cleansing meant. It took time. You digested the patterns reluctantly rather than intuitively, because it made no sense that Europe was falling into madness again at the end of the twentieth century. When I met Munevera, I was struggling with the ABCs of atrocities.

During the interview Munevera said Muslim and Croat men were rounded up in Foca and put into a "concentration camp" on the town's outskirts (her words, not mine). I wrote down the words and forgot about them. Concentration camps were a Nazi invention, and in 1945 we buried the machine that created them. Munevera was being hysterical. Munevera spoke of a girl who lived next door, seventeen years old, who was dragged off by Serb soldiers one day and dumped back at home a few days later, bleeding from her groin. She had been raped an unimaginable number of times, Munevera said, and she died at home. I jotted it down. Munevera was being hysterical.

"I tried to call a friend in Foca today," Munevera said. "She stayed behind. I told her not to. When I called, a strange man answered the phone. I asked for my friend, and he said, 'This is a Serb apartment now.'"

I felt a tug at my sleeve.

"Hey, mister, come here, this man, my cousin, he had seven brothers killed."

My visit was turning into a freak show. I couldn't refuse to see the next exhibit, free of charge, satisfaction guaranteed. The guy with seven dead brothers. I said good-bye to Munevera and her sorrows and moved over to the next blanket. A farmer named Adem sat in the corner, hunched over, face toward the ground. His cousin, the one who lured me over, coaxed Adem to life, barely. Adem extended one of his hands, a big, muscle-bound paw of a man of the earth. I shook the hand, and it was limp. It had gone limp, like his spirit, on the night when thirty-five men from his village were rounded up by Serbs from a neighboring village and had their throats slit. He told the story in a whispered mumble. They were killed by Serbs who had been their friends, people who had helped harvest their fields the previous autumn, people with whom they shared adolescent adventures and secrets, skinny-dipping in the Drina River on hot summer days, groping with the naughty girls of the village at night. All of a sudden, seemingly without reason, they had turned into killers.

Adem, who was twenty-eight, fled in time, just as the roundup started on an evening in the first week of April. There were others who got out, fleeing to the forests and fields around the village. The Serbs chased after them, shooting wildly into the darkness with assault rifles and hollering like drunken hillbillies, which they were, "Muslim scum, hah, we'll get you tomorrow. We've got your women for tonight. We're going to fuck them real good. Did you hear that? *We're going to fuck them real good tonight!*" Some of the men were injured while fleeing. They begged their friends to kill them so that would not be captured by the Serbs, who were sure to comb the fields once dawn broke. Adem didn't say whether their whishes were granted, but his silence was ominous. His face hung toward the ground, his eyes staring at a spot on the blanket that only he could see. His hands started to shake.

"Mister," the cousin said. "Do you want to hear more? I know another man who..."

I didn't really listen to the rest. What could be done with more stories of death and thuggery, none of it reliable, most of it beyond the realm of credibility? From the sound of it, Bosnia was alight with atrocities. But who knows? The Serbs said it wasn't. Which side do you believe? A teenage girl explained to me how one of the Muslim men in her village had been nailed to the front door of the mosque, his arms spread out, so that he was like Christ on the cross, and he was still alive at the time. "Excuse me," I said. "He was nailed to the door?" Yes, she replied, she saw it herself, as the women of her village were marched past the mosque, being herded toward buses that would take them to train stations where they were loaded into cattle cars, yes, cattle cars, and expunged from their homeland, because it was no longer their homeland. The prettiest girls were taken off the trains at one of the stations. "They were all raped," she said. "I was lucky because I wasn't one of them." Girls did their best to avoid becoming war booty by cutting their hair into a crew cut, by smearing their faces with dirt, by binding up their breasts so that they could pass as boys. It worked, some of the time.

I needed a breath of fresh air. The stories, the smells, it was enough for one day. I stepped outside and was blinded by a bright sun that repudiated everything I heard in the dim bowels of the sports hall. When you are in pleasant Split, the wretchedness of Bosnia seems impossible, as unlikely as nighttime enveloping your neighbor's home while your house is soaked in sunshine. If you wanted to find the truth, to find out whether men would act like animals as well as smell like them, you had to leave the sunshine and head for the darkness. There, you would learn that the refugees you felt such pity for in Split were among the luckiest Bosnians of all, because they had escaped the darkness.

TWO

The whole truth emerged as journalists and diplomats talked to Bosnians who had gotten out of the camps and reached safety in Croatia, where they could speak freely. I interviewed several dozen survivors in Croatia and read the written testimony of scores of others. The best overall picture was drawn, belatedly, by the State Department, with far greater resources than any single journalist, in a series of reports sent to the United Nations Security Council. The reports amount to a catalogue of the unimaginable and the unbearable. One of the most chilling passages is in an October 22, 1992, report under the heading of "Abuse of Civilians in Detention Centers." This is how it summarized the experience of one ex-prisoner from Omarska:

"The witness stated that a young Muslim man from Kozarac who had owned a Suzuki motorcycle was tortured in front of the other prisoners. He was severely beaten all over his body and his teeth were knocked out. The guards then tied one end of a wire tightly around his testicles and tied the other end to the victim's motorcycle. A guard got on the motorcycle and sped off."

Do you believe that Europeans did this at the end of the twentieth century? Excuse me, the question should be rephrased. Europeans, as Bosnia reminds us, do not have an inside track on virtue. Ugandans, Europeans, Cambodians—there is no difference in the cruelty sweepstakes, it is a dead heat. Here's the question again: Do you believe humans can do this at the end of the twentieth century? I find it hard to believe that a man can get on a motorcycle and ride off with another man's testicles attached to the tailpipe. Yet the testimony from camp survivors is consistent. It gnaws away at me.

One survivor, Emin Jakubovic, told journalists he was ordered by his Omarska jailers to castrate three prisoners. "They forced me to tear off their testicles, with my teeth, so I tore off their testicles with my teeth. They were screaming with pain." Impossible? At a refugee center in Croatia, I interviewed a man who said he witnessed the episode. It was wintertime, and we were sitting in a bare, unheated room littered with cigarette butts and trampled-on newspapers. My overcoat was buttoned up against the cold, and the ink in my pen was freezing up, as was my right hand, which became too stiff to write legibly. I had been interviewing prison survivors for several hours, and I was tired, fed up with it all. I looked at the man, whose name was Ibrahim, still half-emaciated from his ordeal, and shook my head. Even though I had heard of such things before, I could not believe it. No, I told him, I do not believe your story. I do not believe it. Even among torturers, there is a line beyond which they do not go, such as castration. I asked Ibrahim, Would you believe someone who said the things you have just said? He stared back at me.

"I know," he replied. "I wouldn't believe it unless I had seen it."

On February 13, 1995, in its first batch of indictments, the United Nations War Crimes Tribunal issued international arrest warrants for twenty-one Serbs on charges of committing war crimes and crimes against humanity. The indicted men included Dušan Tadic who according to the tribunal, forced a Muslim prisoner to bite off the testicles of another prisoner.

Bosnia makes you question basic assumptions about humanity, and one of the questions concerns torture. Why, after all, should there be any limit? For a person capable of torture, no form of it is out of bounds. The big moral leap backward has already been taken once the door marked Torture has been opened and the first cut made in the prisoner's skin, or the first butt-blow landed to the prisoner's face. Suddenly, the torturer realizes that he, or she, has entered a new universe of sadistic pleasures. The wild beast has been set free and taken up residence in his soul. What's the moral difference between slitting a man's throat or slicing off his balls? Please tell me, anyone. There is none. If you have the stomach to crush a man's head under your boots, then you probably have the stomach to cut off a woman's breasts. Will God treat you better because you killed but refrained from mutilating? No. You can do as you please and you have nothing to fear. You have entered a world that would sicken Edgar Allan Poe.

You can, for example, barge into a house and put a gun to a father's head and tell him that you will pull the trigger unless he rapes his daughter or at least simulates the rape. (I heard of such things in Bosnia.) The father will refuse and say, I will die before doing that. You shrug your shoulders and reply, Okay, old man, I won't shoot you, but I will shoot your daughter. What does the father do now, dear reader? He pleads, he begs, but then you, the man with the gun, put the gun to the daughter's head, you pull back the hammer, and you shout, *Now!* Do it! Or I shoot! The father starts weeping, yet slowly he unties his belt, moving like a dazed zombie, he can't believe what he must do.

You laugh and say, That's right, old man, pull down those pants, pull up your daughter's dress, *and do it!*

You are the law, and you feel divine.

Prison survivors describe an odd enthusiasm on the part of their torturers, who laughed, sang and got drunk while inflicting their crimes. They weren't just doing a job, there were doing something they enjoyed. They felt liberated. They could smash every crystal glass in the shop and break every taboo in the book, and no law could touch these men. The only prying eyes belonged to foreign journalists, and we could be kept away from hot spots and lied to. Torture became entertainment. For kicks, guards even made prisoners assault one another.

"After beating us for a while one night, the guards got tired," Ibrahim told me. "They decided it would be a good idea to have the prisoners fight each other. A guard singled out me and another prisoner. He told the other prisoner to stand still and he told me to punch the prisoner as hard as possible in the face. I did it. But the guard said I wasn't doing it hard enough, and so he hit me in the back of my head with the butt of his gun. He kept hitting me until I was covered in blood. And then he took another prisoner out of the line and told him to hit me."

It was gladiator time. For the next two hours, the guards at Omarska ordered scores of prisoners to fight each other. It amused them to no end, except when they spotted a prisoner pulling a punch, and then a guard would hit the laggard with a rifle butt. They drew particular pleasure from having members of the same family beat each other. Brothers would be ordered to hit each other. Hard. I talked to an American diplomat who debriefed prisoners freed from Omarska. "It was often a plaything between the guards," she said. "It was like [the] Roman Colosseum. You have to hit the other guy as hard as you can if you want to stay alive. If you don't hit hard enough, then you get shot."

The guards even opened the camp gates and allowed their friends to share in the fun. Civilians came from the outside and would spend a night beating or killing or raping. What's extraordinary is the reasons these Serbs entered the gates of hell for a night of twisted pleasure. They wanted to settle old scores. Survivors told me of hiding behind the backs of other prisoners when Serbs they knew suddenly showed up on the camp grounds. A poor Serb might search for the wealthy Muslim who refused to give him a job five years earlier; a farmer might try to find the Croat who, a decade before, refused to lend his tractor for a day; a middle-aged man might look around for the Muslim who, twenty-five years ago, stole away his high school sweetheart. Petty quarrels were settled with major crimes.

It sounds unbelievable, yet it happened. It makes me wonder what would happen if half the population of Peoria were put into a prison camp, and other half was told it could go into the camp and do whatever it wanted to whomever it wanted, and that no punishment need be feared, because any violent or sexual act committed against a prisoner would be an act of patriotism. It is an official invitation for the wild beast to come out from its hiding place. How many citizens of Peoria would yield to the temptation? How many would resist?

The thousands of pages pumped out by the U.S. Government Printing Office on behalf of the State Department are a valuable addition to the annals of human sadism. A passage in one report outlines the fate of a high school girl from Kozarac who was interned at Trnopolje:

> Three days after her arrival at the prison, she went with a large number of women and other girls to fetch water from a well about 50 meters from the prison gates. Returning from the well, Trnopolje guards held back six girls, including the witness, and stopped them from reentering the prison gates. They were then joined by four more female prisoners. The guards took the 10 girls to a house across the meadow. They were taken to the side yard of the house, out of sight of the roadway. Thirty Serbian soldiers—including "some dressed like a tank crew"—were there and they taunted the girls, calling them "Turkish whores." The girls were ordered to undress or have their clothes pulled off. Three girls resisted or hesitated from their fear. Their clothes were cut off with knives.
>
> The Serbian soldiers told the naked girls to parade slowly in a circle. The men sat at the outside of the circle—smoking, drinking, calling out foul names. The witness estimated the "parade" lasted about 15 minutes. Three soldiers took one girl—one to rape her while the two others held her down. The three men took turns. A soldier approached the witness and mocked her, saying he had seen her before. Though she did not recognize him, he pulled out a photo of the witness with her 19-year-old Muslim boyfriend, whom he cursed for being in the Bosnian Territorial Defense Forces. The man with the photograph raped her first. The witness said she fought and pulled his hair, but he bit her and hit her face. Her lips bled. He hit her hard with the butt of his gun on her cheek, causing extreme pain. Another rapist ran the blade of a knife across her breasts as if to slice the skin off, leaving bleeding scratches. After that, she was raped by eight more men before losing consciousness.

The reports become pornographic. It was the sort of pornography that repulses most people, but some are titillated by it. For a while, everyone in America and Western Europe was fascinated by it, for whatever reasons. The misery of Bosnia, it must be said, sold well in the summer and fall of 1992. Interest gradually tailed off, not because the atrocities were declining, but because America was growing tired of hearing about them. Even snuff films get boring after a while.

Nobel Peace Prize Lecture, December 10, 2004

Wangari Maathai

Wangari Maathai was born in 1940 in Nyeri, Kenya. She received her college education in the United States, earning her B.A. in biology from Mt. Scholastica College in Kansas and her M.A. from the University of Pittsburgh. She became the first woman in East and Central Africa to earn a Ph.D. when she graduated from the University of Nairobi in 1971. Maathai later became the head of the Department of Veterinary Anatomy at the University of Nairobi, again being the first woman in that region of Africa to ascend to such a high academic position. Maathai was awarded the Nobel Peace Prize in 2004 for her efforts to reverse African deforestation through the Green Belt Movement, a grassroots organization she began in Kenya in 1977. The program has been responsible for preventing soil erosion and has employed thousands of village women, who are paid for their efforts, money that has allowed them to better care for their children. The following selection is the lecture Maathai delivered when she received her Nobel Prize in Oslo, Norway, on December 10, 2004.

Your Majesties
Your Royal Highnesses
Honourable Members of the Norwegian Nobel Committee
Excellencies
Ladies and Gentlemen

I stand before you and the world humbled by this recognition and uplifted by the honour of being the 2004 Nobel Peace Laureate.

As the first African woman to receive this prize, I accept it on behalf of the people of Kenya and Africa, and indeed the world. I am especially mindful of women and the girl child. I hope it will encourage them to raise their voices and take more space for leadership. I know the honour also gives a deep sense of pride to our men, both old and young. As a mother, I appreciate the inspiration this brings to the youth and urge them to use it to pursue their dreams.

Although this prize comes to me, it acknowledges the work of countless individuals and groups across the globe. They work quietly and often without recognition to protect the environment, promote democracy, defend human rights and ensure equality between women and men. By so doing, they plant seeds of peace. I know they, too, are proud today. To all who feel represented by this prize I say use it to advance your mission and meet the high expectations the world will place on us.

This honour is also for my family, friends, partners and supporters throughout the world. All of them helped shape the vision and sustain our work, which was often accomplished under hostile conditions. I am also grateful to the people of Kenya — who remained stubbornly hopeful that democracy could be realized and their environment managed sustainably. Because of this support, I am here today to accept this great honour.

I am immensely privileged to join my fellow African Peace laureates, Presidents Nelson Mandela and F.W. de Klerk, Archbishop Desmond Tutu, the late Chief Albert Luthuli, the late Anwar el-Sadat and the UN Secretary General, Kofi Annan.

I know that African people everywhere are encouraged by this news. My fellow Africans, as we embrace this recognition, let us use it to intensify our commitment to our people, to reduce conflicts and poverty and thereby improve their quality of life. Let us embrace democratic governance, protect human rights and protect our environment. I am confident that we shall rise to the occasion. I have always believed that solutions to most of our problems must come from us.

In this year's prize, the Norwegian Nobel Committee has placed the critical issue of environment and its linkage to democracy and peace before the world. For their visionary action, I am profoundly grateful. Recognizing that sustainable development, democracy and peace are indivisible is an idea whose time has come. Our work over the past 30 years has always appreciated and engaged these linkages.

My inspiration partly comes from my childhood experiences and observations of Nature in rural Kenya. It has been influenced and nurtured by the formal education I was privileged to receive in Kenya, the United States and Germany. As I was growing up, I witnessed forests being cleared and replaced by commercial plantations, which destroyed local biodiversity and the capacity of the forests to conserve water.

Excellencies, ladies and gentlemen,

In 1977, when we started the Green Belt Movement, I was partly responding to needs identified by rural women, namely lack of firewood, clean drinking water, balanced diets, shelter and income.

Throughout Africa, women are the primary caretakers, holding significant responsibility for tilling the land and feeding their families. As a result, they are often the first to become aware of environmental damage as resources become scarce and incapable of sustaining their families.

The women we worked with recounted that unlike in the past, they were unable to meet their basic needs. This was due to the degradation of their immediate environment as well as the introduction of commercial farming, which replaced the growing of household food crops. But international trade controlled the price of the exports from these small-scale farmers and a reasonable and just income could not be guaranteed. I came to understand that when the environment is destroyed, plundered or mismanaged, we undermine our quality of life and that of future generations.

Tree planting became a natural choice to address some of the initial basic needs identified by women. Also, tree planting is simple, attainable and guarantees quick, successful results within a reasonable amount time. This sustains interest and commitment.

So, together, we have planted over 30 million trees that provide fuel, food, shelter, and income to support their children's education and household needs. The activity also creates employment and improves soils and watersheds. Through their involvement, women gain some degree of power over their lives, especially their social and economic position and relevance in the family. This work continues.

Initially, the work was difficult because historically our people have been persuaded to believe that because they are poor, they lack not only capital, but also knowledge and skills to address their challenges. Instead they are conditioned to believe that solutions to their problems must come from 'outside'. Further, women did not realize that meeting their needs depended on their environment being healthy and well managed. They were also unaware that a degraded environment leads to a scramble for scarce resources and may culminate in poverty and even conflict. They were also unaware of the injustices of international economic arrangements.

In order to assist communities to understand these linkages, we developed a citizen education program, during which people identify their problems, the causes and possible solutions. They then make connections between their own personal actions and the problems they witness in the environment and in society. They learn that our world is confronted with a litany of woes: corruption, violence against women and children, disruption and breakdown of families, and disintegration of cultures and communities. They also identify the abuse of drugs and chemical substances, especially among young people. There are also devastating diseases that are defying cures or occurring in epidemic proportions. Of particular concern are HIV/AIDS, malaria and diseases associated with malnutrition.

On the environment front, they are exposed to many human activities that are devastating to the environment and societies. These include widespread destruction of ecosystems, especially through deforestation, climatic instability, and contamination in the soils and waters that all contribute to excruciating poverty.

In the process, the participants discover that they must be part of the solutions. They realize their hidden potential and are empowered to overcome inertia and take action. They come to recognize that they are the primary custodians and beneficiaries of the environment that sustains them.

Entire communities also come to understand that while it is necessary to hold their governments accountable, it is equally important that in their own relationships with each other, they exemplify the leadership values they wish to see in their own leaders, namely justice, integrity and trust.

Although initially the Green Belt Movement's tree planting activities did not address issues of democracy and peace, it soon became clear that responsible governance of the environment was impossible without democratic space. Therefore, the tree became a symbol for the democratic struggle in Kenya. Citizens were mobilised to challenge widespread abuses of power, corruption and environmental mismanagement. In Nairobi's Uhuru Park, at Freedom Corner, and in many parts of the country, trees of peace were planted to demand the release of prisoners of conscience and a peaceful transition to democracy.

Through the Green Belt Movement, thousands of ordinary citizens were mobilized and empowered to take action and effect change. They learned to overcome fear and a sense of helplessness and moved to defend democratic rights.

In time, the tree also became a symbol for peace and conflict resolution, especially during ethnic conflicts in Kenya when the Green Belt Movement used peace trees to reconcile disputing communities. During the ongoing re-writing of the Kenyan constitution, similar trees of peace were planted in many parts of the country to promote a culture of peace. Using trees as a symbol of peace is in keeping with a widespread African tradition. For example, the elders of the Kikuyu carried a staff from the *thigi* tree that, when placed between two disputing sides, caused them to stop fighting and seek reconciliation. Many communities in Africa have these traditions.

Such practises are part of an extensive cultural heritage, which contributes both to the conservation of habitats and to cultures of peace. With the destruction of these cultures and the introduction of new values, local biodiversity is no longer valued or protected and as a result, it is quickly degraded and disappears. For this reason, The Green Belt Movement explores the concept of cultural biodiversity, especially with respect to indigenous seeds and medicinal plants.

As we progressively understood the causes of environmental degradation, we saw the need for good governance. Indeed, the state of any county's environment is a reflection of the kind of governance in place, and without good governance there can be no peace. Many countries, which have poor governance systems, are also likely to have conflicts and poor laws protecting the environment.

In 2002, the courage, resilience, patience and commitment of members of the Green Belt Movement, other civil society organizations, and the Kenyan public culminated in the peaceful transition to a democratic government and laid the foundation for a more stable society.

Excellencies, friends, ladies and gentlemen,

It is 30 years since we started this work. Activities that devastate the environment and societies continue unabated. Today we are faced with a challenge that calls for a shift in our thinking, so that humanity stops threatening its life-support system. We are called to assist the Earth to heal her wounds and in the process heal our own — indeed, to embrace the whole creation in all its diversity, beauty and wonder. This will happen if we see the need to revive our sense of belonging to a larger family of life, with which we have shared our evolutionary process.

In the course of history, there comes a time when humanity is called to shift to a new level of consciousness, to reach a higher moral ground. A time when we have to shed our fear and give hope to each other.

That time is now.

The Norwegian Nobel Committee has challenged the world to broaden the understanding of peace: there can be no peace without equitable development; and there can be no development without sustainable management of the environment in a democratic and peaceful space. This shift is an idea whose time has come.

I call on leaders, especially from Africa, to expand democratic space and build fair and just societies that allow the creativity and energy of their citizens to flourish.

Those of us who have been privileged to receive education, skills, and experiences and even power must be role models for the next generation of leadership. In this regard, I would also like to appeal for the freedom of my fellow laureate Aung San Suu Kyi so that she can continue her work for peace and democracy for the people of Burma and the world at large.

Culture plays a central role in the political, economic and social life of communities. Indeed, culture may be the missing link in the development of Africa. Culture is dynamic and evolves over time, consciously discarding retrogressive traditions, like female genital mutilation (FGM), and embracing aspects that are good and useful.

Africans, especially, should re-discover positive aspects of their culture. In accepting them, they would give themselves a sense of belonging, identity and self-confidence.

Ladies and Gentlemen,

There is also need to galvanize civil society and grassroots movements to catalyse change. I call upon governments to recognize the role of these social movements in building a critical mass of responsible citizens, who help maintain checks and balances in society. On their part, civil society should embrace not only their rights but also their responsibilities.

Further, industry and global institutions must appreciate that ensuring economic justice, equity and ecological integrity are of greater value than profits at any cost.

The extreme global inequities and prevailing consumption patterns continue at the expense of the environment and peaceful co-existence. The choice is ours.

I would like to call on young people to commit themselves to activities that contribute toward achieving their long-term dreams. They have the energy and creativity to shape a sustainable future. To the young people I say, you are a gift to your communities and indeed the world. You are our hope and our future.

The holistic approach to development, as exemplified by the Green Belt Movement, could be embraced and replicated in more parts of Africa and beyond. It is for this reason that I have established the Wangari Maathai Foundation to ensure the continuation and expansion of these activities. Although a lot has been achieved, much remains to be done.

Excellencies, ladies and gentlemen,

As I conclude I reflect on my childhood experience when I would visit a stream next to our home to fetch water for my mother. I would drink water straight from the stream. Playing among the arrowroot leaves I tried in vain to pick up the strands of frogs' eggs, believing they were beads. But every time I put my little fingers under them they would break. Later, I saw thousands of tadpoles:

black, energetic and wriggling through the clear water against the background of the brown earth. This is the world I inherited from my parents.

Today, over 50 years later, the stream has dried up, women walk long distances for water, which is not always clean, and children will never know what they have lost. The challenge is to restore the home of the tadpoles and give back to our children a world of beauty and wonder.

Thank you very much.

The Prince

Niccolò Machiavelli

Niccolò Machiavelli (1469–1527) was born in Florence, Italy and, in his 30s, was actively engaged in the political life of the Republic of Florence. After a shift in the political structure of Florence, Machiavelli was forced out of politics and exiled outside the city, where he continued his study of literature and history and began to write. He wrote The Prince *(1513),* The Discourses *(1519),* The Art of War *(1520), and* The Florentine History *(1525). These works were not actually published until later in the eighteenth century, and he has become widely read since as a political analyst and theorist. The following selection, which tells a prince how to rule, has been called "cold-blooded" by some; in fact, the adjective "machiavellian" means cunning, deceitful, and cynical. However, though his emphasis in* The Prince *on situational ethics may seem to pave the way for immoral behavior by rulers, Machiavelli's discussion of the relationship between morality and the negotiation of political power asks rulers to think about not only their actions but also the consequences of those actions.*

It is customary for those who wish to gain the favour of a prince to endeavour to do so by offering him gifts of those things which they hold most precious, or in which they know him to take especial delight. In this way princes are often presented with horses, arms, cloth of gold, gems, and such-like ornaments worthy of their grandeur. In my desire, however, to offer to Your Highness some humble testimony of my devotion, I have been unable to find among my possessions anything which I hold so dear or esteem so highly as that knowledge of the deeds of great men which I have acquired through a long experience of modern events and a constant study of the past.

With the utmost diligence I have long pondered and scrutinised the actions of the great, and now I offer the results to Your Highness within the compass of a small volume: and although I deem this work unworthy of Your Highness's acceptance, yet my confidence in your humanity assures me that you will receive it with favour, knowing that it is not in my power to offer you a greater gift than that of enabling you to understand in a very short time all those things which I have learnt at the cost of privation and danger in the course of many years. I have not sought to adorn my work with long phrases or high-sounding words or any of those superficial attractions and ornaments with which many writers seek to embellish their material, as I desire no honour for my work but such as the novelty and gravity of its subject may justly deserve. Nor will it, I trust, be deemed presumptuous on the part of a man of humble and obscure condition to attempt to discuss and direct the government of princes; for in the same way that landscape painters station themselves in the valleys in order to draw mountains or high ground, and ascend an eminence in order to get a good view of the plains, so it is necessary to be a prince to know thoroughly the nature of the people, and one of the populace to know the nature of princes.

May I trust, therefore, that Your Highness will accept this little gift in the spirit in which it is offered; and if Your Highness will deign to peruse it, you will recognize in it my ardent desire that you may attain to that grandeur which fortune and your own merits presage for you.

And should Your Highness gaze down from the summit of your lofty position towards this humble spot, you will recognise the great and unmerited sufferings inflicted on me by a cruel fate.

The Duties of a Prince with Regard to the Militia

A Prince should have no other aim or thought, nor take up any other thing for his study, but war and its organization and discipline, for that is the only art that is necessary to one who commands, and it is of such virtue that it not only maintains those who are born princes, but often enables men of private fortune to attain to that rank. And one sees, on the other hand, that when princes think more of luxury than of arms, they lose their state. The chief cause of the loss of states, is the contempt of this art, and the way to acquire them is to be well versed in the same.

Francesco Sforza, through being well armed, became, from private status, Duke of Milan; his sons, through wishing to avoid the fatigue and hardships of war, from dukes became private persons. For among other evils caused by being disarmed, it renders you contemptible; which is one of those disgraceful things which a prince must guard against, as will be explained later. Because there is no comparison whatever between an armed and a disarmed man; it is not reasonable to suppose that one who is armed will obey willingly one who is unarmed; or that any unarmed man will remain safe among armed servants. For one being disdainful and the other suspicious, it is not possible for them to act well together. And therefore a prince who is ignorant of military matters, besides the other misfortunes already mentioned, cannot be esteemed by his soldiers, nor have confidence in them.

He ought, therefore, never to let his thoughts stray from the exercise of war; and in peace he ought to practise it more than in war, which he can do in two ways: by action and by study. As to action, he must, besides keeping his men well disciplined and exercised, engage continually in hunting, and thus accustom his body to hardships; and meanwhile learn the nature of the land, how steep the mountains are, how the valleys debouch, where the plains lie, and understand the nature of rivers and swamps. To all this he should devote great attention. This knowledge is useful in two ways. In the first place, one learns to know one's country, and can the better see how to defend it. Then by means of the knowledge and experience gained in one locality, one can easily understand any other that it may be necessary to observe; for the hills and valleys, plains and rivers of Tuscany, for instance, have a certain resemblance to those of other provinces, so that from a knowledge of the country in one province one can easily arrive at a knowledge of others. And that prince who is lacking in this skill is wanting in the first essentials of a leader; for it is this which teaches how to find the enemy, take up quarters, lead armies, plan battles and lay siege to towns with advantage.

Philopoemen, prince of the Achaei, among other praises bestowed on him by writers, is lauded because in times of peace he thought of nothing but the methods of warfare, and when he was in the country with his friends, he often stopped and asked them: If the enemy were on that hill and we found ourselves here with our army, which of us would have the advantage? How could we safely approach him maintaining our order? If we wished to retire, what ought we to do? If they retired, how should we follow them? And he put before them as they went along all the contingencies that might happen to an army, heard their opinion, gave his own, fortifying it by argument; so that thanks to these constant reflections there could never happen any incident when actually leading his armies for which he was not prepared.

But as to exercise for the mind, the prince ought to read history and study the actions of eminent men, see how they acted in warfare, examine the causes of their victories and defeats in order to imitate the former and avoid the latter, and above all, do as some men have done in the past, who have imitated some one, who has been much praised and glorified, and have always kept his deeds and actions before them, as they say Alexander the Great imitated

Achilles, Caesar Alexander, and Scipio Cyrus. And whoever reads the life of Cyrus written by Xenophon, will perceive in the life of Scipio how gloriously he imitated the former, and how, in chastity, affability, humanity, and liberality Scipio conformed to those qualities of Cyrus as described by Xenophon.

A wise prince should follow similar methods and never remain idle in peaceful times, but industriously make good use of them, so that when fortune changes she may find him prepared to resist her blows, and to prevail in adversity.

Of the Things for Which Men, and Especially Princes, are Praised or Blamed

It now remains to be seen what are the methods and rules for a prince as regards his subjects and friends. And as I know that many have written of this, I fear that my writing about it may be deemed presumptuous, differing as I do, especially in this matter, from the opinions of others. But my intention being to write something of use to those who understand, it appears to me more proper to go to the real truth of the matter than to its imagination; and many have imagined republics and principalities which have never been seen or known to exist in reality; for how we live is so far removed from how we ought to live, that he who abandons what is done for what ought to be done, will rather learn to bring about his own ruin than his preservation. A man who wishes to make a profession of goodness in everything must necessarily come to grief among so many who are not good. Therefore it is necessary for a prince, who wishes to maintain himself, to learn how not to be good, and to use this knowledge and not use it, according to the necessity of the case.

Leaving on one side, then, those things which concern only an imaginary prince, and speaking of those that are real, I state that all men, and especially princes, who are placed at a greater height, are reputed for certain qualities which bring them either praise or blame. Thus one is considered liberal, another *misero* or miserly (using a Tuscan term, seeing that *avaro* with us still means one who is rapaciously acquisitive and *misero* one who makes grudging use of his own); one a free giver, another rapacious; one cruel, another merciful; one a breaker of his word, another trustworthy; one effeminate and pusillanimous, another fierce and high-spirited; one humane, another haughty; one lascivious, another chaste; one frank, another astute; one hard, another easy; one serious, another frivolous; one religious, another an unbeliever, and so on. I know that every one will admit that it would be highly praiseworthy in a prince to possess all the above-named qualities that are reputed good, but as they cannot all be possessed or observed, human conditions not permitting of it, it is necessary that he should be prudent enough to avoid the scandal of those vices which would lose him the state, and guard himself if possible against those which will not lose it him, but if not able to, he can indulge them with less scruple. And yet he must not mind incurring the scandal of those vices, without which it would be difficult to save the state, for if one considers well, it will be found that some things which seem virtues would, if followed, lead to one's ruin, and some others which appear vices result in one's greater security and wellbeing.

Of Liberality and Niggardliness

Beginning now with the first qualities above named, I say that it would be well to be considered liberal; nevertheless liberality such as the world understands it will injure you, because if used virtuously and in the proper way, it will not be known, and you will incur the disgrace of the contrary vice. But one who wishes to obtain the reputation of liberality among men, must not omit every kind of sumptuous display, and to such an extent that a prince of this character will consume by such means all his resources, and will be at last compelled, if he wishes to maintain his name for liberality, to impose heavy taxes on his people, become extortionate, and do everything possible to obtain money. This will make his subjects begin to hate him, and he will be little esteemed being poor, so that having by this liberality injured many and benefited but few, he will feel the first little disturbance and be endangered by every peril. If he recognises this and wishes to change his system, he incurs at once the charge of niggardliness.

A prince, therefore, not being able to exercise this virtue of liberality without risk if it be known, must not, if he be prudent, object to be called miserly. In course of time he will be thought more liberal, when it is seen that by his parsimony his revenue is sufficient, that he can defend himself against those who make war on him, and undertake enterprises without burdening his people, so that he is really liberal to all those from whom he does not take, who are infinite in number, and niggardly to all to whom he does not give, who are few. In our times we have seen nothing great done except by those who have been esteemed niggardly; the others have all been ruined. Pope Julius II, although he had made use of a reputation for liberality in order to attain the papacy, did not seek to retain it afterwards, so that he might be able to wage war. The present King of France has carried on so many wars without imposing an extraordinary tax, because his extra expenses were covered by the parsimony he had so long practised. The present King of Spain, if he had been thought liberal, would not have engaged in and been successful in so many enterprises.

For these reasons a prince must care little for the reputation of being a miser, if he wishes to avoid robbing his subjects, if he wishes to be able to defend himself, to avoid becoming poor and contemptible, and not to be forced to become rapacious; his niggardliness is one of those vices which enable him to reign. If it is said that Caesar attained the empire through liberality, and that many others have reached the highest positions through being liberal or being thought so, I would reply that you are either a prince already or else on the way to become one. In the first case, this liberality is harmful; in the second, it is certainly necessary to be considered liberal. Caesar was one of those who wished to attain the mastery over Rome, but if after attaining it he had lived and had not moderated his expenses, he would have destroyed that empire. And should any one reply that there have been many princes, who have done great things with their armies, who have been thought extremely liberal, I would answer by saying that the prince may either spend his own wealth and that of his subjects or the wealth of others. In the first case he must be sparing, but for the rest he must not neglect to be very liberal. The liberality is very necessary to a prince who marches with his armies, and lives by plunder, sack and ransom, and is dealing with the wealth of others, for without it he would not be followed by his soldiers. And you may be very generous indeed with what is not the property of yourself or your subjects, as were Cyrus, Caesar, and Alexander; for spending the wealth of others will not diminish your reputation, but increase it, only spending your own resources will injure you. There is nothing which destroys itself so much as liberality, for by using it you lose the power of using it, and become either poor and despicable, or, to escape poverty, rapacious and hated. And of all things that a prince must guard against, the most important are being despicable or hated, and liberality will lead you to one or the other of these conditions. It is, therefore, wiser to have the name of a miser, which produces disgrace without hatred, than to incur of necessity the name of being rapacious, which produces both disgrace and hatred.

Of Cruelty and Clemency, and Whether It Is Better To Be Loved or Feared

Proceeding to the other qualities before named, I say that every prince must desire to be considered merciful and not cruel. He must, however, take care not to misuse this mercifulness. Cesare Borgia was considered cruel, but his cruelty had brought order to the Romagna, united it, and reduced it to peace and fealty. If this is considered well, it will be seen that he was really much more merciful than the Florentine people, who, to avoid the name of cruelty, allowed Pistoia to be destroyed. A prince, therefore, must not mind incurring the charge of cruelty for the purpose of keeping his subjects united and faithful; for, with a very few examples, he will be more merciful than those who, from excess of tenderness, allow disorders to arise, from whence spring bloodshed and rapine; for these as a rule injure the whole community, while the executions carried out by the prince injure only individuals. And of all princes, it is impossible for a new prince to escape the reputation of cruelty, new states being always full of dangers. Wherefore Virgil through the mouth of Dido says:

> Res dura, et regni novitas me talia cogunt[1]
> Moliri, et late fines custode tueri.

Nevertheless, he must be cautious in believing and acting, and must not be afraid of his own shadow, and must proceed in a temperate manner with prudence and humanity, so that too much confidence does not render him incautious, and too much diffidence does not render him intolerant.

From this arises the question whether it is better to be loved more than feared, or feared more than loved. The reply is, that one ought to be both feared and loved, but as it is difficult for the two to go together, it is much safer to be feared than loved, if one of the two has to be wanting. For it may be said of men in general that they are ungrateful, voluble, dissemblers, anxious to avoid danger, and covetous of gain; as long as you benefit them, they are entirely yours; they offer you their blood, their goods, their life, and their children, as I have before said, when the necessity is remote; but when it approaches, they revolt. And the prince who has relied solely on their words, without making other preparations, is ruined; for the friendship which is gained by purchase and not through grandeur and nobility of spirit is bought but not secured, and at a pinch is not to be expended in your service. And men have less scruple in offending one who makes himself loved than one who makes himself feared; for love is held by a chain of obligation which, men being selfish, is broken whenever it serves their purpose; but fear is maintained by a dread of punishment which never fails.

Still, a prince should make himself feared in such a way that if he does not gain love, he at any rate avoids hatred; for fear and the absence of hatred may well go together, and will be always attained by one who abstains from interfering with the property of his citizens and subjects or with their women. And when he is obliged to take the life of any one, let him do so when there is a proper justification and manifest reason for it; but above all he must abstain from taking the property of others, for men forget more easily the death of their father than the loss of their patrimony. Then also pretexts for seizing property are never wanting, and one who begins to live by rapine will always find some reason for taking the goods of others, whereas causes for taking life are rarer and more fleeting.

But when the prince is with his army and has a large number of soldiers under his control, then it is extremely necessary that he should not mind being thought cruel; for without this reputation he could not keep an army united or disposed to any duty. Among the noteworthy actions of Hannibal is numbered this, that although he had an enormous army, composed of men of all nations and fighting in foreign countries, there never arose any dissension either among them or against the prince, either in good fortune or in bad. This could not be due to anything but his inhuman cruelty, which together with his infinite other virtues, made him always venerated and terrible in the sight of his soldiers, and without it his other virtues would not have sufficed to produce that effect. Thoughtless writers admire on the one hand his actions, and on the other blame the principal cause of them.

And that it is true that his other virtues would not have sufficed may be seen from the case of Scipio (famous not only in regard to his own times, but all times of which memory remains), whose armies rebelled against him in Spain, which arose from nothing but his excessive kindness, which allowed more licence to the soldiers than was consonant with military discipline. He was reproached with this in the senate by Fabius Maximus, who called him a corrupter of the Roman militia. Locri having been destroyed by one of Scipio's officers was not revenged by him, nor was the insolence of that officer punished, simply by reason of his easy nature; so much so, that some one wishing to excuse him in the senate, said that there were many men who knew rather how not to err, than how to correct the errors of others. This disposition would in time have tarnished the fame and glory of Scipio had he persevered in it under the empire, but living under the rule of the senate this harmful quality was not only concealed but became a glory to him.

I conclude, therefore, with regard to being feared and loved, that men love at their own free will, but fear at the will of the prince, and that a wise prince must rely on what is in his power and not on what is in the power of others, and he must only contrive to avoid incurring hatred, as has been explained.

In What Ways Princes Must Keep Faith

How laudable it is for a prince to keep good faith and live with integrity, and not with astuteness, every one knows. Still the experience of our times shows those princes to have done great things who have had little regard for good faith, and have been able by astuteness to confuse men's brains, and who have ultimately overcome those who have made loyalty their foundation.

You must know, then, that there are two methods of fighting, the one by law, the other by force: the first method is that of men, the second of beasts; but as the first method is often insufficient, one must have recourse to the second. It is therefore necessary for a prince to know well how to use both the beast and the man. This was covertly taught to rulers by ancient writers, who relate how Achilles and many others of those ancient princes were given to Chiron the centaur to be brought up and educated under his discipline. The parable of this semi-animal, semi-human teacher is meant to indicate that a prince must know how to use both natures, and that the one without the other is not durable.

A prince being thus obliged to know well how to act as a beast must imitate the fox and the lion, for the lion cannot protect himself from traps, and the fox cannot defend himself from wolves. One must therefore be a fox to recognise traps, and a lion to frighten wolves. Those that wish to be only lions do not understand this. Therefore, a prudent ruler ought not to keep faith when by so doing it would be against his interest, and when the reasons which made him bind himself no longer exist. If men were all good, this precept would not be a good one; but as they are bad, and would not observe their faith with you, so you are not bound to keep faith with them. Nor have legitimate grounds ever failed a prince who wished to show colourable excuse for the non-fulfilment of his promise. Of this one could furnish an infinite number of modern examples, and show how many times peace has been broken, and how many promises rendered worthless, by the faithlessness of princes, and those that have been best able to imitate the fox have succeeded best. But it is necessary to be able to disguise this character well, and to be a great feigner and dissembler; and men are so simple and so ready to obey present necessities, that one who deceives will always find those who allow themselves to be deceived.

I will only mention one modern instance. Alexander VI did nothing else but deceive men, he thought of nothing else, and found the occasion for it; no man was ever more able to give assurances, or affirmed things with stronger oaths, and no man observed them less; however, he always succeeded in his deceptions, as he well knew this aspect of things.

It is not, therefore, necessary for a prince to have all the above-named qualities, but it is very necessary to seem to have them. I would even be bold to say that to possess them and always to observe them is dangerous, but to appear to possess them is useful. Thus it is well to seem merciful, faithful, humane, sincere, religious, and also to be so; but you must have the mind so disposed that when it is needful to be otherwise you may be able to change to the opposite qualities. And it must be understood that a prince, and especially a new prince, cannot observe all those things which are considered good in men, being often obliged, in order to maintain the state, to act against faith, against charity, against humanity, and against religion. And, therefore, he must have a mind disposed to adapt itself according to the wind, and as the variations of fortune dictate, and, as I said before, not deviate from what is good, if possible, but be able to do evil if constrained.

A prince must take great care that nothing goes out of his mouth which is not full of the above-named five qualities, and, to see and hear him, he should seem to be all mercy, faith, integrity, humanity, and religion. And nothing is more necessary than to seem to have this last quality, for men in general judge more by the eyes than by the hands, for every one can see, but very few have to feel. Everybody sees what you appear to be, few feel what you are, and those few will not dare to oppose themselves to the many, who have the majesty of the state to defend them; and in the actions of men, and especially of princes, from which there is no appeal, the end justifies the means. Let a prince therefore aim at conquering and maintaining the state, and the means will always be judged honourable and praised by every one, for the vulgar is always taken by appearances and the issue of the event; and the world consists only of the vulgar, and the few who are not vulgar are isolated when the many have a rallying point in the prince. A certain prince of the present time, whom it is well not to name, never does anything but preach peace and good faith, but he is really a great enemy to both, and either of them, had he observed them, would have lost him state or reputation on many occasions.

That We Must Avoid Being Despised and Hated

But as I have now spoken of the most important of the qualities in question, I will now deal briefly and generally with the rest. The prince must, as already stated, avoid those things which will make him hated or despised; and whenever he succeeds in this, he will have done his part, and will find no danger in other vices. He will chiefly become hated, as I said, by being rapacious, and usurping the property and women of his subjects, which he must abstain from doing, and whenever one does not attack the property or honour of the generality of men, they will live contented; and one will only have to combat the ambition of a few, who can be easily held in check in many ways. He is rendered despicable by being thought changeable, frivolous, effeminate, timid, and irresolute; which a prince must guard against as a rock of danger, and so contrive that his actions show grandeur, spirit, gravity, and fortitude; and as to the government of his subjects, let his sentence be irrevocable, and let him adhere to his decisions so that no one may think of deceiving or cozening him.

The prince who creates such an opinion of himself gets a great reputation, and it is very difficult to conspire against one who has a great reputation, and he will not easily be attacked, so long as it is known that he is capable and reverenced by his subjects. For a prince must have two kinds of fear: one internal as regards his subjects, one external as regards foreign powers. From the latter he can defend himself with good arms and good friends, and he will always have good friends if he has good arms; and internal matters will always remain quiet, if they are not perturbed by conspiracy and there is no disturbance from without; and even if external powers sought to attack him, if he has ruled and lived as I have described, he will always if he stands firm, be able to sustain every shock, as I have shown that Nabis the Spartan did. But with regard to the subjects, if not acted on from outside, it is still to be feared lest they conspire in secret, from which the prince may guard himself well by avoiding hatred and contempt, and keeping the people satisfied with him, which it is necessary to accomplish, as has been related at length. And one of the most potent remedies that a prince has against conspiracies, is that of not being hated by the mass of the people; for whoever conspires always believes that he will satisfy the people by the death of their prince; but if he thought to offend them by doing this, he would fear to engage in such an undertaking, for the difficulties that conspirators have to meet are infinite. Experience shows that there have been very many conspiracies, but few have turned out well, for whoever conspires cannot act alone, and cannot find companions except among those who are discontented; and as soon as you have disclosed your intention to a malcontent, you give him the means of satisfying himself, for by revealing it he can hope to secure everything he wants; to such an extent that seeing a certain gain by doing this, and seeing on the other hand only a doubtful one and full of danger, he must either be a rare friend to you or else a very bitter enemy to the prince if he keeps faith with you. And to express the matter in a few words, I say, that on the side of the conspirator there is nothing but fear, jealousy, suspicion, and dread of punishment which frightens him; and on the side of the prince there is the majesty of government, the laws, the protection of friends and of the state which guard him. When to these things is added the goodwill of the people, it is impossible that any one should have the temerity to conspire. For whereas generally a conspirator has to fear before the execution of his plot, in this case, having the people for an enemy, he must also fear after his crime is accomplished, and thus he is not able to hope for any refuge.

Endnote

1. "Harsh necessity and newness of the kingdom force me to take such stern measures, and far and wide to secure my borders with guards."

I Am Prepared to Die

Nelson Mandela

Nelson Rolihlahla Mandela (1918–) was born to the Thembu Xhosa family in the village of Mvezo in the Umtata district, capital of the Transkei, in the Eastern Cape Province of South Africa. Mandela's father, Gadla Henry Mphakanyiswa, was a counsel to the Thembu king, a position for which Mandela was groomed from birth and was destined to inherit. When he was seven, Rolihlahla Mandela became the first member of his family to attend a school, where a Methodist teacher named him Nelson. As a student, Mandela became involved in political opposition to the white minority government's denial of political, social, and economic rights to South Africa's black majority and joined the African National Congress (ANC) in 1942. Although Mandela is well-known for the violent tactics he used against the apartheid regime in South Africa, he was initially committed to ending apartheid through non-violent mehtods. In 1961, however, he became the co-founder and leader of the ANC's armed wing, Umkhonto we Sizwe (translated as Spear of the Nation*). With Umkhonto, he co-ordinated a sabotage campaign against military and government targets and made plans to wage a guerilla war against the South African regime if sabotage failed to end apartheid. The apartheid regime considered him and the ANC to be terrorists, and, on August 5, 1962, after living on the run for seventeen months, Mandela was arrested and imprisoned in the Johannesburg Fort. On October 25, 1962, he was sentenced to five years in prison. Two years later, on June 11, 1964, a second verdict was reached concerning his previous involvement with the ANC. While Mandela was in prison, the South Arican government had brought more charges of the capital crimes of sabotage and treason against Mandela and other ANC leaders. These charges included planning armed action, in particular sabotage, to which Mandela admitted, and conspiring to help other countries invade South Africa, which he denied. Mandela was found guilty, and, on June 12, 1964, he was sentenced to* *life imprisonment. Over the next twenty-six years, Mandela became increasingly associated with opposition to apartheid, and the slogan "Free Nelson Mandela" became the rallying cry for anti-apartheid activists around the world. In February 1985, he refused an offer of conditional release in return for renouncing armed struggle. He remained in prison until February 11, 1990, when State President F.W. de Klerk, giving in to sustained ANC campaigning and international pressure, ordered Mandela's release and ended the ban on the ANC; Mandela and De Klerk shared the Nobel Peace Prize in 1993. On April 27, 1994, Mandela became the first President of South Africa to be elected in fully-representative democratic elections. As President (1994–1999), Mandela presided over the transition from minority rule and apartheid, winning international respect for his advocacy of national and international reconciliation.*

Second Court Statement, 1964

Mandela's statement from the dock in Pretoria Supreme Court, 20 April 1964, at the opening of the defense case.

I am the First Accused.

I hold a Bachelor's Degree in Arts and practised as an attorney in Johannesburg for a number of years in partnership with Oliver Tambo. I am a convicted prisoner serving five years for leaving the country without a permit and for inciting people to go on strike at the end of May 1961.

At the outset, I want to say that the suggestion made by the State in its opening that the struggle in South Africa is under the influence of foreigners or communists is wholly incorrect. I have done whatever I did, both as an individual and as a leader of my people, because of my experience in South Africa and my own proudly felt African background, and not because of what any outsider might have said.

In my youth in the Transkei I listened to the elders of my tribe telling stories of the old days. Amongst the tales they related to me were those of wars fought by our ancestors in defense of the fatherland. The names of Dingane and Bambata, Hintsa and Makana, Squngthi and Dalasile, Moshoeshoe and Sekhukhuni, were praised as the glory of the entire African nation. I hoped then that life might offer me the opportunity to serve my people and make my own humble contribution to their freedom struggle. This is what has motivated me in all that I have done in relation to the charges made against me in this case.

Having said this, I must deal immediately and at some length with the question of violence. Some of the things so far told to the Court are true and some are untrue. I do not, however, deny that I planned sabotage. I did not plan it in a spirit of recklessness, nor because I have any love of violence. I planned it as a result of a calm and sober assessment of the political situation that had arisen after many years of tyranny, exploitation, and oppression of my people by the Whites.

I admit immediately that I was one of the persons who helped to form Umkhonto we Sizwe, and that I played a prominent role in its affairs until I was arrested in August 1962.

In the statement which I am about to make I shall correct certain false impressions which have been created by State witnesses. Amongst other things, I will demonstrate that certain of the acts referred to in the evidence were not and could not have been committed by Umkhonto. I will also deal with the relationship between the African National Congress and Umkhonto, and with the part which I personally have played in the affairs of both organizations. I shall deal also with the part played by the Communist Party. In order to explain these matters properly, I will have to explain what Umkhonto set out to achieve; what methods it prescribed for the achievement of these objects; and why these methods were chosen. I will also have to explain how I became involved in the activities of these organizations.

I deny that Umkhonto was responsible for a number of acts which clearly fell outside the policy of the organization, and which have been charged in the indictment against us. I do not know what justification there was for these acts, but to demonstrate that they could not have been authorized by Umkhonto, I want to refer briefly to the roots and policy of the organization.

I have already mentioned that I was one of the persons who helped to form Umkhonto. I, and the others who started the organization, did so for two reasons. Firstly, we believed that as a result of Government policy, violence by the African people had become inevitable, and that unless responsible leadership was given to canalize and control the feelings of our people, there would be outbreaks of terrorism which would produce an intensity of bitterness and hostility between the various races of this country which is not produced even by war. Secondly, we felt that without violence there would be no way open to the African people to succeed in their struggle against the principle of white supremacy. All lawful modes of expressing opposition to this principle had been closed by legislation, and we were placed in a position in which we had either to accept a permanent state of inferiority, or to defy the Government. We chose to defy the law. We first broke the law in a way which avoided any recourse to violence; when this form was legislated against, and then the Government resorted to a show of force to crush opposition to its policies, only then did we decide to answer violence with violence.

But the violence which we chose to adopt was not terrorism. We who formed Umkhonto were all members of the African National Congress, and had behind us the ANC tradition of non-violence and negotiation as a means of solving political disputes. We believe that South Africa belongs to all the people who live in it, and not to one group, be it black or white. We did not want an interracial war, and tried to avoid it to the last minute. If the Court is in doubt about this, it will be seen that the whole history of our organization bears out what I have said, and what I will subsequently say, when I describe the tactics which Umkhonto decided to adopt. I want, therefore, to say something about the African National Congress.

The African National Congress was formed in 1912 to defend the rights of the African people which had been seriously curtailed by the South Africa Act, and which were then being threatened by the Native Land Act. For thirty-seven years—that is until 1949—it adhered strictly to a constitutional struggle. It put forward demands and resolutions; it sent delegations to the Government in the belief that African grievances could be settled through peaceful discussion and that Africans could advance gradually to full political rights. But White Governments remained unmoved, and the rights of Africans became less instead of becoming greater. In the words of my leader, Chief Lutuli, who became President of the ANC in 1952, and who was later awarded the Nobel Peace Prize:

> Who will deny that thirty years of my life have been spent knocking in vain, patiently, moderately, and modestly at a closed and barred door? What have been the fruits of moderation? The past thirty years have seen the greatest number of laws restricting our rights and progress, until today we have reached a stage where we have almost no rights at all.

Even after 1949, the ANC remained determined to avoid violence. At this time, however, there was a change from the strictly constitutional means of protest which had been employed in the past. The change was embodied in a decision which was taken to protest against apartheid legislation by peaceful, but unlawful, demonstrations against certain laws. Pursuant to this policy the ANC launched the Defiance Campaign, in which I was placed in charge of volunteers. This campaign was based on the principles of passive resistance. More than 8,500 people defied apartheid laws and went to jail. Yet there was not a single instance of violence in the course of this campaign on the part of any defier. I and nineteen colleagues were convicted for the role which we played in organizing the campaign, but our sentences were suspended mainly because the judge found that discipline and non-violence had been stressed throughout. This was the time when the volunteer section of the ANC was established, and when the word "Amadelakufa"[1] was first used: This was the time when the volunteers were asked to take a pledge to uphold certain principles. Evidence dealing with volunteers and their pledges has been introduced into this case, but completely out of context. The volunteers were not, and are not, the soldiers of a black army pledged to fight a civil war against the whites. They were, and are, dedicated workers who are prepared to lead campaigns initiated by the ANC to distribute leaflets, to organize strikes, or do whatever the particular campaign required. They are called volunteers because they volunteer to face the penalties of imprisonment and whipping which are now prescribed by the legislature for such acts.

During the Defiance Campaign, the Public Safety Act and the Criminal Law Amendment Act were passed. These Statutes provided harsher penalties for offences committed by way of protests against laws. Despite this, the protests continued and the ANC adhered to its policy of non-violence. In 1956, 156 leading members of the Congress Alliance, including myself, were arrested on a charge of high treason and charges under the Suppression of Communism Act. The non-violent policy of the ANC was put in issue by the State, but when the Court gave judgement some five years later, it found that the ANC did not have a policy of violence. We were acquitted on all counts, which included a count that the ANC sought to set up a communist state in place of the existing regime. The Government has always sought to label all its opponents as communists. This allegation has been repeated in the present case, but as I will show, the ANC is not, and never has been, a communist organization.

In 1960 there was the shooting at Sharpeville,[2] which resulted in the proclamation of a state of emergency and the declaration of the ANC as an unlawful organization. My colleagues and I, after careful consideration, decided that we would not obey this decree. The African people were not part of the Government and did not make the laws by which they were governed. We believed in the words of the Universal Declaration of Human Rights, that "the will of the people shall be the basis of authority of the Government," and for us to accept the banning was equivalent to accepting the silencing of the Africans for all time. The ANC refused to dissolve, but instead went underground. We believed it was our duty to preserve this organization which had been built up with almost fifty years of unremitting toil. I have no doubt that no self-respecting White political organization would disband itself if declared illegal by a government in which it had no say.

In 1960 the Government held a referendum which led to the establishment of the Republic. Africans, who constituted approximately 70 per cent of the population of South Africa, were not entitled to vote, and were not even consulted about the proposed constitutional change. All of us were apprehensive of our future under the proposed White Republic, and a resolution was taken to hold an All-In African Conference to call for a National Convention, and to organize mass demonstrations on the eve of the unwanted Republic, if the Government failed to call the Convention. The conference was attended by Africans of various political persuasions. I was the Secretary of the conference and undertook to be responsible for organizing the national stay-at-home which was subsequently called to coincide with the declaration of the Republic. As all strikes by Africans are illegal, the person organizing such a strike must avoid arrest. I was chosen to be this person, and consequently I had to leave my home and family and my practice and go into hiding to avoid arrest.

The stay-at-home, in accordance with ANC policy, was to be a peaceful demonstration. Careful instructions were given to organizers and members to avoid any recourse to violence. The Government's answer was to introduce new and harsher laws, to mobilize its armed forces, and to send Saracens,[3] armed vehicles, and soldiers into the townships in a massive show of force designed to intimidate the people. This was an indication that the Government had decided to rule by force alone, and this decision was a milestone on the road to Umkhonto.

Some of this may appear irrelevant to this trial. In fact, I believe none of it is irrelevant because it will, I hope, enable the Court to appreciate the attitude eventually adopted by the various persons and bodies concerned in the National Liberation Movement. When I went to jail in 1962, the dominant idea was that loss of life should be avoided. I now know that this was still so in 1963.

I must return to June 1961. What were we, the leaders of our people, to do? Were we to give in to the show of force and the implied threat against future action, or were we to fight it and, if so, how?

We had no doubt that we had to continue the fight. Anything else would have been abject surrender. Our problem was not whether to fight, but was how to continue the fight. We of the ANC had always stood for a non-racial democracy, and we shrank from any action which might drive the races further apart than they already were. But the hard facts were that fifty years of non-violence had brought the African people nothing but more and more repressive legislation, and fewer and fewer rights. It may not be easy for this Court to understand, but it is a fact that for a long time the people had been talking of violence—of the day when they would fight the White man and win back their country—and we, the leaders of the ANC, had nevertheless always prevailed upon them to avoid violence and to pursue peaceful methods. When some of us discussed this in May and June of 1961, it could not be denied that our policy to achieve a nonracial State by non-violence had achieved nothing, and that our followers were beginning to lose confidence in this policy and were developing disturbing ideas of terrorism.

It must not be forgotten that by this time violence had, in fact, become a feature of the South African political scene. There had been violence in 1957 when the women of Zeerust were ordered to carry passes; there was violence in 1958 with the enforcement of cattle culling in Sekhukhuniland; there was violence in 1959 when the people of Cato Manor protested against pass raids; there was violence in 1960 when the Government attempted to impose Bantu Authorities in Pondoland. Thirty-nine Africans died in these disturbances. In 1961 there had been riots in Warmbaths, and all this time the Transkei had been a seething mass of unrest. Each disturbance pointed clearly to the inevitable growth among Africans of the belief that violence was the only way out—it showed that a Government which uses force to maintain its rule teaches the oppressed to use force to oppose it. Already small groups had arisen in the urban areas and were spontaneously making plans for violent forms of political struggle. There now arose a danger that these groups would adopt terrorism against Africans, as well as Whites, if not properly directed. Particularly disturbing was the type of violence engendered in places such as Zeerust, Sekhukhuniland, and Pondoland amongst Africans. It was increasingly taking the form, not of struggle against the Government—though this is what prompted it—but of civil strife amongst themselves, conducted in such a way that it could not hope to achieve anything other than a loss of life and bitterness.

At the beginning of June 1961, after a long and anxious assessment of the South African situation, I, and some colleagues, came to the conclusion that as violence in this country was inevitable, it would be unrealistic and wrong for African leaders to continue preaching peace and non-violence at a time when the Government met our peaceful demands with force.

This conclusion was not easily arrived at. It was only when all else had failed, when all channels of peaceful protest had been barred to us, that the decision was made to embark on violent forms of political struggle, and to form Umkhonto we Sizwe. We did so not because we desired such a course, but solely because the Government had left us with no other choice. In the Manifesto of Umkhonto published on 16 December 1961, which is Exhibit AD, we said:

> The time comes in the life of any nation when there remain only two choices—submit or fight. That time has now come to South Africa. We shall not submit and we have no choice but to hit back by all means in our power in defense of our people, our future, and our freedom.

This was our feeling in June of 1961 when we decided to press for a change in the policy of the National Liberation Movement. I can only say that I felt morally obliged to do what I did.

We who had taken this decision started to consult leaders of various organizations, including the ANC. I will not say whom we spoke to, or what they said, but I wish to deal with the role of the African National Congress in this phase of the struggle, and with the policy and objectives of Umkhonto we Sizwe.

As far as the ANC was concerned, it formed a clear view which can be summarized as follows:

a. It was a mass political organization with a political function to fulfill. Its members had joined on the express policy of non-violence.

b. Because of all this, it could not and would not undertake violence. This must be stressed. One cannot turn such a body into the small, closely knit organization required for sabotage. Nor would this be politically correct, because it would result in members ceasing to carry out this essential activity: political propaganda and organization. Nor was it permissible to change the whole nature of the organization.

c. On the other hand, in view of this situation I have described, the ANC was prepared to depart from its fifty-year-old policy of nonviolence to this extent that it would no longer disapprove of properly controlled violence. Hence members who undertook such activity would not be subject to disciplinary action by the ANC.

I say "properly controlled violence" because I made it clear that if I formed the organization I would at all times subject it to the political guidance of the ANC and would not undertake any different form of activity from that contemplated without the consent of the ANC. And I shall now tell the Court how that form of violence came to be determined.

As a result of this decision, Umkhonto was formed in November 1961. When we took this decision, and subsequently formulated our plans, the ANC heritage of nonviolence and racial harmony was very much with us. We felt that the country was drifting towards a civil war in which Blacks and Whites would fight each other. We viewed the situation with alarm. Civil war could mean the destruction of what the ANC stood for; with civil war, racial peace would be more difficult than ever to achieve. We already have examples in South African history of the results of war. It has taken more than fifty years for the scars of the South African War to disappear. How much longer would it take to eradicate the scars of inter-racial civil war, which could not be fought without a great loss of life on both sides?

The avoidance of civil war had dominated our thinking for many years, but when we decided to adopt violence as part of our policy, we realized that we might one day have to face the prospect of such a war. This had to be taken into account in formulating our plans. We required a plan which was flexible and which permitted us to act in accordance with the needs of the times; above all, the plan had to be one which recognized civil war as the last resort, and left the decision on this question to the future. We did not want to be committed to civil war, but we wanted to be ready if it became inevitable.

Four forms of violence were possible. There is sabotage, there is guerrilla warfare, there is terrorism, and there is open revolution. We chose to adopt the first method and to exhaust it before taking any other decision.

In the light of our political background the choice was a logical one. Sabotage did not involve loss of life, and it offered the best hope for future race relations. Bitterness would be kept to a minimum and, if the policy bore fruit, democratic government could become a reality. This is what we felt at the time, and this is what we said in our Manifesto (Exhibit AD):

> We of Umkhonto We Sizwe have always sought to achieve liberation without bloodshed and civil clash. We hope, even at this late hour, that our first actions will awaken everyone to a realization of the disastrous situation to which the Nationalist policy is leading. We hope that we will bring the Government and its supporters to their senses before it is too late, so that both the Government and its policies can be changed before matters reach the desperate stage of civil war.

The initial plan was based on a careful analysis of the political and economic situation of our country. We believed that South Africa depended to a large extent on foreign capital and foreign trade. We felt that planned destruction of power plants, and interference with rail and telephone communications, would tend to scare away capital from the country, make it more difficult for goods from the industrial areas to reach the seaports on schedule, and would in the long run be a heavy drain on the economic life of the country, thus compelling the voters of the country to reconsider their position.

Attacks on the economic life lines of the country were to be linked with sabotage on Government buildings and other symbols of apartheid. These attacks would serve as a source of inspiration to our people. In addition, they would provide an outlet for those people who were urging the adoption of violent methods and would enable us to give concrete proof to our followers that we had adopted a stronger line and were fighting back against Government violence.

In addition, if mass action were successfully organized, and mass reprisals taken, we felt that sympathy for our cause would be roused in other countries, and that greater pressure would be brought to bear on the South African Government.

This then was the plan. Umkhonto was to perform sabotage, and strict instructions were given to its members right from the start, that on no account were they to injure or kill people in planning or carrying out operations. These instructions have been referred to in the evidence of "Mr. X" and "Mr. Z."[4]

The affairs of the Umkhonto were controlled and directed by a National High Command, which had powers of co-option and which could, and did, appoint Regional Commands. The High Command was the body which determined tactics and targets and was in charge of training and finance. Under the High Command there were Regional Commands which were responsible for the direction of the local sabotage groups. Within the framework of the policy laid down by the National High Command, the Regional Commands had authority to select the targets to be attacked. They had no authority to go beyond the prescribed framework and thus had no authority to embark upon acts which endangered life, or which did not fit into the overall plan of sabotage. For instance, Umkhonto members were forbidden ever to go armed into operation. Incidentally, the terms High Command and Regional Command were an importation from the Jewish national underground organization Irgun Zvai Leumi, which operated in Israel between 1944 and 1948.

Umkhonto had its first operation on 16 December 1961, when Government buildings in Johannesburg, Port Elizabeth and Durban were attacked. The selection of targets is proof of the policy to which I have referred. Had we intended to attack life we would have selected targets where people congregated and not empty buildings and power stations. The sabotage which was committed before 16 December 1961 was the work of isolated groups and had no connection whatever with Umkhonto. In fact, some of these and a number of later acts were claimed by other organizations.

The Manifesto of Umkhonto was issued on the day that operations commenced. The response to our actions and Manifesto among the white population was characteristically violent. The Government threatened to take strong action, and called upon its supporters to stand firm and to ignore the demands of the Africans. The Whites failed to respond by suggesting change; they responded to our call by suggesting the laager [Afrikaans: a defensive military action].

In contrast, the response of the Africans was one of encouragement. Suddenly there was hope again. Things were happening. People in the townships became eager for political news. A great deal of enthusiasm was generated by the initial successes, and people began to speculate on how soon freedom would be obtained.

But we in Umkhonto weighed up the white response with anxiety. The lines were being drawn. The whites and blacks were moving into separate camps, and the prospects of avoiding a civil war were made less. The white newspapers carried reports that sabotage would be punished by death. If this was so, how could we continue to keep Africans away from terrorism?

Already scores of Africans had died as a result of racial friction. In 1920 when the famous leader, Masabala, was held in Port Elizabeth jail, twenty-four of a group of Africans who had gathered to demand his release were killed by the police and white civilians. In 1921, more than one hundred Africans died in the Bulhoek affair. In 1924 over two hundred Africans were killed when the Administrator of South-West Africa led a force against a group which had rebelled against the imposition of dog tax. On 1 May 1950, eighteen Africans died as a result of police shootings during the strike. On 21 March 1960, sixty-nine unarmed Africans died at Sharpeville.

How many more Sharpevilles would there be in the history of our country? And how many more Sharpevilles could the country stand without violence and terror becoming the order of the day? And what would happen to our people when that stage was reached? In the long run we felt certain we must succeed, but at what cost to ourselves and the rest of the country?

And if this happened, how could black and white ever live together again in peace and harmony? These were the problems that faced us, and these were our decisions.

Experience convinced us that rebellion would offer the Government limitless opportunities for the indiscriminate slaughter of our people. But it was precisely because the soil of South Africa is already drenched with the blood of innocent Africans that we felt it our duty to make preparations as a long-term undertaking to use force in order to defend ourselves against force. If war were inevitable, we wanted the fight to be conducted on terms most favourable to our people. The fight which held out prospects best for us and the least risk of life to both sides was guerrilla warfare. We decided, therefore, in our preparations for the future, to make provision for the possibility of guerrilla warfare.

All whites undergo compulsory military training, but no such training was given to Africans. It was in our view essential to build up a nucleus of trained men who would be able to provide the leadership which would be required if guerrilla warfare started. We had to prepare for such a situation before it became too late to make proper preparations. It was also necessary to build up a nucleus of men trained in civil administration and other professions, so that Africans would be equipped to participate in the government of this country as soon as they were allowed to do so.

At this stage it was decided that I should attend the Conference of the Pan-African Freedom Movement for Central, East, and Southern Africa, which was to be held early in 1962 in Addis Ababa, and, because of our need for preparation, it was also decided that, after the conference, I would undertake a tour of the African States with a view to obtaining facilities for the training of soldiers, and that I would also solicit scholarships for the higher education of matriculated Africans. Training in both fields would be necessary, even if changes came about by peaceful means. Administrators would be necessary who would be willing and able to administer a non-racial State and so would men be necessary to control the army and police force of such a State.

It was on this note that I left South Africa to proceed to Addis Ababa as a delegate of the ANC. My tour was a success. Wherever I went I met sympathy for our cause and promises to help. All Africa was united against the stand of White South Africa, and even in London I was received with great sympathy by political leaders, such as Mr. Gaitskell and Mr. Grimond. In Africa I was promised support by such men as Julius Nyerere, now President of Tanganyika; Mr. Kawawa, then Prime Minister of Tanganyika; Emperor Haile Selassie of Ethiopia; General Abboud, President of the Sudan; Habib Bourguiba, President of Tunisia; Ben Bella, now President of Algeria; Modibo Keita, President of Mali; Leopold Senghor, President of Senegal; Sékou Touré, President of Guinea; President Tubman of Liberia; and Milton Obote, Prime Minister of Uganda. It was Ben Bella who invited me to visit Oujda, the Headquarters of the Algerian Army of National Liberation, the visit which is described in my diary, one of the Exhibits.

I started to make a study of the art of war and revolution and, whilst abroad, underwent a course in military training. If there was to be guerrilla warfare, I wanted to be able to stand and fight with my people and to share the hazards of war with them. Notes of lectures which I received in Algeria are contained in Exhibit 16, produced in evidence. Summaries of books on guerrilla warfare and military strategy have also been produced. I have already admitted that these documents are in my writing, and I acknowledge that I made these studies to equip myself for the role which I might have to play if the struggle drifted into guerrilla warfare. I approached this question as every African Nationalist should do. I was completely objective. The Court will see that I attempted to examine all types of authority on the subject—from the East and from the West, going back to the classic work of Clausewitz, and covering such a variety as Mao Tse Tung and Che Guevara on the one hand, and the writings on the Anglo-Boer War on the other. Of course, these notes are merely summaries of the books I read and do not contain my personal views.

I also made arrangements for our recruits to undergo military training. But here it was impossible to organize any scheme without the co-operation of the ANC offices in Africa. I consequently obtained the permission of the ANC in South Africa to do this. To this extent then there was a departure from the original decision of the ANC, but it applied outside South Africa only. The first batch of recruits actually arrived in Tanganyika when I was passing through that country on my way back to South Africa.

I returned to South Africa and reported to my colleagues on the results of my trip. On my return I found that there had been little alteration in the political scene save that the threat of a death penalty for sabotage had now become a fact. The attitude of my colleagues in Umkhonto was much the same as it had been before I left. They were feeling their way cautiously and felt that it would be a long time before the possibilities of sabotage were exhausted. In fact, the view was expressed by some that the training of recruits was premature. This is recorded by me in the document which is Exhibit R 14. After a full discussion, however, it was decided to go ahead with the plans for military training because of the fact that it would take many years to build up a sufficient nucleus of trained soldiers to start a guerrilla campaign, and whatever happened the training would be of value.

I wish to turn now to certain general allegations made in this case by the State. . . .

[One] of the allegations made by the State is that the aims and objects of the ANC and the Communist Party are the same. I wish to deal with this and with my own political position, because I must assume that the State may try to argue from certain Exhibits that I tried to introduce Marxism into the

ANC. The allegation as to the ANC is false. This is an old allegation which was disproved at the Treason Trial and which has again reared its head. But since the allegation has been made again, I shall deal with it as well as with the relationship between the ANC and the Communist Party and Umkhonto and that party.

The ideological creed of the ANC is, and always has been, the creed of African Nationalism. It is not the concept of African Nationalism expressed in the cry, "Drive the White man into the sea." The African Nationalism for which the ANC stands is the concept of freedom and fulfilment for the African people in their own land. The most important political document ever adopted by the ANC is the "Freedom Charter." It is by no means a blueprint for a socialist state. It calls for redistribution, but not nationalization, of land; it provides for nationalization of mines, banks, and monopoly industry, because big monopolies are owned by one race only, and without such nationalization racial domination would be perpetuated despite the spread of political power. It would be a hollow gesture to repeal the Gold Law prohibitions against Africans when all gold mines are owned by European companies. In this respect the ANC's policy corresponds with the old policy of the present Nationalist Party which, for many years, had as part of its programme the nationalization of the gold mines which, at that time, were controlled by foreign capital. Under the Freedom Charter, nationalization would take place in an economy based on private enterprise. The realization of the Freedom Charter would open up fresh fields for a prosperous African population of all classes, including the middle class. The ANC has never at any period of its history advocated a revolutionary change in the economic structure of the country, nor has it, to the best of my recollection, ever condemned capitalist society.

As far as the Communist Party is concerned, and if I understand its policy correctly, it stands for the establishment of a State based on the principles of Marxism. Although it is prepared to work for the Freedom Charter, as a short-term solution to the problems created by white supremacy, it regards the Freedom Charter as the beginning, and not the end, of its programme.

The ANC, unlike the Communist Party, admitted Africans only as members. Its chief goal was, and is, for the African people to win unity and full political rights. The Communist Party's main aim, on the other hand, was to remove the capitalists and to replace them with a working-class government. The Communist Party sought to emphasize class distinctions whilst the ANC seeks to harmonize them. This is a vital distinction.

It is true that there has often been close co-operation between the ANC and the Communist Party. But co-operation is merely proof of a common goal—in this case the removal of white supremacy—and is not proof of a complete community of interests.

The history of the world is full of similar examples. Perhaps the most striking illustration is to be found in the co-operation between Great Britain, the United States of America, and the Soviet Union in the fight against Hitler. Nobody but Hitler would have dared to suggest that such co-operation turned Churchill or Roosevelt into communists or communist tools, or that Britain and America were working to bring about a communist world.

Another instance of such co-operation is to be found precisely in Umkhonto. Shortly after Umkhonto was constituted, I was informed by some of its members that the Communist Party would support Umkhonto, and this then occurred. At a later stage the support was made openly.

I believe that communists have always played an active role in the fight by colonial countries for their freedom; because the short-term objects of communism would always correspond with the long-term objects of freedom movements. Thus communists have played an important role in the freedom struggles fought in countries such as Malaya, Algeria, and Indonesia, yet none of these States today are communist countries. Similarly in the underground resistance movements which sprung up in Europe during the last World War, communists played an important role. Even General Chiang Kai-Shek, today one of the bitterest enemies of communism, fought together with the communists against the ruling class in the struggle which led to his assumption of power in China in the 1930s.

This pattern of co-operation between communists and non-communists has been repeated in the National Liberation Movement of South Africa. Prior to the banning of the Communist Party, joint campaigns involving the Communist Party and the Congress movements were accepted practice. African communists could, and did, become members of the ANC, and some served on the National, Provincial, and local committees. Amongst those who served on the National Executive are Albert Nzula, a former Secretary of the Communist Party; Moses Kotane, another former Secretary; and J. B. Marks, a former member of the Central Committee.

I joined the ANC in 1944, and in my younger days I held the view that the policy of admitting communists to the ANC, and the close co-operation which existed at times on specific issues between the ANC and the Communist Party, would lead to a watering down of the concept of African Nationalism. At that stage I was a member of the African National Congress Youth League, and was one of a group which moved for the expulsion of communists from the ANC. This proposal was heavily defeated. Amongst those who voted against the proposal were some of the most conservative sections of African political opinion. They defended the policy on the ground that from its inception the ANC was formed and built up, not as a political party with one school of political thought, but as a Parliament of the African people, accommodating people of various political convictions, all united by the common goal of national liberation. I was eventually won over to this point of view and I have upheld it ever since.

It is perhaps difficult for white South Africans, with an ingrained prejudice against communism, to understand why experienced African politicians so readily accept communists as their friends. But to us the reason is obvious. Theoretical differences amongst those fighting against oppression is a luxury we cannot afford at this stage. What is more, for many decades communists were the only political group in South Africa who were prepared to treat Africans as human beings and their equals; who were prepared to eat with us, talk with us, live with us, and work with us. They were the only political group which was prepared to work with the Africans for the attainment of political rights and a stake in society. Because of this, there are many Africans who, today, tend to equate freedom with communism. They are supported in this belief by a legislature which brands all exponents of democratic government and African freedom as communists and bans many of them (who are not communists) under the Suppression of Communism Act. Although I have never been a member of the Communist Party, I myself have been named under that pernicious Act because of the role I played in the Defiance Campaign. I have also been banned and imprisoned under that Act.

It is not only in internal politics that we count communists as amongst those who support our cause. In the international field, communist countries have always come to our aid. In the United Nations and other Councils of the world the communist *bloc* has supported the Afro-Asian struggle against colonialism and often seems to be more sympathetic to our plight than some of the Western powers. Although there is a universal condemnation of apartheid, the communist *bloc* speaks out against it with a louder voice than most of the white world. In these circumstances, it would take a brash young politician, such as I was in 1949, to proclaim that the Communists are our enemies.

I turn now to my own position. I have denied that I am a communist, and I think that in the circumstances I am obliged to state exactly what my political beliefs are.

I have always regarded myself, in the first place, as an African patriot. After all, I was born in Umtata, forty-six years ago. My guardian was my cousin, who was the acting paramount chief of Tembuland, and I am related both to the present paramount chief of Tembuland, Sabata Dalindyebo, and to Kaizer Matanzima, the Chief Minister of the Transkei.

Today I am attracted by the idea of a classless society, an attraction which springs in part from Marxist reading and, in part, from my admiration of the structure and organization of early African societies in this country. The land, then the main means of production, belonged to the tribe. There were no rich or poor and there was no exploitation.

It is true, as I have already stated, that I have been influenced by Marxist thought. But this is also true of many of the leaders of the new independent States. Such widely different persons as Gandhi, Nehru, Nkrumah, and Nasser all acknowledge this fact. We all accept the need for some form of socialism to enable our people to catch up with the advanced countries of this world and to overcome their legacy of extreme poverty. But this does not mean we are Marxists.

Indeed, for my own part, I believe that it is open to debate whether the Communist Party has any specific role to play at this particular stage of our political struggle. The basic task at the present moment is the removal of race discrimination and the attainment of democratic rights on the basis of the Freedom Charter. In so far as that Party furthers this task, I welcome its assistance. I realize that it is one of the means by which people of all races can be drawn into our struggle.

From my reading of Marxist literature and from conversations with Marxists, I have gained the impression that communists regard the parliamentary system of the West as undemocratic and reactionary. But, on the contrary, I am an admirer of such a system.

The Magna Carta, the Petition of Rights, and the Bill of Rights are documents which are held in veneration by democrats throughout the world.

I have great respect for British political institutions, and for the country's system of justice. I regard the British Parliament as the most democratic institution in the world, and the independence and impartiality of its judiciary never fail to arouse my admiration.

The American Congress, that country's doctrine of separation of powers, as well as the independence of its judiciary, arouses in me similar sentiments.

I have been influenced in my thinking by both West and East. All this has led me to feel that in my search for a political formula, I should be absolutely impartial and objective. I should tie myself to no particular system of society other than of socialism. I must leave myself free to borrow the best from the West and from the East. . . .

There are certain Exhibits which suggest that we received financial support from abroad, and I wish to deal with this question.

Our political struggle has always been financed from internal sources—from funds raised by our own people and by our own supporters. Whenever we had a special campaign or an important political case—for example, the Treason Trial—we received financial assistance from sympathetic individuals and organizations in the Western countries. We had never felt it necessary to go beyond these sources.

But when in 1961 the Umkhonto was formed, and a new phase of struggle introduced, we realized that these events would make a heavy call on our slender resources, and that the scale of our activities would be hampered by the lack of funds. One of my instructions, as I went abroad in January 1962, was to raise funds from the African states.

I must add that, whilst abroad, I had discussions with leaders of political movements in Africa and discovered that almost every single one of them, in areas which had still not attained independence, had received all forms of assistance from the socialist countries, as well as from the West, including that of financial support. I also discovered that some well-known African states, all of them non-communists, and even anti-communists, had received similar assistance.

On my return to the Republic, I made a strong recommendation to the ANC that we should not confine ourselves to Africa and the Western countries, but that we should also send a mission to the socialist countries to raise the funds which we so urgently needed.

I have been told that after I was convicted such a mission was sent, but I am not prepared to name any countries to which it went, nor am I at liberty to disclose the names of the organizations and countries which gave us support or promised to do so.

As I understand the State case, and in particular the evidence of "Mr. X," the suggestion is that Umkhonto was the inspiration of the Communist Party which sought by playing upon imaginary grievances to enroll the African people into an army which ostensibly was to fight for African freedom, but in reality was fighting for a communist state. Nothing could be further from the truth. In fact the suggestion is preposterous. Umkhonto was formed by Africans to further their struggle for freedom in their own land. Communists and others supported the movement, and we only wish that more sections of the community would join us.

Our fight is against real, and not imaginary, hardships or, to use the language of the State Prosecutor, "so-called hardships." Basically, we fight against two features which are the hallmarks of African life in South Africa and which are entrenched by legislation which we seek to have repealed. These features are poverty and lack of human dignity, and we do not need communists or so-called "agitators" to teach us about these things.

South Africa is the richest country in Africa, and could be one of the richest countries in the world. But it is a land of extremes and remarkable contrasts. The whites enjoy what may well be the highest standard of living in the world, whilst Africans live in poverty and misery. Forty per cent of the Africans live in hopelessly overcrowded and, in some cases, drought-stricken Reserves, where soil erosion and the overworking of the soil makes it impossible for them to live properly off the land. Thirty per cent are labourers, labour tenants, and squatters on white farms and work and live under conditions similar to those of the serfs of the Middle Ages. The other 30 per cent live in towns where they have developed economic and social habits which bring them closer in many respects to white standards. Yet most Africans, even in this group, are impoverished by low incomes and high cost of living.

The highest-paid and the most prosperous section of urban African life is in Johannesburg. Yet their actual position is desperate. The latest figures were given on 25 March 1964 by Mr. Carr, Manager of the Johannesburg Non-European Affairs Department. The poverty datum line for the average African family in Johannesburg (according to Mr. Carr's department) is R42.84 per month. He showed that the average monthly wage is R32.24 and that 46 per cent of all African families in Johannesburg do not earn enough to keep them going.

Poverty goes hand in hand with malnutrition and disease. The incidence of malnutrition and deficiency diseases is very high amongst Africans. Tuberculosis, pellagra, kwashiorkor, gastro-enteritis, and scurvy bring death and destruction of health. The incidence of infant mortality is one of the highest in the world. According to the Medical Officer of Health for Pretoria, tuberculosis kills forty people a day (almost all Africans), and in 1961 there were 58,491 new cases reported. These diseases not only destroy the vital organs of the body, but they result in retarded mental conditions and lack of initiative, and reduce powers of concentration. The secondary results of such conditions affect the whole community and the standard of work performed by African labourers.

The complaint of Africans, however, is not only that they are poor and the whites are rich, but that the laws which are made by the whites are designed to preserve this situation. There are two ways to break out of poverty. The first is by formal education, and the second is by the worker acquiring a greater skill at his work and thus higher wages. As far as Africans are concerned, both these avenues of advancement are deliberately curtailed by legislation.

The present Government has always sought to hamper Africans in their search for education. One of their early acts, after coming into power, was to stop subsidies for African school feeding. Many African children who attended schools depended on this supplement to their diet. This was a cruel act.

There is compulsory education for all white children at virtually no cost to their parents, be they rich or poor. Similar facilities are not provided for the African children, though there are some who receive such assistance. African children, however, generally have to pay more for their schooling than whites. According to figures quoted by the South African Institute of Race Relations in its 1963 journal, approximately 40 per cent of African children in the age group between seven to fourteen do not attend school. For those who do attend school, the standards are vastly different from those afforded to white children. In 1960–61 the *per capita* Government spending on African students at State-aided schools was estimated at R12.46. In the same years, the *per capita* spending on white children in the Cape Province (which are the only figures available to me) was R144.57. Although there are no figures available to me, it can be stated, without doubt, that the white children on whom R144.57 per head was being spent all came from wealthier homes than African children on whom R12.46 per head was being spent.

The quality of education is also different. According to the Bantu Educational journal, only 5,660 African children in the whole of South Africa passed their Junior Certificate in 1962, and in that year only 362 passed matric.[5] This is presumably consistent with the policy of Bantu education about which the present Prime Minister said, during the debate on the Bantu Education Bill in 1953:

> When I have control of Native education I will reform it, so that Natives will be taught from childhood to realize that equality with Europeans is not for them. . . . People who believe in equality are not desirable teachers for Natives. When my Department controls Native education it will know for what class of higher education a Native is fitted, and whether he will have a chance in life to use his knowledge.

The other main obstacle to the economic advancement of the African is the industrial colour-bar under which all the better jobs of industry are reserved for Whites only. Moreover, Africans who do obtain employment in the unskilled and semi-skilled occupations which are open to them are not allowed to form trade unions which have recognition under the Industrial Conciliation Act. This means that strikes of African workers are illegal, and that they are denied the right of collective bargaining which is permitted to the better-paid White workers. The discrimination in the policy of successive South African Governments towards African workers is demonstrated by the so-called "civilized labour policy" under which sheltered, unskilled Government jobs are found for those white workers who cannot make the grade in industry, at wages which far exceed the earnings of the average African employee in industry.

The Government often answers its critics by saying that Africans in South Africa are economically better off than the inhabitants of the other countries in Africa. I do not know whether this statement is true and doubt whether any comparison can be made without having regard to the cost-of-living index in such countries. But even if it is true, as far as the African people are concerned it is irrelevant. Our complaint is not that we are poor by comparison with people in other countries, but that we are poor by comparison with the white people in our own country, and that we are prevented by legislation from altering this imbalance.

The lack of human dignity experienced by Africans is the direct result of the policy of white supremacy. White supremacy implies black inferiority. Legislation designed to preserve white supremacy entrenches this notion. Menial tasks in South Africa are invariably performed by Africans. When anything has to be carried or cleaned the white man will look around for an African to do it for him, whether the African is employed by him or not. Because of this sort of attitude, whites tend to regard Africans as a separate breed. They do not look upon them as people with families of their own; they do not realize that they have emotions—that they fall in love like white people do; that they want to be with their wives and children like white people want to be with theirs; that they want to earn enough money to support their families properly, to feed and clothe them and send them to school. And what "house-boy" or "garden-boy" or labourer can ever hope to do this?

Pass laws, which to the Africans are among the most hated bits of legislation in South Africa, render any African liable to police surveillance at any time. I doubt whether there is a single African male in South Africa who has not at some stage had a brush with the police over his pass. Hundreds and thousands of Africans are thrown into jail each year under pass laws. Even worse than this is the fact that pass laws keep husband and wife apart and lead to the breakdown of family life.

Poverty and the breakdown of family life have secondary effects. Children wander about the streets of the townships because they have no schools to go to, or no money to enable them to go to school, or no parents at home to see that they go to school, because both parents (if there be two) have to work to keep the family alive. This leads to a breakdown in moral standards, to an alarming rise in illegitimacy, and to growing violence which erupts not only politically, but everywhere. Life in the townships is dangerous. There is not a day that goes by without somebody being stabbed or assaulted. And violence is carried out of the townships in the white living areas. People are afraid to walk alone in the streets after dark. Housebreakings and robberies are increasing, despite the fact that the death sentence can now be imposed for such offences. Death sentences cannot cure the festering sore.

Africans want to be paid a living wage. Africans want to perform work which they are capable of doing, and not work which the Government declares them to be capable of. Africans want to be allowed to live where they obtain work, and not be endorsed out of an area because they were not born there. Africans want to be allowed to own land in places where they work, and not to be obliged to live in rented houses which they can never call their own. Africans want to be part of the general population, and not confined to living in their own ghettoes. African men want to have their wives and children to live with them where they work, and not be forced into an unnatural existence in men's hostels. African women want to be with their menfolk and not be left permanently widowed in the Reserves. Africans want to be allowed out after eleven o'clock at night and not to be confined to their rooms like little children. Africans want to be allowed to travel in their own country and to seek work where they want to and not where the Labour Bureau tells them to. Africans want a just share in the whole of South Africa; they want security and a stake in society.

Above all, we want equal political rights, because without them our disabilities will be permanent. I know this sounds revolutionary to the whites in this country, because the majority of voters will be Africans. This makes the white man fear democracy.

But this fear cannot be allowed to stand in the way of the only solution which will guarantee racial harmony and freedom for all. It is not true that the enfranchisement of all will result in racial domination. Political division, based on colour, is entirely artificial and, when it disappears, so will the domination of one colour group by another. The ANC has spent half a century fighting against racialism. When it triumphs it will not change that policy.

This then is what the ANC is fighting. Their struggle is a truly national one. It is a struggle of the African people, inspired by their own suffering and their own experience. It is a struggle for the right to live.

During my lifetime I have dedicated myself to this struggle of the African people. I have fought against white domination, and I have fought against black domination. I have cherished the ideal of a democratic and free society in which all persons live together in harmony and with equal opportunities. It is an ideal which I hope to live for and to achieve. But if needs be, it is an ideal for which I am prepared to die.

On 11 June 1964, at the conclusion of the trial, Mandela and seven others—Walter Sisulu, Govan Mbeki, Raymond Mhlaba, Elias Motsoaledi, Andrew Mlangeni, Ahmed Kathrada and Denis Goldberg—were convicted. Mandela was found guilty on four charges of sabotage and, like the others, was sentenced to life imprisonment. On 11 February 1990, after intense international pressure, he was released from prison.

Endnotes

1. **Amadelakufa** Those who are prepared to make sacrifices.
2. **Sharpeville** The location where South African police killed 69 and wounded 178 demonstrators who were protesting South Africa's pass laws. [Ed. note.]
3. **Saracens** British-made military troop carriers.
4. State witnesses in the trial whose names were withheld for their protection.
5. The junior Certificate examination was generally taken by white children at the age of 15, and they cannot normally leave school before this. Matriculation is taken two years later and qualifies students for higher education. The educational system, however, ensures that very few Africans reach junior Certificate level, so that what represents a basic standard for whites is one of achievement for Africans. Even fewer attain matriculation level.

The Movement: The Rise of Tea Party Activism

Ben McGrath

Ben McGrath started at The New Yorker *in 1999 as a contributor and fact checker, and has been a staff writer since 2003. He has contributed more than two hundred stories to the magazine's "The Talk of the Town," and his feature subjects have been as diverse as Pro Bowling, Michael Bloomberg, hip-hop radio station Hot 97, Formula One racing, and a Native American community in the hill country of New Jersey. McGrath is known for his incisive articles about polarizing sports figures like Lenny Dykstra and Kobe Bryant.*

McGrath wrote "The Movement: The Rise of Tea Party Activism" for the February 1, 2010 edition of The New Yorker. *The piece explains the genesis of this Libertarian themed movement that pays homage to the Boston Tea party of the American Revolution. McGrath recalls his visit in the fall of 2009 to a "Take Back America" rally in Burlington, Kentucky. He profiles the people he met, the politicians and media influences on the movement, and some of the "inflammatory" platforms on which members stand. The essay also explores the historical connections to not only the American Revolution, but of Andrew Jackson's boisterous presidency and reactions to the excesses of the Gilded Age.*

In a 2010 "Ask the Author" piece for The New Yorker, *McGrath stated the following observation about the ideology within the Tea Party movement:*

As with most if not all social movements, what you have here is a diverse collection of people with some overlapping concerns. In this case, I'd say that the primary thing that unites them is a strong opposition to the status quo, and, if I could identify one primary ideological point, it'd be a belief in smaller government. For a start.

Regarding style, it has been said that McGrath quotes his subjects often, but not excessively. He has the gift of economy, and allows his subject, not his writing, be the focal point of the piece.

McGrath lives in the lower Hudson Valley.

My first immersion in the social movement that helped take Ted Kennedy's Massachusetts Senate seat away from the Democrats, and may have derailed the President's chief domestic initiative, occurred last fall, in Burlington, Kentucky, at a Take Back America rally. My escort was an exceptionally genial sixty-seven-year-old man named Don Seely, an electrical engineer who said that he was between jobs and using the unwanted free time to volunteer his services to the Northern Kentucky Tea Party, the rally's host organization, as a Webmaster. "I've never been a Webmaster, but I've *known* Webmasters," he explained, with a chuckle, as he walked around a muddy field, near a horse-jumping ring, and introduced me to some of his colleagues, one of whom was a fireman. "And he's also our finance guy." Being the finance guy, from what I could gather, entailed volunteering a personal credit card to be used for the group's PayPal account. The amateur nature of the operation was a matter of pride to all those who were taking an active interest, in many cases for the first time in their lives, in the cause of governance. Several of the volunteers had met at Bulldog's Roadhouse, in a nearby town named Independence, where they assembled on weekdays for what you might call happy hour, were it not for the fact that Bulldog's is a Fox News joint and five o'clock is when Glenn Beck comes on, warning from a studio that he likes to call the "doom room" about the return of a Marxist fifth column.

Seely wore a muted plaid shirt, rumpled khakis, and large, round glasses that seemed to magnify his curiosity, a trait that he attributed to his training as an engineer—an urge to understand the way things work. He told me that he used to listen to Beck on the radio, before Beck got his Fox show. "I didn't like him," he said. "He was always making fun of people. You know, he's basically a comedian. But the reason I like him now is he's kind of had a mind-set change. Instead of making fun of everybody, he started asking himself questions. His point was 'Get out there, talk to your neighbor, see what they feel. Don't sit back under your tree boohooing.' " The Bulldog's gang was a collection of citizens who were, as one of them put it, "tired of talking to the TV."

So they watched Beck together, over beer, and then spent an hour consoling one another, although lately their personal anxieties had overtaken the more general ones of the host on the screen, and Beck's chalkboard lectures about the fundamental transformation of the Republic had become more like the usual barroom ballgame: background noise. "We found that you really have to let people get the things off their chests," Seely said.

Burlington is the seat of Boone County, and the rally took place at the Boone County fairgrounds, on an afternoon that was chilly enough to inspire one of the speakers, the ghostwriter of Joe the Plumber's autobiography, to dismiss global warming, to great applause. A second-generation Chrysler dealer, whose lot had just been shut down, complained that the Harvard-educated experts on Wall Street and in Washington knew nothing about automobiles. ("I've been in this business since 1958, and what I know is that the American public does not want small cars!") The district's congressional representative, Geoff Davis, brought up the proposed cap-and-trade legislation favored by Democrats, and called it an "economic colonization of the hardworking states that produce the energy, the food, and the manufactured goods of the heartland, to take that and pay for social programs in the large coastal states."

Boone County borders both Indiana and Ohio, and was described to me by a couple of people I met there as "flyover country," with a mixture of provincial anxiety and defensive skepticism—as in "What brings you to flyover country?" The phrase is not quite apt. Home to the Cincinnati airport, which serves as a Delta hub, the county owes much of its growth and relative prosperity over the past two decades to large numbers of people flying in and out, not over. But Delta's recent struggles, and rumors about the impending contraction of its local subsidiary, Comair, have contributed to a deeper sense of economic anxiety. "You go to the warehouses around the airport, probably at least a third or twenty-five per cent are empty," Seely said. "We need to give somebody a break here, so people can start making money." As it happens, the largest employer in northern Kentucky today is the I.R.S.

Another Bulldog's regular, a middle-aged woman dressed in jeans, a turtleneck, and a red sweatshirt, stood beside some stables, hustling for signatures to add to the Tea Party mailing list. "I tell you, it's an enthusiastic group," she said. "Talk about grassroots. This is as grassroots as it gets."

"And she works full time," Seely added.

"Not as full time as I'd like."

About a thousand people had turned up at the rally, most of them old enough to remember a time when the threats to the nation's long-term security, at home and abroad, were more easily defined and acknowledged. Suspicious of decadent élites and concerned about a central government whose ambitions had grown unmanageably large, they sounded, at least in broad strokes, a little like the left-wing secessionists I'd met at a rally in Vermont in the waning days of the Bush Administration. Large assemblies of like-minded people, even profoundly anxious people anticipating the imminent death of empire, have an unmistakable allure: festive despair. A young man in a camouflage jacket sold T-shirts ("Fox News Fan," for example), while a local district judge doled out play money: trillion-dollar bills featuring the face of Ben Bernanke. An insurance salesman paraded around, dressed as though guiding a tour of Colonial Williamsburg. "Oh, this is George Washington!" Seely said. "Hey, George, come over here a minute."

"I'm back for the Second American Revolution," the man said. "My weapons this time will be the Constitution, the Internet, and my talk-radio ads."

If there was a central theme to the proceedings, it was probably best expressed in the refrain "Can you hear us now?," conveying a long-standing grievance that the political class in Washington is unresponsive to the needs and worries of ordinary Americans. Republicans and Democrats alike were targets of derision. "Their constituency is George Soros," one man grumbled, and I was reminded of the dangerous terrain where populism slides into a kind of nativist paranoia—the subject of Richard Hofstadter's famous essay linking anti-Masonic sentiment in the eighteen-twenties with McCarthyism and with the John Birch Society founder Robert Welch's contention that Dwight Eisenhower was "a dedicated, conscious agent of the Communist conspiracy." The name Soros, understood in the context of this recurring strain—the "paranoid style in American politics," Hofstadter called it—is synonymous, like Rockefeller or Rothschild, with a New World Order.

The Soros grumbler, who had also labelled John McCain a Communist, was dressed in jeans pulled up well above his waist with suspenders, and wearing thick, oversized shades. When he saw my notebook, he turned to Seely and asked, "Where's he from, supposedly?" Informed that I live in New York, he replied, "There's a nightmare right there." What he had in mind was not a concentration of godless liberals, as it turned out, but something more troubling. "*Major* earthquake faults," he said. "It's hard in spots, but basically it's like a bag of bricks." Some more discussion revolved around a super-volcano in Yellowstone ("It'll fry Denver and Salt Lake at the same time") and the dire geological forecasts of Edgar Cayce, the so-called Sleeping Prophet, which involved the sudden emergence of coastlines in what, for the time being, is known as the Midwest. I asked the man his name. "T. J. Randall," he said. "That's not my real name, but that's the one I'm using."

Seely saw our encounter with the doomsayer more charitably than Hofstadter might have. "That's an example of an intelligent person who's not quite got it all together," he said. "You can tell that. But he's pretty interesting to talk to." Seely's own reaction, upon learning where I'd come from, had been to ask if I was familiar with the New School, in Greenwich Village. His youngest daughter, Amber, had gone there.

I asked Seely what Amber thought of the Tea Party. "We kind of hit a happy medium where we don't discuss certain things," he said, and added that at the moment Amber, who now works for a nonprofit that builds affordable housing in New Orleans, was visiting his son, Denver, who is enrolled in a Ph.D. program in mechanical engineering at Mississippi State.

By most accounts, the Paul Revere figure of this Second American Revolution is an excitable cable-news reporter named Rick Santelli, a former futures trader and Drexel Burnham Lambert vice-president who stood on the floor of the Chicago Mercantile Exchange last February and sounded the alarm on CNBC about the new Administration's planned assistance for home-owners facing foreclosure. He proposed a nationwide referendum, via the Internet, on the matter of subsidizing "the losers' mortgages," winning both the attention and the vocal support of the working traders in his midst. "President Obama, are you listening?" he shouted, and then said that he'd been thinking of organizing a Chicago Tea Party in July, urging "all you capitalists" to come join him on Lake Michigan, where "we're going to be dumping in some derivative securities." It was a delicate pose—financial professionals more or less laughing at debtors while disavowing the lending techniques that had occasioned the crisis—but within a matter of hours a Web site, Offi-cialChicagoTeaParty.com, had gone live, and by the end of the following week dozens of small protests were occurring simultaneously around the country, invoking the legacy of early New England colonists in their revolt against King George.

Santelli's rant was delivered at 7:10 A.M., Chicago time, but it was highly YouTubeable, and all the more effective to the alienated masses—"the rabble," as some have taken to calling themselves—because Santelli was not a known conservative mouthpiece like Rush Limbaugh or Beck or Sean Hannity. The primal narrative of any insurrection benefits from the appearance of unlikely spontaneity. Another early agitator who merits a retrospective footnote is Keli Carender, a.k.a. the Liberty Belle, a blogger and "random woman," as one admirer says, "from Seattle, of all places." Carender was a week ahead of Santelli in voicing her dissent; her mistake was choosing the wrong animating metaphor. Borrowing terminology from Limbaugh, she organized a Porkulus Protest in response to the economic-stimulus bill, and tried tagging Democratic leaders with epithets like Porky and Piggy and Porker. (Not the least of tea's advantages is the ease with which it can be converted into a handy acronym: Taxed Enough Already.) But Carender identified a tactic that would prove invaluable in the months of raucous town-hall meetings and demonstrations to follow: adopting the idealistic energy of liberal college students. "Unlike the melodramatic lefties, I do not want to get arrested," she wrote. "I do, however, want to take a page from their playbook and be loud, obnoxious, and in their faces."

Spring brought the founding of the Tea Party Patriots, a centralized Web destination for decentralized malcontents, and the start of Glenn Beck's side gig as a social organizer, through his 9.12 Project. The numbers nine and twelve referred to a checklist of principles and values, but their greater significance lay in the allusion to September 11th. "The day after America was attacked, we were not obsessed with Red States, Blue States or political parties," the project's mission statement read. "We want to get everyone thinking like it is September 12, 2001, again." The chosen values were inarguable: things like honesty and hope and courage. Only two of the principles ("I believe in God and He is the center of my life"; "I work hard for what I have and I will share it with who I want to. Government cannot force me to be charitable") indicated any kind of political agenda. Inclusiveness was the point.

As spring passed into summer, the scores at local Tea Party gatherings turned to hundreds, and then thousands, collecting along the way footloose Ron Paul supporters, goldbugs, evangelicals, Atlas Shruggers, militiamen, strict Constitutionalists, swine-flu skeptics, scattered 9/11 "truthers," neo-"Birchers," and, of course, "birthers"—those who remained convinced that the President was a Muslim double agent born in Kenya. "We'll meet back here in six months," Beck had said in March, and when September 12th arrived even the truest of believers were surprised by the apparent strength of the new movement, as measured by the throngs who made the pilgrimage to the Capitol for a Taxpayer March on Washington, swarming the Mall with signs reading " '1984' Is Not an Instruction Manual" and "The Zoo Has an African Lion and the White House Has a Lyin' African!"

Politics is ultimately a numbers game, and the natural excitement surrounding 9.12 drove crowd estimates upward, from an early lowball figure of sixty thousand, reported by ABC News, into the hundreds of thousands and across the million mark, eventually nearing two million—an upper limit of some significance, because 1.8 million was the figure commonly reported in mainstream or "state-run" media outlets as the attendance at President Obama's Inauguration. "There are more of us than there are of them, and we know the truth," one of the Kentucky organizers, who had carpooled to D.C. with a couple of co-workers from an auto-parts warehouse, told me. The fact that the mainstream media generally declined to acknowledge the parallel, regarding the marchers as a loud and motley long tail of disaffection, and not a silent majority, only hardened their resolve.

Consider our peculiar political situation at the end of this first decade of the new century. An African-American Democrat is elected President, following the collapse of the two great symbols of postwar prosperity, Detroit and Wall Street. Seizing on the erosion of public trust in élite institutions, the C.E.O. of World Wrestling Entertainment, Linda McMahon, announces her candidacy for the U.S. Senate, touting her opposition to a federal banking bailout whose principal beneficiaries include many of her neighbors in Greenwich, Connecticut. Another pro-wrestling eminence, the former Minnesota governor Jesse (the Body) Ventura, begins hosting a new television show called "Conspiracy Theory," evincing a distrust in government so deep that it equates environmental crusaders with the Bilderbergs. A multimillionaire pornographer, Larry Flynt, is moved to branch out from his regular perch as an enemy of moral hypocrisy with an expanded sense of purpose, lamenting the takeover of Washington by "Wall Street, the mega-corporations and the super-rich," in an op-ed for the Huffington Post, and calling for an unspecified form of national strike inspired by Shays's Rebellion. And an obscure state senator who once posed naked for *Cosmopolitan* emerges, after driving a pickup truck around Massachusetts, as a leading contender to unseat the aforementioned President.

American history is dotted with moments like this, when, as the Princeton historian Sean Wilentz says, "panic and vitriol come to the fore," occasioning a temporary realignment of political interests. Flynt cited Franklin Roosevelt's use of the phrase "economic royalists," which was itself an echo of the moneyed interests targeted by Andrew Jackson, who earned the nickname King Mob after his Inauguration, in 1829, brought hordes of precursors of the *Hustler* subscribers and WrestleMania fans of our time to the White House lawn. Jackson's staunch opposition to the Second Bank of the United States set a precedent for generations of Wall Street resentment to come.

Between the demise of the Whig Party and the consolidation of the modern Republican Party, under Lincoln, there came a nativist movement of Know Nothings, as they called themselves—or "the Lou Dobbs party," as Michael Kazin, the author of "The Populist Persuasion," now says. Marx and Engels had just published their manifesto, and German immigrants were suspected of importing Socialist ideas. The new waves of Irish Catholics couldn't be trusted, either: who was to say they wouldn't take their orders from the Pope instead of the President?

Gilded Age excesses gave rise to a new People's Party, a movement of Southern and Western farmers and miners united in opposition to railroad speculators, and the panic of 1893 accelerated their cause. By 1896, William Jennings Bryan was addressing the Democratic Convention with his famous critique of "the idle holders of idle capital." (The convention, held in Chicago, loosed "a wild, raging, irresistible mob which nothing can turn from its abominable foolishness," as the *Times* put it.) "That basic kind of vocabulary, against the monarchy and the aristocracy, has informed every conceivable American dissident group in one way or another," Wilentz says. "Lyndon

LaRouche does that whole Queen of England thing. He's *still* fighting the American Revolution."

The Tea Party movement, identified by some commentators as the first right-wing street-protest movement of our time, may be a reflection of how far populist sentiment has drifted away from the political left in the decades since the New Deal. "The original Populists were the ones who came up with the income tax," Charles Postel, the author of "The Populist Vision," said recently. "They were for the nationalization of everything. Their idea of a model institution was the Post Office." Bryan believed that the "right to coin money and issue money is a function of the government," and railed, most memorably, against the "cross of gold." Yet few ideas stir the Tea Party faithful more than a fear of creeping nationalization and the dangers—both moral and practical—associated with printing money to suit momentary needs. The sponsors of Glenn Beck's nightly history lessons on the depredations of American progressivism frequently include purveyors of gold.

One historical comparison that some Tea Party champions have made is to the civil-rights movement, and, to the extent that the analogy holds, it may reflect the fact that the Tea Party seems to derive much of its energy from the members of that generation who did not participate in the cultural revolution of the sixties, and are only belatedly coming to terms with social and demographic trends set in motion fifty years ago. Don Seely invited me to his house for coffee the day after the rally at the Kentucky fairgrounds, and showed me his Air Force Commendation Medal, awarded for meritorious service from 1967 to 1971. "At this age, I was so ignorant," he said. "Every once in a while, you'd catch a glimpse on TV of Martin Luther King—all that kind of stuff was going on. I graduated college in December of '66. About a year after I left, that's when all the riots happened. I'm thinking, *What* is going *on?*" Seely had always wanted to be a pilot, but, because of poor eyesight, he ended up an engineer in a satellite-control facility. The medal was accompanied by a photograph of Seely in his captain's uniform, and he said that Amber, after looking at the image, had proclaimed that he was the only person she knew who'd kept the same hair style for nearly fifty years: short, straight, and parted neatly on the far right.

Seely grew up across the street from a dairy farm that his father owned, in Ohio, and he considers himself a "green," by the mid-century standards relating to productive use of the land, in contrast with the "weirdos" whom he now associates with environmental causes. "If they had their way, all the buildings, all industry, all fossil fuel would stop," he said. "And you can't have that." He and his wife, who works at the Creation Museum, an institution dedicated to promoting a Biblically literal account of the earth's origins, raised their family in a Columbus suburb and moved south across the Ohio River about a year ago, to be closer to their grandchildren. Their new Kentucky home has a large expanse of freshly mowed grass out back that Seely's brother-in-law at first mistook for a golf course. "Those towers over there, that's actually Ohio," Seely said, stepping onto his back porch and pointing at the nearest tall buildings. "Ohio has a problem: money is leaving, educated people are leaving. 'Cause we have a lot of good universities in Ohio, but there's no jobs there, so you educate your kids and then you send them off."

Seely had a history in local politics to reflect on as he thought about how to reverse the tide of urban progressivism. Many of his cohorts did not, however, and he worried about the transition from the strange euphoria of collective exasperation. Like the sixties radicals, they risked suffering from a kind of idealistic naïveté. "I don't think the Tea Party quite understands how the system actually works," he said. For about a decade, he served as a Republican central committeeman, a volunteer position, in Ohio's Franklin County, where the general level of civic engagement was such that politicians were known to be willing to appear at any home where five or six neighbors might assemble. Democracy as he experienced it was practiced in a largely backroom fashion, with the committeemen and the county chairs trading favors for endorsements. The local Republican Party, in his telling, consisted of three competing factions: moderates, fiscal conservatives, and Seely's group, the social conservatives. A few years ago, when the longtime Franklin County chair, a friend of Seely's, stepped down, the first two groups banded together to block the social conservatives from retaining power. "And guess who they elected to be the chairman?" he asked me. "An open homosexual!"

"People are finally getting to the point where they want to educate themselves," Seely went on. "We've got to get to the point where people are educated enough to find out about 'Well, how *do* you endorse candidates?' That's really where the power is. It's been very frustrating to me, because I tell people about my experience and it goes *pffft pffft*"—he gestured to indicate something passing over his head. "They say, 'You know, we're not interested in local things. We're interested in national things.' I go, 'Well, fine. That's good. But, really, you got to be local.' "

After we finished our coffee, Seely took me to the Creation Museum, a mile down the road. The museum, which opened in 2007, at a cost of twenty-seven million dollars, features a planetarium, animatronic dinosaurs, and a partial replica, built to exacting scale, of Noah's Ark. Several staff Ph.D.s work on site. The first exhibit showed two paleontologists, a Darwinist and a Biblical literalist, examining a fossil. "Depending on what your world view is, and what you believe and what you've been taught, you can look at the same thing and come to a different conclusion," Seely explained. The exhibit, called "Starting Points," was intended to demonstrate the plausible divergence in theories about man's relation to dinosaurs, but it could just as easily have spoken for the assumptions we make about Barack Obama's past associations with figures like Bill Ayers and Bernardine Dohrn.

Obama's selection last summer of the Republican congressman John McHugh to be his Secretary of the Army created the need for a special election, and provided the first opportunity for Tea Party activists to make an electoral impact both locally and nationally. It served as a dress rehearsal for the Massachusetts Senate race, and enabled activists to learn from their mistakes. McHugh's district, New York's Twenty-third, covers most of what locals call the North Country, from the Adirondacks to the St. Lawrence River and extending west to Lake Ontario. Primarily rural, its politics and class markers have more in common with Kentucky than with Manhattan, and the Republican Party had been in control since before the turn of the twentieth century. But Obama carried the district, with fifty-two per cent of the vote, and the eleven Republican county chairs made what seemed like an expedient choice in nominating the veteran state assemblywoman Dede Scozzafava to run for McHugh's seat. Scozzafava was a big-tent selection: pro-choice, in favor of gay marriage, and a friend of the teachers' union.

Tea Party adherents responded by backing a third-party challenge from an earnest accountant named Doug Hoffman, who had served as the C.F.O. for the Lake Placid Olympics in 1980. "We formed the foundation that created the Miracle, and I think the miracle was the start of the Reagan Revolution, and it eventually brought down the Soviet Union," Hoffman told a group of supporters. "Since this is the first congressional race of 2010, we're going to break down the wall again. And the miracle is we're going to take America back, and we're going to get our freedom back."

Shortly before the election, I went to Cicero, New York, to hear the former House majority leader Dick Armey address what one listener referred to as a "glorified sticker club." A group of about thirty people had assembled in the cavernous interior of Drivers Village, a cluster of adjoined auto dealerships. They had been meeting regularly for months to talk politics. "This could be the single most important election that any of us will ever get to work on in our lifetime—the game-changer," Armey, who now heads a supply-side nonprofit called Freedom Works, declared. He predicted—correctly—that Scozzafava would end up conceding before Election Day, and said that the only remaining question was whether Hoffman, who was polling in third place, could manage to overcome the Democrats' likely election fraud, which he estimated to be worth three percentage points. "In '93, when the worm started to turn, it started to turn with a special election in Kentucky," he said, referring to a 1994 contest that was prompted by the death of an incumbent Democrat, and won by a little-known Republican, a Christian-bookstore owner named Ron Lewis. "That election changed everybody's mood," Armey said. It also paved the way for the Republican takeover of the House in the '94 midterms.

"None of us knew this was going to hit," a young woman named Jennifer Bernstone said, looking up from a laptop. "We all went to D.C. in September: '*Woo hoo,* that was awesome!' We all came home. '*Now* what?' This is the what. Who the heck knew? I sing for a living. I'm an actress. I don't *do* this stuff." Her immediate concern was the effective deployment of Hoffman supporters from Connecticut and Westchester, with whom she'd been e-mailing. They were coming to canvass for the weekend, and needed places to crash.

"I feel a kinship with the Afghan hill men," a young man with wavy hair and glasses said, eying Armey's young associates with an air of caution. "We're a bunch of ordinary people, and a bunch of very powerful groups are coming in with very different philosophies—maybe sometimes I agree with them, most of the time I don't—and they're having a proxy war in our back yard."

The group at Drivers Village had organized through Meetup.com under the name Central New York 9.12, and, according to one of them, a Constitutionalist, they represented about eight political subgroups, including that most prized Tea Party scalp: Obama voters. They had brought no props, and none were dressed in period garb. They seemed united principally by their acute sensitivity to the raging-teabagger stereotype, and, as if to reassure each other, compared notes of their experiences on the Mall:

"You saw the lack of litter."

"I think it had more to do with the calibre of the people involved."

"As you can see, we're not really what a lot of people portray us as," William Wells, the Afghanistan analogist, told me, after apologizing for the mud stains on his jeans, which he attributed to harvesting pinot gris earlier in the day. Wells's father is an astronomer turned vintner, and his mother is a doctor. "I used to work at Fannie Mae," he said. "I was a research analyst in the loss-forecasting division. If you understand that, you understand kind of why I'm here. In some ways, this, for me, is paying off my debt when I should have said something." He added that Sean Hannity and Keith Olbermann had each got the story of the housing crisis about half right, despite "very different angles of approach," and that Glenn Beck, "whatever you think of his histrionics," had been closer to ninety per cent correct.

As the meeting was breaking up, a soft-spoken project manager, and father of six, named Paul Dopp asked me if I knew who had won the Battle of Saratoga. "It was General Arnold," he said—Benedict Arnold. "Part of the reason he turned traitor was that he didn't get the recognition for it. He got ticked. But what he did is he rode right out in front between the soldiers, looked at the Americans, and said, 'I'm fighting. Are you coming?' And they came. Someone is going to stand up for principle." Dopp said that his brother had travelled to the Soviet Union in the nineteen-eighties, while studying détente, and returned with a sober lesson on the corrupting effects of power.

"For a lot of people, government is their religion," he said. "That's their place of worship, because they truly believe in the betterment of man."

At night, with the dealerships closed, Drivers Village felt vast and lonely. "This used to be a mall before the economy crashed around here," Dopp said, referring not to the recent tumult but to the Rockefeller era. "We've been ravaged so well, so long, we're kind of like, 'The last person that leaves Schenectady, please turn the lights off.' The only reason we're still alive is because of the bubble created by the financial system down in the city." The mall had been resuscitated by a born-again car salesman whose political sympathies inclined him to let the Commons, as the interior corridors of Drivers Village are known, be put to revolutionary use.

Without paying attention, I followed the group out a different exit from the way I'd come in, and quickly realized that it would take a long time to find my car—parked amid acres of cars awaiting sale in a recession. One of the men at the meeting offered to drive me around the lot to speed up the search, taking the opportunity to show me a three-ring binder that he kept in the back seat of his van, full of homemade graphs showing the growth of the national debt, and Internet printouts that hinted at links between, for instance, ACORN and an Obama campaign office in Louisiana. "That's what got us mad, those sorts of things," he said. "You know, it drives us nuts. I would love for someone to actually come out and say this—someone that is credible, other than myself, in my own mind."

The involvement of people like Dick Armey in the Tea Party movement led many Democrats, including Speaker of the House Nancy Pelosi, to dismiss the significance of the activism as a creation of right-wing moguls. Freedom Works and a host of lobbying firms and think tanks, including Americans for Tax Reform, the Club for Growth, Campaign for Liberty, and the Ayn Rand Center for Individual Rights, sponsored the march in Washington last September. Lobbyists and think tanks in turn rely on financial support from corporate interests with enormous stakes in much of the prospective legislation on Capitol Hill. "Astroturfing" is the critics' preferred term for this phenomenon, with its imputation of a synthetic, top-down structure to contrast with the outward appearance of grassroots independence. Yet the presence of paid Freedom Works operatives at meetings like the one in Cicero, handing out Obamacare Translator leaflets and legislator "leave-behinds," would be cause for greater skepticism if the civilians in attendance weren't already compiling binders of their own and reciting from memory the troublesome implications buried on page 59 of House Resolution 3200. The blogosphere can make trained foot soldiers of us all, with or without corporate funding.

"If you listen to the Democrats, they're completely convinced somebody's in charge of all this," Dick Armey said, sitting at a hotel café in Syracuse with a press aide, the day after his pep talk to the sticker club. He took off his

Stetson and said that he'd only just learned about the existence of the Tea Party Patriots and "a group that call themselves the 9.12 Project, and I'm not quite sure where they come from."

"It's Glenn Beck," his press aide interjected.

"I don't know Glenn Beck," Armey said. "I think I was on his show one time. Was I?"

Freedom Works has an annual budget of only seven million dollars and a paid staff of eighteen, most of whom travel comfortably within the Washington establishment, where debating the sanity of Beck remains a common cocktail-party gambit. Its employees are well versed in the differences between the Austrian and Chicago economic schools, and in the biographical details of Howard Roark and John Galt, but tend to cringe at some of the paranoid elements within the Ron Paul contingent. They provide logistical support and tactical know-how, like the dreaded community organizers mocked by Rudy Giuliani, to a network of some four hundred activists scattered around the country. In their advisory capacity, their aims are to push fiscal concerns, not social issues, and to deëmphasize personal attacks on Obama, which could be perceived as having racial overtones; instead, they take on Pelosi and Harry Reid.

"Where did MoveOn.org come from?" Armey asked, citing the grassroots liberal group that was until recently the envy of all its conservative counterparts, and then answered his own question, incorrectly: "From George Bush." In fact, as Armey's aide was quick to point out, MoveOn originated in the Clinton impeachment proceedings, and subsequently gained wider attention under Bush, and specifically through its unofficial association with the grassroots campaign of Howard Dean—or "the governor from back East that ran for President," as Armey put it, adding, "His name will come to me tomorrow."

An absent-minded professor in cowboy boots, Armey saw his role as eliciting coverage of the growing conservative opposition from news organizations (like this one) that exist outside the Fox and Friends echo chamber. "I don't know if you noticed, but in August, all of a sudden, I became the bogeyman," he told me, with undisguised pleasure, and said that he'd received an e-mail from an old friend, "a liberal English prof from a small college down the road," in Dallas, that read "Shame on you." The outburst had been prompted by a blog post linking Freedom Works to a town-hall strategy memo distributed by activists in Fairfield County, Connecticut. (The memo, which was written by a Tea Party Patriots volunteer, included such suggestions as "Watch for an opportunity to yell out and challenge the Rep's statements early" and "The goal is to rattle him.") In his defense, Armey offered the folksy alibi of having been "back in Texas, tending to two sick goats," on the weekend of the town-hall event in question, with the veterinary receipts to prove it. "They made a walking, talking, attention-getting device out of me," he said.

Even as Armey welcomes the attention, he must be wary of attracting too much. The Tea Party Express, a road show funded by a PAC called Our Country Deserves Better, has earned the scorn of many activists for being too slickly produced—its buses too flashy, its steak-house tabs too high. Some even call it the Astroturf Express, in an attempt to own the opposition's slur. "That's a Republican PAC," one board member of the defiantly nonpartisan Tea Party Patriots declared recently, and, to be sure, Armey's side recommended "a great YouTube" in which the Republican Senator John Cornyn can be seen being booed and heckled on a stage in Austin for his support of the Troubled Asset Relief Program. TARP, because it happened on President Bush's watch, makes for a better Tea Party litmus test than anything since.

"There you are, Leader," the aide said at another point, drawing Armey's attention to a television above the hotel bar, which was showing the local news. Armey was standing behind a lectern, touting the virtues of a flat tax, while Doug Hoffman stood off to the side, smiling. The footage was from a boisterous rally in downtown Syracuse, which is not part of District Twenty-three. Most liberals mistook Hoffman's eventual defeat, which came after a bitter Scozzafava endorsed the Democrat Bill Owens, as a sign that the movement had overshot. "If the tea party right can't win there, imagine how it might fare in the nation where most Americans live," Frank Rich wrote in the *Times*, noting that New York's Twenty-third District is ninety-three per cent white. The headline over Rich's column was "THE NIGHT THEY DROVE THE TEA PARTIERS DOWN." Rich and others, including senior members of the Obama Administration, underestimated the strength of the movement, and the extent of the resentment that fed it. By fixating on the most egregious protest signs, and making sport of Tea Party infighting, they ignored the movement's gradual consolidation.

Meanwhile, Freedom Works and other activist groups refocussed their attention on Florida, where a thirty-eight-year-old fiscal conservative named Marco Rubio was mounting a strong primary challenge for the Senate against the popular but moderate governor, Charlie Crist. Rand Paul, son of Ron, caught up with Kentucky's Secretary of State, Trey Grayson, in the race to succeed Senator Jim Bunning. And in Tennessee's Eighth Congressional District, earlier this month, a conservative named Donn Janes opted out of the Republican primary in order to run as "an independent Tea Party candidate." Bill O'Reilly, who has never seemed entirely comfortable with the anarchic impulses of the activist fringe, told his new Fox News colleague Sarah Palin that he wouldn't be surprised to see her lead a Tea Party ticket in 2012. "Well, there is no Tea Party ticket," Palin demurred. "There could be," he said. If a registered national Tea Party existed, a recent Rasmussen poll suggested, its popularity would exceed that of the Republicans. Among independent voters, a hypothetical Tea Party candidate beat a Democrat, too.

The lesson that the Republican establishment drew from upstate New York was not to shun the movement, for fear of losing moderates, but to court it (the embattled Republican National Committee chairman Michael Steele recently used teacups as props during a speech) or get out of its way, as evidenced by last week's special election in Massachusetts. While Scott Brown, a telegenic state senator, visited the kinds of coastal New England towns that had always counted Ted Kennedy as their own, the National Republican Senatorial Committee deliberately chose not to offer him much public support, because of voters' dissatisfaction with party politics.

As in upstate New York, volunteers from elsewhere flocked to canvass and man phone banks: not crazed sign-carriers but quietly dedicated engineers and winemakers and singers. By the end, Brown was raising a million dollars a day from donors who saw an opportunity to make the election a referendum on health care.

The Democrats were "caught napping," as David Axelrod admitted to the *Times*. Massachusetts already has a more generous health-care system than anything that either the Senate or the House has yet proposed. Attorney General Martha Coakley, the Democratic candidate, appeared at times barely to campaign at all, and flubbed the kinds of exchanges—about the Red Sox, say—designed to showcase blue-collar cred. While Coakley carried the city of Boston, the site of the original Tea Party, with nearly seventy per cent of the vote, Brown, notably, won the neighborhood of South Boston, where the sting of forced busing still lingers from the seventies.

The lesson that the Tea Party movement seems to have learned is, in effect, Don Seely's: to respect local preferences and work selectively within the system. Rather than back a libertarian third-party candidate, the activists this time rallied behind the equivalent of Dede Scozzafava. Scott Brown at one point likened himself to a "Reagan Democrat" and is something of a moderate on abortion rights. One of Dick Armey's associates told me in November, "We have got to show that this movement can be successful outside the South." Now they have, and New York's Senator Chuck Schumer, who made the mistake of describing Brown as a "far-right teabagger," in a last-ditch fund-raising appeal on behalf of Coakley, has invited talk of a movement to depose him in November by drafting Rick Santelli's CNBC colleague Larry Kudlow.

What remains to be seen is whether the anti-establishment bent of the Tea Partiers will drive them to disown their greatest coup in the weeks to come. Less than twenty-four hours after the victory, Glenn Beck was suggesting that Brown might be morally unfit for office. ("This one could end with a dead intern. I'm just saying.")

Back in New York City, you can feel the tremors in the social bedrock, if not in the earth's crust, as T. J. Randall would have it. An online video game, designed recently by libertarians in Brooklyn, called "2011: Obama's Coup Fails" imagines a scenario in which the Democrats lose seventeen of nineteen seats in the Senate and a hundred and seventy-eight in the House during the midterm elections, prompting the President to dissolve the Constitution and implement an emergency North American People's Union, with help from Mexico's Felipe Calderón, Canada's Stephen Harper, and various civilian defense troops with names like the Black Tigers, the International Service Union Empire, and CORNY, or the Congress of Rejected and Neglected Youth. Lou Dobbs has gone missing, Glenn Beck and Rush Limbaugh turn up dead at a FEMA concentration camp, and you, a lone militiaman in a police state where private gun ownership has been outlawed, are charged with defeating the enemies of patriotism, one county at a time.

Not long ago, at a restaurant in the shadow of the Brooklyn Bridge, I stood next to Kellen Giuda, a twenty-seven-year-old self-described "party guy" (in the night-life sense) and the proprietor of a Web site, parcbench.com, that he describes as a "*Rolling Stone* from the right." He was listening to a couple of deficit hawks from Hoboken who were worried about potential demagogic influences on the Tea Party movement from the likes of Sarah Palin. Giuda is a co-founder of Tea Party 365, a local New York City battalion, which had convened this particular meeting, as well as a national board member for the Tea Party Patriots. While the Hoboken pair were making their case, he glanced at his iPhone and skimmed a newly arriving e-mail from yet another upstart organization, Tea Party Nation. It announced a national convention to be held in Nashville on the first weekend in February, with Sarah Palin as the keynote speaker.

Dick Armey, despite his contention that "the Republican Party is undergoing the most massive identity crisis in the history of politics," was nearby, talking happily with Ed Cox, the newly elected chair of the New York Republican State Committee, who seemed to recognize that a shift in the power center had occurred.

Eventually, a couple of men dressed in black silenced the crowd with an impassioned presentation that called to mind lefty gatherings of the sixties, or even the thirties. One of them was from Maine, the other from Fresno, and they were driving across the country to raise awareness of the plight of farmers in California's Central Valley, where a water shortage had been creating a "new dust bowl" and threatening the local way of life. Women handed out flyers for a campaign called Saving the Valley that Hope Forgot. ("Americans need to ask themselves whether they are willing to settle for foreign food, like they have settled for foreign oil.") A gray-haired man in a blue velvet jacket and sneakers started inching toward the center of the room with an acoustic guitar. He had a "Reagan for President" button on his shoulder strap and a "Hoffman for Congress" sticker on his case.

The cause of the water shortage was not a natural drought, the men in black explained, but "radical environmentalism": a government effort to protect an endangered "two-inch bait fish" called the Delta smelt. (They had recently barbecued a smelt and found it wanting.) And they had opted for a four-wheel-drive S.U.V. instead of a beat-up van for their road trip. But they invited the guitarist to play, and before long Hank from Gravesend and Julie from Chelsea and Kellen from Morningside Heights were singing along to the chorus of a folk anthem in that great American tradition:

Take it back,

Take our country back.

Our way of life is now under attack.

Draw a line in the sand, so they all understand

And our values stay intact.

Take it back.

The Logic of Stupid Poor People

Tressie McMillan

Tressie McMillan Cottom earned her Ph.D in Sociology from Emory University and is currently an assistant professor at Virginia Commonwealth University. She is also the writer of the blog tressiemc, where she blogs about issues involving gender, racial, and socioeconomic inequality. Cottom is the author of several books, such as Profit U: The Rise of For-Profit Higher Education *on for-profit colleges and their admission practices. Her writing has appeared in Inside Higher Education,* The Chronical of Higher Education, Slate, Dissent Magazine, *and* The New York Times. *She has also appeared on NPR and "Dan Rather Reports."*

"The Logic of Stupid Poor People" is an essay from her blog in which she addresses the issue of status symbols and the dichotomy in the judgements made by the not-poor about the poor who have them. The essay was written in response to a tweet issued by Errol Louis on October 29, 2013. Louis, a journalist and talk-show host, wrote that "I totally get that it's horrible and illegal to profile people. But still #SMFH over a not-filthy-rich person spending $2,500 on a handbag." Cottom's response in her essay highlights the controversy concerning purchasing-power and the growing class-divide.

We hates us some poor people. First, they insist on being poor when it is so easy to not be poor. They do things like buy expensive designer belts and $2500 luxury handbags.

To be fair, this isn't about Errol Louis. His is a belief held by many people, including lots of black people, poor people, formerly poor people, etc. It is, I suspect, an honest expression of incredulity. If you are poor, why do you spend money on useless status symbols like handbags and belts and clothes and shoes and televisions and cars?

One thing I've learned is that one person's illogical belief is another person's survival skill. And nothing is more logical than trying to survive.

My family is a classic black American migration family. We have rural Southern roots, moved north and almost all have returned. I grew up watching my great-grandmother, and later my grandmother and mother, use our minimal resources to help other people make ends meet. We were those good poors, the kind who live mostly within our means. We had a little luck when a male relative got extra military pay when they came home a paraplegic or used the VA to buy a Jim Walter house. If you were really blessed when a relative died with a paid up insurance policy you might be gifted a lump sum to buy the land that Jim Walters used as collateral to secure your home lease. That's how generational wealth happens where I'm from: lose a leg, a part of your spine, die right and maybe you can lease-to-own a modular home.

We had a little of that kind of rural black wealth so we were often in a position to help folks less fortunate. But perhaps the greatest resource we had was a bit more education. We were big readers and we encouraged the girl children, especially, to go to some kind of college. Consequently, my grandmother and mother had a particular set of social resources that helped us navigate mostly white bureaucracies to our benefit. We could, as my grandfather would say, talk like white folks. We loaned that privilege out to folks a lot.

I remember my mother taking a next door neighbor down to the social service agency. The elderly woman had been denied benefits to care for the granddaughter she was raising. The woman had been denied in the genteel bureaucratic way — lots of waiting, forms, and deadlines she could not quite navigate. I watched my mother put on her best Diana Ross "Mahogany" outfit: a camel colored cape with matching slacks and knee high boots. I was miffed, as only an only child could be, about sharing my mother's time with the neighbor girl. I must have said something about why we had to do this. Vivian fixed me with a stare as she was slipping on her pearl earrings and told me that people who can do, must do. It took half a day but something about my mother's performance of respectable black person — her Queen's English, her Mahogany outfit, her straight bob and pearl earrings — got done what the elderly lady next door had not been able to get done in over a year. I learned, watching my mother, that there was a price we had to pay to signal to gatekeepers that we were worthy of engaging. It meant dressing well and speaking well. It might not work. It likely wouldn't work but on the off chance that it would, you had to try. It was unfair but, as Vivian also always said, "life isn't fair little girl."

I internalized that lesson and I think it has worked out for me, if unevenly. A woman at Belk's once refused to show me the Dooney and Burke purse I was interested in buying. Vivian once made a salesgirl cry after she ignored us in an empty store. I have walked away from many of hotly desired purchases, like the impractical off-white winter coat I desperately wanted, after some bigot at the counter insulted me and my mother. But, I have half a PhD and I support myself aping the white male privileged life of the mind. It's a mixed bag. Of course, the trick is you can never know the counterfactual of your life. There is no evidence of access denied. Who knows what I was not granted for not enacting the right status behaviors or symbols at the right time for an agreeable authority? Respectability rewards are a crap-shoot but we do what we can within the limits of the constraints imposed by a complex set of structural and social interactions designed to limit access to status, wealth, and power.

I do not know how much my mother spent on her camel colored cape or knee-high boots but I know that whatever she paid it returned in hard-to-measure dividends. How do you put a price on the double-take of a clerk at the welfare office who decides you might not be like those other trifling women in the waiting room and provides an extra bit of information about completing a form that you would not have known to ask about? What is the retail value of a school principal who defers a bit more to your child because your mother's presentation of self signals that she might unleash the bureaucratic savvy of middle class parents to advocate for her child? I don't know the price of these critical engagements with organizations and gatekeepers relative to our poverty when I was growing up. But, I am living proof of its investment yield.

Why do poor people make stupid, illogical decisions to buy status symbols? For the same reason all but only the most wealthy buy status symbols, I suppose. We want to belong. And, not just for the psychic rewards, but belonging to one group at the right time can mean the difference between unemployment and employment, a good job as opposed to a bad job, housing or a shelter, and so on. Someone mentioned on twitter that poor people can be presentable with affordable options from Kmart. But the issue is not about being presentable. Presentable is the bare minimum of social civility. It means being clean, not smelling, wearing shirts and shoes for service and the like. Presentable as a sufficient condition for gainful, dignified work or successful social interactions is a privilege. It's the aging white hippie who can cut the ponytail of his youthful rebellion and walk into senior management while aging black panthers can never completely outrun the effects of stigmatization against which they were courting a revolution. Presentable is relative and, like life, it ain't fair.

In contrast, "acceptable" is about gaining access to a limited set of rewards granted upon group membership. I cannot know exactly how often my presentation of acceptable has helped me but I have enough feedback to know it is not inconsequential. One manager at the apartment complex where I worked while in college told me, repeatedly, that she knew I was "Okay" because my little Nissan was clean. That I had worn a Jones of New York suit to the interview really sealed the deal. She could call the suit by name because she asked me about the label in the interview. Another hiring manager at my first professional job looked me up and down in the waiting room, cataloging my outfit, and later told me that she had decided I was too classy to be on the call center floor. I was hired as a trainer instead. The difference meant no shift work, greater prestige, better pay and a baseline salary for all my future employment.

I have about a half dozen other stories like this. What is remarkable is not that this happened. There is empirical evidence that women and people of color are judged by appearances differently and more harshly than are white men. What is remarkable is that these gatekeepers *told me the story*. They wanted me to know how I had properly signaled that I was not a typical black or a typical woman, two identities that in combination are almost always conflated with being poor.

I sat in on an interview for a new administrative assistant once. My regional vice president was doing the hiring. A long line of mostly black and brown women applied because we were a cosmetology school. Trade schools at the margins of skilled labor in a gendered field are necessarily classed and raced. I found one candidate particularly charming. She was trying to get out of a salon because 10 hours on her feet cutting hair would average out to an hourly rate below minimum wage. A desk job with 40 set hours and medical benefits represented mobility for her. When she left my VP turned to me and said, "did you see that tank top she had on under her blouse?! OMG, you wear a silk*shell* not a tank top!" Both of the women were black.

The VP had constructed her job as senior management. She drove a brand new BMW because she, "should treat herself" and liked to tell us that ours was an image business. A girl wearing a cotton tank top as a shell was incompatible with BMW-driving VPs in the image business. Gatekeeping is a complex job of managing boundaries that do not just define others but that also define ourselves. Status symbols—silk shells, designer shoes, luxury handbags—become keys to unlock these gates. If I need a job that will save my lower back and move my baby from medicaid to an HMO, how much should I spend signaling to people like my former VP that I will not compromise her status by opening the door to me? That candidate maybe could not afford a proper shell. I will never know. But I do know that had she gone hungry for two days to pay for it or missed wages for a trip to the store to buy it, she may have been rewarded a job that could have lifted her above minimum wage. Shells aren't designer handbags, perhaps. But a cosmetology school in a strip mall isn't a job at Bank of America, either.

At the heart of these incredulous statements about the poor decisions poor people make is a belief that we would never be like them. We would know better. We would know to save our money, eschew status symbols, cut coupons, practice puritanical sacrifice to amass a million dollars. There is a regular news story of a lunch lady who, unbeknownst to all who knew her, died rich and leaves it all to a cat or a charity or some such. Books about the modest lives of the rich like to tell us how they drive Buicks instead of BMWs. What we forget, if we ever know, is that what we know now about status and wealth creation and sacrifice are predicated on who we are, i.e. not poor. If you change the conditions of your not-poor status, you change everything you know as a result of being a not-poor. You have no idea what you would do if you were poor until you are poor. And not intermittently poor or formerly not-poor, but born poor, expected to be poor and treated by bureaucracies, gatekeepers and well-meaning respectability authorities as inherently poor. Then, and only then, will you understand the relative value of a ridiculous status symbol to someone who intuits that they cannot afford to not have it.

Body Ritual among the Nacirema

Horace Miner

University of Michigan

Horace Mitchell Miner, an anthropologist and specialist in the cultures of primitive peoples, is considered one of the more versatile social scientists of the mid-twentieth century. Miner was born on May 26, 1912, in St. Paul, Minnesota, and grew up in Lexington, Kentucky, where his father, James Burt Miner, was a professor at the University of Kentucky. As a young man, he studied at L'Ecole Alasacienne in Paris and, later, at the University of Munich before returning home to Kentucky, where he received his A.B. degree in Sociology from the University of Kentucky. He became interested in archeology and participated in excavations conducted in conjunction with the university. After working as an assistant museum curator at the university's Museum of Anthropology, he changed his focus to anthropology, eventually earning his doctorate from the University of Chicago. Well-traveled, Miner taught at several universities across the United States and, on a Fulbright Fellowship, at a college in Uganda. He published numerous books, including Culture and Agriculture *(1949) and* City in Modern Africa *(1967). However, he is best known for his 1956 essay, "Body Ritual Among the Nacirema" ("American" spelled backwards), a satire of American culture from an anthropological perspective that underscores the way cultural context defines meaning and dictates behavior within that culture. Horace Miner died in Ann Arbor, Michigan, on November 26, 1993.*

The anthropologist has become so familiar with the diversity of ways in which different peoples behave in similar situations that he is not apt to be surprised by even the most exotic customs. In fact, if all of the logically possible combinations of behavior have not been found somewhere in the world, he is apt to suspect that they must be present in some yet undescribed tribe. This point has, in fact, been expressed with respect to clan organization by Murdock (1949:71). In this light, the magical beliefs and practices of the Nacirema present such unusual aspects that it seems desirable to describe them as an example of the extremes to which human behavior can go.

Professor Linton first brought the ritual of the Nacirema to the attention of anthropologists twenty years ago (1936:326), but the culture of this people is still very poorly understood. They are a North American group living in the territory between the Canadian Cree, the Yaqui and Tarahumare of Mexico, and the Carib and Arawak of the Antilles. Little is known of their origin, although tradition states that they came from the east. According to Nacirema mythology, their nation was originated by a culture hero, Notgnihsaw, who is otherwise known for two great feats of strength—the throwing of a piece of wampum across the river Pa-To-Mac and the chopping down of a cherry tree in which the Spirit of Truth resided.

Nacirema culture is characterized by a highly developed market economy which has evolved in a rich natural habitat. While much of the people's time is devoted to economic pursuits, a large part of the fruits of these labors and a considerable portion of the day are spent in ritual activity. The focus of this activity is the human body, the appearance and health of which loom as a dominant concern in the ethos of the people. While such a concern is certainly not unusual, its ceremonial aspects and associated philosophy are unique.

The fundamental belief underlying the whole system appears to be that the human body is ugly and that its natural tendency is to debility and disease. Incarcerated in such a body, man's only hope is to avert these characteristics through the use of the powerful influences of ritual and ceremony. Every household has one or more shrines devoted to this purpose. The more powerful individuals in the society have several shrines in their houses and, in fact, the opulence of a house is often referred to in terms of the number of such ritual centers it possesses. Most houses are of wattle and daub construction, but the shrine rooms of the more wealthy are walled with stone. Poorer families imitate the rich by applying pottery plaques to their shrine walls.

While each family has at least one such shrine, the rituals associated with it are not family ceremonies but are private and secret. The rites are normally only discussed with children, and then only during the period when they are being initiated into these mysteries. I was able, however, to establish sufficient rapport with the natives to examine these shrines and to have the rituals described to me.

The focal point of the shrine is a box or chest which is built into the wall. In this chest are kept the many charms and magical potions without which no native believes he could live. These preparations are secured from a variety of specialized practitioners. The most powerful of these are the medicine men, whose assistance must be rewarded with substantial gifts. However, the medicine men do not provide the curative potions for their clients, but decide what the ingredients should be and then write them down in an ancient and secret language. This writing is understood only by the medicine men and by the herbalists who, for another gift, provide the required charm.

The charm is not disposed of after it has served its purpose, but is placed in the charm-box of the household shrine. As these magical materials are specific for certain ills, and the real or imagined maladies of the people are many, the charm-box is usually full to overflowing. The magical packets are so numerous that people forget what their purposes were and fear to use them again. While the natives are very vague on this point, we can only assume that the idea in retaining all the old magical materials is that their presence in the charm-box, before which the body rituals are conducted, will in some way protect the worshipper.

Beneath the charm-box is a small font. Each day every member of the family, in succession, enters the shrine room, bows his head before the charm-box, mingles different sorts of holy water in the font, and proceeds with a brief rite of ablution. The holy waters are secured from the Water Temple of the community, where the priests conduct elaborate ceremonies to make the liquid ritually pure.

In the hierarchy of magical practitioners, and below the medicine men in prestige, are specialists whose designation is best translated "holy-mouth-men." The Nacirema have an almost pathological horror of and fascination with the mouth, the condition of which is believed to have a supernatural influence on all social relationships. Were it not for the rituals of the mouth, they believe that their teeth would fall out, their gums bleed, their jaws shrink, their friends desert them, and their lovers reject them. They also believe that a strong relationship exists between oral and moral characteristics. For example, there is a ritual ablution of the mouth for children which is supposed to improve their moral fiber.

The daily body ritual performed by everyone includes a mouth-rite. Despite the fact that these people are so punctilious about care of the mouth, this rite involves a practice which strikes the uninitiated stranger as revolting. It was reported to me that the ritual consists of inserting a small bundle of hog hairs into the mouth, along with certain magical powders, and then moving the bundle in a highly formalized series of gestures.

In addition to the private mouth-rite, the people seek out a holy-mouth-man once or twice a year. These practitioners have an impressive set of paraphernalia, consisting of a variety of augers, awls, probes, and prods. The use of these objects in the exorcism of the evils of the mouth involves almost unbelievable ritual torture of the client. The holy-mouth-man opens the client's mouth and, using the above mentioned tools, enlarges any holes which decay may have created in the teeth. Magical materials are put into these holes. If there are no naturally occurring holes in the teeth, large sections of one or more teeth are gouged out so that the supernatural substance can be applied. In the client's view, the purpose of these ministrations is to arrest decay and to draw friends. The extremely sacred and traditional character of the rite is evident in the fact that the natives return to the holy-mouth-men year after year, despite the fact that their teeth continue to decay.

It is to be hoped that, when a thorough study of the Nacirema is made, there will be careful inquiry into the personality structure of these people. One has but to watch the gleam in the eye of a holy-mouth-man, as he jabs an awl into an exposed nerve, to suspect that a certain amount of sadism is involved. If this can be established, a very interesting pattern emerges, for most of the population shows definite masochistic tendencies. It was to these that Professor Linton referred in discussing a distinctive part of the daily body ritual which is performed only by men. This part of the rite involves scraping and lacerating the surface of the face with a sharp instrument. Special women's rites are performed only four times during each lunar month, but what they lack in frequency is made up in barbarity. As part of this ceremony, women bake their heads in small ovens for about an hour. The theoretically interesting point is that what seems to be a preponderantly masochistic people have developed sadistic specialists.

The medicine men have an imposing temple, or *lati pso*, in every community of any size. The more elaborate ceremonies required to treat very sick patients can only be performed at this temple. These ceremonies involve not only the thaumaturge but a permanent group of vestal maidens who move sedately about the temple chambers in distinctive costume and headdress.

The *lati pso* ceremonies are so harsh that it is phenomenal that a fair proportion of the really sick natives who enter the temple ever recover. Small children whose indoctrination is still incomplete have been known to resist attempts to take them to the temple because "that is where you go to die." Despite this fact, sick adults are not only willing but eager to undergo the protracted ritual purification, if they can afford to do so. No matter how ill the supplicant or how grave the emergency, the guardians of many temples will not admit a client if he cannot give a rich gift to the custodian. Even after one has gained admission and survived the ceremonies, the guardians will not permit the neophyte to leave until he makes still another gift.

The supplicant entering the temple is first stripped of all his or her clothes. In every-day life the Nacirema avoids exposure of his body and its natural functions. Bathing and excretory acts are performed only in the secrecy of the household shrine, where they are ritualized as part of the body-rites.

Psychological shock results from the fact that body secrecy is suddenly lost upon entry into the *lati pso*. A man, whose own wife has never seen him in an excretory act, suddenly finds himself naked and assisted by a vestal maiden while he performs his natural functions into a sacred vessel. This sort of ceremonial treatment is necessitated by the fact that the excreta are used by a diviner to ascertain the course and nature of the client's sickness. Female clients, on the other hand, find their naked bodies are subjected to the scrutiny, manipulation and prodding of the medicine men.

Few supplicants in the temple are well enough to do anything but lie on their hard beds. The daily ceremonies, like the rites of the holy-mouth-men, involve discomfort and torture. With ritual precision, the vestals awaken their miserable charges each dawn and roll them about on their beds of pain while performing ablutions, in the formal movements of which the maidens are highly trained. At other times they insert magic wands in the supplicant's mouth or force him to eat substances which are supposed to be healing. From time to time the medicine men come to their clients and jab magically treated needles into their flesh. The fact that these temple ceremonies may not cure, and may even kill the neophyte, in no way decreases the people's faith in the medicine men.

There remains one other kind of practitioner, known as a "listener." This witch-doctor has the power to exorcise the devils that lodge in the heads of people who have been bewitched. The Nacirema believe that parents bewitch their own children. Mothers are particularly suspected of putting a curse on children while teaching them the secret body rituals. The counter-magic of the witch-doctor is unusual in its lack of ritual. The patient simply tells the "listener" all his troubles and fears, beginning with the earliest difficulties he can remember. The memory displayed by the Nacirema in these exorcism sessions is truly remarkable. It is not uncommon for the patient to bemoan the rejection he felt upon being weaned as a babe, and a few individuals even see their troubles going back to the traumatic effects of their own birth.

In conclusion, mention must be made of certain practices which have their base in native esthetics but which depend upon the pervasive aversion to the natural body and its functions. There are ritual fasts to make fat people thin and ceremonial feasts to make thin people fat. Still other rites are used to make women's breasts larger if they are small, and smaller if they are large. General dissatisfaction with breast shape is symbolized in the fact that the ideal form is virtually outside the range of human variation. A few women afflicted with almost inhuman hypermammary development are so idolized that they make a handsome living by simply going from village to village and permitting the natives to stare at them for a fee.

Reference has already been made to the fact that excretory functions are ritualized, routinized, and relegated to secrecy. Natural reproductive functions are similarly distorted. Intercourse is taboo as a topic and scheduled as an act.

Efforts are made to avoid pregnancy by the use of magical materials or by limiting intercourse to certain phases of the moon. Conception is actually very infrequent. When pregnant, women dress so as to hide their condition. Parturition takes place in secret, without friends or relatives to assist, and the majority of women do not nurse their infants.

Our review of the ritual life of the Nacirema has certainly shown them to be a magic-ridden people. It is hard to understand how they have managed to exist so long under the burdens which they have imposed upon themselves. But even such exotic customs as these take on real meaning when they are viewed with the insight provided by Malinowski when he wrote (1948:70):

> Looking from far and above, from our high places of safety in the developed civilization, it is easy to see all the crudity and irrelevance of magic. But without its power and guidance early man could not have mastered his practical difficulties as he has done, nor could man have advanced to the higher stages of civilization.

References Cited

Linton, Ralph (1936). The Study of Man. New York, D. Appleton-Century Co.

Malinowski, Bronislaw (1948). Magic, Science, and Religion. Glencoe, The Free Press.

Murdock, George P. (1949). Social Structure. New York, The Macmillan Co.

Arranging a Marriage
in India

Serena Nanda

Serena Nanda is an American cultural anthropologist whose fields of interest are visual anthropology, gender, and culture and law. Nanda is known for her pioneering ethnographic work with the hijra, *or third gender, of India.* Neither Man Nor Woman: The Hijras of India *(1998), which won the Ruth Benedict prize, is one of the earliest works in a non-Western context about transgendered identity. In* Gender Diversity: Crosscultural Variations *(1999), Nanda describes what she calls "gender variance" in not only India but also Native America, Polynesia, Brazil, Thailand, the Philippines, and Euro-America. She has co-authored* American Cultural Pluralism and Law *(1996) with Jill Norgren;* Cultural Anthropology *(1997) with Richard L. Warms;* New York More Than Ever *(2003) with Joan Gregg and Beth Pacheco; and* 40 Perfect New York Days: Walks and Rambles in and Around the City *(2004) with Gregg and Pacheco. Nanda is Professor Emerita in the Department of Anthropology at John Jay College of Criminal Justice, CUNY. The following selection, which was included in* The Naked Anthropologist: Tales from Around the World, *edited by Philip R. De Vita (1992), explores the cultural influences surrounding the practice of arranged marriage in Indian society.*

> Sister and doctor brother-in-law invite correspondence from North Indian professionals only, for a beautiful, talented, sophisticated, intelligent sister, 5'3", slim, M.A. in textile design, father a senior civil officer. Would prefer immigrant doctors, between 26–29 years. Reply with full details and returnable photo.

A well-settled uncle invites matrimonial correspondence from slim, fair, educated South Indian girl, for his nephew, 25 years, smart, M.B.A., green card holder, 5'6". Full particulars with returnable photo appreciated.

Matrimonial Advertisements, *India Abroad*

In India, almost all marriages are arranged. Even among the educated middle classes in modern, urban India, marriage is as much a concern of the families as it is of the individuals. So customary is the practice of arranged marriage that there is a special name for a marriage which is not arranged: It is called a "love match."

On my first field trip to India, I met many young men and women whose parents were in the process of "getting them married." In many cases, the bride and groom would not meet each other before the marriage. At most they might meet for a brief conversation, and this meeting would take place only after their parents had decided that the match was suitable. Parents do not compel their children to marry a person who either marriage partner finds objectionable. But only after one match is refused will another be sought.

As a young American woman in India for the first time, I found this custom of arranged marriage oppressive. How could any intelligent young person agree to such a marriage without great reluctance? It was contrary to everything I believed about the importance of romantic love as the only basis of a happy marriage. It also clashed with my strongly held notions that the choice of such an intimate and permanent relationship could be made only by the individuals involved. Had anyone tried to arrange my marriage, I would have been defiant and rebellious!

At the first opportunity, I began, with more curiosity than tact, to question the young people I met on how they felt about this practice. Sita, one of my young informants, was a college graduate with a degree in political science. She had been waiting for over a year while her parents were arranging a match for her. I found it difficult to accept the docile manner in which this well-educated young woman awaited the outcome of a process that would result in her spending the rest of her life with a man she hardly knew, a virtual stranger, picked out by her parents.

"How can you go along with this?" I asked her, in frustration and distress. "Don't you care who you marry?"

"Of course I care," she answered. "This is why I must let my parents choose a boy for me. My marriage is too important to be arranged by such an inexperienced person as myself. In such matters, it is better to have my parents' guidance."

I had learned that young men and women in India do not date and have very little social life involving members of the opposite sex. Although I could not disagree with Sita's reasoning, I continued to pursue the subject.

"But how can you marry the first man you have ever met? Not only have you missed the fun of meeting a lot of different people, but you have not given yourself the chance to know who is the right man for you."

"Meeting with a lot of different people doesn't sound like any fun at all," Sita answered. "One hears that in America the girls are spending more time worrying about whether they will meet a man and get married. Here we have the chance to enjoy our life and let our parents do this work and worrying for us."

She had me there. The high anxiety of the competition to "be popular" with the opposite sex certainly was the most prominent feature of life as an American teenager in the late fifties. The endless worrying about the rules that governed our behavior and about our popularity ratings sapped both our self-esteem and our enjoyment of adolescence. I reflected that absence of this competition in India most certainly may have contributed to the self-confidence and natural charm of so many of the young women I met.

And yet, the idea of marrying a perfect stranger, whom one did not know and did not "love," so offended my American ideas of individualism and romanticism, that I persisted with my objections.

"I still can't imagine it," I said. "How can you agree to marry a man you hardly know?"

"But of course he will be known. My parents would never arrange a marriage for me without knowing all about the boy's family background. Naturally we will not rely only on what the family tells us. We will check the particulars out ourselves. No one will want their daughter to marry into a family that is not good. All these things we will know beforehand."

Impatiently, I responded, "Sita, I don't mean know the family, I mean, know the man. How can you marry someone you don't know personally and don't love? How can you think of spending your life with someone you may not even like?"

"If he is a good man, why should I not like him?" she said. "With you people, you know the boy so well before you marry, where will be the fun to get married? There will be no mystery and no romance. Here we have the whole of our married life to get to know and love our husband. This way is better, is it not?"

Her response made further sense, and I began to have second thoughts on the matter. Indeed, during months of meeting many intelligent young Indian people, both male and female, who had the same ideas as Sita, I saw arranged marriages in a different light. I also saw the importance of the family in Indian life and realized that a couple who took their marriage into their own hands was taking a big risk, particularly if their families were irreconcilably opposed to the match. In a country where every important resource in life—a job, a house, a social circle—is gained through family connections, it seemed foolhardy to cut oneself off from a supportive social network and depend solely on one person for happiness and success.

⋙

Six years later I returned to India to again do fieldwork, this time among the middle class in Bombay, a modern, sophisticated city. From the experience of my earlier visit, I decided to include a study of arranged marriages in my project. By this time I had met many Indian couples whose marriages had been arranged and who seemed very happy. Particularly in contrast to the fate of many of my married friends in the United States who were already in the process of divorce, the positive aspects of arranged marriages appeared to me to outweigh the negatives. In fact, I thought I might even participate in arranging a marriage myself. I had been fairly successful in the United States in "fixing up" many of my friends, and I was confident that my matchmaking skills could be easily applied to this new situation, once I learned the basic rules. "After all," I thought, "how complicated can it be? People want pretty much the same things in a marriage whether it is in India or America."

An opportunity presented itself almost immediately. A friend from my previous Indian trip was in the process of arranging for the marriage of her eldest son. In India there is a perceived shortage of "good boys," and since my friend's family was eminently respectable and the boy himself personable, well educated, and nice looking, I was sure that by the end of my year's fieldwork, we would have found a match.

The basic rule seems to be that a family's reputation is most important. It is understood that matches would be arranged only within the same caste and general social class, although some crossing of subcastes is permissible if the class positions of the bride's and groom's families are similar. Although dowry is now prohibited by law in India, extensive gift exchanges took place with every marriage. Even when the boy's family does not "make demands," every girl's family nevertheless feels the obligation to give the traditional gifts, to the girl, to the boy, and to the boy's family. Particularly when the couple would be living in the joint family—that is, with the boy's parents and his married brothers and their families, as well as with unmarried siblings—which is still very common even among the urban, upper-middle class in India, the girl's parents are anxious to establish smooth relations between their family and that of the boy. Offering the proper gifts, even when not called "dowry," is often an important factor in influencing the relationship between the bride's and groom's families and perhaps, also, the treatment of the bride in her new home.

In a society where divorce is still a scandal and where, in fact, the divorce rate is exceedingly low, an arranged marriage is the beginning of a lifetime relationship not just between the bride and groom but between their families as well. Thus, while a girl's looks are important, her character is even more so, for she is being judged as a prospective daughter-in-law as much as a prospective bride. Where she would be living in a joint family, as was the case with my friend, the girl's ability to get along harmoniously in a family is perhaps the single most important quality in assessing her suitability.

My friend is a highly esteemed wife, mother, and daughter-in-law. She is religious, soft-spoken, modest, and deferential. She rarely gossips and never quarrels, two qualities highly desirable in a woman. A family that has the reputation for gossip and conflict among its womenfolk will not find it easy to get good wives for their sons. Parents will not want to send their daughter to a house in which there is conflict.

My friend's family were originally from North India. They had lived in Bombay, where her husband owned a business, for forty years. The family had delayed in seeking a match for their eldest son because he had been an Air Force pilot for several years, stationed in such remote places that it had seemed fruitless to try to find a girl who would be willing to accompany him. In their social class, a military career, despite its economic security, has little prestige and is considered a drawback in finding a suitable bride. Many families would not allow their daughters to marry a man in an occupation so potentially dangerous and which requires so much moving around.

The son had recently left the military and joined his father's business. Since he was a college graduate, modern, and well traveled, from such a good family, and, I thought, quite handsome, it seemed to me that he, or rather his family, was in a position to pick and choose. I said as much to my friend.

While she agreed that there were many advantages on their side, she also said, "We must keep in mind that my son is both short and dark; these are drawbacks in finding the right match." While the boy's height had not escaped my notice, "dark" seemed to me inaccurate; I would have called him "wheat" colored perhaps, and in any case, I did not realize that color would be a consideration. I discovered, however, that while a boy's skin color is a less important consideration than a girl's, it is still a factor.

An important source of contacts in trying to arrange her son's marriage was my friend's social club in Bombay. Many of the women had daughters of the right age, and some had already expressed an interest in my friend's son. I was most enthusiastic about the possibilities of one particular family who had five daughters, all of whom were pretty, demure, and well educated. Their mother had told my friend, "You can have your pick for your son, whichever one of my daughters appeals to you most."

I saw a match in sight. "Surely," I said to my friend, "we will find one there. Let's go visit and make our choice." But my friend held back; she did not seem to share my enthusiasm, for reasons I could not then fathom.

When I kept pressing for an explanation of her reluctance, she admitted, "See, Serena, here is the problem. The family has so many daughters, how will they be able to provide nicely for any of them? We are not making any demands, but still, with so many daughters to marry off, one wonders whether she will even be able to make a proper wedding. Since this is our eldest son, it's best if we marry him to a girl who is the only daughter, then the wedding will truly be a gala affair." I argued that surely the quality of the girls them-selves made up for any deficiency in the elaborateness of the wedding. My friend admitted this point but still seemed reluctant to proceed.

"Is there something else," I asked her, "some factor I have missed?" "Well," she finally said, "there is one other thing. They have one daughter already mar-ried and living in Bombay. The mother is always complaining to me that the girl's in-laws don't let her visit her own family often enough. So it makes me wonder, will she be that kind of mother who always wants her daughter at her own home? This will prevent the girl from adjusting to our house. It is not a good thing." And so, this family of five daughters was dropped as a possibility.

Somewhat disappointed, I nevertheless respected my friend's reasoning and geared up for the next prospect. This was also the daughter of a woman in my friend's social club. There was clear interest in this family and I could see why. The family's reputation was excellent; in fact, they came from a sub-caste slightly higher than my friend's own. The girl, who was an only daughter, was pretty and well educated and had a brother studying in the United States. Yet, after expressing an interest to me in this family, all talk of them suddenly died down and the search began elsewhere.

"What happened to that girl as a prospect?" I asked one day. "You never men-tion her any more. She is so pretty and so educated, what did you find wrong?"

"She is too educated. We've decided against it. My husband's father saw the girl on the bus the other day and thought her forward: A girl who 'roams about' the city by herself is not the girl for our family." My disappointment this time was even greater, as I thought the son would have liked the girl very much. But then I thought, my friend is right, a girl who is going to live in a joint family cannot be too independent or she will make life miserable for everyone. I also learned that if the family of the girl has even a slightly higher social status than the family of the boy, the bride may think herself too good for them, and this too will cause problems. Later my friend admitted to me that this had been an important factor in her decision not to pursue the match.

The next candidate was the daughter of a client of my friend's husband. When the client learned that the family was looking for a match for their son, he said, "Look no further, we have a daughter." This man then invited my friends to dinner to see the girl. He had already seen their son at the office and decided that "he liked the boy." We all went together for tea, rather than dinner—it was less of a commitment—and while we were there, the girl's mother showed us around the house. The girl was studying for her exams and was briefly introduced to us.

After we left, I was anxious to hear my friend's opinion. While her hus-band liked the family very much and was impressed with his client's business accomplishments and reputation, the wife didn't like the girl's looks. "She is short, no doubt, which is an important plus point, but she is also fat and wears glasses." My friend obviously thought she could do better for her son and asked her husband to make his excuses to his client by saying that they had decided to postpone the boy's marriage indefinitely.

By this time almost six months had passed and I was becoming impatient. What I had thought would be an easy matter to arrange was turning out to be quite complicated. I began to believe that between my friend's desire for a girl who was modest enough to fit into her joint family, yet attractive and educated enough to be an acceptable partner for her son, she would not find anyone suitable. My friend laughed at my impatience: "Don't be so much in a hurry," she said. "You Americans want everything done so quickly. You get married quickly and then just as quickly get divorced. Here we take marriage more seriously. We must take all the factors into account. It is not enough for us to learn by our mistakes. This is too serious a business. If a mistake is made we have not only ruined the life of our son or daughter, but we have spoiled the reputation of our family as well. And that will make it much harder for their brothers and sisters to get married. So we must be very careful."

What she said was true and I promised myself to be more patient, though it was not easy. I had really hoped and expected that the match would be made before my year in India was up. But it was not to be. When I left India my friend seemed no further along in finding a suitable match for her son than when I had arrived.

Two years later, I returned to India and still my friend had not found a girl for her son. By this time, he was close to thirty, and I think she was a little worried. Since she knew I had friends all over India, and I was going to be there for a year, she asked me to "help her in this work" and keep an eye out for someone suitable. I was flattered that my judgment was respected, but knowing now how complicated the process was, I had lost my earlier confidence as a matchmaker. Nevertheless, I promised that I would try.

It was almost at the end of my year's stay in India that I met a family with a marriageable daughter whom I felt might be a good possibility for my friend's son. The girl's father was related to a good friend of mine and by coincidence came from the same village as my friend's husband. This new family had a successful business in a medium-sized city in central India and were from the same subcaste as my friend. The daughter was pretty and chic; in fact, she had studied fashion design in college. Her parents would not allow her to go off by herself to any of the major cities in India where she could make a career, but they had compromised with her wish to work by allowing her to run a small dressmaking boutique from their home. In spite of her desire to have a career, the daughter was both modest and home-loving and had had a traditional, sheltered upbringing. She had only one other sister, already married, and a brother who was in his father's business.

I mentioned the possibility of a match with my friend's son. The girl's parents were most interested. Although their daughter was not eager to marry just yet, the idea of living in Bombay—a sophisticated, extremely fashion-conscious city where she could continue her education in clothing design—was a great inducement. I gave the girl's father my friend's address and suggested that when they went to Bombay on some business or whatever, they look up the boy's family.

Returning to Bombay on my way to New York, I told my friend of this newly discovered possibility. She seemed to feel there was potential but, in spite of my urging, would not make any moves herself. She rather preferred to wait for the girl's family to call upon them. I hoped something would come of this introduction, though by now I had learned to rein in my optimism.

A year later I received a letter from my friend. The family had indeed come to visit Bombay, and their daughter and my friend's daughter, who were near in age, had become very good friends. During that year, the two girls had frequently visited each other. I thought things looked promising.

Last week I received an invitation to a wedding: My friend's son and the girl were getting married. Since I had found the match, my presence was particularly requested at the wedding. I was thrilled. Success at last! As I prepared to leave for India, I began thinking, "Now, my friend's younger son, who do I know who has a nice girl for him . . .?"

Further Reflections on Arranged Marriage

This essay was written from the point of view of a family seeking a daughter-in-law. Arranged marriage looks different from the perspective of the prospective bride and her family. Young women do get excited about the prospects of marriage, but there is also ambivalence and increasing uncertainty, as the bride contemplates leaving the familiarity of her own home, where as a "temporary guest" she was often indulged, to live among strangers. She will now come under the close scrutiny of her husband's family: how she dresses, how she behaves, how she gets along with others, where she goes, how she spends her time, her domestic abilities -- all of this and much more -- will be observed and commented on by a whole new set of relations. Her interaction with her family of birth will be monitored and substantially curtailed. Not only will she leave their home, but with increasing geographic mobility, she may also live very far away, perhaps even on another continent. Expressed desires to visit her natal family may be interpreted as an inability to adjust to her husband's family, is a potential source of conflict. Even in the best situations, the burdens of adjustment in an arranged marriage are heavier for a woman than for a man.

The new bride may be a target of resentment and hostility from her mother-in-law or her husband's unmarried sisters, for whom she is now a source of competition for his affection, loyalty, and economic resources. Even if she is psychologically or physically abused, returning to her parent's home is a highly stigmatized option, as is divorce, which is still rare, though increasing, particularly in urban areas. Marriage and motherhood are still considered the essential roles for a woman, both for lower class working woman and even middle-class and professional women. Most families still consider "marrying off" their daughters as a compelling religious duty and social necessity. This increases a bride's sense of obligation to make the marriage a success, at whatever cost to her own personal happiness.

The vulnerability of a new bride may be intensified by the issue of dowry. Although illegal, dowry is an increasingly pressing issue with the increasing value of consumerism as a source of status. If a groom's family is not satisfied with the dowry, the young bride may be harassed to get her parents to give more. In extreme cases, she may even be murdered, with her death claimed as an accident or suicide . These "dowry deaths" offers the husband's family an opportunity to arrange another match for him, thus bringing in another dowry.

Changes in Indian marriage patterns diverge within the contexts of class, rural/urban location; generational differences and divergent gender perspectives. Arranged marriage continues to be preferred in India, though more by men than by women, and more by the older than the younger generation, as it continues to provide a source of stability and security. Additionally, the traditional Indian orientation to the family and kinship group, of which arranged marriage is an essential component, provides many women with an "Indian" cultural identity they wish to maintain, in contrast to the values of individualism associated with globalization, Westernization, and modernization.

An emerging alternative to arranged marriage, is what are called "love marriages" but this simple opposition obscures a more complicated picture, in which there are actually a range of alternatives. In a "love marriage" the initial contact between the couple does not involve traditional matchmakers and choices dictated by family members, and may – or may not, be accepted by parents; this is particularly true where the potential couple's free choice of a spouse crosses religious, caste, or social class lines.

Another alternative to traditional arranged marriages are "self-arranged" marriage, where the individuals meet on their own, but then seek their parents' approval. If the parents agree, the process follows that of a traditional arranged marriage. Middle class parents sometimes adjust to the changes in the marriage landscape by arranging for their marriage-ready children to meet several potential partners (though this is done covertly), giving them the right of refusal.

The changes in contemporary Indian marriages must be understood in the context of globalization of values, and also, perhaps even more importantly, in the increasing number of women in the work force. Whether for call center professionals, or poor garment factory workers, it is mainly the workplace that has opened up opportunities for men and women to meet each other and develop intimate relationships. Also important is the diffusion of "modern" cultural values regarding "love," reflected in the Indian media and discussed endlessly by young women. Even within traditionally arranged marriages, there is an emerging expectation of what scholars call "companionate" marriage, in which the traditional emphasis on familial obligation is slowly giving way to an idealization of intimacy, trust and equality between the conjugal couple.

Partly because of geographic dislocation, in both arranged and "love" marriages, partners are increasingly sought through newspaper advertisements and the internet, though the traditional criteria of similar caste, ethnicity, professional status, religion, and physical qualities and sometimes horoscopes, remain important. After an exchange of "bios" and photos, a short list is created, with some attempts to verify the information and for the potential spouses to contact each other. These channels increase the possibilities for exaggeration and outright fraud, resulting in an emerging profession of private detectives hired to check the backgrounds of the potential spouse and their family.

Abetted by both global values and because of the importance of women's earnings to their families, Indian women today are increasingly asserting their autonomy. They are, however, still more powerless than men, and particularly among the poor, vulnerable to marital abuse, often related to alcoholism, and abandonment. If they choose a "love match," they almost always live in nuclear families, even if their families become reconciled to their choice. This deprives them of the support – however tenuous – of their own families. Poorer working women often use their wages to amass a dowry, hoping that this will encourage their families to find them a suitable mate or that it will cement a "love match." The traditional Indian folk saying that a woman leaves her home twice in her life, first when she marries and the second time when she dies, no longer holds true, bringing with it changes that are both welcome and a new source of concern.

References

Abraham, Margaret (2000). *Speaking the Unspeakable: Marital Violence against South Asian Immigrants in the United States.* New Brunswick, NJ: Rutgers University Press.

Divakaruni, Chitra Banerjee (1995). *Arranged Marriage: Stories.* New York: Doubleday/Anchor.

Nanda, Serena and Joan Gregg (2009). *The Gift of a Bride: a Tale of Anthropology, Matrimony, and Murder.* Lanham, MD: Altamira/Rowman and Littlefield.

Stone, Linda, and Caroline James (2005). "Dowry, Bride-Burning, and Female Power in India." In Gender in Cross-Cultural Perspective. 4th Edition. Caroline B. Brettell and Carolyn F. Sargent, eds. pp. 310–320. Upper Saddle River, NJ: Pearson/Prentice Hall.

Films

Provoked. Jag Mundhra, director. Distributed by Private Moments Ltd., UK, 2007.

Monsoon Wedding. Mira Nair, director. Distributed by Mirabai Films, Inc. USA. 2001.

Politics and the English Language

George Orwell

George Orwell, the pen name of Eric Arthur Blair (1903-1950), was a British novelist devoted to exposing, through his writing, the dangers of political oppression. His novels came to include, not only criticism of the British Empire both abroad and at home, but what he believed were other oppressive systems on the rise in the early twentieth century, such as Communism in Russia and Nazism in Germany. Orwell did this with two of his most famous novels, Animal Farm *(1945) and* 1984 *(1949), both published closely following World War II.*

Animal Farm *is a novel-length fable in which the animals take over a farm and set up their own form of government. They begin with democratic ideals, but gradually treat each other more and more unequally. This is achieved, partly, through the manipulation of language. For example, the tenet (painted on the farmyard's barn wall), "All animals are equal." eventually becomes amended to "All animals are equal, but some animals are more equal than others."*

Orwell deepens this exploration of the part language plays in oppression in his novel 1984. *This book is a warning. It describes a dystopia in which the government has grown to have near-complete control over its citizens. This government, called "Big Brother," is always watching (there is no privacy, even of thought). Authority figures also engage in "Newspeak," a pervasive form of double-talk that allows them to change facts to fit whatever "truth" thy find useful to brainwash and control the population. Examples of this are slogans such as "War is Peace", "Freedom is Slavery" and "Ignorance is Strength." The government is comprised of four deliberately misnamed*

"Ministries" of "Truth," where documents are systematically falsified, of "Love," where dissidents are imprisoned and tortured by the "Thought Police," of "Plenty," in charge of rationing food, and of "Peace," engaged in waging constant war.

The use of language to manipulate people is the idea central to "Politics and the English Language," the essay you are about to read. It was written in 1946, between the two novels just mentioned. Orwell saw the erosion of language as a weakness that made people vulnerable to just the sort of manipulation he describes in his novels. In his essay, he points out how clichés, dead metaphors, unnecessarily difficult words, jargon, wordiness, and complex and unclear constructions, such as the passive voice, are not only examples of bad style, but are politically dangerous. Insincere speakers, those with an agenda, who are only using words to manipulate their hearers, he suggests, intentionally use these forms of speech to obscure actual meaning and to disrupt communication so as to gain an advantage over those who will allow it. His essay is meant to warn us that we are in such danger, but to encourage us that, by improving our use of language, we will not only do better in our English classes, we may be better able to resist political oppression.

Most people who bother with the matter at all would admit that the English language is in a bad way, but it is generally assumed that we cannot by conscious action do anything about it. Our civilization is decadent and our language — so the argument runs — must inevitably share in the general collapse. It follows that any struggle against the abuse of language is a sentimental archaism, like preferring candles to electric light or hansom cabs to aeroplanes. Underneath this lies the half-conscious belief that language is a natural growth and not an instrument which we shape for our own purposes.

Now, it is clear that the decline of a language must ultimately have political and economic causes: it is not due simply to the bad influence of this or that individual writer. But an effect can become a cause, reinforcing the original cause and producing the same effect in an intensified form, and so on indefinitely. A man may take to drink because he feels himself to be a failure, and then fail all the more completely because he drinks. It is rather the same thing that is happening to the English language. It becomes ugly and inaccurate because our thoughts are foolish, but the slovenliness of our language makes it easier for us to have foolish thoughts. The point is that the process is reversible. Modern English, especially written English, is full of bad habits which spread by imitation and which can be avoided if one is willing to take the necessary trouble. If one gets rid of these habits one can think more clearly, and to think clearly is a necessary first step toward political regeneration: so that the fight against bad English is not frivolous and is not the exclusive concern of professional writers. I will come back to this presently, and I hope that by that time the meaning of what I have said here will have become clearer. Meanwhile, here are five specimens of the English language as it is now habitually written.

These five passages have not been picked out because they are especially bad — I could have quoted far worse if I had chosen — but because they illustrate various of the mental vices from which we now suffer. They are a little below the average, but are fairly representative examples. I number them so that I can refer back to them when necessary:

1. I am not, indeed, sure whether it is not true to say that the Milton who once seemed not unlike a seventeenth-century Shelley had not become, out of an experience ever more bitter in each year, more alien [sic] to the founder of that Jesuit sect which nothing could induce him to tolerate.

Professor Harold Laski (*Essay in Freedom of Expression*)

2. Above all, we cannot play ducks and drakes with a native battery of idioms which prescribes egregious collocations of vocables as the Basic *put up with* for *tolerate*, or *put at a loss* for *bewilder*.

Professor Lancelot Hogben (*Interglossa*)

3. On the one side we have the free personality: by definition it is not neurotic, for it has neither conflict nor dream. Its desires, such as they are, are transparent, for they are just what institutional approval keeps in the forefront of consciousness; another institutional pattern would alter their number and intensity; there is little in them that is natural, irreducible, or culturally dangerous. But *on the other side*, the social bond itself is nothing but the mutual reflection of these self-secure integrities. Recall the definition of love. Is not this the very picture of a small academic? Where is there a place in this hall of mirrors for either personality or fraternity?

Essay on psychology in *Politics* (New York)

4. All the "best people" from the gentlemen's clubs, and all the frantic fascist captains, united in common hatred of Socialism and bestial horror at the rising tide of the mass revolutionary movement, have turned to acts of provocation, to foul incendiarism, to medieval legends of poisoned wells, to legalize their own destruction of proletarian organizations, and rouse the agitated petty-bourgeoise to chauvinistic fervor on behalf of the fight against the revolutionary way out of the crisis.

Communist pamphlet

5. If a new spirit is to be infused into this old country, there is one thorny and contentious reform which must be tackled, and that is the humanization and galvanization of the B.B.C. Timidity here will bespeak canker and atrophy of the soul. The heart of Britain may be sound and of strong beat, for instance, but the British lion's roar at present is like that of Bottom in Shakespeare's *Midsummer Night's Dream* — as gentle as any sucking dove. A virile new Britain cannot con-

tinue indefinitely to be traduced in the eyes or rather ears, of the world by the effete languors of Langham Place, brazenly masquerading as "standard English." When the Voice of Britain is heard at nine o'clock, better far and infinitely less ludicrous to hear aitches honestly dropped than the present priggish, inflated, inhibited, school-ma'amish arch braying of blameless bashful mewing maidens!

Letter in *Tribune*

Each of these passages has faults of its own, but, quite apart from avoidable ugliness, two qualities are common to all of them. The first is staleness of imagery; the other is lack of precision. The writer either has a meaning and cannot express it, or he inadvertently says something else, or he is almost indifferent as to whether his words mean anything or not. This mixture of vagueness and sheer incompetence is the most marked characteristic of modern English prose, and especially of any kind of political writing. As soon as certain topics are raised, the concrete melts into the abstract and no one seems able to think of turns of speech that are not hackneyed: prose consists less and less of *words* chosen for the sake of their meaning, and more and more of *phrases* tacked together like the sections of a prefabricated henhouse. I list below, with notes and examples, various of the tricks by means of which the work of prose construction is habitually dodged:

Dying metaphors. A newly invented metaphor assists thought by evoking a visual image, while on the other hand a metaphor which is technically "dead" (e.g. *iron resolution*) has in effect reverted to being an ordinary word and can generally be used without loss of vividness. But in between these two classes there is a huge dump of worn-out metaphors which have lost all evocative power and are merely used because they save people the trouble of inventing phrases for themselves. Examples are: *Ring the changes on, take up the cudgel for, toe the line, ride roughshod over, stand shoulder to shoulder with, play into the hands of, no axe to grind, grist to the mill, fishing in troubled waters, on the order of the day, Achilles' heel, swan song, hotbed.* Many of these are used without knowledge of their meaning (what is a "rift," for instance?), and incompatible metaphors are frequently mixed, a sure sign that the writer is not interested in what he is saying. Some metaphors now current have been twisted out of their original meaning withouth those who use them even being aware of the fact. For example, *toe the line* is sometimes written as *tow the line*. Another example is *the hammer and the anvil*, now always used with the implication that the anvil gets the worst of it. In real life it is always the anvil that breaks the hammer, never the other way about: a writer who stopped to think what he was saying would avoid perverting the original phrase.

Operators or verbal false limbs. These save the trouble of picking out appropriate verbs and nouns, and at the same time pad each sentence with extra syllables which give it an appearance of symmetry. Characteristic phrases are *render inoperative, militate against, make contact with, be subjected to, give rise to, give grounds for, have the effect of, play a leading part (role) in, make itself felt, take effect, exhibit a tendency to, serve the purpose of, etc., etc.* The keynote is the elimination of simple verbs. Instead of being a single word, such as *break, stop, spoil, mend, kill*, a verb becomes a *phrase*, made up of a noun or adjective tacked on to some general-purpose verb such as *prove, serve, form, play, render*. In addition, the passive voice is wherever possible used in preference to the active, and noun constructions are used instead of gerunds (*by examination of* instead of *by examining*). The range of verbs is further cut down by means of the *-ize* and *de-* formations, and the banal statements are given an appearance of profundity by means of the *not un-* formation. Simple conjunctions and prepositions are replaced by such phrases as *with respect to, having regard to, the fact that, by dint of, in view of, in the interests of, on the hypothesis that;* and the ends of sentences are saved by anticlimax by such resounding commonplaces as *greatly to be desired, cannot be left out of account, a development to be expected in the near future, deserving of serious consideration, brought to a satisfactory conclusion,* and so on and so forth.

Pretentious diction. Words like *phenomenon, element, individual* (as noun), *objective, categorical, effective, virtual, basic, primary, promote, constitute, exhibit, exploit, utilize, eliminate, liquidate,* are used to dress up a simple statement and give an air of scientific impartiality to biased judgements. Adjectives like *epoch-making, epic, historic, unforgettable, triumphant, age-old, inevitable, inexorable, veritable,* are used to dignify the sordid process of international politics, while writing that aims at glorifying war usually takes on an archaic color, its characteristic words being: *realm, throne, chariot, mailed fist, trident, sword, shield, buckler, banner, jackboot, clarion.* Foreign words and expressions such as *cul de sac, ancien regime, deus ex machina, mutatis mutandis, status quo, gleichschaltung, weltanschauung,* are used to give an air of culture and elegance. Except for the useful abbreviations *i.e., e.g.,* and *etc.*, there is no real need for any of the hundreds of foreign phrases now current in the English language. Bad writers, and especially scientific, political, and sociological writers, are nearly always haunted by the notion that Latin or Greek words are grander than Saxon ones, and unnecessary words like *expedite, ameliorate, predict, extraneous, deracinated, clandestine, subaqueous,* and hundreds of others constantly gain ground from their Anglo-Saxon numbers.[*] The jargon peculiar to Marxist writing (*hyena, hangman, cannibal, petty bourgeois, these gentry, lackey, flunkey, mad dog, White Guard,* etc.) consists largely of words translated from Russian, German, or French; but the normal way of coining a new word is to

---

[*] An interesting illustration of this is the way in which English flower names were in use till very recently are being ousted by Greek ones, *Snapdragon* becoming *antirrhinum, forget-me-not* becoming *myosotis,* etc. It is hard to see any practical reason for this change of fashion: it is probably due to an instinctive turning away from the more homely word and a vague feeling that the Greek word is scientific.

use Latin or Greek root with the appropriate affix and, where necessary, the size formation. It is often easier to make up words of this kind (*deregionalize, impermissible, extramarital, non-fragmentary* and so forth) than to think up the English words that will cover one's meaning. The result, in general, is an increase in slovenliness and vagueness.

Meaningless words. In certain kinds of writing, particularly in art criticism and literary criticism, it is normal to come across long passages which are almost completely lacking in meaning.† Words like *romantic, plastic, values, human, dead, sentimental, natural, vitality,* as used in art criticism, are strictly meaningless, in the sense that they not only do not point to any discoverable object, but are hardly ever expected to do so by the reader. When one critic writes, "The outstanding feature of Mr. X's work is its living quality," while another writes, "The immediately striking thing about Mr. X's work is its peculiar deadness," the reader accepts this as a simple difference opinion. If words like *black* and *white* were involved, instead of the jargon words *dead* and *living,* he would see at once that language was being used in an improper way. Many political words are similarly abused. The word *Fascism* has now no meaning except in so far as it signifies "something not desirable." The words *democracy, socialism, freedom, patriotic, realistic, justice* have each of them several different meanings which cannot be reconciled with one another. In the case of a word like *democracy,* not only is there no agreed definition, but the attempt to make one is resisted from all sides. It is almost universally felt that when we call a country democratic we are praising it: consequently the defenders of every kind of regime claim that it is a democracy, and fear that they might have to stop using that word if it were tied down to any one meaning. Words of this kind are often used in a consciously dishonest way. That is, the person who uses them has his own private definition, but allows his hearer to think he means something quite different. Statements like *Marshal Pétain was a true patriot, The Soviet press is the freest in the world, The Catholic Church is opposed to persecution,* are almost always made with intent to deceive. Other words used in variable meanings, in most cases more or less dishonestly, are: *class, totalitarian, science, progressive, reactionary, bourgeois, equality.*

Now that I have made this catalogue of swindles and perversions, let me give another example of the kind of writing that they lead to. This time it must of its nature be an imaginary one. I am going to translate a passage of

---

† Example: Comfort's catholicity of perception and image, strangely Whitmanesque in range, almost the exact opposite in aesthetic compulsion, continues to evoke that trembling atmospheric accumulative hinting at a cruel, an inexorably serene timelessness . . . Wrey Gardiner scores by aiming at simple bull's-eyes with precision. Only they are not so simple, and through this contented sadness runs more than the surface bittersweet of resignation." (*Poetry Quarterly*)

good English into modern English of the worst sort. Here is a well-known verse from *Ecclesiastes*:

I returned and saw under the sun, that the race is not to the swift, nor the battle to the strong, neither yet bread to the wise, nor yet riches to men of understanding, nor yet favour to men of skill; but time and chance happeneth to them all.

Here it is in modern English:

Objective considerations of contemporary phenomena compel the conclusion that success or failure in competitive activities exhibits no tendency to be commensurate with innate capacity, but that a considerable element of the unpredictable must invariably be taken into account.

This is a parody, but not a very gross one. Exhibit (3) above, for instance, contains several patches of the same kind of English. It will be seen that I have not made a full translation. The beginning and ending of the sentence follow the original meaning fairly closely, but in the middle the concrete illustrations — race, battle, bread — dissolve into the vague phrases "success or failure in competitive activities." This had to be so, because no modern writer of the kind I am discussing — no one capable of using phrases like "objective considerations of contemporary phenomena" — would ever tabulate his thoughts in that precise and detailed way. The whole tendency of modern prose is away from concreteness. Now analyze these two sentences a little more closely. The first contains forty-nine words but only sixty syllables, and all its words are those of everyday life. The second contains thirty-eight words of ninety syllables: eighteen of those words are from Latin roots, and one from Greek. The first sentence contains six vivid images, and only one phrase ("time and chance") that could be called vague. The second contains not a single fresh, arresting phrase, and in spite of its ninety syllables it gives only a shortened version of the meaning contained in the first. Yet without a doubt it is the second kind of sentence that is gaining ground in modern English. I do not want to exaggerate. This kind of writing is not yet universal, and outcrops of simplicity will occur here and there in the worst-written page. Still, if you or I were told to write a few lines on the uncertainty of human fortunes, we should probably come much nearer to my imaginary sentence than to the one from *Ecclesiastes*.

As I have tried to show, modern writing at its worst does not consist in picking out words for the sake of their meaning and inventing images in order to make the meaning clearer. It consists in gumming together long strips of words which have already been set in order by someone else, and making the results presentable by sheer humbug. The attraction of this way of writing is that it is easy. It is easier — even quicker, once you have the habit — to say *In my opinion it is not an unjustifiable assumption that* than to say *I think*. If you use ready-made phrases, you not only don't have to hunt about for the words; you also don't have to bother with the rhythms of your sentences since these phrases are generally so arranged as to be more or less euphonious. When you are composing in a hurry — when you are dictating to a stenographer, for instance, or making a public speech — it is natural to fall into a pretentious, Latinized style. Tags like *a consideration which we should do well to bear in mind* or *a conclusion to which all of us would readily assent* will save many a sentence from coming down with a bump. By using stale metaphors, similes, and idioms, you save much mental effort, at the cost of leaving your meaning vague, not only for your reader but for yourself. This is the significance of mixed metaphors. The sole aim of a metaphor is to call up a visual image. When these images clash — as in *The Fascist octopus has sung its swan song, the jackboot is thrown into the melting pot* — it can be taken as certain that the writer is not seeing a mental image of the objects he is naming; in other words he is not really thinking. Look again at the examples I gave at the beginning of this essay. Professor Laski (I) uses five negatives in fifty three words. One of these is superfluous, making nonsense of the whole passage, and in addition there is the slip — alien for akin — making further nonsense, and several avoidable pieces of clumsiness which increase the general vagueness. Professor Hogben (2) plays ducks and drakes with a battery which is able to write prescriptions, and, while disapproving of the everyday phrase *put up with*, is unwilling to look *egregious* up in the dictionary and see what it means; (3), if one takes an uncharitable attitude towards it, is simply meaningless: probably one could work out its intended meaning by reading the whole of the article in which it occurs. In (4), the writer knows more or less what he wants to say, but an accumulation of stale phrases chokes him like tea leaves blocking a sink. In (5), words and meaning have almost parted company. People who write in this manner usually have a general emotional meaning — they dislike one thing and want to express solidarity with another — but they are not interested in the detail of what they are saying. A scrupulous writer, in every sentence that he writes, will ask himself at least four questions, thus: I. What am I trying to say? 2. What words will express it? 3. What image or idiom will make it clearer? 4. Is this image fresh enough to have an effect? And he will probably ask himself two more: I. Could I put it more shortly? 2. Have I said anything that is avoidably ugly? But you are not obliged to go to all this trouble. You can shirk it by simply throwing your mind open and letting the ready-made phrases come crowding in. They will construct your sentences for you — even think your thoughts for you, to a certain extent — and at need they will perform the important service of partially concealing your meaning even from yourself. It is at this point that the special connection between politics and the debasement of language becomes clear.

In our time it is broadly true that political writing is bad writing. Where it is not true, it will generally be found that the writer is some kind of rebel, expressing his private opinions and not a "party line." Orthodoxy, of whatever color, seems to demand a lifeless, imitative style. The political dialects to be found in pamphlets, leading articles, manifestoes, White papers and the speeches of undersecretaries do, of course, vary from party to party, but they are all alike in that one almost never finds in them a fresh, vivid, homemade turn of speech. When one watches some tired hack on the platform mechanically repeating the familiar phrases — *bestial atrocities, iron heel, bloodstained tyranny, free peoples of the world, stand shoulder to shoulder* — one often has a curious feeling that one is not watching a live human being but some kind of dummy: a feeling which suddenly becomes stronger at moments when the light catches the speaker's spectacles and turns them into blank discs which seem to have no eyes behind them. And this is not altogether fanciful. A speaker who uses that kind of phraseology has gone some distance toward turning himself into a machine. The appropriate noises are coming out of his larynx, but his brain is not involved as it would be if he were choosing his words for himself. If the speech he is making is one that he is accustomed to make over and over again, he may be almost unconscious of what he is saying, as one is when one utters the responses in church. And this reduced state of consciousness, if not indispensable, is at any rate favorable to political conformity.

In our time, political speech and writing are largely the defense of the indefensible. Things like the continuance of British rule in India, the Russian purges and deportations, the dropping of the atom bombs on Japan, can indeed be defended, but only by arguments which are too brutal for most people to face, and which do not square with the professed aims of the political parties. Thus political language has to consist largely of euphemism., question-begging and sheer cloudy vagueness. Defenseless villages are bombarded from the air, the inhabitants driven out into the countryside, the cattle machine-gunned, the huts set on fire with incendiary bullets: this is called *pacification*. Millions of peasants are robbed of their farms and sent trudging along the roads with no more than they can carry: this is called *transfer of population* or *rectification of frontiers*. People are imprisoned for years without trial, or shot in the back of the neck or sent to die of scurvy in Arctic lumber camps: this is called *elimination of unreliable elements*. Such phraseology is needed if one wants to name things without calling up mental pictures of them. Consider for instance some comfortable English professor defending Russian totalitarianism. He cannot say outright, "I believe in killing off your opponents when you can get good results by doing so." Probably, therefore, he will say something like this:

While freely conceding that the Soviet regime exhibits certain features which the humanitarian may be inclined to deplore, we must, I think, agree that a certain curtailment of the right to political opposition is an unavoidable concomitant of transitional periods, and that the rigors which the

Russian people have been called upon to undergo have been amply justified in the sphere of concrete achievement."

The inflated style itself is a kind of euphemism. A mass of Latin words falls upon the facts like soft snow, blurring the outline and covering up all the details. The great enemy of clear language is insincerity. When there is a gap between one's real and one's declared aims, one turns as it were instinctively to long words and exhausted idioms, like a cuttlefish spurting out ink. In our age there is no such thing as "keeping out of politics." All issues are political issues, and politics itself is a mass of lies, evasions, folly, hatred, and schizophrenia. When the general atmosphere is bad, language must suffer. I should expect to find — this is a guess which I have not sufficient knowledge to verify — that the German, Russian and Italian languages have all deteriorated in the last ten or fifteen years, as a result of dictatorship.

But if thought corrupts language, language can also corrupt thought. A bad usage can spread by tradition and imitation even among people who should and do know better. The debased language that I have been discussing is in some ways very convenient. Phrases like *a not unjustifiable assumption, leaves much to be desired, would serve no good purpose, a consideration which we should do well to bear in mind,* are a continuous temptation, a packet of aspirins always at one's elbow. Look back through this essay, and for certain you will find that I have again and again committed the very faults I am protesting against. By this morning's post I have received a pamphlet dealing with conditions in Germany. The author tells me that he "felt impelled" to write it. I open it at random, and here is almost the first sentence I see: "[The Allies] have an opportunity not only of achieving a radical transformation of Germany's social and political structure in such a way as to avoid a nationalistic reaction in Germany itself, but at the same time of laying the foundations of a cooperative and unified Europe." You see, he "feels impelled" to write — feels, presumably, that he has something new to say — and yet his words, like cavalry horses answering the bugle, group themselves automatically into the familiar dreary pattern. This invasion of one's mind by ready-made phrases (*lay the foundations, achieve a radical transformation*) can only be prevented if one is constantly on guard against them, and every such phrase anaesthetizes a portion of one's brain.

I said earlier that the decadence of our language is probably curable. Those who deny this would argue, if they produced an argument at all, that language merely reflects existing social conditions, and that we cannot influence its development by any direct tinkering with words and constructions. So far as the general tone or spirit of a language goes, this may be true, but it is not true in detail. Silly words and expressions have often disappeared, not through any evolutionary process but owing to the conscious action of a minority. Two recent examples were *explore every avenue* and *leave no stone unturned,* which were killed by the jeers of a few journalists. There is a long list of flyblown metaphors which could similarly be got rid of if enough people would interest themselves in the job; and it should also be possible to laugh the *not un-* formation out of existence*, to reduce the amount of Latin and Greek in the average sentence, to drive out foreign phrases and strayed scientific words, and, in general, to make pretentiousness unfashionable. But all these are minor points. The defense of the English language implies more than this, and perhaps it is best to start by saying what it does *not* imply.

To begin with it has nothing to do with archaism, with the salvaging of obsolete words and turns of speech, or with the setting up of a "standard English" which must never be departed from. On the contrary, it is especially concerned with the scrapping of every word or idiom which has outworn its usefulness. It has nothing to do with correct grammar and syntax, which are of no importance so long as one makes one's meaning clear, or with the avoidance of Americanisms, or with having what is called a "good prose style." On the other hand, it is not concerned with fake simplicity and the attempt to make written English colloquial. Nor does it even imply in every case preferring the Saxon word to the Latin one, though it does imply using the fewest and shortest words that will cover one's meaning. What is above all needed is to let the meaning choose the word, and not the other way around. In prose, the worst thing one can do with words is surrender to them. When you think of a concrete object, you think wordlessly, and then, if you want to describe the thing you have been visualizing you probably hunt about until you find the exact words that seem to fit it. When you think of something abstract you are more inclined to use words from the start, and unless you make a conscious effort to prevent it, the existing dialect will come rushing in and do the job for you, at the expense of blurring or even changing your meaning. Probably it is better to put off using words as long as possible and get one's meaning as clear as one can through pictures and sensations. Afterward one can choose — not simply *accept* — the phrases that will best cover the meaning, and then switch round and decide what impressions one's words are likely to make on another person. This last effort of the mind cuts out all stale or mixed images, all prefabricated phrases, needless repetitions, and humbug and vagueness generally. But one can often be in doubt about the effect of a word or a phrase, and one needs rules that one can rely on when instinct fails. I think the following rules will cover most cases:

(i) Never use a metaphor, simile, or other figure of speech which you are used to seeing in print.

---

*One can cure oneself of the *not un-* formation by memorizing this sentence: *A not unblack dog was chasing a not unsmall rabbit across a not ungreen field.*

(ii) Never use a long word where a short one will do.

(iii) If it is possible to cut a word out, always cut it out.

(iv) Never use the passive where you can use the active.

(v) Never use a foreign phrase, a scientific word, or a jargon word if you can think of an everyday English equivalent.

(vi) Break any of these rules sooner than say anything outright barbarous.

These rules sound elementary, and so they are, but they demand a deep change of attitude in anyone who has grown used to writing in the style now fashionable. One could keep all of them and still write bad English, but one could not write the kind of stuff that I quoted in those five specimens at the beginning of this article.

I have not here been considering the literary use of language, but merely language as an instrument for expressing and not for concealing or preventing thought. Stuart Chase and others have come near to claiming that all abstract words are meaningless, and have used this as a pretext for advocating a kind of political quietism. Since you don't know what Fascism is, how can you struggle against Fascism? One need not swallow such absurdities as this, but one ought to recognize that the present political chaos is connected with the decay of language, and that one can probably bring about some improvement by starting at the verbal end. If you simplify your English, you are freed from the worst follies of orthodoxy. You cannot speak any of the necessary dialects, and when you make a stupid remark its stupidity will be obvious, even to yourself. Political language — and with variations this is true of all political parties, from Conservatives to Anarchists — is designed to make lies sound truthful and murder respectable, and to give an appearance of solidity to pure wind. One cannot change this all in a moment, but one can at least change one's own habits, and from time to time one can even, if one jeers loudly enough, send some worn-out and useless phrase — some *jackboot, Achilles' heel, hotbed, melting pot, acid test, veritable inferno,* or other lump of verbal refuse — into the dustbin, where it belongs.

Shooting an Elephant

George Orwell

George Orwell was born Eric Blair (1903–1950) in the northern Indian village of Motihari, where his English father was stationed in the Civil Service at a time when India was still part of the British Empire. Orwell was educated in England, but returned to India and Burma (a province of British India; now Myanmar) in 1922 and held a position in the British Imperial Police until 1927. It was his experience as a police officer in Lower Burma that he drew upon for the material in the present selection, first written in 1936 and later published (in 1950) in a collection of essays under the same title. Whether he ever actually shot an elephant while serving in Burma is a matter of some controversy. According to the testimony of one of his fellow officers, he was involved in such a shooting and was punished with a transfer to another district, but his biographers note that there is no official record of the incident. After returning to Europe, he wrote both fiction and nonfiction on a range of topics, and was perhaps best known as a political writer with an affinity for socialist causes. His reputation as one of the 20th century's greatest writers rests largely upon two works of political satire: the allegorical Animal Farm *(1945) and* 1984 *(1949).*

In Moulmein, in lower Burma, I was hated by large numbers of people—the only time in my life that I have been important enough for this to happen to me. I was subdivisional police officer of the town, and in an aimless, petty kind of way anti-European feeling was very bitter. No one had the guts to raise a riot, but if a European woman went through the bazaars alone somebody would probably spit betel juice over her dress. As a police officer I was an obvious target and was baited whenever it seemed safe to do so. When a nimble Burman tripped me up on the football field and the referee (another Burman) looked the other way, the crowd yelled with hideous laughter. This happened more than once. In the end the sneering yellow faces of young men that met me everywhere, the insults hooted after me when I was at a safe distance, got badly on my nerves. The young Buddhist priests were the worst of all. There were several thousands of them in the town and none of them seemed to have anything to do except stand on street corners and jeer at Europeans.

All this was perplexing and upsetting. For at that time I had already made up my mind that imperialism was an evil thing and the sooner I chucked up my job and got out of it the better. Theoretically—and secretly, of course— I was all for the Burmese and all against their oppressors, the British. As for the job I was doing, I hated it more bitterly than I can perhaps make clear. In a job like that you see the dirty work of Empire at close quarters. The wretched prisoners huddling in the stinking cages of the lock-ups, the grey, cowed faces of the long-term convicts, the scarred buttocks of the men who had been flogged with bamboos—all these oppressed me with an intolerable sense of guilt. But I could get nothing into perspective. I was young and ill-educated and I had had to think out my problems in the utter silence that is imposed on every Englishman in the East. I did not even know that the British Empire is dying, still less did I know that it is a great deal better than the younger empires that are going to supplant it. All I knew was that I was stuck between my hatred of the empire I served and my rage against the evil-spirited little beasts who tried to make my job impossible. With one part of my mind I thought of the British Raj as an unbreakable tyranny, as something clamped down, in *saecula saeculorum*,[1] upon the will of prostrate peoples; with another part I thought that the greatest joy in the world would be to drive a bayonet into a Buddhist priest's guts. Feelings like these are the normal by-products of imperialism; ask any Anglo-Indian official, if you can catch him off duty.

One day something happened which in a roundabout way was enlightening. It was a tiny incident in itself, but it gave me a better glimpse than I had had before of the real nature of imperialism—the real motives for which despotic governments act. Early one morning the sub-inspector at a police station the other end of the town rang me up on the phone and said that an elephant was ravaging the bazaar. Would I please come and do something about it? I did not know what I could do, but I wanted to see what was happening and I got on to a pony and started out. I took my rifle, an old 44 Winchester and much too small to kill an elephant, but I thought the noise might be useful *in terrorem*. Various Burmans stopped me on the way and told me about the elephant's doings. It was not, of course, a wild elephant, but a tame one which had gone "must." It had been chained up, as tame elephants always are when their attack of "must" is due, but on the previous night it had broken its chain and escaped. Its mahout, the only person who could manage it when it was in that state, had set out in pursuit, but had taken the wrong direction and was now twelve hours' journey away, and in the morning the elephant had suddenly reappeared in the town. The Burmese population had no weapons and were quite helpless against it. It had already destroyed somebody's bamboo hut, killed a cow and raided some fruit-stalls and devoured the stock; also it had met the municipal rubbish van and, when the driver jumped out and took to his heels, had turned the van over and inflicted violences upon it.

The Burmese sub-inspector and some Indian constables were waiting for me in the quarter where the elephant had been seen. It was a very poor quarter, a labyrinth of squalid bamboo huts, thatched with palm-leaf, winding all over a steep hillside. I remember that it was a cloudy, stuffy morning at the beginning of the rains. We began questioning the people as to where the elephant had gone and, as usual, failed to get any definite information. That is invariably the case in the East; a story always sounds clear enough at a distance, but the nearer you get to the scene of events the vaguer it becomes. Some of the people said that the elephant had gone in one direction, some said that he had gone in another, some professed not even to have heard of any elephant. I had almost made up my mind that the whole story was a pack of lies, when we heard yells a little distance away. There was a loud, scandalized cry of "Go away, child! Go away this instant!" and an old woman with a switch in her hand came round the corner of a hut, violently shooing away a crowd of naked children. Some more women followed, clicking their tongues and exclaiming; evidently there was something that the children ought not to have seen. I rounded the hut and saw a man's dead body sprawling in the mud. He was an Indian, a black Dravidian coolie, almost naked, and he could not have been dead many minutes. The people said that the elephant had come suddenly upon him round the corner of the hut, caught him with its trunk, put its foot on his back and ground him into the earth. This was the rainy season and the ground was soft, and his face had scored a trench a foot deep and a couple of yards long. He was lying on his belly with arms crucified and head sharply twisted to one side. His face was coated with mud, the eyes wide open, the teeth bared and grinning with an expression of unendurable agony. (Never tell me, by the way, that the dead look peaceful. Most of the corpses I have seen looked devilish.) The friction of the great beast's foot had stripped the skin from his back as neatly as one skins a rabbit. As soon as I saw the dead man I sent an orderly to a friend's house nearby to borrow an elephant rifle. I had already sent back the pony, not wanting it to go mad with fright and throw me if it smelt the elephant.

The orderly came back in a few minutes with a rifle and five cartridges, and meanwhile some Burmans had arrived and told us that the elephant was in the paddy fields below, only a few hundred yards away. As I started forward practically the whole population of the quarter flocked out of the houses and followed me. They had seen the rifle and were all shouting excitedly that I was going to shoot the elephant. They had not shown much interest in the elephant when he was merely ravaging their homes, but it was different now that he was going to be shot. It was a bit of fun to them, as it would be to an English crowd; besides they wanted the meat. It made me vaguely uneasy. I had no intention of shooting the elephant—I had merely sent for the rifle to defend myself if necessary—and it is always unnerving to have a crowd following you. I marched down the hill, looking and feeling a fool, with the rifle over my shoulder and an ever-growing army of people jostling at my heels. At the bottom, when you got away from the huts, there was a metalled road and beyond that a miry waste of paddy fields a thousand yards across, not yet ploughed but soggy from the first rains and dotted with coarse grass. The elephant was standing eight yards from the road, his left side towards us. He took not the slightest notice of the crowd's approach. He was tearing up bunches of grass, beating them against his knees to clean them and stuffing them into his mouth.

I had halted on the road. As soon as I saw the elephant I knew with perfect certainty that I ought not to shoot him. It is a serious matter to shoot a working elephant—it is comparable to destroying a huge and costly piece of machinery—and obviously one ought not to do it if it can possibly be avoided. And at that distance, peacefully eating, the elephant looked no more dangerous than a cow. I thought then and I think now that his attack of "must" was already passing off, in which case he would merely wander harmlessly about until the mahout came back and caught him. Moreover, I did not in the least want to shoot him. I decided that I would watch him for a little while to make sure that he did not turn savage again, and then go home.

But at that moment I glanced round at the crowd that had followed me. It was an immense crowd, two thousand at the least and growing every minute: It blocked the road for a long distance on either side. I looked at the sea of yellow faces above the garish clothes—faces all happy and excited over this bit of fun, all certain that the elephant was going to be shot. They were watching me as they would watch a conjurer about to perform a trick. They did not like me, but with the magical rifle in my hands I was momentarily worth watching. And suddenly I realized that I should have to shoot the elephant after all. The people expected it of me and I had got to do it; I could feel their two thousand wills pressing me forward, irresistibly. And it was at this moment, as I stood there with the rifle in my hands, that I first grasped the hollowness, the futility of the white man's dominion in the East. Here was I, the white man with his gun, standing in front of the unarmed native crowd—seemingly the leading actor of the piece; but in reality I was only an absurd puppet pushed to and fro by the will of those yellow faces behind. I perceived in this moment that when the white man turns tyrant it is his own freedom that he destroys. He becomes a sort of hollow, posing dummy, the conventionalized figure of a sahib. For it is the condition of his rule that he shall spend his life in trying to impress the "natives," and so in every crisis he has got to do what the "natives" expect of him. He wears a mask, and his face grows to fit it. I had got to shoot the elephant. I had committed myself to doing it when I sent for the rifle. A sahib has got to act like a sahib; he has got to appear resolute, to know his own mind and do definite things. To come all that way, rifle in hand, with two thousand people marching at my heels, and then to trail feebly away, having done nothing—no, that was impossible. The crowd would laugh at me. And my whole life, every white man's life in the East, was one long struggle not to be laughed at.

But I did not want to shoot the elephant. I watched him beating his bunch of grass against his knees, with that preoccupied grandmotherly air that elephants have. It seemed to me that it would be murder to shoot him. At that age I was not squeamish about killing animals, but I had never shot an elephant and never wanted to. (Somehow it always seems worse to kill a *large* animal.) Besides, there was the beast's owner to be considered. Alive, the elephant was worth at least a hundred pounds; dead, he would only be worth the value of his tusks, five pounds, possibly. But I had got to act quickly. I turned to some experienced-looking Burmans who had been there when we arrived, and asked them how the elephant had been behaving. They all said the same thing: he took no notice of you if you left him alone, but he might charge if you went too close to him.

It was perfectly clear to me what I ought to do. I ought to walk up to within, say, twenty-five yards of the elephant and test his behavior. If he charged, I could shoot; if he took no notice of me, it would be safe to leave him until the mahout came back. But also I knew that I was going to do no such thing. I was a poor shot with a rifle and the ground was soft mud into which one would sink at every step. If the elephant charged and I missed him, I should have about as much chance as a toad under a steamroller. But even then I was not thinking particularly of my own skin, only of the watchful yellow faces behind. For at that moment, with the crowd watching me, I was not afraid in the ordinary sense, as I would have been if I had been alone. A white man mustn't be frightened in front of "natives"; and so, in general, he isn't frightened. The sole thought in my mind was that if anything went wrong those two thousand Burmans would see me pursued, caught, trampled on and reduced to a grinning corpse like that Indian up the hill. And if that happened it was quite probable that some of them would laugh. That would never do. There was only one alternative. I shoved the cartridges into the magazine and lay down on the road to get a better aim.

The crowd grew very still, and a deep, low, happy sigh, as of people who see the theatre curtain go up at last, breathed from innumerable throats. They were going to have their bit of fun after all. The rifle was a beautiful German thing with cross-hair sights. I did not then know that in shooting an elephant one would shoot to cut an imaginary bar running from ear-hole to ear-hole. I ought, therefore, as the elephant was sideways on, to have aimed straight at his ear-hole; actually I aimed several inches in front of this, thinking the brain would be further forward.

When I pulled the trigger I did not hear the bang or feel the kick—one never does when a shot goes home—but I heard the devilish roar of glee that went up from the crowd. In that instant, in too short a time, one would have thought, even for the bullet to get there, a mysterious, terrible change had come over the elephant. He neither stirred nor fell, but every line of his body had altered. He looked suddenly stricken, shrunken, immensely old, as though the frightful impact of the bullet had paralysed him without knocking him down. At last, after what seemed a long time—it might have been five seconds, I dare say—he sagged flabbily to his knees. His mouth slobbered. An enormous senility seemed to have settled upon him. One could have imagined him thousands of years old. I fired again into the same spot. At the second shot he did not collapse but climbed with desperate slowness to his feet and stood weakly upright, with legs sagging and head drooping. I fired a third time. That was the shot that did for him. You could see the agony of it jolt his whole body and knock the last remnant of strength from his legs. But in falling he seemed for a moment to rise, for as his hind legs collapsed beneath him he seemed to tower upward like a huge rock toppling, his trunk reaching skywards like a tree. He trumpeted, for the first and only time. And then down he came, his belly towards me, with a crash that seemed to shake the ground even where I lay.

I got up. The Burmans were already racing past me across the mud. It was obvious that the elephant would never rise again, but he was not dead. He was breathing very rhythmically with long rattling gasps, his great mound of a side painfully rising and failing. His mouth was wide open—I could see far down into caverns of pale pink throat. I waited a long time for him to die, but his breathing did not weaken. Finally I fired my two remaining shots into the spot where I thought his heart must be. The thick blood welled out of him like red velvet, but still he did not die. His body did not even jerk when the shots hit him, the tortured breathing continued without a pause. He was dying, very slowly and in great agony, but in some world remote from me where not even a bullet could damage him further. I felt that I had got to put an end to that dreadful noise. It seemed dreadful to see the great beast lying there, powerless to move and yet powerless to die, and not even to be able to finish him. I sent back for my small rifle and poured shot after shot into his heart and down his throat. They seemed to make no impression. The tortured gasps continued as steadily as the ticking of a clock.

In the end I could not stand it any longer and went away. I heard later that it took him half an hour to die. Burmans were bringing dahs and baskets even before I left, and I was told they had stripped his body almost to the bones by the afternoon.

Afterwards, of course, there were endless discussions about the shooting of the elephant. The owner was furious, but he was only an Indian and could do nothing. Besides, legally I had done the right thing, for a mad elephant has to be killed, like a mad dog, if its owner fails to control it. Among the Europeans opinion was divided. The older men said I was right, the younger men said it was a damn shame to shoot an elephant for killing a coolie, because an elephant was worth more than any damn Coringhee coolie. And afterwards I was very glad that the coolie had been killed; it put me legally in the right and it gave me a sufficient pretext for shooting the elephant. I often wondered whether any of the others grasped that I had done it solely to avoid looking a fool.

Endnote

1. **saecula saeculorum** For ever and ever. [Ed. note.]

Zen and the Art of Motorcycle Maintenance

Robert M. Pirsig

Robert M. Pirsig (1928 —), born in Minneapolis, Minnesota, is a philosopher and teacher as much as he is a novelist. He is the author of the semi-autobiographical and semi-philosophical novel Zen *and the* Art *of* Motorcycle Maintenance *(1974). The book has very little to do with either Zen Buddhism or, for that matter, motorcycle maintenance. Its subtitle calls the book an* Inquiry into Values. *It is a novel tracing a road trip that the narrator and his son take across America on motorcycles. The narrator does not identify himself by name, though his experience closely resembles that of the author himself. He does refer to his past self as "Phaedrus" (a character in Plato's* Dialogues*) and explains that, after teaching English Composition for some time at a small community college, he had a nervous breakdown. Upon recovering, he notices some of the same tendencies toward mental stress in his son, Chris, and takes him on a road trip to help him think things through.*

The novel unfolds through a series of conversations with his son, discussions with adult friends, and internal meditations. The chief question on the narrator's mind has to do with what "quality" is. He comes to this in response to student questions about what he wants from their papers. He says, simply, that he wants the papers to be "good," to be high in quality. His students, of course, ask him what that means! It is this question, "What is quality?" that he assigns as a paper topic to his class; but he finds that he, himself, has a hard time answering it. We know what it is, but we just can't explain it . . . not fully, anyway. In fact, this difficulty lends to the mental distress that causes him to leave his teaching job at the college. And it is this question that remains central to the real-world Pirsig's continued philosophical inquiry, called the

"*Metaphysics of Quality.*"

In a nutshell, Pirsig thinks that, though we believe that we have some idea of value, when pressed, we find the essence, or quality, of quality itself very hard, perhaps impossible, to define. Nevertheless, our innate sense of what is good or bad, better or worse, is predicated on just such an intuitive understanding. It is this effort to artic- ulate the intuitive that explains the "Zen" in the title. Zen Buddhism stresses an immediate intuitive grasp over intellectual understanding.

The following excerpt is drawn from the narrator's school teaching days as "Phaedrus" and describes his effort to help a student narrow down a topic for a paper. The advice he gives his student is quite practical and leads to an idea of writing small *that might be helpful to many a student struggling to write a better, more focused and coherent essay!*

Today now I want to take up the first phase of his journey into Quality, the nonmetaphys- ical phase, and this will be pleasant. It's nice to start journeys pleasantly, even when you know they won't end that way. Using his class notes as reference material I want to reconstruct the way in which Quality became a working con- cept for him in the teaching of rhetoric. His second phase, the metaphysical one, was tenuous and speculative, but this first phase, in which he simply taught rhetoric, was by all accounts solid and pragmatic and probably deserves to be judged on its own merits, independently of the second phase.

He'd been innovating extensively. He'd been having trouble with students who had nothing to say. At first he thought it was laziness but later it became apparent that it wasn't. They just couldn't think of anything to say.

One of them, a girl with strong-lensed glasses, wanted to write a five-hun- dred-word essay about the United States. He was used to the sinking feeling that comes from statements like this, and suggested without disparagement that she narrow it down to just Bozeman.

When the paper came due she didn't have it and was quite upset. She had tried and tried but she just couldn't think of anything to say.

He had already discussed her with her previous instructors and they'd con- firmed his impressions of her. She was very serious, disciplined and hard- working, but extremely dull. Not a spark of creativity in her anywhere. Her eyes, behind the thick-lensed glasses, were the eyes of a drudge. She wasn't bluffing him, she really couldn't think of anything to say, and was upset by her inability to do as she was told.

It just stumped him. Now *he* couldn't think of anything to say. A silence occurred, and then a peculiar answer: "Narrow it down to the *main street* of Bozeman." It was a stroke of insight.

She nodded dutifully and went out. But just before her next class she came back in *real* distress, tears this time, distress that had obviously been there for a long time. She still couldn't think of anything to say, and couldn't understand why, if she couldn't think of anything about *all* of Bozeman, she should be able to think of something about just one street.

He was furious. *"You're not looking!"* he said. A memory came back of his own dismissal from the University for having *too much* to say. For every fact there is an *infinity* of hypotheses. The more you *look* the more you *see*. She really wasn't looking and yet somehow didn't understand this.

He told her angrily, *"Narrow it down* to the *front of one building* on the main street of Bozeman. The Opera House. Start with the upper left-hand brick."

Her eyes, behind the thick-lensed glasses, opened wide.

She came in the next class with a puzzled look and handed him a five-thousand-word essay on the front of the Opera House on the main street of Bozeman, Montana. "I sat in the hamburger stand across the street," she said, "and started writing about the first brick, and the second brick, and then by the third brick it all started to come and I couldn't stop. They thought I was crazy, and they kept kidding me, but here it all is. I don't understand it."

Neither did he, but on long walks through the streets of town he thought about it and concluded she was evidently stopped with the same kind of blockage that had paralyzed him on his first day of teaching. She was blocked because she was trying to repeat, in her writing, things she had already heard, just as on the first day he had tried to repeat things he had already decided to say. She couldn't think of anything to write about Bozeman because she couldn't recall anything she had heard worth repeating. She was strangely unaware that she could look and see freshly for herself, as she wrote, without primary regard for what had been said before. The narrowing down to one brick destroyed the blockage because it was so obvious she *had* to do some original and direct seeing.

He experimented further. In one class he had everyone write all hour about the back of his thumb. Everyone gave him funny looks at the beginning of the hour, but everyone did it, and there wasn't a single complaint about "nothing to say."

In another class he changed the subject from the thumb to a coin, and got a full hour's writing from every student. In other classes it was the same. Some asked, "Do you have to write about both sides?" Once they got into the idea of seeing directly for themselves they also saw there was no limit to the amount they could say. It was a confidence-building assignment too, because what they wrote, even though seemingly trivial, was nevertheless their own thing, not a mimicking of someone else's. Classes where he used that coin exercise were always less balky and more interested.

As a result of his experiments he concluded that imitation was a real evil that had to be broken before real rhetoric teaching could begin. This imitation seemed to be an external compulsion. Little children didn't have it. It seemed to come later on, possibly as a result of school itself.

That sounded right, and the more he thought about it the more right it sounded. Schools teach you to imitate. If you don't imitate what the teacher wants you get a bad grade. Here, in college, it was more sophisticated, of course; you were supposed to imitate the teacher in such a way as to convince the teacher you were not imitating, but taking the essence of the instruction and going ahead with it on your own. That got you A's. Originality on the other hand could get you anything—from A to F. The whole grading system cautioned against it.

He discussed this with a professor of psychology who lived next door to him, an extremely imaginative teacher, who said, "Right. Eliminate the whole degree-and-grading system and then you'll get real education."

Phaedrus thought about this, and when weeks later a very bright student couldn't think of a subject for a term paper, it was still on his mind, so he gave it to her as a topic. She didn't like the topic at first, but agreed to take it anyway.

Within a week she was talking about it to everyone, and within two weeks had worked up a superb paper. The class she delivered it to didn't have the advantage of two weeks to think about the subject, however, and was quite hostile to the whole idea of eliminating grades and degrees. This didn't slow her down at all. Her tone took on an old-time religious fervor. She begged the other students to *listen*, to understand this was really *right*. "I'm not saying this for *him*," she said and glanced at Phaedrus. "It's for *you*."

Her pleading tone, her religious fervor, greatly impressed him, along with the fact that her college entrance examinations had placed her in the upper one percent of the class. During the next quarter, when teaching "persuasive writing," he chose this topic as a "demonstrator," a piece of persuasive writing he worked up by himself, day by day, in front of and with the help of the class.

He used the demonstrator to avoid talking in terms of principles of composition, all of which he had deep doubts about. He felt that by exposing classes to his own sentences as he made them, with all the misgivings and hang-ups and erasures, he would give a more honest picture of what writing was like than by spending class time picking nits in completed student work or holding up the completed work of masters for emulation. This time he developed the argument that the whole grading system and degree should be eliminated, and to make it something that truly involved the students in what they were hearing, he withheld all grades during the quarter.

Just up above the top of the ridge the snow can be seen now. On foot it's many days away though. The rocks below it are too steep for a direct hiking climb, particularly with the heavy loads we are carrying, and Chris is way too young for any kind of ropes-and-pitons stuff. We must cross over the forested ridge we are now approaching, enter another canyon, follow it to its end and then come back at an upward angle along to the ridge. Three days hard to the snow. Four days easy. If we don't show up in nine, DeWeese will start looking for us.

We stop for a rest, sit down and brace against a tree so that we don't topple over backward from the packs. After a while I reach around over my shoulder, take the machete from the top of my pack and hand it to Chris.

"See those two aspens over there? The straight ones? At the edge?" I point to them. "Cut those down about a foot from the ground."

"Why?"

"We'll need them later for hiking sticks and tent poles."

Chris takes the machete, starts to rise but then settles back again. "You cut them," he says.

So I take the machete and go over and cut the poles. They both cut neatly in one swing, except for the final strip of bark, which I sever with the back hook of the machete. Up in the rocks you need the poles for balancing and the pine up above is no good for poles, and this is about the last of the aspen here. It bothers me a little though that Chris is turning down work. Not a good sign in the mountains.

A short rest and then on we go. It'll take a while to get used to this load. There's a negative reaction to all the weight. As we go on though, it'll become more natural. . . .

Phaedrus' argument for the abolition of the degree-and-grading system produced a nonplussed or negative reaction in all but a few students at first, since it seemed, on first judgment, to destroy the whole University system. One student laid it wide open when she said with complete candor, "Of course you can't eliminate the degree and grading system. After all, that's what we're here for."

She spoke the complete truth. The idea that the majority of students attend a university for an education independent of the degree and grades is a little hypocrisy everyone is happier not to expose. Occasionally some students do arrive for an education but rote and the mechanical nature of the institution soon converts them to a less idealistic attitude.

The demonstrator was an argument that elimination of grades and degrees would destroy this hypocrisy. Rather than deal with generalities it dealt with the specific career of an imaginary student who more or less typified what was found in the classroom, a student completely conditioned to work for a grade rather than for the knowledge the grade was supposed to represent.

Such a student, the demonstrator hypothesized, would go to his first class, get his first assignment and probably do it out of habit. He might go to his second and third as well. But eventually the novelty of the course would wear off and, because his academic life was not his only life, the pressure of other obligations or desires would create circumstances where he just would not be able to get an assignment in.

Since there was no degree or grading system he would incur no penalty for this. Subsequent lectures which presumed he'd completed the assignment might be a little more difficult to understand, however, and this difficulty, in turn, might weaken his interest to a point where the next assignment, which he would find quite hard, would also be dropped. Again no penalty.

In time his weaker and weaker understanding of what the lectures were about would make it more and more difficult for him to pay attention in class. Eventually he would see he wasn't learning much; and facing the continual pressure of outside obligations, he would stop studying, feel guilty about this and stop attending class. Again, no penalty would be attached.

But what had happened? The student, with no hard feelings on anybody's part, would have flunked himself out. Good! This is what should have happened. He wasn't there for a real education in the first place and had no real business there at all. A large amount of money and effort had been saved and there would be no stigma of failure and ruin to haunt him the rest of his life. No bridges had been burned.

The student's biggest problem was a slave mentality which had been built into him by years of carrot-and-whip grading, a mule mentality which said, "If you don't whip me, I won't work." He didn't get whipped. He didn't work. And the cart of civilization, which he supposedly was being trained to pull, was just going to have to creak along a little slower without him.

This is a tragedy, however, only if you presume that the cart of civilization, "the system," is pulled by mules. This is a common, vocational, "location" point of view, but it's not the Church attitude.

The Church attitude is that civilization, or "the system" or "society" or whatever you want to call it, is best served not by mules but by free men. The purpose of abolishing grades and degrees is not to punish mules or to get rid of them but to provide an environment in which that mule can turn into a free man.

The hypothetical student, still a mule, would drift around for a while. He would get another kind of education quite as valuable as the one he'd abandoned, in what used to be called the "school of hard knocks." Instead of wasting money and time as a high-status mule, he would now have to get a job as a low-status mule, maybe as a mechanic. Actually his *real* status would go up. He would be making a contribution for a change. Maybe that's what he would do for the rest of his life. Maybe he'd found his level. But don't count on it.

In time—six months; five years, perhaps—a change could easily begin to take place. He would become less and less satisfied with a kind of dumb, day-to-day shopwork. His creative intelligence, stifled by too much theory and too many grades in college, would now become reawakened by the boredom of the shop. Thousands of hours of frustrating mechanical problems would have made him more interested in machine design. He would like to design machinery himself. He'd think he could do a better job. He would try modifying a few engines, meet with success, look for more success, but feel blocked because he didn't have the theoretical information. He would discover that when before he felt stupid because of his lack of interest in theoretical information, he'd now find a brand of theoretical information which he'd have a lot of respect for, namely, mechanical engineering.

So he would come back to our degreeless and gradeless school, but with a difference. He'd no longer be a grade-motivated person. He'd be a knowledge-motivated person. He would need no external pushing to learn. His push would come from inside. He'd be a free man. He wouldn't need a lot of discipline to shape him up. In fact, if the instructors assigned him were slacking on the job he would be likely to shape *them* up by asking rude questions. He'd be there to learn something, would be paying to learn something and they'd better come up with it.

Motivation of this sort, once it catches hold, is a ferocious force, and in the gradeless, degreeless institution where our student would find himself, he wouldn't stop with rote engineering information. Physics and mathematics were going to come within his sphere of interest because *he'd see he needed them*. Metallurgy and electrical engineering would come up for attention. And, in the process of intellectual maturing that these abstract studies gave him, he would be likely to branch out into other theoretical areas that weren't directly related to machines but had become a part of a newer larger goal. This larger goal wouldn't be the imitation of education in Universities today, glossed over and concealed by grades and degrees that give the appearance of something happening when, in fact, almost nothing is going on. It would be the real thing.

Such was Phaedrus' demonstrator, his unpopular argument, and he worked on it all quarter long, building it up and modifying it, arguing for it, defending it. All quarter long papers would go back to the students with comments but no grades, although the grades were entered in a book.

As I said before, at first almost everyone was sort of nonplussed. The majority probably figured they were stuck with some idealist who thought removal of grades would make them happier and thus work harder, when it was obvious that without grades everyone would just loaf. Many of the students with A records in previous quarters were contemptuous and angry at first, but because of their acquired self-discipline went ahead and did the work anyway. The B students and high-C students missed some of the early assignments or turned in sloppy work. Many of the low-C and D students didn't even show up for class. At this time another teacher asked him what he was going to do about this lack of response.

"Outwait them," he said.

His lack of harshness puzzled the students at first, then made them suspicious. Some began to ask sarcastic questions. These received soft answers and the lectures and speeches proceeded as usual, except with no grades.

Then a hoped-for phenomenon began. During the third or fourth week some of the A students began to get nervous and started to turn in superb work and hang around after class with questions that fished for some indication as to how they were doing. The B and high-C students began to notice this and work a little and bring up the quality of their papers to a more usual level. The low C, D and future F's began to show up for class just to see what was going on.

After midquarter an even more hoped-for phenomenon took place. The A-rated students lost their nervousness and became active participants in everything that went on with a friendliness that was uncommon in a grade-getting class. At this point the B and C students were in a panic, and turned in stuff that looked as though they'd spent hours of pains-taking work on it. The D's and F's turned in satisfactory assignments.

In the final weeks of the quarter, a time when normally everyone knows what his grade will be and just sits back half asleep, Phaedrus was getting a kind of class participation that made other teachers take notice. The B's and C's had joined the A's in friendly free-for-all discussion that made the class seem like a successful party. Only the D's and F's sat frozen in their chairs, in a complete internal panic.

The phenomenon of relaxation and friendliness was explained later by a couple of students who told him, "A lot of us got together outside of class to try to figure out how to beat this system. Everyone decided the best way was just to figure you were going to fail and then go ahead and do what you could anyway. Then you start to relax. Otherwise you go out of your mind!"

The students added that once you got used to it it wasn't so bad, you were more interested in the subject matter, but repeated that it wasn't easy to get used to.

At the end of the quarter the students were asked to write an essay evaluating the system. None of them knew at the time of writing what his or her grade would be. Fifty-four percent opposed it. Thirty-seven percent favored it. Nine percent were neutral.

On the basis of one man, one vote, the system was very unpopular. The majority of students definitely wanted their grades as they went along. But when Phaedrus broke down the returns according to the grades that were in his book—and the grades were not out of line with grades predicted by previous classes and entrance evaluations—another story was told. The A students were 2 to 1 in favor of the system. The B and C students were evenly divided. And the D's and F's were *unanimously* opposed!

This surprising result supported a hunch he had had for a long time: that the brighter, more serious students were the *least* desirous of grades, possibly because they were more interested in the subject matter of the course, whereas the dull or lazy students were the *most* desirous of grades, possibly because grades told them if they were getting by.

The Allegory of the Cave

Plato

Plato (427 B.C.–348 B.C.) was born to a noble family in the Greek city-state of Athens. One of the greatest of ancient philosophers, he was a student of Socrates, the founder of Western philosophy. After Socrates' death in 399 B.C., Plato carried on the Socratic tradition by way of public lectures at the Athenian Academy and through his written works. Although Plato considered the spoken word to be superior to the written, he wrote extensively and virtually all of his compositions have survived intact. With a few exceptions, these works take the form of philosophical dialogues featuring Socrates as the central figure who interrogates and refutes the views of a variety of interlocutors. While Plato's thought is Socratic in its inspiration, it developed — especially in his later works — in directions that went well beyond its Socratic origins. At the heart of the Platonic philosophy is the Theory of Ideas. According to this theory, behind the phenomenal world perceived by the senses and typified by transience is another unchanging and perfect world of "ideas" or forms. Understanding of this eternal realm can be achieved only through a process of pure reason. Moreover, the world of the ideas is hierarchical and at its apex is the supreme Idea of the Good— a concept consistent with the Socratic emphasis on virtue as the highest of human pursuits. In one of Plato's greatest and most influential dialogues, The Republic, *Socrates and his interlocutors explore the design and the aims of the ideal political state. In the present selection, taken from* The Republic, *Socrates expounds in allegorical fashion upon the process of education required to shape the minds of the ruling elite of this ideal state, a process which seeks to inculcate a vision of the Idea of the Good.*

And now, I said, let me show in a figure how far our nature is enlightened or unenlightened:—Behold! human beings living in an underground den, which has a mouth open towards the light and reaching all along the den; here they have been from their childhood, and have their legs and necks chained so that they cannot move, and can only see before them, being prevented by the chains from turning round their heads. Above and behind them a fire is blazing at a distance, and between the fire and the prisoners there is a raised way; and you will see, if you look, a low wall built along the way, like the screen which marionette players have in front of them, over which they show the puppets.

I see.

And do you see, I said, men passing along the wall carrying all sorts of vessels, and statues and figures of animals made of wood and stone and various materials, which appear over the wall? Some of them are talking, others silent.

You have shown me a strange image, and they are strange prisoners.

Like ourselves, I replied; and they see only their own shadows, or the shadows of one another, which the fire throws on the opposite wall of the cave?

True, he said; how could they see anything but the shadows if they were never allowed to move their heads?

And of the objects which are being carried in like manner they would only see the shadows?

Yes, he said.

And if they were able to converse with one another, would they not suppose that they were naming what was actually before them?

Very true.

And suppose further that the prison had an echo which came from the other side, would they not be sure to fancy when one of the passers-by spoke that the voice which they heard came from the passing shadow?

No question, he replied.

To them, I said, the truth would be literally nothing but the shadows of the images.

That is certain.

And now look again, and see what will naturally follow if the prisoners are released and disabused of their error. At first, when any of them is liberated and compelled suddenly to stand up and turn his neck round and walk and look towards the light, he will suffer sharp pains; the glare will distress him, and he will be unable to see the realities of which in his former state he had seen the shadows; and then conceive some one saying to him, that what he saw before was an illusion, but that now, when he is approaching nearer to being and his eye is turned towards more real existence, he has a clearer vision—what will be his reply? And you may further imagine that his instructor is pointing to the objects as they pass and requiring him to name them,—will he not be perplexed? Will he not fancy that the shadows which he formerly saw are truer than the objects which are now shown to him?

Far truer.

And if he is compelled to look straight at the light, will he not have a pain in his eyes which will make him turn away to take refuge in the objects of vision which he can see, and which he will conceive to be in reality clearer than the things which are now being shown to him?

True, he said.

And suppose once more, that he is reluctantly dragged up a steep and rugged ascent, and held fast until he is forced into the presence of the sun himself, is he not likely to be pained and irritated? When he approaches the light his eyes will be dazzled, and he will not be able to see anything at all of what are now called realities.

Not all in a moment, he said.

He will require to grow accustomed to the sight of the upper world. And first he will see the shadows best, next the reflections of men and other objects in the water, and then the objects themselves; then he will gaze upon the light of the moon and the stars and the spangled heaven; and he will see the sky and the stars by night better than the sun or the light of the sun by day?

Certainly.

Last of all he will be able to see the sun, and not mere reflections of him in the water, but he will see him in his own proper place, and not in another, and he will contemplate him as he is.

Certainly.

He will then proceed to argue that this is he who gives the season and the years, and is the guardian of all that is in the visible world, and in a certain way the cause of all things which he and his fellows have been accustomed to behold?

Clearly, he said, he would first see the sun and then reason about him.

And when he remembered his old habitation, and the wisdom of the den and his fellow prisoners, do you not suppose that he would felicitate himself on the change, and pity them?

Certainly, he would.

And if they were in the habit of conferring honors among themselves on those who were quickest to observe the passing shadows and to remark which of them went before, and which followed after, and which were together; and who were therefore best able to draw conclusions as to the future, do you think that he would care for such honors and glories, or envy the possessors of them? Would he not say with Homer,

> Better to be the poor servant of a poor master,

and to endure anything, rather than think as they do and live after their manner?

Yes, he said, I think that he would rather suffer anything than entertain these false notions and live in this miserable manner.

Imagine once more, I said, such a one coming suddenly out of the sun to be replaced in his old situation; would he not be certain to have his eyes full of darkness?

To be sure, he said.

And if there were a contest, and he had to compete in measuring the shadows with the prisoners who had never moved out of the den, while his sight was still weak, and before his eyes had become steady (and the time which would be needed to acquire this new habit of sight might be very considerable), would he not be ridiculous? Men would say of him that up he went and down he came without his eyes; and that it was better not even to think of ascending; and if any one tried to loose another and lead him up to the light, let them only catch the offender, and they would put him to death.

No question, he said.

This entire allegory, I said, you may now append, dear Glaucon, to the previous argument; the prison house is the world of sight, the light of the fire is the sun, and you will not misapprehend me if you interpret the journey upwards to be the ascent of the soul into the intellectual world according to my poor belief, which, at your desire, I have expressed—whether rightly or wrongly God knows. But, whether true or false, my opinion is that in the world of knowledge the idea of good appears last of all, and is seen only with an effort; and, when seen, is also inferred to be the universal author of all things beautiful and right, parent of light and of the lord of light in this visible world, and the immediate source of reason and truth in the intellectual; and that this is the power upon which he who would act rationally either in public or private life must have his eye fixed.

I agree, he said, as far as I am able to understand you.

Moreover, I said, you must not wonder that those who attain to this beatific vision are unwilling to descend to human affairs; for their souls are ever hastening into the upper world where they desire to dwell; which desire of theirs is very natural, if our allegory may be trusted.

Yes, very natural.

And is there anything surprising in one who passes from divine contemplations to the evil state of man, misbehaving himself in a ridiculous manner; if, while his eyes are blinking and before he has become accustomed to the surrounding darkness, he is compelled to fight in courts of law, or in other places, about the images or the shadows of images of justice, and is endeavoring to meet the conceptions of those who have never yet seen absolute justice?

Anything but surprising, he replied.

Anyone who has common sense will remember that the bewilderments of the eyes are of two kinds, and arise from two causes, either from coming out of the light or from going into the light, which is true of the mind's eye, quite as much as of the bodily eye; and he who remembers this when he sees anyone whose vision is perplexed and weak, will not be too ready to laugh; he will first ask whether that soul of man has come out of the brighter life, and is unable to see because unaccustomed to the dark, or having turned from darkness to the day is dazzled by excess of light. And he will count the one happy in his condition and state of being, and he will pity the other; or, if he have a mind to laugh at the soul which comes from below into the light, there will be more reason in this than in the laugh which greets him who returns from above out of the light into the den.

That, he said, is a very just distinction.

But then, if I am right, certain professors of education must be wrong when they say that they can put a knowledge into the soul which was not there before, like sight into blind eyes.

They undoubtedly say this, he replied.

Whereas, our argument shows that the power and capacity of learning exists in the soul already; and that just as the eye was unable to turn from darkness to light without the whole body, so too the instrument of knowledge can only by the movement of the whole soul be turned from the world of becoming into that of being, and learn by degrees to endure the sight of being, and of the brightest and best of being, or in other words, of the good.

Very true.

And must there not be some art which will effect conversion in the easiest and quickest manner; not implanting the faculty of sight, for that exists already, but has been turned in the wrong direction, and is looking away from the truth?

Yes, he said, such an art may be presumed.

And whereas the other so-called virtues of the soul seem to be akin to bodily qualities, for even when they are not originally innate they can be implanted later by habit and exercise, the virtue of wisdom more than anything else contains a divine element which always remains, and by this conversion is rendered useful and profitable; or, on the other hand, hurtful and useless. Did you never observe the narrow intelligence flashing from the keen eye of a clever rogue—how eager he is, how clearly his paltry soul sees the way to his end; he is the reverse of blind, but his keen eyesight is forced into the service of evil, and he is mischievous in proportion to his cleverness?

Very true, he said.

But what if there had been a circumcision of such natures in the days of their youth; and they had been severed from those sensual pleasures, such as eating and drinking, which, like leaden weights, were attached to them at their birth, and which drag them down and turn the vision of their souls upon the things that are below—if, I say, they had been released from these impediments and turned in the opposite direction, the very same faculty in them would have seen the truth as keenly as they see what their eyes are turned to now.

Very likely.

Yes, I said; and there is another thing which is likely, or rather a necessary inference from what has preceded, that neither the uneducated and uninformed of the truth, nor yet those who never make an end of their education, will be able ministers of State; not the former, because they have no single aim of duty which is the rule of all their actions, private as well as public; nor the latter, because they will not act at all except upon compulsion, fancying that they are already dwelling apart in the islands of the blessed.

Very true, he replied.

Then, I said, the business of us who are the founders of the State will be to compel the best minds to attain that knowledge which we have already shown to be the greatest of all—they must continue to ascend until they arrive at the good; but when they have ascended and seen enough we must not allow them to do as they do now.

What do you mean?

I mean that they remain in the upper world: but this must not be allowed; they must be made to descend again among the prisoners in the den, to partake of their labors and honors, whether they are worth having or not.

But is not this unjust? he said; ought we to give them a worse life, when they might have a better?

You have again forgotten, my friend, I said, the intention of the legislator, who did not aim at making any one class in the State happy above the rest; the happiness was to be in the whole State, and he held the citizens together by persuasion and necessity, making them benefactors of the State, and therefore benefactors of one another; to this end he created them, not to please themselves, but to be his instruments in binding up the State.

True, he said, I had forgotten.

Observe, Glaucon, that there will be no injustice in compelling our philosophers to have a care and providence of others; we shall explain to them that in other States, men of their class are not obliged to share in the tolls of politics: and this is reasonable, for they grow up at their own sweet will, and the government would rather not have them. Being self-taught, they cannot be expected to show any gratitude for a culture which they have never received. But we have brought you into the world to be rulers of the hive, kings of yourselves and of the other citizens, and have educated you for better and more perfectly than they have been educated, and you are better able to share in the double duty. Wherefore each of you, when his turn comes, must go down to the general underground abode, and get the habit of seeing in the dark. When you have acquired the habit, you will see ten thousand times better than the inhabitants of the den, and you will know what the several images are, and what they represent, because you have seen the beautiful and just and good in their truth. And thus our State, which is also yours, will be a reality, and not a dream only, and will be administered in a spirit unlike that of other States, in which men fight with one another about shadows only and are distracted in the struggle for power, which in their eyes is a great good. Whereas the truth is that the State in which the rulers are most reluctant to govern is always the best and most quietly governed, and the State in which they are most eager, the worst.

Quite true, he replied.

And will our pupils, when they hear this, refuse to take their turn at the toils of State, when they are allowed to spend the greater part of their time with one another in the heavenly light?

Impossible, he answered; for they are just men, and the commands which we impose upon them are just; there can be no doubt that every one of them will take office as a stern necessity, and not after the fashion of our present rulers of State.

Yes, my friend, I said; and there lies the point. You must contrive for your future rulers another and a better life than that of a ruler, and then you may have a well-ordered State; for only in the State which offers this, will they rule who are truly rich, not in silver and gold, but in virtue and wisdom, which are the true blessings of life. Whereas if they go to the administration of public affairs, poor and hungering after their own private advantage, thinking that hence they are to snatch the chief good, order there can never be; for they will be fighting about office, and the civil and domestic broils which thus arise will be the ruin of the rulers themselves and of the whole State.

Most true, he replied.

And the only life which looks down upon the life of political ambition is that of true philosophy. Do you know of any other?

Indeed, I do not, he said.

The Men We Carry in Our Minds

Scott Russell Sanders

Scott Russell Sanders is a prolific writer of novels, short stories, and personal non-fiction and one of America's most vocal proponents of environmental concerns. He was born in Memphis, Tennessee, in 1945. Sanders studied physics and English at Brown University until 1967 and earned a Ph.D. in English from Cambridge University in 1971. From then until his retirement in 2009, he taught at Indiana University. His memoir A Private History of Awe (2006) was nominated for the Pulitzer Prize. In much of his writing, such as his most recent work, A Conservationist Manifesto (2009), Sanders celebrates the beauty of nature and the need to maintain a sustainable relationship to the environment. The personal essay "The Men We Carry in Our Minds," from his collection The Paradise of Bombs (1987) reflects a different strain in Sanders' writing: his attempts to honestly explore the impacts of social, cultural, and economic structures on people's lives and personal identities.

This must be a hard time for women," I say to my friend Anneke. "They have so many paths to choose from, and so many voices calling them."

"I think it's a lot harder for men," she replies.

"How do you figure that?"

"The women I know feel excited, innocent, like crusaders in a just cause. The men I know are eaten up with guilt."

We are sitting at the kitchen table drinking sassafras tea, our hands wrapped around the mugs because this April morning is cool and drizzly. "Like a Dutch morning," Anneke told me earlier. She is Dutch herself, a writer and midwife and peacemaker, with the round face and sad eyes of a woman in a Vermeer painting who might be waiting for the rain to stop, for a door to open. She leans over to sniff a sprig of lilac, pale lavender, that rises from a vase of a cobalt blue.

"Women feel such pressure to be everything, do everything," I say. "Career, kids, art, politics. Have their babies and get back to the office a week later. It's as if they're trying to overcome a million years' worth of evolution in one life-time."

"But we help one another. We don't try to lumber on alone, like so many wounded grizzly bears, the way men do." Anneke sips her tea. I gave her the mug with owls on it, for wisdom. "And we have this deep-down sense that we're in the *right*—we've been held back, passed over, used—while men feel they're in the wrong. Men are the ones who've been discredited, who have to search their souls."

I search my soul. I discover guilty feelings aplenty—toward the poor, the Vietnamese, Native Americans, the whales, an endless list of debts—a guilt in each case that is as bright and unambiguous as a neon sign. But toward women I feel something more confused, a snarl of shame, envy, wary tenderness, and amazement. This muddle troubles me. To hide my unease I say, "You're right, it's tough being a man these days."

"Don't laugh." Anneke frowns at me, mournful-eyed, through the sassafras steam. "I wouldn't be a man for anything. It's much easier being the victim. All the victim has to do is break free. The persecutor has to live with his past."

How deep is that past? I find myself wondering after Anneke has left. How much of an inheritance do I have to throw off? Is it just the beliefs I breathed in as a child? Do I have to scour memory back through father and grandfather? Through St. Paul? Beyond Stonehenge and into the twilit caves? I'm convinced the past we must contend with is deeper even than speech. When I think back on my childhood, on how I learned to see men and women, I have a sense of ancient, dizzying depths. The back roads of Ten-nessee and Ohio where I grew up were probably closer, in their sexual patterns, to the campsites of Stone Age hunters than to the genderless cities of the future into which we are rushing.

The first men, besides my father, I remember seeing were black convicts and white guards, in the cottonfield across the road from our farm on the out-skirts of Memphis. I must have been three or four. The prisoners wore dingy gray-and-black zebra suits, heavy as canvas, sodden with sweat. Hatless, stooped, they chopped weeds in the fierce heat, row after row, breathing the acrid dust of boll-weevil poison. The overseers wore dazzling white shirts and broad shadowy hats. The oiled barrels of their shotguns flashed in the sun-light. Their faces in memory are utterly blank. Of course those men, white and black, have become for me an emblem of racial hatred. But they have also come to stand for the twin poles of my early vision of manhood—the brute toiling animal and the boss.

When I was a boy, the men I knew labored with their bodies. They were marginal farmers, just scraping by, or welders, steel-workers, carpenters; they swept floors, dug ditches, mined coal, or drove trucks, their forearms ropy with muscle; they trained horses, stoked furnaces, built tires, stood on assembly lines wrestling parts onto cars and refrigerators. They got up before light, worked all day long whatever the weather, and when they came home at night they looked as though somebody had been whipping them. In the evenings and on weekends they worked on their own places, tilling gardens that were lumpy with clay, fixing broken-down cars, hammering on houses that were always too drafty, too leaky, too small.

The bodies of the men I knew were twisted and maimed in ways visible and invisible. The nails of their hands were black and split, the hands tattooed with scars. Some had lost fingers. Heavy lifting had given many of them finicky backs and guts weak from hernias. Racing against conveyor belts had given them ulcers. Their ankles and knees ached from years of standing on concrete. Anyone who had worked for long around machines was hard of hearing. They squinted, and the skin of their faces was creased like the leather of old work gloves. There were times, studying them, when I dreaded growing up. Most of them coughed, from dust or cigarettes, and most of them drank cheap wine or whiskey, so their eyes looked bloodshot and bruised. The fathers of my friends always seemed older than the mothers. Men wore out sooner. Only women lived into old age.

As a boy I also knew another sort of men, who did not sweat and break down like mules. They were soldiers, and so far as I could tell they scarcely worked at all. During my early school years we lived on a military base, an arsenal in Ohio, and every day I saw GIs in the guardshacks, on the stoops of barracks, at the wheels of olive drab Chevrolets. The chief fact of their lives was boredom. Long after I left the Arsenal I came to recognize the sour smell the soldiers gave off as that of souls in limbo. They were all waiting—for wars, for transfers, for leaves, for promotions, for the end of their hitch—like so many braves waiting for the hunt to begin. Unlike the warriors of older tribes, however, they would have no say about when the battle would start or how it would be waged. Their waiting was broken only when they practiced for war. They fired guns at targets, drove tanks across the churned-up fields of the military reservation, set off bombs in the wrecks of old fighter planes. I knew this was all play. But I also felt certain that when the hour for killing arrived, they would kill. When the real shooting started, many of them would die. This was what soldiers were *for*, just as a hammer was for driving nails.

Warriors and toilers: those seemed, in my boyhood vision, to be the chief destinies for men. They weren't the only destinies, as I learned from having a few male teachers, from reading books, and from watching television. But the men on television—the politicians, the astronauts, the generals, the savvy lawyers, the philosophical doctors, the bosses who gave orders to both soldiers and laborers—seemed as remote and unreal to me as the figures in tapestries. I could no more imagine growing up to become one of these cool, potent creatures than I could imagine becoming a prince.

A nearer and more hopeful example was that of my father, who had escaped from a red-dirt farm to a tire factory, and from the assembly line to the front office. Eventually he dressed in a white shirt and tie. He carried himself as if he had been born to work with his mind. But his body, remembering the earlier years of slogging work, began to give out on him in his fifties, and it quit on him entirely before he turned sixty-five. Even such a partial escape from man's fate as he had accomplished did not seem possible for most of the boys I knew. They joined the Army, stood in line for jobs in the smoky plants, helped build highways. They were bound to work as their fathers had worked, killing themselves or preparing to kill others.

A scholarship enabled me not only to attend college, a rare enough feat in my circle, but even to study in a university meant for the children of the rich. Here I met for the first time young men who had assumed from birth that they would lead lives of comfort and power. And for the first time I met women who told me that men were guilty of having kept all the joys and privileges of the earth for themselves. I was baffled. What privileges? What joys? I thought about the maimed, dismal lives of most of the men back home. What had they stolen from their wives and daughters? The right to go five days a week, twelve months a year, for thirty or forty years to a steel mill or a coal mine? The right to drop bombs and die in war? The right to feel every leak in the roof, every gap in the fence, every cough in the engine, as a wound they must mend? The right to feel, when the lay-off comes or the plant shuts down, not only afraid but ashamed?

I was slow to understand the deep grievances of women. This was because, as a boy, I had envied them. Before college, the only people I had ever known who were interested in art or music or literature, the only ones who read books, the only ones who ever seemed to enjoy a sense of ease and grace were the mothers and daughters. Like the menfolk, they fretted about money, they scrimped and made-do. But, when the pay stopped coming in, they were not the ones who had failed. Nor did they have to go to war, and that seemed to me a blessed fact. By comparison with the narrow, ironclad days of fathers, there was an expansiveness, I thought, in the days of mothers. They went to see neighbors, to shop in town, to run errands at school, at the library, at church. No doubt, had I looked harder at their lives, I would have envied them less. It was not my fate to become a woman, so it was easier for me to see the graces. Few of them held jobs outside of the home, and those who did filled thankless roles as clerks and waitresses. I didn't see, then, what a prison a house could be, since houses seemed to me brighter, handsomer places than any factory. I did not realize—because such things were never spoken of—how often women suffered from men's bullying. I did learn about the wretchedness of abandoned wives, single mothers, widows; but I also learned about the wretchedness of lone men. Even then I could see how exhausting it was for a mother to cater all day to the needs of young children. But if I had been asked, as a boy, to choose between tending a baby and tending a machine, I think I would have chosen the baby. (Having now tended both, I know I would choose the baby.)

So I was baffled when the women at college accused me and my sex of having cornered the world's pleasures. I think something like my bafflement has been felt by other boys (and by girls as well) who grew up in dirt-poor farm country, in mining country, in black ghettos, in Hispanic barrios, in the shadows of factories, in Third World nations—any place where the fate of men is as grim and bleak as the fate of women. Toilers and warriors. I realize now how ancient these identities are, how deep the tug they exert on men, the undertow of a thousand generations. The miseries I saw, as a boy, in the lives of nearly all men I continue to see in the lives of many—the body-breaking toil, the tedium, the call to be tough, the humiliating powerlessness, the battle for a living and for territory.

When the women I met at college thought about the joys and privileges of men, they did not carry in their minds the sort of men I had known in my childhood. They thought of their fathers, who were bankers, physicians, architects, stockbrokers, the big wheels of the big cities. These fathers rode the train to work or drove cars that cost more than any of my childhood houses. They were attended from morning to night by female helpers, wives and nurses and secretaries. They were never laid off, never short of cash at month's end, never lined up for welfare. These fathers made decisions that mattered. They ran the world.

The daughters of such men wanted to share in this power, this glory. So did I. They yearned for a say over their future, for jobs worthy of their abilities, for the right to live at peace, unmolested, whole. Yes, I thought, yes yes. The difference between me and these daughters was that they saw me, because of my sex, as destined from birth to become like their fathers, and therefore as an enemy to their desires. But I knew better. I wasn't an enemy, in fact or in feeling. I was an ally. If I had known, then, how to tell them so, would they have believed me? Would they now?

Sermon on the Mount, Matthew 5-7

The Sermon on the Mount, which appears in the fifth, sixth, and seventh chapters of the Book of Matthew in the New Testament are seen as a key element in Christian ethics and provides instructions in how a true follower of Jesus should live his or her life. St. Augustine noted, "If any one will piously and soberly consider the sermon which our Lord Jesus Christ spoke on the mount, as we read it in the Gospel according to Matthew, I think that he will find in it, so far as regards the highest morals, a perfect standard of the Christian life."

It presents the most extensive teachings of Jesus in the New Testament and is believed to have been delivered to his followers soon after his baptism by John the Baptist. Because of its similarity to Jesus's Sermon on the Plain, which is found in the Book of Luke, biblical scholars believe that there were not two different sermons; instead, both are compilations of the teachings delivered at various times and then constructed into a single sermon.

The Beatitudes

When Jesus saw the crowds, he went up the mountain; and after he sat down, his disciples came to him. Then he began to speak, and taught them, saying:
   "Blessed are the poor in spirit, for theirs is the kingdom of heaven.
   "Blessed are those who mourn, for they will be comforted.

"Blessed are the meek, for they will inherit the earth.

"Blessed are those who hunger and thirst for righteousness, for they will be filled.

"Blessed are the merciful, for they will receive mercy.

"Blessed are the pure in heart, for they will see God.

"Blessed are the peacemakers, for they will be called children of God.

"Blessed are those who are persecuted for righteousness' sake, for theirs is the kingdom of heaven.

"Blessed are you when people revile you and persecute you and utter all kinds of evil against you falsely on my account. Rejoice and be glad, for your reward is great in heaven, for in the same way they persecuted the prophets who were before you.

Salt and Light

"You are the salt of the earth; but if salt has lost its taste, how can its saltiness be restored? It is no longer good for anything, but is thrown out and trampled under foot.

"You are the light of the world. A city built on a hill cannot be hid. No one after lighting a lamp puts it under the bushel basket, but on the lampstand, and it gives light to all in the house. In the same way, let your light shine before others, so that they may see your good works and give glory to your Father in heaven.

The Law and the Prophets

"Do not think that I have come to abolish the law or the prophets; I have come not to abolish but to fulfill. For truly I tell you, until heaven and earth pass away, not one letter, not one stroke of a letter, will pass from the law until all is accomplished. Therefore, whoever breaks one of the least of these commandments, and teaches others to do the same, will be called least in the kingdom of heaven; but whoever does them and teaches them will be called great in the kingdom of heaven. For I tell you, unless your righteousness exceeds that of the scribes and Pharisees, you will never enter the kingdom of heaven.

Concerning Anger

"You have heard that it was said to those of ancient times, 'You shall not murder'; and 'whoever murders shall be liable to judgment.' But I say to you that if you are angry with a brother or sister, you will be liable to judgment; and if you insult a brother or sister, you will be liable to the council; and if you say, 'You fool,' you will be liable to the hell of fire. So when you are offering your gift at the altar, if you remember that your brother or sister has something against you, leave your gift there before the altar and go; first be reconciled to your brother or sister, and then come and offer your gift. Come to terms quickly with your accuser while you are on the way to court with him, or your accuser may hand you over to the judge, and the judge to the guard, and you will be thrown into prison, Truly I tell you, you will never get out until you have paid the last penny.

Concerning Adultery

"You have heard that it was said, 'You shall not commit adultery.' But I say to you that everyone who looks at a woman with lust has already committed adultery with her in his heart. If your right eye causes you to sin, tear it out and throw it away; it is better for you to lose one of your members than for your whole body to be thrown into hell. And if your right hand causes you to sin, cut it off and throw it away; it is better for you to lose one of your members than for your whole body to go into hell.

Concerning Divorce

"It was also said, 'Whoever divorces his wife, let him give her a certificate of divorce.' But I say to you that anyone who divorces his wife, except on the ground of unchastity, causes her to commit adultery; and whoever marries a divorced woman commits adultery.

Concerning Oaths

"Again, you have heard that it was said to those of ancient times, 'You shall not swear falsely, but carry out the vows you have made to the Lord.' But I say to you, Do not swear at all, either by heaven, for it is the throne of God, or by the earth, for it is his footstool, or by Jerusalem, for it is the city of the great King. And do not swear by your head, for you cannot make one hair white or black. Let your word be 'Yes, Yes' or 'No, No'; anything more than this comes from the evil one.

Concerning Retaliation

"You have heard that it was said, 'An eye for an eye and a tooth for a tooth.' But I say to you, Do not resist an evildoer. But if anyone strikes you on the right cheek, turn the other also; and if anyone wants to sue you and take your coat, give your cloak as well; and if anyone forces you to go one mile, go also the second mile. Give to everyone who begs from you, and do not refuse anyone who wants to borrow from you.

Love for Enemies

"You have heard that it was said, 'You shall love your neighbor and hate your enemy.' But I say to you, Love your enemies and pray for those who persecute you, so that you may be children of your Father in heaven; for he makes his sun rise on the evil and on the good, and sends rain on the righteous and on the unrighteous. For if you love those who love you, what reward do you have? Do not even the tax collectors do the same? And if you greet only your brothers and sisters, what more are you doing than others? Do not even the Gentiles do the same? Be perfect, therefore, as your heavenly Father is perfect.

Concerning Almsgiving

6 "Beware of practicing your piety before others in order to be seen by them; for then you have no reward from your Father in heaven.

"So whenever you give alms, do not sound a trumpet before you, as the hypocrites do in the synagogues and in the streets, so that they may be praised by others. Truly I tell you, they have received their reward. But when you give alms, do not let your left hand know what your right hand is doing, so that your alms may be done in secret; and your Father who sees in secret will reward you.

Concerning Prayer

"And whenever you pray, do not be like the hypocrites; for they love to stand and pray in the synagogues and at the street corners, so that they may be seen by others. Truly I tell you, they have received their reward. But whenever you pray, go into your room and shut the door and pray to your Father who is in secret; and your Father who sees in secret will reward you.

"When you are praying, do not heap up empty phrases as the Gentiles do; for they think that they will be heard because of their many words. Do not be like them, for your Father knows what you need before you ask him.

"Pray then in this way:
      Our Father in heaven,
        hallowed be your name.
    Your kingdom come.
      Your will be done,
        on earth as it is in heaven.
      Give us this day our daily bread.
      And forgive us our debts,
        as we also have forgiven our debtors.
      And do not bring us to the time of trial,
        but rescue us from the evil one.

For if you forgive others their trespasses, your heavenly Father will also forgive you; but if you do not forgive others, neither will your Father forgive your trespasses.

Concerning Fasting

"And whenever you fast, do not look dismal, like the hypocrites, for they disfigure their faces so as to show others that they are fasting. Truly I tell you, they have received their reward. But when you fast, put oil on your head and wash your face, so that your fasting may be seen not by others but by your Father who is in secret; and your Father who sees in secret will reward you.

Concerning Treasures

"Do not store up for yourselves treasures on earth, where moth and rust consume and where thieves break in and steal; but store up for yourselves treasures in heaven, where neither moth nor rust consumes and where thieves do not break in and steal. For where your treasure is, there your heart will be also.

The Sound Eye

"The eye is the lamp of the body. So, if your eye is healthy, your whole body will be full of light; but if your eye is unhealthy, your whole body will be full of darkness. If then the light in you is darkness, how great is the darkness!

Serving Two Masters

"No one can serve two masters; for a slave will either hate the one and love the other, or be devoted to the one and despise the other. You cannot serve God and wealth.

Do Not Worry

"Therefore I tell you, do not worry about your life, what you will eat or what you will drink, or about your body, what you will wear. Is not life more than food, and the body more than clothing? Look at the birds of the air; they neither sow nor reap nor gather into barns, and yet your heavenly Father feeds them. Are you not of more value than they? And can any of you by worrying add a single hour to your span of life? And why do you worry about clothing? Consider the lilies of the field, how they grow; they neither toil nor spin, yet I tell you, even Solomon in all his glory was not clothed like one of these. But if God so clothes the grass of the field, which is alive today and tomorrow is thrown into the oven, will he not much more clothe you—you of little faith?

Therefore do not worry, saying, 'What will we eat?' or 'What will we drink?' or 'What will we wear?' For it is the Gentiles who strive for all these things; and indeed your heavenly Father knows that you need all these things. But strive first for the kingdom of God and his righteousness, and all these things will be given to you as well.

"So do not worry about tomorrow, for tomorrow will bring worries of its own. Today's trouble is enough for today.

Judging Others

7 "Do not judge, so that you may not be judged. For with the judgment you make you will be judged, and the measure you give will be the measure you get. Why do you see the speck in your neighbor's eye, but do not notice the log in your own eye? Or how can you say to your neighbor, 'Let me take the speck out of your eye,' while the log is in your own eye? You hypocrite, first take the log out of your own eye, and then you will see clearly to take the speck out of your neighbor's eye.

Profaning the Holy

"Do not give what is holy to dogs; and do not throw your pearls before swine, or they will trample them under foot and turn and maul you.

Ask, Search, Knock

"Ask, and it will be given you; search, and you will find; knock, and the door will be opened for you. For everyone who asks receives, and everyone who searches finds, and for everyone who knocks, the door will be opened. Is there anyone among you who, if your child asks for bread, will give a stone? Or if the child asks for a fish, will give a snake? If you then, who are evil, know how to give good gifts to your children, how much more will your Father in heaven give good things to those who ask him!

The Golden Rule

"In everything do to others as you would have them do to you; for this is the law and the prophets.

The Narrow Gate

"Enter through the narrow gate; for the gate is wide and the road is easy that leads to destruction, and there are many who take it. For the gate is narrow and the road is hard that leads to life, and there are few who find it.

A Tree and Its Fruit

"Beware of false prophets, who come to you in sheep's clothing but inwardly are ravenous wolves. You will know them by their fruits. Are grapes gathered from thorns, or figs from thistles? In the same way, every good tree bears good fruit, but the bad tree bears bad fruit. A good tree cannot bear bad fruit, nor can a bad tree bear good fruit. Every tree that does not bear good fruit is cut down and thrown into the fire. Thus you will know them by their fruits.

Concerning Self-Deception

"Not everyone who says to me, 'Lord, Lord,' will enter the kingdom of heaven, but only the one who does the will of my Father in heaven. On that day many will say to me, 'Lord, Lord, did we not prophesy in your name, and cast out demons in your name, and do many deeds of power in your name?' Then I will declare to them, 'I never knew you; go away from me, you evildoers.'

Hearers and Doers

"Everyone then who hears these words of mine and acts on them will be like a wise man who built his house on rock. The rain fell, the floods came, and the winds blew and beat on that house, but it did not fall, because it had been founded on rock. And everyone who hears these words of mine and does not act on them will be like a foolish man who built his house on sand. The rain fell, and the floods came, and the winds blew and beat against that house, and it fell—and great was its fall!"

Now when Jesus had finished saying these things, the crowds were astounded at his teaching, for he taught them as one having authority, and not as their scribes.

First Days at Carlisle

Luther Standing Bear

It is disputed as to whether Luther standing bear was born in 1868 in the Lakota tribe of the Sioux nation or five years earlier, in 1863, to a white father and Lakota woman. What is known is that he was raised to be a warrior and a hunter during the time period of General George Armstrong Custer's defeat at Little Big Horn.

Not long after the defeat of Custer and the U.S. Cavalry, the Lakota were forced onto reservations. The government slaughtered all of the buffalo the Lakota depended upon for their survival as part of its effort to force assimilation and to eliminate the tribal traditions that held the people together.

Another policy in the government's attempts to assimilate the Native Americans and to eradicate their culture and traditions was the creation of federal boarding schools for Native American children. The first of these schools was established in Carlisle, Pennsylvania, in 1879. Luther Standing Bear was among the first group of students to arrive at the school.

This excerpt is taken from My People, the Sioux, *by Standing Bear, and offers his reflections on his experiences upon his arrival about the treatment he encountered at the hands of the white teachers and administrators.*

In his later life, Standing Bear traveled with Buffalo Bill's Wild West Show when it was touring in Europe and worked as an actor in American films. He also published four books about his life, his tribe and native customs and traditions.

First Days at Carlisle

At last the train arrived at a junction where we were told we were at the end of our journey. Here we left the train and walked about two miles to the Carlisle Barracks. Soon we came to a big gate in a great high wall. The gate was locked, but after quite a long wait, it was unlocked and we marched in through it. I was the first boy inside. At that time I thought nothing of it, but now I realize that I was the first Indian boy to step inside the Carlisle Indian School grounds.

Here the girls were all called to one side by Louise McCoz, the girls' interpreter. She took them into one of the big buildings, which was very brilliantly lighted, and it looked good to us from the outside.

When our interpreter told us to go to a certain building which he pointed out to us, we ran very fast, expecting to find nice little beds like those the white people had. We were so tired and worn out from the long trip that we wanted a good long sleep. From Springfield, Dakota, to Carlisle, Pennsylvania, riding in day coaches all the way, with no chance to sleep, is an exhausting journey for a bunch of little Indians.

But the first room we entered was empty. A cast-iron stove stood in the middle of the room, on which was placed a coal-oil lamp. There was no fire in the stove. We ran through all the rooms, but they were all the same—no fire, no beds. This was a two-story building, but we were all herded into two rooms on the upper floor.

Well, we had to make the best of the situation, so we took off our leggins and rolled them up for a pillow. All the covering we had was the blanket which each had brought. We went to sleep on the hard floor, and it was so cold! We had been used to sleeping on the ground, but the floor was so much colder.

Next morning we were called downstairs for breakfast. All we were given was bread and water. How disappointed we were! At noon we had some meat, bread, and coffee, so we felt a little better. But how lonesome the big boys and girls were for their far-away Dakota homes where there was plenty to eat! The big boys seemed to take it worse than we smaller chaps did. I guess we little fellows did not know any better. The big boys would sing brave songs, and that would start the girls to crying. They did this for several nights. The girls' quarters were about a hundred and fifty yards from ours, so we could hear them crying. After some time the food began to get better; but it was far from being what we had been used to receiving back home.

At this point I must tell you how the Carlisle Indian School was started. A few years previously, four or five tribes in Oklahoma had some trouble. They were Cheyennes, Arapahoes, Comanches, and Wichitas. There was another tribe with them, but I have forgotten the name. The Government arrested some braves from these various tribes and took them to Virginia as prisoners.

Captain Pratt was in charge of them. He conceived the idea of placing these Indians in a school to see if they could learn anything in that manner. So they were put into the Hampton School, where negroes were sent. They were good-sized young men, having been on the war-path already, but old as they were, they were getting on splendidly with their studies.

That gave Captain Pratt another idea. He thought if he could get some young Indian children and educate them, it would help their people. He went to the Government officials and put the proposition up to them, and asked permission to try the experiment. They told him to go ahead and see what he could do, providing he could get any Indians to educate. Captain Pratt was not at all sure he could do this.

He had nothing prepared to start such a school, but the Government gave him the use of some empty buildings at Carlisle, Pennsylvania. He brought some of the Indian prisoners from Virginia with him, and they remained in the Carlisle Barracks until Captain Pratt could go to Dakota and return with his first consignment of "scholars." Carlisle School had been a soldiers' home at one time; so at the start it was not built for the education of the Indian people.

I had come to this school merely to show my people that I was brave enough to leave the reservation and go East, not knowing what it meant and not caring.

When we first arrived at Carlisle, we had nothing to do. There were no school regulations, no rules of order or anything of that sort. We just ran all over the school grounds and did about as we pleased.

Soon some white people began to come in from nearby towns to see us. Then we would all go up on the second floor and stand against the railings to look down at them. One of our boys was named Lone Hill. He watched the people closely, and if he saw a negro in the crowd he would run inside and put his war-shirt on. Then he would come out and chase the negro all over the grounds until he left. How the people laughed at this!

For some time we continued sleeping on the hard floor, and it was far from being as comfortable as the nice, soft beds in our tipis back home. One evening the interpreter called us all together, and gave each a big bag. He said these were to be our mattresses, but that we would have to fill them ourselves with straw. He said, "Our behind the stable is a large haystack. Go there and fill these bags all full."

So we all ran as fast as we could to the haystack and filled our sacks as quickly as possible, pushing and scuffling to see who would get finished first. When the bags were all full, we carried them to one of the big rooms on the second floor. Here the bags were all laid out in a row. We little fellows certainly did look funny, lugging those great bags across the yard and upstairs.

That night we had the first good sleep in a long time. These bags were sewed all around, and in the center there was a slit through which they were filled with the straw; but there was nobody to sew the slit up after the bag was filled. We had no sheets and no extra blankets thus far—nothing but the blankets we had brought from the reservation.

The next day we played back and forth over these bags of straw, and soon it began to filter out through the slits. Presently it was scattered all over the floor, and as we had no brooms with which to sweep it up, you can imagine the looks of the room at the starting of our school!

Although we were yet wearing our Indian clothes, the interpreter came to us and told us we must go to school. We were marched into a schoolroom, where we were each given a pencil and slate. We were seated at single desks. We soon discovered that the pencils made marks on the slates. So we covered our heads with our blankets, holding the slate inside so the other fellow would not know what we were doing. Here we would draw a man on a pony chasing buffalo, or a boy shooting birds in a tree, or it might be one of our Indian games, or anything that suited our fancy to try and portray.

When we had all finished, we dropped our blankets down on the seat and marched up to the teacher with our slates to show what we had drawn. Our teacher was a woman. She bowed her head as she examined the slates and smiled, indicating that we were doing pretty well—at least we interpreted it that way.

One day when we came to school there was a lot of writing on one of the blackboards. We did not know what it meant, but our interpreter came into the room and said, "Do you see all these marks on the blackboard? Well, each word is a white man's name. They are going to give each one of you one of these names by which you will hereafter be known." None of the names were read or explained to us, so of course we did not know the sound or meaning of any of them.

The teacher had a long pointed stick in her hand, and the interpreter told the boy in the front seat to come up. The teacher handed the stick to him, and the interpreter then told him to pick out any name he wanted. The boy had gone up with his blanket on. When the long stick was handed to him, he turned to us as much as to say, 'Shall I—or will you help me—to take one of these names? Is it right for me to take a white man's name?' He did not know what to do for a time, not uttering a single word—but he acted a lot and was doing a lot of thinking.

Finally he pointed out one of the names written on the blackboard. Then the teacher took a piece of white tape and wrote the name on it. Then she cut off a length of the tape and sewed it on the back of the boy's shirt. Then that name was erased from the board. There was no duplication of names in the first class at Carlisle School!

Then the next boy took the pointer and selected a name. He was also labeled in the same manner as Number One. When my turn came, I took the pointer and acted as if I were about to touch an enemy. Soon we all had the names of white men sewed on our backs. When we went to school, we knew enough to take our proper places in the class, but that was all. When the teacher called the roll, no one answered his name. Then she would walk around and look at the back of the boys' shirts. When she had the right name located, she made the boy stand up and say "Present." She kept this up for about a week before we knew what the sound of our new names was.

I was one of the "bright fellows" to learn my name quickly. How proud I was to answer when the teachers called the roll! I would put my blanket down and half raise myself in my seat, all ready to answer to my new name. I had selected the name "Luther"—not "Lutheran" as many people call me. "Lutheran" is the name of a church denomination, not a person.

Next we had to learn to write our names. Our good teacher had a lot of patience with us. She is now living in Los Angeles, California, and I still like to go and ask her any question which may come up in my mind. She first wrote my name on the slate for me, and then, by motions, indicated that I was to write it just like that. She held the pencil in her hand just so, then made first one stroke, then another, and by signs I was given to understand that I was to follow in exactly the same way.

The first few times I wrote my new name, it was scratched so deeply into the slate that I was never able to erase it. But I copied my name all over both sides of the slate until there was no more room to write. Then I took my slate up to show it to the teacher, and she indicated, by the expression of her face, that it was very good. I soon learned to write it very well; then I took a piece of chalk downstairs and wrote 'Luther' all over everything I could copy it on.

Next the teacher wrote out the alphabet on my slate and indicated to me that I was to take the slate to my room and study. I was pleased to do this, as I expected to have a lot of fun. I went up on the second floor, to the end of the building, where I thought nobody would bother me. There I sat down and looked at those queer letters, trying hard to figure out what they meant. No one was there to tell me that the first letter was "A" the next "B" and so on. This was the first time in my life that I was really disgusted. It was something I could not decipher, and all this study business was not what I had come East for anyhow—so I thought.

How lonesome I felt for my father and mother! I stayed upstairs all by myself, thinking of the good times I might be having if I were only back home, where I could ride my ponies, go wherever I wanted to and do as I pleased, and, when it came night, could lie down and sleep well. Right then and there I learned that no matter how humble your home is, it is yet home.

So it did me no good to take my slate with me that day. It only made me lonesome. The next time the teacher told me by signs to take my slate to my room, I shook my head, meaning "no." She came and talked to me in English, but of course I did not know what she was saying.

A few days later, she wrote the alphabet on the blackboard, then brought the interpreter into the room. Through him she told us to repeat each letter after her, calling out "A," and we all said "A"; then "B," and so on. This was our real beginning. The first day we learned the first three letters of the alphabet, both the pronunciation and the reading of them.

I had not determined to learn anything yet. All I could think of was my free life at home. How long would these people keep us here? When were we going home? At home we could eat any time we wished, but here we had to watch the sun all the time. On cloudy days the waits between meals seemed terribly long.

There soon came a time when the church people fixed up an old building which was to be used as our dining-room. In it they placed some long tables, but with no cover on. Our meals were dished up and brought to each plate before we entered. I very quickly learned to be right there when the bell rang, and get in first. Then I would run along down the table until I came to a plate which I thought contained the most meat, when I would sit down and begin eating without waiting for anyone.

We soon "got wise" when it came to looking out for the biggest portion of meat. When we knew by the sun that it was near dinner time, we would play close to the dining-room, until the woman in charge came out with a big bell in her hand to announce that the meal was ready. We never had to be called twice! We were right there when it came meal-time!

After a while they hung a big bell on a walnut tree near the office. This was to be rung for school hours and meals. One of the Indian boys named Edgar Fire Thunder used to sneak around the building and ring the bell before it was time to eat. Of course we would all rush for the dining-room, only to find the doors locked. Nobody seemed to object to this boy playing such pranks, but we did not like it.

We were still wearing our Indian clothes. One of the Indian prisoners was delegated to teach us to march in to the dining-room and to school. Some of the boys had bells on their leggins, which helped us to keep time as we stepped off.

One day we had a strange experience. We were all called together by the interpreter and told that we were to have our hair cut off. We listened to what he had to say, but we did not reply. This was something that would require some thought, so that evening the big boys held a council, and I recall very distinctly that Nakpa Kesela, or Robert American Horse, made a serious speech. Said he, "If I am to learn the ways of the white people, I can do it just as well with my hair on." To this we all exclaimed "Hau!"—meaning that we agreed with him.

In spite of this meeting, a few days later we saw some white men come inside the school grounds carrying big chairs. The interpreter told us these were the men who had come to cut our hair. We did not watch to see where the chairs were carried, as it was school time, and we went to our classroom. One of the big boys named Ya Slo, or Whistler, was missing. In a short time he came in with his hair cut off. They then called another boy out, and when he returned, he also wore short hair. In this way we were called out one by one.

When I saw most of them with short hair, I began to feel anxious to be "in style" and wanted mine cut, too. Finally I was called out of the schoolroom, and when I went into the next room, the barber was waiting for me. He motioned for me to sit down, and then he commenced work. But when my hair was cut short, it hurt my feelings to such an extent that the tears came into my eyes. I do not recall whether the barber noticed my agitation or not, nor did I care. All I was thinking about was that hair he had taken away from me.

Right here I must state how this hair-cutting affected me in various ways. I have recounted that I always wanted to please my father in every way possible. All his instructions to me had been along this line: "Son, be brave and get killed." This expression had been moulded into my brain to such an extent that I knew nothing else.

But my father had made a mistake. He should have told me, upon leaving home, to go and learn all I could of the white man's ways, and be like them. That would have given a new idea from a different slant; but Father did not advise me along that line. I had come away from home with the intention of never returning alive unless I had done something very brave.

Now, after having had my hair cut, a new thought came into my head. I felt that I was no more Indian, but would be an imitation of a white man. And we are still imitations of white men, and the white men are imitations of the Americans.

We all looked so funny with short hair. It had been cut with a machine and was cropped very close. We still had our Indian clothes, but were all "bald-headed." None of us slept well that night; we felt so queer. I wanted to feel my head all the time. But in a short time I became anxious to learn all I could.

Next we heard that we were soon to have white men's clothes. We were all very excited and anxious when this was announced to us. One day some wagons came in, loaded with big boxes, which were unloaded in front of the office. Of course we were all very curious, and gathered around to watch the proceedings and see all we could.

Here, one at a time, we were "sized up" and a whole suit handed to each of us. The clothes were some sort of dark heavy gray goods, consisting of coat, pants, and vest. We were also given a dark woolen shirt, a cap, a pair of suspenders, socks, and heavy farmer's boots.

Up to this time we had all been wearing our thin shirts, leggins, and a blanket. Now we had received new outfits of white men's clothes, and to us it seemed a whole lot of clothing to wear at once, but even at that, we had not yet received any underwear.

As soon as we had received our outfits, we ran to our rooms to dress up. The Indian prisoners were kept busy helping us put the clothes on. Although the suits were too big for many of us, we did not know the difference. I remember that my boots were far too large, but as long as they were "screechy" or squeaky, I didn't worry about the size! I liked the noise they made when I walked, and the other boys were likewise pleased.

How proud we were with clothes that had pockets and with boots that squeaked! We walked the floor nearly all the night. Many of the boys even went to bed with their clothes all on. But in the morning, the boys who had taken off their pants had a most terrible time. They did not know whether they were to button up in front or behind. Some of the boys said the open part went in front; others said, "No, it goes at the back." There is where the boys who had kept all their clothes on came in handy to look at. They showed the others that the pants buttoned up in front and not at the back. So here we learned something again.

Another boy and I received some money from home. His name was Waniyetula, or Winter, and he was my cousin. We concluded we might as well dress up like white men; so we took all our money to the interpreter and asked him if he would buy us some nice clothes. He promised he would.

We did not know the amount of money which we handed over to him, but we gave him all we had received, as we did not know values then. He took the money and went to town. When he returned he brought us each a big bundle. We took them and went into an empty room to dress up, as we did not want the other boys to see us until we had the clothes on. When we opened the bundles, we were surprised to see how many things we had received for our money. Each bundle contained a black suit of clothes, a pair of shoes and socks, stiff bosom shirt, two paper collars, a necktie, a pair of cuffs, derby hat, cuff buttons, and some colored glass studs for our stiff shirt fronts.

We were greatly pleased with our purchases, which we examined with great curiosity and eagerness. As it was nearly time for supper, we tied the bundles together again and took them into one of the rooms where an Indian prisoner was staying, asking him to keep the bundles for us until the next day. We had to talk to him in the sign language, as he was from a different tribe. The sign language, by the way, was invented by the Indian. White men never use it correctly.

We felt very proud of our new purchases and spent most of that evening getting off by ourselves and discussing them. We found out later that our wonderful clothes cost all together about eleven dollars. The interpreter had bought the cheapest things he could get in the town of Carlisle.

All the next day we were together. We kept our eyes on our disciplinarian, Mr. Campbell, because we wanted to see how he put on his collar. We were studying not very far away from him and we watched him constantly, trying to figure out how he had put that collar on his shirt.

When evening came at last, we carried our bundles up to the second floor where we could be alone. Here we opened the things up and started to dress up. While we were thus engaged, in came the prisoner with whom we had left the bundles the night before. We were glad, in a way, that he had come in, because he knew more about how the clothes ought to be worn than we did, and he helped us dress.

Just as we were through, the bell rang for supper. The other boys were already in line. We came down the outside stairway, and when they observed us, what a war-whoop went up! The boys made all kinds of remarks about our outfits, and called us "white men." But our teachers and the other white people were greatly pleased at our new appearance.

We had only two paper collars apiece, and when they became soiled we had to go without collars. We tried our best to wear the ties without the collars, but I guess we must have looked funny.

It was now winter and very cold, so we were supplied with red flannel underwear. These looked pretty to us, but we did not like the warmth and the "itching" they produced. I soon received some more money from my father, and another boy named Knaska, or Frog, and I bought us some white under-wear. This was all right, but we did not dare let any one else know it, as the rules were that we had to wear the red flannels. So every Sunday morning we would put the red ones on, because they held inspection on Sunday morning. Captain Pratt and others always looked us over that day very carefully; but as soon as the inspection was through, we would slip into our white underclothes and get ready to attend Sunday School in town.

All the boys and girls were given permission to choose the religious denomination which appealed to them best, so they were at liberty to go where they pleased to Sunday School. Most of us selected the Episcopal Church. I was baptized in that church under the name of Luther.

In our room lived a boy named Kaici Inyanke, or Running Against. While not exactly bad, he was always up to some mischief. His father's name was Black Bear, so when the boy was baptized he took his father's name, while his Christian name was Paul. He is yet living at Pine Ridge Agency, South Dakota. More than once Captain Pratt had to hold Paul up. He would play until the very last minute and then try to clean his shoes and comb his hair, all at once seemingly. On this particular Sunday Paul rushed in and was so busy that he did not get half finished. He had combed his hair, but had applied too much water, which was running down his face, while one of his shoes was cleaned and the other was dirty.

We had been taught to stand erect like soldiers when Captain Pratt, Dr. Givens, and others entered the room for inspection. First, Captain Pratt would "size us up" from head to foot, notice if we had our hair combed nicely, if our clothes were neatly brushed, and if we had cleaned our shoes. Then he would look the room over to see if our beds were made up right, often lifting the mattresses to see that everything was clean underneath. Often they would look into our wooden boxes where we kept our clothes, to see that everything was spick and span.

Paul Black Bear had not been able—as usual—to finish getting ready for inspection, and when Captain Pratt looked at his feet, Paul tried to hide the shoe that was not polished, by putting it behind the other one. Captain Pratt also noticed the water running down his face. We all expected to see Paul get a "calling down," but Captain Pratt only laughed and told Paul to do better next time.

At Carlisle it was the rule that we were not to be permitted to smoke, but Paul smoked every time he had a chance. One day he made a "long smoke" and stood by one of the big fireplaces, puffing away very fast. All at once he got sick at the stomach and fainted. We had to drag him out of the fireplace and pour water on him.

One day our teacher brought some wooden plates into the schoolroom. She told us they were to paint on. She gave me about half a dozen of them. We each received a small box of watercolors. I painted Indian designs on all my plates. On some of them I had a man chasing buffalo, shooting them with the bow and arrow. Others represented a small boy shooting at birds in the trees. When I had them all painted, I gave them back to the teacher. She seemed to be well pleased with my work, and sent them all away somewhere. Possibly some persons yet have those wooden plates which were painted by the first class of Indian boys and girls at Carlisle.

About this time there were many additions to the school from various tribes in other States and from other reservations. We were not allowed to converse in the Indian tongue, and we knew so little English that we had a hard time to get along. With these other tribes coming in, we were doing our best to talk as much English as we could.

One night in December we were all marched down to the chapel. When the doors were opened, how surprised we were! Everything was decorated with green. We all took seats, but we could not keep still. There was a big tree in the room, all trimmed and decorated. We stretched our necks to see everything. Then a minister stood up in front and talked to us, but I did not mind a thing he said—in fact, I could not understand him anyway.

This was our first Christmas celebration, and we were all so happy. I saw the others were getting gifts from off that tree, and I was anxious to get something myself. Finally my name was called, and I received several presents, which had been put on the tree for me by the people for whom I had painted the plates. Others were from my teacher, Miss M. Burgess, and some from my Sunday School teacher, Miss Eggee. I was very happy for all the things I had received.

I now began to realize that I would have to learn the ways of the white man. With that idea in mind, the thought also came to me that I must please my father as well. So my little brain began to work hard. I thought that some day I might be able to become an interpreter for my father, as he could not speak English. Or I thought I might be able to keep books for him if he again started a store. So I worked very hard.

One day they selected a few boys and told us we were to learn trades. I was to be a tinsmith. I did not care for this, but I tried my best to learn this trade. Mr. Walker was our instructor. I was getting along very well. I made hundreds of tin cups, coffee pots, and buckets. These were sent away and issued to the Indians on various reservations.

After I had left the school and returned home, this trade did not benefit me any, as the Indians had plenty of tinware that I had made at school.

Mornings I went to the tin shop, and in the afternoon attended school. I tried several times to drop this trade and go to school the entire day, but Captain Pratt said, "No, you must go to the tin shop—that is all there is to it," so I had to go. Half school and half work took away a great deal of study time. I figure that I spent only about a year and a half in school, while the rest of the time was wasted, as the school was not started properly to begin with. Possibly you wonder why I did not remain longer, but the Government had made an agreement with our parents as to the length of time we were to be away.

A short time later, some boys, myself among the number, were called into one of the schoolrooms. There we found a little white woman. There was a long table in front of her, on which were many packages tied in paper. She opened up one package and it contained a bright, shining horn. Other packages disclosed more horns, but they seemed to be different sizes.

The little white woman picked up a horn and then looked the boys over. Finally she handed it to a boy who she thought might be able to use it. Then she picked out a shorter horn and gave it to me. I learned afterward that it was a B-flat cornet. When she had finished, all the boys had horns in their hands. We were to be taught how to play on them and form a band.

The little woman had a black case with her, which she opened. It held a beautiful horn, and when she blew on it it sounded beautiful. Then she motioned to us that we were to blow our horns. Some of the boys tried to blow from the large end. Although we tried our best, we could not produce a sound from them. She then tried to talk to us, but we did not understand her. Then she showed us how to wet the end of the mouthpiece. We thought she wanted us to spit into the horns, so we did. She finally got so discouraged with us that she started crying.

We just stood there and waited for her to get through, then we all tried again. Finally, some of the boys managed to make a noise through their horns. But if you could have heard it! It was terrible! But we thought we were doing fine.

So now I had more to occupy my attention. In the morning I had one hour to practice for the band. Then I must run to my room and change my clothes and go to work in the tin shop. From there I had to run again to my room and change my clothes and get ready for dinner. After that, I had a little time to study my lessons.

Then the school bell would ring and it was time for school. After that, we played and studied our music. Then we went to bed. All lights had to be out at nine o'clock. The first piece of music our band was able to play was the alphabet, from "a" to "z." It was a great day for us when we were able to play this simple little thing in public. But it was a good thing we were not asked to give an encore, for that was all we knew!

After I had learned to play a little, I was chosen to give all the bugle calls. I had to get up in the morning before the others and arouse everybody by blowing the morning call. Evenings at ten minutes before nine o'clock I blew again. Then all the boys would run for their rooms. At nine o'clock the second call was given, when all lights were turned out and we were supposed to be in bed. Later on I learned the mess call, and eventually I could blow all the calls of the regular army.

I did these duties all the time I was at Carlisle School, so in the early part of 1880, although I was a young boy of but twelve, I was busy learning everything my instructors handed me.

One Sunday morning we were busy getting ready to get to Sunday School in town. Suddenly there was great excitement among some of the boys on the floor below. One of the boys came running upstairs shouting, "Luther Standing Bear's father is here!" Everybody ran downstairs to see my father. We had several tribes at the school now, many of whom had heard of my father, and they were anxious to see him.

When I got downstairs, my father was in the center of a large crowd of the boys, who were all shaking hands with him. I had to fight my way through to reach him. He was so glad to see me, and I was delighted to see him. But our rules were that we were not to speak the Indian language under any consideration. And here was my father, and he could not talk English!

My first act was to write a note to Captain Pratt, asking if he would permit me to speak to my father in the Sioux tongue. I said, "My father is here. Please allow me to speak to him in Indian." Captain Pratt answered, "Yes, my boy; bring your father over to my house."

This was another happy day for me. I took my father over to meet Captain Pratt, who was so glad to see him, and was very respectful to him. Father was so well dressed. He wore a gray suit, nice shoes, and a derby hat. But he wore his hair long. He looked very nice in white men's clothes. He even sported a gold watch and chain. Captain Pratt gave father a room with Robert American Horse, in the boys' quarters. He allowed the boys to talk to him in the Indian tongue, and that pleased the boys very much. Here Father remained for a time with us.

Declaration of Sentiments

Elizabeth Cady Stanton

Elizabeth Cady Stanton (1818-1902) was born in Johnstown, New York and was from an early age involved in various political movements, including abolition and temperance. She is best known, however, for her early advocacy of women's rights and is generally credited as one of the founders of the 19ᵗʰ century women's suffrage (voting rights) movement. In addition, she supported liberalization of divorce laws, the right of women to keep their wages, and equal guardianship of children. The present selection, modeled after the Declaration of Independence, was composed for the 1848 Seneca Falls Convention, the inaugural gathering of the women's suffrage movement. In addition to rearing seven children, she wrote a number of books on the suffrage movement, lectured widely, and ran for Congress in 1866.

When, in the course of human events, it becomes necessary for one portion of the family of man to assume among the people of the earth a position different from that which they have hitherto occupied, but one to which the laws of nature and of nature's God entitle them, a decent respect to the opinions of mankind requires that they should declare the causes that impel them to such a course.

We hold these truths to be self-evident: that all men and women are created equal; that they are endowed by their Creator with certain inalienable rights; that among these are life, liberty, and the pursuit of happiness; that to secure these rights governments are instituted, deriving their just powers from the consent of the governed. Whenever any form of government becomes destructive of these ends, it is the right of those who suffer from it to refuse allegiance to it, and to insist upon the institution of a new government, laying its foundation on such principles, and organizing its powers in such form, as to them shall seem most likely to effect their safety and happiness. Prudence, indeed, will dictate that governments long established should not be changed for light and transient causes; and accordingly all experience hath shown that mankind are more disposed to suffer, while evils are sufferable, than to right themselves by abolishing the forms to which they were accustomed. But when a long train of abuses and usurpations, pursuing invariably the same object evinces a design to reduce them under absolute despotism, it is their duty to throw off such government, and to provide new guards for their future security. Such has been the patient sufferance of the women under this government, and such is now the necessity which constrains them to demand the equal station to which they are entitled.

The history of mankind is a history of repeated injuries and usurpations on the part of man toward woman, having in direct object the establishment of an absolute tyranny over her. To prove this, let facts be submitted to a candid world.

He has never permitted to exercise her inalienable right to the elective franchise.

He has compelled her to submit to laws, in the formation of which she had no voice.

He has withheld from her rights which are given to the most ignorant and degraded men—both natives and foreigners.

Having deprived her of this first right of a citizen, the elective franchise, thereby leaving her without representation in the halls of legislation, he has oppressed her on all sides.

He has made her, if married, in the eye of the law, civilly dead.

He has taken from her all right in property, even to the wages she earns.

He has made her, morally, an irresponsible being, as she can commit many crimes with impunity, provided they be done in the presence of her husband. In the covenant of marriage, she is compelled to promise obedience to her husband, he becoming, to all intents and purposes, her master—the law giving him power to deprive her of her liberty, and to administer chastisement.

He has so framed the laws of divorce, as to what shall be the proper causes, and in case of separation, to whom the guardianship of the children shall be given, as to be wholly regardless of the happiness of women—the law, in all cases, going upon a false supposition of the supremacy of man, and giving all power into his hands.

After depriving her of all rights as a married woman, if single, and the owner of property, he has taxed her to support a government which recognizes her only when her property can be made profitable to it.

He has monopolized nearly all the profitable employments, and from those she is permitted to follow, she receives but a scanty remuneration. He closes against her all the avenues to wealth and distinction which he considers most honorable to himself. As a teacher of theology, medicine, or law, she is not known.

He has denied her the facilities for obtaining a thorough education, all colleges being closed against her.

He allows her in Church, as well as State, but a subordinate position, claiming Apostolic authority for her exclusion from the ministry, and, with some exceptions, from any public participation in the affairs of the Church.

He has created a false public sentiment by giving to the world a different code of morals for men and women, by which moral delinquencies which exclude women from society, are not only tolerated, but deemed of little account in man.

He has usurped the prerogative of Jehovah himself, claiming it as his right to assign for her a sphere of action, when that belongs to her conscience and to her God.

He has endeavored, in every way that he could, to destroy her confidence in her own powers, to lessen her self-respect, and to make her willing to lead a dependent and abject life.

Now, in view of this entire disfranchisement of one-half the people of this county, their social and religious degradation—in view of the unjust laws above mentioned, and because women do feel themselves aggrieved, oppressed, and fraudulently deprived of their most sacred rights, we insist that they have immediate admission to all the rights and privileges which belong to them as citizens of the United States.

In entering upon the great work before us, we anticipate no small amount of misconception, misrepresentation and ridicule: but we shall use every instrumentality within our power to effect our object. We shall employ agents, circulate tracts, petition the State and National legislatures, and endeavor to enlist the pulpit and the press in our behalf. We hope this Convention will be followed by a series of Conventions embracing every part of the country.

1898

Mother Tongue

Amy Tan

Amy Tan (1952–) was born in Oakland, California, to Chinese immigrant parents. Upon the deaths of her older brother and father in 1967 and 1968 from brain tumors, Tan, her mother, and her younger brother moved to Montreux, Switzerland. Tan is perhaps best known for writing The Joy Luck Club *(1989), which was made into a feature film in 1993. This work, Tan's first novel, intertwines the stories of four aging Chinese immigrant women and their four Americanized daughters. The novel explores not only mother-daughter relationships, but also the cultural conflict between immigrant parents and their American children. In much of her work, Tan explores the clash of traditional Chinese and American cultures. Along with* The Joy Luck Club, *her novels, including* The Kitchen God's Wife *(1991),* The Hundred Secret Senses *(1995), and* The Bonesetter's Daughter *(2001), draw heavily from stories Tan's mother recounted about her life in China. Citing her mother as "her inspiration," Tan once told a reporter for the* Seattle Times, *"My books have amounted to taking her stories—a gift to me—and giving them back to her. To me, it was the ultimate thing I ever could have done for myself and my mother." In 1992, Tan adapted one of the stories from* The Joy Luck Club *for a children's book,* The Moon Lady; *her second children's book,* The Chinese Siamese Cat, *was published in 1994 and is the basis for a long-running PBS cartoon.*

In "Mother Tongue," Amy Tan describes the various kinds of English she uses—from the "broken" English she uses in speaking with her mother, to the formal and sophisticated English she employs in public settings. Tan plays upon the meaning of the term "mother tongue," referring both to English as one's native language and to the English her own mother uses, that is, her mother's English, which is not her mother's "mother tongue."

For Amy Tan herself, English is a variety of tongues. English is more than a single and monolithic way of using the language. Tan finds in her mother's "broken" English, for example, a powerful self-presence, even though the mother's use of English is riddled with grammatical errors and idiomatic incongruities. Part of the pleasure of Tan's essay is the way the writer plays off various kinds of English against one another. Part of the essay's power lies in its invitation to see how English provides multiple possibilities for conveying ideas and expressing oneself. An additional but related aspect of Tan's essay is its revelation of culturally conflicting perspectives—and how language, in this case English, both reflects and exacerbates them.

Tan takes up some other issues in this essay as well. She wonders, for example, why so few Asian-American students go into English studies, why so many are directed to math and science. Tan also discusses her aims in writing stories in the various Englishes that she uses with her mother. Among them is her desire to capture an aspect of her mother's language that reveals her mother's "passion, her imagery, the rhythms of her speech, and the nature of her thoughts." In this regard, Tan's essay is a tribute to both her mother and her mother tongue.

I am not a scholar of English or literature. I cannot give you much more than personal opinions on the English language and its variations in this country or others.

I am a writer. And by that definition, I am someone who has always loved language. I am fascinated by language in daily life. I spend a great deal of my time thinking about the power of language—the way it can evoke an emotion, a visual image, a complex idea, or a simple truth. Language is the tool of my trade. And I use them all—all the Englishes I grew up with.

Recently, I was made keenly aware of the different Englishes I do use. I was giving a talk to a large group of people, the same talk I had already given to half a dozen other groups. The nature of the talk was about my writing, my life, and my book, *The Joy Luck Club*. The talk was going along well enough, until I remembered one major difference that made the whole talk sound wrong. My mother was in the room. And it was perhaps the first time she had heard me give a lengthy speech, using the kind of English I have never used with her. I was saying things like "The intersection of memory upon imagination" and "There is an aspect of my fiction that relates to thus-and-thus"—

a speech filled with carefully wrought grammatical phrases, burdened, it suddenly seemed to me, with nominalized forms, past perfect tenses, conditional phrases, all the forms of standard English that I had learned in school and through books, the forms of English I did not use at home with my mother.

Just last week, I was walking down the street with my mother, and I again found myself conscious of the English I was using, the English I do use with her. We were talking about the price of new and used furniture and I heard myself saying this: "Not waste money that way." My husband was with us as well, and he didn't notice any switch in my English. And then I realized why. It's because over the twenty years we've been together I've often used that same kind of English with him, and sometimes he even uses it with me. It has become our language of intimacy, a different sort of English that relates to family talk, the language I grew up with.

So you'll have some idea of what this family talk I heard sounds like, I'll quote what my mother said during a recent conversation which I videotaped and then transcribed. During this conversation, my mother was talking about a political gangster in Shanghai who had the same last name as her family's, Du, and how the gangster in his early years wanted to be adopted by her family, which was rich by comparison. Later, the gangster became more powerful, far richer than my mother's family, and one day showed up at my mother's wedding to pay his respects. Here's what she said in part:

"Du Yusong having business like fruit stand. Like off the street kind. He is Du like Du Zong—but not Tsung-ming, Island people. The local people call putong, the river east side, he belong to that side local people. That man want to ask Du Zong father take him in like become own family Du Zong father wasn't look down on him. But didn't take seriously, until that man big like become a mafia. Now important person, very hard to inviting him. Chinese way, came only to show respect, don't stay for dinner. Respect for making big celebration, he shows up. Mean gives lots of respect. Chinese custom. Chinese social life that way. If too important won't have to stay too long. He come to my wedding. I didn't see, I heard it. I gone to boy's side, they have YMCA dinner. Chinese age I was nineteen."

You should know that my mother's expressive command of English belies how much she actually understands. She reads the *Forbes* report, listens to *Wall Street Week*, converses daily with her stockbroker, reads all of Shirley MacLaine's books with ease—all kinds of things I can't begin to understand. Yet some of my friends tell me they understand 50 percent of what my mother says. Some say they understand 80 to 90 percent. Some say they understand none of it, as if she were speaking pure Chinese. But to me, my mother's English is perfectly clear, perfectly natural. It's my mother tongue. Her language, as I hear it, is vivid, direct, full of observation and imagery. That was the language that helped shape the way I saw things, expressed things, made sense of the world.

Lately, I've been giving more thought to the kind of English my mother speaks. Like others, I have described it to people as "broken" or "fractured" English. But I wince when I say that. It has always bothered me that I can think of no other way to describe it other than "broken," as if it were damaged and needed to be fixed, as if it lacked a certain wholeness and soundness. I've heard other terms used, "limited English," for example. But they seem just as bad, as if everything is limited, including people's perceptions of the limited English speaker.

I know this for a fact, because when I was growing up, my mother's "limited" English limited *my* perception of her. I was ashamed of her English. I believed that her English reflected the quality of what she had to say. That is, because she expressed them imperfectly her thoughts were imperfect. And I had plenty of empirical evidence to support me: the fact that people in department stores, at banks, and at restaurants did not take her seriously, did not give her good service, pretended not to understand her, or even acted as if they did not hear her.

My mother has long realized the limitations of her English as well. When I was fifteen, she used to have me call people on the phone to pretend I was she. In this guise, I was forced to ask for information or even to complain and yell at people who had been rude to her. One time it was a call to her Stockbroker in New York. She had cashed out her small portfolio and it just so happened we were going to go to New York the next week, our very first trip outside California. I had to get on the phone and say in an adolescent voice that was not very convincing, "This is Mrs. Tan."

And my mother was standing in the back whispering loudly, "Why he don't send me check, already two weeks late. So mad he lie to me, losing me money."

And then I said in perfect English, "Yes, I'm getting rather concerned. You had agreed to send the check two weeks ago, but it hasn't arrived."

Then she began to talk more loudly. "What he want, I come to New York tell him front of his boss, you cheating me?" And I was trying to calm her down, make her be quiet, while telling the stockbroker, "I can't tolerate any more excuses. If I don't receive the check immediately, I am going to have to speak to your manager when I'm in New York next week." And sure enough, the following week there we were in front of this astonished stockbroker, and I was sitting there red-faced and quiet, and my mother, the real Mrs. Tan, was shouting at his boss in her impeccable broken English.

We used a similar routine just five days ago, for a situation that was far less humorous. My mother had gone to the hospital for an appointment, to find out about a benign brain tumor a CAT scan had revealed a month ago. She said she had spoken very good English, her best English, no mistakes.

Still, she said, the hospital did not apologize when they said they had lost the CAT scan and she had come for nothing. She said they did not seem to have any sympathy when she told them she was anxious to know the exact diagnosis, since her husband and son had both died of brain tumors. She said they would not give her any more information until the next time and she would have to make another appointment for that. So she said she would not leave until the doctor called her daughter. She wouldn't budge. And when the doctor finally called her daughter, me, who spoke in perfect English—lo and behold—we had assurances the CAT scan would be found, promises that a conference call on Monday would be held, and apologies for any suffering my mother had gone through for a most regrettable mistake.

I think my mother's English almost had an effect on limiting my possibilities in life as well. Sociologists and linguists probably will tell you that a person's developing language skills are more influenced by peers. But I do think that the language spoken in the family, especially in immigrant families which are more insular, plays a large role in shaping the language of the child. And I believe that it affected my results on achievement tests, IQ tests, and the SAT. While my English skills were never judged as poor, compared to math, English could not be considered my strong suit. In grade school I did moderately well, getting perhaps B's, sometimes B-pluses, in English and scoring perhaps in the sixtieth or seventieth percentile on achievement tests. But those scores were not good enough to override the opinion that my true abilities lay in math and science, because in those areas I achieved A's and scored in the ninetieth percentile or higher.

This was understandable. Math is precise: there is only one correct answer. Whereas, for me at least, the answers on English tests were always a judgment call, a matter of opinion and personal experience. Those tests were constructed around items like fill-in-the-blank sentence completion, such as "Even though Tom was _____, Mary thought he was _____." And the correct answer always seemed to be the most bland combinations of thoughts, for example, "Even though Tom was shy, Mary thought he was charming," with the grammatical structure "even though" limiting the correct answer to some sort of semantic opposites, so you wouldn't get answers like, "Even though Tom was foolish, Mary thought he was ridiculous." Well, according to my mother, there were very few limitations as to what Tom could have been and what Mary might have thought of him. So I never did well on tests like that.

The same was true with word analogies, pairs of words in which you were supposed to find some sort of logical, semantic relationship—for example, "*Sunset* is to *nightfall* as _____ is to _____." And here you would be presented with a list of four possible pairs, one of which showed the same kind of relationship: *red* is to *stoplight*, *bus* is to *arrival*, *chills* is to *fever*, *yawn* is to *boring*.

Well, I could never think that way. I knew what the tests were asking, but I could not block out of my mind the images already created by the first pair, "*sunset* is to *nightfall*"—and I would see a burst of colors against a darkening sky, the moon rising, the lowering of a curtain of stars. And all the other pairs of words—red, bus, stoplight, boring—just threw up a mass of confusing images, making it impossible for me to sort out something as logical as saying: "A sunset precedes nightfall" is the same as "a chill precedes a fever." The only way I would have gotten that answer right would have been to imagine an associative situation, for example, my being disobedient and staying out past sunset, catching a chill at night, which turns into feverish pneumonia as punishment, which indeed did happen to me.

I have been thinking about all this lately, about my mother's English, about achievement tests. Because lately I've been asked, as a writer, why there are not more Asian Americans represented in American literature. Why are there few Asian Americans enrolled in creative writing programs? Why do so many Chinese students go into engineering? Well, these are broad sociological questions I can't begin to answer. But I have noticed in surveys—in fact, just last week—that Asian students, as a whole, always do significantly better on Math achievement tests than in English. And this makes me think that there are other Asian-American students whose English spoken in the home might also be described as "broken" or "limited." And perhaps they also have teachers who are steering them away from writing and into math and science, which is what happened to me.

Fortunately, I happen to be rebellious in nature and enjoy the challenge of disproving assumptions made about me. I became an English major my first year in college, after being enrolled as pre-med. I started writing nonfiction as a freelancer the week after I was told by my former boss that writing was my worst skill and I should hone my talents toward account management.

But it wasn't until 1985 that I finally began to write fiction. And at first I wrote using what I thought to be wittily crafted sentences, sentences that would finally prove I had mastery over the English language. Here's an example from the first draft of a story that later made its way into *The Joy Luck Club*, but without this line: "That was my mental quandary in its nascent state." A terrible line, which I can barely pronounce.

Fortunately, for reasons I won't get into today, I later decided I should envision a reader for the stories I would write. And the reader I decided upon was my mother, because these were stories about mothers. So with this reader in mind—and in fact she did read my early drafts—I began to write stories using all the Englishes I grew up with: the English I spoke to my mother, which for lack of a better term might be described as "simple"; the English she used with me, which for lack of a better term might be described as "broken," my translation of her Chinese, which could certainly be described as "watered down," and what I imagined to be her translation of her Chinese if she could speak in perfect English, her internal language, and for that I sought to preserve the essence, but neither an English nor a Chinese structure. I wanted to capture what language ability tests can never reveal: her intent, her passion, her imagery, the rhythms of her speech, and the nature of her thoughts.

Apart from what any critic had to say about my writing, I knew I had succeeded where it counted when my mother finished reading my book and gave me her verdict: "So easy to read."

The Damned
Human Race

Mark Twain

Mark Twain (1835–1910) was born Samuel Clemens in Florida, Missouri. Soon after, his family moved to the Mississippi River town of Hannibal, Missouri, where he grew up watching steamboats ply the river and dreamt of becoming a riverboat pilot. He did become a pilot briefly in the 1850s, but his earliest jobs were in the newspaper business as printer and reporter. In 1865, he wrote "The Celebrated Jumping Frog of Calaveras County," the piece which first brought him national recognition and which marked him as the great American humorist that he was to remain throughout his career. In the 1870s and early 1880s, his most prolific and successful period as a writer, he published the works for which he is best known, among them The Gilded Age *(1873),* The Adventures of Tom Sawyer *(1876), and* The Adventures of Huckleberry Finn *(1884). Throughout his early and middle periods, Twain's artistic vision was largely an optimistic one, but this was altered by a series of painful events that left him deeply embittered. The most tragic of these were the deaths of his eldest daughter, Susy; his wife, Olivia; and his youngest daughter, Jean—all between 1896 and 1909. It is generally agreed that these personal losses influenced the deeply pessimistic vision of the human condition that characterizes his latest writings. Among these was the present selection, "The Damned Human Race" (1909), which was published posthumously many decades after the author's death, in a collection called* Letters from the Earth *(1962).*

I have been studying the traits and dispositions of the "lower animals" (so-called), and contrasting them with the traits and dispositions of man. I find the result humiliating to me. For it obliges me to renounce my allegiance to the Darwinian[1] theory of the Ascent of Man from the Lower Animals; since it now seems plain to me that that theory ought to be vacated in favor of a new and truer one, this new and truer one to be named the Descent of Man from the Higher Animals.

In proceeding toward this unpleasant conclusion I have not guessed or speculated or conjectured, but have used what is commonly called the scientific method. That is to say, I have subjected every postulate that presented itself to the crucial test of actual experiment, and have adopted it or rejected it according to the result. Thus I verified and established each step of my course in its turn before advancing to the next. These experiments were made in the London Zoological Gardens, and covered many months of painstaking and fatiguing work.

Before particularizing any of the experiments, I wish to state one or two things which seem to more properly belong in this place than further along. This in the interest of clearness. The massed experiments established to my satisfaction certain generalizations, to wit:

1. That the human race is of one distinct species. It exhibits slight variations—in color, stature, mental caliber, and so on—due to climate, environment, and so forth; but it is a species by itself, and not to be confounded with any other.

2. That the quadrupeds are a distinct family, also. This family exhibits variations—in color, size, food preferences and so on; but it is a family by itself.

3. That the other families—the birds, the fishes, the insects, the reptiles, etc.—are more or less distinct, also. They are in the procession. They are links in the chain which stretches down from the higher animals to man at the bottom.

Some of my experiments were quite curious. In the course of my reading I had come across a case where, many years ago, some hunters on our Great Plains organized a buffalo hunt for the entertainment of an English earl— that, and to provide some fresh meat for his larder. They had charming sport. They killed seventy-two of those great animals; and ate part of one of them and left the seventy-one to rot. In order to determine the difference between an anaconda and an earl—if any—I caused seven young calves to be turned into the anaconda's cage. The grateful reptile immediately crushed one of them and swallowed it, then lay back satisfied. It showed no further interest in the calves, and no disposition to harm them. I tried this experiment with other anacondas; always with the same result. The fact stood proven that the difference between an earl and an anaconda is that the earl is cruel and the anaconda isn't; and that the earl wantonly destroys what he has no use for, but the anaconda doesn't. This seemed to suggest that the anaconda was not descended from the earl. It also seemed to suggest that the earl was descended from the anaconda, and had lost a good deal in the transition.

I was aware that many men who have accumulated more millions of money than they can ever use have shown a rabid hunger for more, and have not scrupled to cheat the ignorant and the helpless out of their poor servings in order to partially appease that appetite. I furnished a hundred different kinds of wild and tame animals the opportunity to accumulate vast stores of food, but none of them would do it. The squirrels and bees and certain birds made accumulations, but stopped when they had gathered a winter's supply, and could not be persuaded to add to it either honestly or by chicane. In order to bolster up a tottering reputation the ant pretended to store up supplies, but I was not deceived. I know the ant. These experiments convinced me that there is this difference between man and the higher animals: He is avaricious and miserly, they are not.

In the course of my experiments I convinced myself that among the animals man is the only one that harbors insults and injuries, broods over them, waits till a chance offers, then takes revenge. The passion of revenge is unknown to the higher animals.

Roosters keep harems, but it is by consent of their concubines; therefore, no wrong is done. Men keep harems, but it is by brute force, privileged by atrocious laws which the other sex were allowed no hand in making. In this matter man occupies a far lower place than the rooster.

Cats are loose in their morals, but not consciously so. Man, in his descent from the cat, has brought the cat's looseness with him but has left the unconsciousness behind—the saving grace which excuses the cat. The cat is innocent, man is not.

Indecency, vulgarity, obscenity—these are strictly confined to man; he invented them. Among the higher animals there is no trace of them. They hide nothing; they are not ashamed. Man, with his soiled mind, covers himself. He will not even enter a drawing room with his breast and back naked, so alive are he and his mates to indecent suggestion. Man is "The Animal that Laughs." But so does the monkey, as Mr. Darwin pointed out; and so does the Australian bird that is called the laughing jackass. No—Man is the Animal that Blushes. He is the only one that does it—or has occasion to.

At the head of this article[2] we see how "three monks were burnt to death" a few days ago, and a prior "put to death with atrocious cruelty." Do we inquire into the details? No; or we should find out that the prior was subjected to unprintable mutilations. Man—when he is a North American Indian—gouges out his prisoner's eyes; when he is King John, with a nephew to render untroublesome, he uses a red-hot iron; when he is a religious zealot dealing with heretics in the Middle Ages, he skins his captive alive and scatters salt on his back; in the first Richard's time he shuts up a multitude of Jew families in a tower and sets fire to it; in Columbus's time he captures a family of Spanish Jews and—but *that* is not printable; in our day in England a man is fined ten shillings for beating his mother nearly to death with a chair, and another man is fined forty shillings for having four pheasant eggs in his possession without being able to satisfactorily explain how he got them. Of all the animals, man is the only one that is cruel. He is the only one that inflicts pain for the pleasure of doing it. It is a trait that is not known to the higher animals. The cat plays with the frightened mouse; but she has this excuse, that she does not know that the mouse is suffering. The cat is moderate—unhumanly moderate: She only scares the mouse, she does not hurt it; she doesn't dig out its eyes, or tear off its skin, or drive splinters under its nails—manfashion; when she is done playing with it she makes a sudden meal of it and puts it out of its trouble. Man is the Cruel Animal. He is alone in that distinction.

The higher animals engage in individual fights, but never in organized masses. Man is the only animal that deals in that atrocity of atrocities, War. He is the only one that gathers his brethren about him and goes forth in cold blood and with calm pulse to exterminate his kind. He is the only animal that for sordid wages will march out, as the Hessians did in our Revolution,[3] and as the boyish Prince Napoleon did in the Zulu war,[4] and help to slaughter strangers of his own species who have done him no harm and with whom he has no quarrel.

Man is the only animal that robs his helpless fellow of his country—takes possession of it and drives him out of it or destroys him. Man has done this in all the ages. There is not an acre of ground on the globe that is in possession of its rightful owner, or that has not been taken away from owner after owner, cycle after cycle, by force and bloodshed.

Man is the only Slave. And he is the only animal who enslaves. He has always been a slave in one form or another, and has always held other slaves in bondage under him in one way or another. In our day he is always some man's slave for wages, and does that man's work; and this slave has other slaves under him for minor wages, and they do *his* work. The higher animals are the only ones who exclusively do their own work and provide their own living.

Man is the only Patriot. He sets himself apart in his own country, under his own flag, and sneers at the other nations, and keeps multitudinous uniformed assassins on hand at heavy expense to grab slices of other people's countries, and keep *them* from grabbing slices of *his*. And in the intervals between campaigns he washes the blood off his hands and works for "the universal brotherhood of man"—with his mouth.

Man is the Religious Animal. He is the only Religious Animal. He is the only animal that has the True Religion—several of them. He is the only animal that loves his neighbor as himself, and cuts his throat if his theology isn't straight. He has made a graveyard of the globe in trying his honest best to smooth his brother's path to happiness and heaven. He was at it in the time of the Caesars, he was at it in Mahomet's time, he was at it in the time of the Inquisition, he was at it in France a couple of centuries, he was at it in England in Mary's day,[5] he has been at it ever since he first saw the light, he is at it today in Crete—as per the telegrams quoted above—he will be at it somewhere else tomorrow. The higher animals have no religion. And we are told that they are going to be left out, in the Hereafter. I wonder why? It seems questionable taste.

Man is the Reasoning Animal. Such is the claim. I think it is open to dispute. Indeed, my experiments have proven to me that he is the Unreasoning Animal. Note his history, as sketched above. It seems plain to me that whatever he is he is *not* a reasoning animal. His record is the fantastic record of a maniac. I consider that the strongest count against his intelligence is the fact that with that record back of him he blandly sets himself up as the head animal of the lot: Whereas by his own standards he is the bottom one.

In truth, man is incurably foolish. Simple things which the other animals easily learn, he is incapable of learning. Among my experiments was this. In an hour I taught a cat and a dog to be friends. I put them in a cage. In another hour I taught them to be friends with a rabbit. In the course of two days I was able to add a fox, a goose, a squirrel and some doves. Finally a monkey. They lived together in peace; even affectionately.

Next, in another cage I confined an Irish Catholic from Tipperary, and as soon as he seemed tame I added a Scotch Presbyterian from Aberdeen. Next a Turk from Constantinople; a Greek Christian from Crete; an Armenian; a Methodist from the wilds of Arkansas; a Buddhist from China; a Brahman from Benares. Finally, a Salvation Army Colonel from Wapping. Then I stayed away two whole days. When I came back to note results, the cage of Higher Animals was all right, but in the other there was but a chaos of gory odds and ends of turbans and fezzes and plaids and bones and flesh—not a specimen left alive. These Reasoning Animals had disagreed on a theological detail and carried the matter to a Higher Court.

One is obliged to concede that in true loftiness of character, Man cannot claim to approach even the meanest of the Higher Animals. It is plain that he is constitutionally incapable of approaching that altitude; that he is constitutionally afflicted with a Defect which must make such approach forever impossible, for it is manifest that this defect is permanent in him, indestructible, ineradicable.

I find this Defect to be *the Moral Sense.* He is the only animal that has it. It is the secret of his degradation. It is the quality *which enables him to do wrong.* It has no other office. It is incapable of performing any other function. It could never have been intended to perform any other. Without it, man could do no wrong. He would rise at once to the level of the Higher Animals.

Since the Moral Sense has but the one office, the one capacity—to enable man to do wrong—it is plainly without value to him. It is as valueless to him as is disease. In fact, it manifestly *is* a disease. *Rabies is* bad, but it is not so bad as this disease. Rabies enables a man to do a thing which he could not do when in a healthy state: kill his neighbor with a poisonous bite. No one is the better man for having rabies. The Moral Sense enables a man to do wrong. It enables him to do wrong in a thousand ways. Rabies is an innocent disease, compared to the Moral Sense. No one, then, can be the better man for having the Moral Sense. What, now, do we find the Primal Curse to have been? Plainly what it was in the beginning: the infliction upon man of the Moral Sense; the ability to distinguish good from evil; and with it, necessarily, the ability to *do* evil; for there can be no evil act without the presence of consciousness of it in the doer of it.

And so I find that we have descended and degenerated, from some far ancestor—some microscopic atom wandering at its pleasure between the mighty horizons of a drop of water perchance—insect by insect, animal by animal, reptile by reptile, down the long highway of smirchless innocence, till we have reached the bottom stage of development nameable as the Human Being. Below us—nothing. Nothing but the Frenchman.

There is only one possible stage below the Moral Sense; that is the Immoral Sense. The Frenchman has it. Man is but little lower than the angels. This definitely locates him. He is between the angels and the French.

Man seems to be a rickety poor sort of a thing, any way you take him; a kind of British Museum of infirmities and inferiorities. He is always undergoing repairs. A machine that was as unreliable as he is would have no market. On top of his specialty—the Moral Sense—are piled a multitude of minor infirmities; such a multitude, indeed, that one may broadly call them countless. The higher animals get their teeth without pain or inconvenience. Man gets his through months and months of cruel torture; and at a time of life when he is but ill able to bear it. As soon as he has got them they must all be pulled out again, for they were of no value in the first place, not worth the loss of a night's rest. The second set will answer for a while, by being reinforced occasionally with rubber or plugged up with gold; but he will never get a set which can really be depended on till a dentist makes him one. This set will be called "false" teeth as if he had ever worn any other kind.

In a wild state—a natural state—the Higher Animals have a few diseases; diseases of little consequence; the main one is old age. But man starts in as a child and lives on diseases till the end, as a regular diet. He has mumps, measles, whooping cough, croup, tonsillitis, diphtheria, scarlet fever, almost as a matter of course. Afterward, as he goes along, his life continues to be threatened at every turn: by colds, coughs, asthma, bronchitis, itch, cholera, cancer, consumption, yellow fever, bilious fever, typhus fevers, hay fever; ague, chilblains, piles, inflammation of the entrails, indigestion, toothache, earache, deafness, dumbness, blindness, influenza, chicken pox, cowpox, smallpox, liver complaint, constipation, bloody flux, warts, pimples, boils, carbuncles, abscesses, bunions, corns, tumors, fistulas, pneumonia, softening of the brain, melancholia and fifteen other kinds of insanity; dysentery, jaundice, diseases of the heart, the bones, the skin, the scalp, the spleen, the kidneys, the nerves, the brain, the blood; scrofula, paralysis, leprosy, neuralgia, palsy, fits, headache, thirteen kinds of rheumatism, forty-six of gout, and a formidable supply of gross and unprintable disorders of one sort and another. Also—but why continue the list? The mere names of the agents appointed to keep this shackly machine out of repair would hide him from sight if printed on his body in the smallest type known to the founder's art. He is but a basket of pestilent corruption provided for the support and entertainment of swarming armies of bacilli—armies commissioned to rot him and destroy him, and each army equipped with a special detail of the work. The process of waylaying him, persecuting him, rotting him, killing him, begins with his first breath, and there is no mercy, no pity, no truce till he draws his last one.

Look at the workmanship of him, in certain of its particulars. What are his tonsils for? They perform no useful function; they have no value. They have no business there. They are but a trap. They have but the one office, the one industry: to provide tonsillitis and quinsy and such things for the possessor of them. And what is the vermiform appendix for? It has no value; it cannot perform any useful service. It is but an ambuscaded enemy whose sole interest in life is to lie in wait for stray grapeseeds and employ them to breed strangulated hernia. And what are the male's mammals for? For business, they are out of the question; as an ornament, they are a mistake. What is his beard for? It performs no useful function; it is a nuisance and a discomfort; all nations hate it; all nations persecute it with a razor. And because it is a nuisance and a discomfort, Nature never allows the supply of it to fall short, in any man's case, between puberty and the grave. You never see a man baldheaded on his chin. But his hair! It is a graceful ornament, it is a comfort, it is the best of all protections against certain perilous ailments, man prizes it above emeralds and rubies. And because of these things Nature puts it on, half the time, so that it won't stay. Man's sight, smell, hearing, sense of locality—how inferior they are. The condor sees a corpse at five miles; man has no telescope that can do it. The bloodhound follows a scent that is two days old. The robin hears the earthworm burrowing his course under the ground. The cat, deported in a closed basket, finds its way home again through twenty miles of country which it has never seen.

Certain functions lodged in the other sex perform in a lamentably inferior way as compared with the performance of the same functions in the Higher Animals. In the human being, menstruation, gestation and parturition are terms which stand for horrors. In the Higher Animals these things are hardly even inconveniences.

For style, look at the Bengal tiger—that ideal of grace, beauty, physical perfection, majesty. And then look at Man—that poor thing. He is the Animal of the Wig, the Trepanned Skull, the Ear Trumpet, the Glass Eye, the Pasteboard Nose, the Porcelain Teeth, the Silver Windpipe, the Wooden Leg—a creature that is mended and patched all over, from top to bottom. If he can't get renewals of his bric-a-brac in the next world, what will he look like?

He has just one stupendous superiority. In his intellect he is supreme. The Higher Animals cannot touch him there. It is curious, it is noteworthy, that no heaven has ever been offered him wherein his one sole superiority was provided with a chance to enjoy itself. Even when he himself has imagined a heaven, he has never made provision in it for intellectual joys. It is a striking omission. It seems a tacit confession that heavens are provided for the Higher Animals alone. This is matter for thought; and for serious thought. And it is full of a grim suggestion: that we are not as important, perhaps, as we had all along supposed we were.

Endnotes

1. Charles Darwin (1809–1882) published *The Descent of Man* in 1871, a highly controversial book in which he argued that humankind had descended from "lower" forms of life. —EDS.

2. In his nonfiction Twain often introduced newsclippings as evidence of human atrocity. In this instance the article has been lost, but Twain is most likely referring to the religious persecutions that followed the 1897 Cretan revolt. —EDS.

3. **Revolution.** Approximately 17,000 mercenaries from Hesse, a part of Germany, fought for the British during the American Revolution. —EDS.

4. **Zulu war:** Napolean III's son died while fighting for the British during the 1879 Zulu rebellion in what is now the Republic of South Africa. Great Britain annexed the Zulu territory shortly after, and that is the context for Twain's remarks in the next paragraph. —EDS.

5. **Mary's day:** In the time of Mary I, who reigned as Queen of England between 1553 and mid 1558; her vigorous persecution of Protestants earned her the nickname "Bloody Mary." —EDS.

The Perimeter of
Ignorance

Neil deGrasse Tyson

Neil deGrasse Tyson (1958 —) believes that we all need to be more scientifically literate in order for our culture to progress. Tyson is an astrophysicist who has become a world-renowned "science communicator," as he calls himself. He was born and raised in New York City, where he still lives with his wife and two children. He is both a scientist and a gifted speaker who regularly goes on lecture tours to explain scientific ideas. His ability to get across these ideas in down-to-earth, and often humorous ways, has made him very popular with a broad audience (though his idea that Pluto is not a planet has earned him some hate mail, even from third graders). Tyson is a graduate of Harvard and Columbia Universities and is the Frederick P. Rose Director of the Hayden Planetarium where, among other things, visitors can learn about our eight planet solar system.

In 2013, Tyson became the host for the series Cosmos: A Spacetime Odyssey, *an updated version of Carl Sagan's* Cosmos: A Personal Voyage, *a television series popular in the 1970s. That popularity came with some controversy when Sagan's description of the cosmos raised questions among some in the audience about the scientist's thoughts on God. When asked whether he believed in God, Sagan, who was fond of saying that we are made of "star stuff," responded famously that "extraordinary claims demand extraordinary evidence." (He said the same thing when asked whether he believed in U.F.O visitations.)*

Sagan (now deceased) and Tyson met when Tyson was a young man just deciding to become a scientist. They both shared a love of the universe and the desire to introduce it to others. With Tyson's subsequent inheritance of the Cosmos *mantle, came the same inevitable questions that were posed to his predecessor, this time concerning the divine or "intelligent design" of the universe. Tyson has responded to what he calls a "God-of-the-gaps" approach to explaining what we do not know, declaring, "I don't even care if someone wants to say, 'You don't understand that; God did it.' That doesn't even bother me. What would bother me is if you were so content in that answer that you no longer had curiosity to learn how it happened. The day you stop looking because you're content God did it, I don't need you in the lab."*

In the following essay, which first appeared in the November, 2005 issue of Natural History *magazine, Tyson elaborates more fully. He demonstrates that some of the greatest scientists in history, Ptolemy, Galileo, and Newton among them, have only started talking about God when they have reached the limit of their understanding of something, what Tyson calls "The Perimeter of Ignorance." Tyson believes that this use of the idea of a divine designer as a place-holder, not only often marks the stopping point of scientific progress, it may, in fact, become an obstacle to it.*

Writing in centuries past, many scientists felt compelled to wax poetic about cosmic mysteries and God's handiwork. Perhaps one should not be surprised at this: most scientists back then, as well as many scientists today, identify themselves as spiritually devout.

But a careful reading of older texts, particularly those concerned with the universe itself, shows that the authors invoke divinity only when they reach the boundaries of their understanding. They appeal to a higher power only when staring into the ocean of their own ignorance. They call on God only from the lonely and precarious edge of incomprehension. Where they feel certain about their explanations, however, God gets hardly a mention.

Let's start at the top. Isaac Newton was one of the greatest intellects the world has ever seen. His laws of motion and his universal law of gravitation, conceived in the mid-seventeenth century, account for cosmic phenomena that had eluded philosophers for millennia. Through those laws, one could understand the gravitational attraction of bodies in a system, and thus come to understand orbits.

In the *Principia*, Newton distinguishes between hypotheses and experimental philosophy, and declares, "Hypotheses, whether metaphysical or physical, whether of occult qualities or mechanical, have no place in experimental philosophy." What he wants is data, "inferr'd from the phænomena." But in the absence of data, at the border between what he could explain and what he

could only honor—the causes he could identify and those he could not—
Newton rapturously invokes God:

> Eternal and Infinite, Onmipotent and Omniscient; . . . he governs all
> things, and knows all things that are or can be done. . . . We know him
> only by his most wise and excellent contrivances of things, and final
> causes; we admire him for his perfections; but we reverence and adore
> him on account of his dominion.

A century later, the French astronomer and mathematician Pierre-Simon de
Laplace confronted Newton's dilemma of unstable orbits head-on. Rather
than view the mysterious stability of the solar system as the unknowable work
of God, Laplace declared it a scientific challenge. In his multipart masterpiece,
Mécanique Céleste, the first volume of which appeared in 1798, Laplace
demonstrates that the solar system is stable over periods of time longer than
Newton could predict. To do so, Laplace pioneered a new kind of mathematics called perturbation theory, which enabled him to examine the cumula-
tive effects of many small forces. According to an oft-repeated but probably
embellished account, when Laplace gave a copy of Mécanique Céleste to his
physics-literate friend Napoleon Bonaparte, Napoleon asked him what role
God played in the construction and regulation of the heavens. "Sire," Laplace
replied, "I have no need of that hypothesis."

Laplace notwithstanding, plenty of scientists besides Newton have called
on God—or the gods—wherever their comprehension fades to ignorance.
Consider the second-century A.D. Alexandrian astronomer Ptolemy. Armed
with a description, but no real understanding, of what the planets were doing
up there, he could not contain his religious fervor:

> I know that I am mortal by nature, and ephemeral; but when I trace,
> at my pleasure, the windings to and fro of the heavenly bodies, I no
> longer touch Earth with my feet: I stand in the presence of Zeus him-
> self and take my fill of ambrosia.

Or consider the seventeenth-century Dutch astronomer Christian Huygens,
whose achievements include constructing the first working pendulum clock
and discovering the rings of Saturn. In his charming book *The Celestial Worlds
Discover'd*, posthumously published in 1696, most of the opening chapter celebrates all that was then known of planetary orbits, shapes, and sizes, as well
as the planets' relative brightness and presumed rockiness. The book even
includes foldout charts illustrating the structure of the solar system. God is
absent from this discussion—even though a mere century earlier, before
Newton's achievements, planetary orbits were supreme mysteries.

Celestial Worlds also brims with speculations about life in the solar system,
and that's where Huygens raises questions to which he has no answer. That's

where he mentions the biological conundrums of the day, such as the origin of life's complexity. And sure enough, because seventeenth-century physics was more advanced than seventeenth-century biology, Huygens invokes the hand of God only when he talks about biology:

> I suppose no body will deny but that there's somewhat more of Contrivance, somewhat more of Miracle in the production and growth of Plants and Animals than in lifeless heaps of inanimate Bodies. . . . For the finger of God, and the Wisdom of Divine Providence, is in them much more clearly manifested than in the other.

Today secular philosophers call that kind of divine invocation "God of the gaps"—which comes in handy, because there has never been a shortage of gaps in people's knowledge.

As reverent as Newton, Huygens, and other great scientists of earlier centuries may have been, they were also empiricists. They did not retreat from the conclusions their evidence forced them to draw, and when their discoveries conflicted with prevailing articles of faith, they upheld the discoveries. That doesn't mean it was easy: sometimes they met fierce opposition, as did Galileo, who had to defend his telescopic evidence against formidable objections drawn from both scripture and "common" sense.

Galileo clearly distinguished the role of religion from the role of science. To him, religion was the service of God and the salvation of souls, whereas science was the source of exact observations and demonstrated truths. In a long, famous, bristly letter written in the summer of 1615 to the Grand Duchess Christina of Tuscany (but, like so many epistles of the day, circulated among the literati), he quotes, in his own defense, an unnamed yet sympathetic church official saying that the Bible "tells you how to go to heaven, not how the heavens go."

The letter to the duchess leaves no doubt about where Galileo stood on the literal word of the Holy Writ:

> In expounding the Bible if one were always to confine oneself to the unadorned grammatical meaning, one might fall into error. . . .

> Nothing physical which . . . demonstrations prove to us, ought to be called in question (much less condemned) upon the testimony of biblical passages which may have some different meaning beneath their words. . . .

> I do not feel obliged to believe that the same God who has endowed us with senses, reason and intellect has intended us to forgo their use.

A rare exception among scientists, Galileo saw the unknown as a place to explore rather than as an eternal mystery controlled by the hand of God.

As long as the celestial sphere was generally regarded as the domain of the divine, the fact that mere mortals could not explain its workings could safely be cited as proof of the higher wisdom and power of God. But beginning in the sixteenth century, the work of Copernicus, Kepler, Galileo, and Newton—not to mention Maxwell, Heisenberg, Einstein, and everybody else who discovered fundamental laws of physics—provided rational explanations for an increasing range of phenomena. Little by little, the universe was subjected to the methods and tools of science, and became a demonstrably knowable place.

Then, in what amounts to a stunning yet unheralded philosophical inversion, throngs of ecclesiastics and scholars began to declare that it was the laws of physics themselves that served as proof of the wisdom and power of God.

One popular theme of the seventeenth and eighteenth centuries was the "clockwork universe"—an ordered, rational, predictable mechanism fashioned and run by God and his physical laws. The early telescopes, which all relied on visible light, did little to undercut that image of an ordered system. The Moon revolved around Earth. Earth and other planets rotated on their axes and revolved around the Sun. The stars shone. The nebulae floated freely in space.

Not until the nineteenth century was it evident that visible light is just one band of a broad spectrum of electromagnetic radiation—the band that human beings just happen to see. Infrared was discovered in 1800, ultraviolet in 1801, radio waves in 1888, X rays in 1895, and gamma rays in 1900. Decade by decade in the following century, new kinds of telescopes came into use, fitted with detectors that could "see" these formerly invisible parts of the electromagnetic spectrum. Now astrophysicists began to unmask the true character of the universe.

Turns out that some celestial bodies give off more light in the invisible bands of the spectrum than in the visible. And the invisible light picked up by the new telescopes showed that mayhem abounds in the cosmos: monstrous gamma-ray bursts, deadly pulsars, matter-crushing gravitational fields, matter-hungry black holes that flay their bloated stellar neighbors, newborn stars igniting within pockets of collapsing gas. And as our ordinary, optical telescopes got bigger and better, more mayhem emerged: galaxies that collide and cannibalize each other, explosions of supermassive stars, chaotic stellar and planetary orbits. Our own cosmic neighborhood—the inner solar system—turned out to be a shooting gallery, full of rogue asteroids and comets that collide with planets from time to time. Occasionally they've even wiped out stupendous masses of Earth's flora and fauna. The evidence all points to the fact that we occupy not a well-mannered clockwork universe, but a destructive, violent, and hostile zoo.

Of course, Earth can be bad for your health too. On land, grizzly bears want to maul you; in the oceans, sharks want to eat you. Snowdrifts can freeze you, deserts dehydrate you, earthquakes bury you, volcanoes incinerate you. Viruses can infect you, parasites suck your vital fluids, cancers take over your body, congenital diseases force an early death. And even if you have the good luck to be healthy, a swarm of locusts could devour your crops, a tsunami could wash away your family, or a hurricane could blow apart your town.

So the universe wants to kill us all. But let's ignore that complication for the moment.

Many, perhaps countless, questions hover at the front lines of science. In some cases, answers have eluded the best minds of our species for decades or even centuries. And in contemporary America, the notion that a higher intelligence is the single answer to all enigmas has been enjoying a resurgence. This present-day version of God of the gaps goes by a fresh name: "intelligent design." the term suggests that some entity, endowed with a mental capacity far greater than the human mind can muster, created or enabled all the things in the physical world that we cannot explain through scientific methods.

An interesting hypothesis.

But why confine ourselves to things too wondrous or intricate for us to understand, whose existence and attributes we then credit to a super-intelligence? Instead, why not tally all those things whose design is so clunky, goofy, impractical, or unworkable that they reflect the absence of intelligence?

Take the human form. We eat, drink, and breathe through the same hole in the head, and so, despite Henry J. Heimlich's eponymous maneuver, choking is the fourth leading cause of "unintentional injury death" in the United States. How about drowning, the fifth leading cause? Water coffers almost three-quarters of Earth's surface, yet we are land creatures—submerge your head for just a few minutes, and you die.

Or take our collection of useless body parts. What good is the pinky toenail? How about the appendix, which stops functioning after childhood and thereafter serves only as the source of appendicitis? Useful parts, too, can be problematic. I happen to like my knees, but nobody ever accused them of being well protected from bumps and bangs. These days, people with problem knees can get them surgically replaced. As for our pain-prone spine, it may be a while before someone finds a way to swap that out.

How about the silent killers? High blood pressure, colon cancer, and diabetes each cause tens of thousands of deaths in the U.S. every year, but it's possible not to know you're afflicted until your coroner tells you so. Wouldn't it be nice if we had built-in biogauges to warn us of such dangers well in advance? Even cheap cars, after all, have engine gauges. And what comedian designer configured the region between our legs—an entertainment complex built around a sewage system?

The eye is often held up as a marvel of biological engineering. To the astrophysicist, though, it's only a so-so detector. A better one would be much more sensitive to dark things in the sky, and to all the invisible parts of the spectrum. How much more breathtaking sunsets would be if we could see ultraviolet and infrared. How useful it would be if, at a glance, we could see every source of microwaves' in the environment, or know which radio station transmitters were active. How helpful it would be if we could spot police radar detectors at night.

Think how easy it would be to navigate an unfamiliar city if we, like birds, could always tell which way was north because of the magnetite in our heads. Think how much better off we'd be if we had gills as well as lungs, how much more productive if we had six arms instead of two. And if we had eight, we could safely drive a car while simultaneously talking on a cell phone, changing the radio station, applying makeup, sipping a drink, and scratching our left ear.

Stupid design could fuel a movement unto itself. It may not be nature's default, but it's ubiquitous. Yet people seem to enjoy thinking that our bodies, our minds, and even our universe represent pinnacles of form and reason. Maybe it's a good antidepressant to think so. But it's not science—not now, not in the past, not ever.

Another practice that isn't science is embracing ignorance. Yet it's fundamental to the philosophy of intelligent design: I don't know what this is. I don't know how it works. It's too complicated for me to figure out. It's too complicated for any human being to figure out. So it must be the product of a higher intelligence.

What do you do with that line of reasoning? Do you just cede the solving of problems to someone smarter than you, someone who's not even human? Do you tell students to pursue only questions with easy answers?

There may be a limit to what the human mind can figure out about out universe. But how presumptuous it would be for me to claim that if I can't solve a problem, neither can any other person who has ever lived or who will ever be born. Suppose Galileo and Laplace had felt that way? Better yet, what if Newton had not? He might then have solved Laplace's problem a century earlier, making it Possible for Laplace to cross the next frontier of ignorance.

Science is a philosophy of discovery. Intelligent design is a philosophy of ignorance. You cannot build a program of discovery on the assumption that nobody is smart enough to figure out the answer to a problem. Once upon a time, people identified the god Neptune as the source of storms at sea. Today we call these storms hurricanes. We know when and where they start. We know what drives them. We know what mitigates their destructive power. And anyone who has studied global warming can tell you what makes them worse. The only people Who still call hurricanes "acts of God" are the people Who write insurance forms.

To deny or erase the rich, colorful *history* of scientists and other thinkers who have invoked divinity in their work would be intellectually dishonest.

Surely there's an appropriate place for intelligent design to live in the academic landscape. How about the *history* of religion? How about philosophy or psychology? The one place it doesn't belong is the science classroom.

If you're not swayed by academic arguments, consider the financial consequences. Allow intelligent design into science textbooks, lecture halls, and laboratories, and the cost to the frontier of scientific discovery—the frontier that drives the economies of the future—would be incalculable. I don't want students who could make the next major breakthrough in renewable energy sources or space travel to have been taught that anything they don't understand, and that nobody yet understands, is divinely constructed and therefore beyond their intellectual capacity. The day that happens, Americans will just sit in awe of what we don't understand, while we watch the rest of the world boldly go where no mortal has gone before.

Newton's law of gravity enables you to calculate the force of attraction between any two objects. If you introduce a third object, then each one attracts the other two, and the orbits they trace become much harder to compute. Add another object, and another, and another, and soon you have the planets in our solar system. Earth and the Sun pull on each other, but Jupiter also pulls on Earth, Saturn pulls on Earth, Mars pulls on Earth, Jupiter pulls on Saturn, Saturn pulls on Mars, and on and on.

Newton feared that all this pulling would render the orbits in the solar system unstable. His equations indicated that the planets should long ago have either fallen into the Sun or flown the coop—leaving the Sun, in either case, devoid of planets. Yet the solar system, as well as the larger cosmos, appeared to be the very model of order and durability. So Newton, in his greatest work, the *Principia*, concludes that God must occasionally step in and make things right:

> The six primary Planets are revolv'd about the Sun, in circles concentric with the Sun, and with motions directed towards the same parts, and almost in the same plane. . . . But it is not to be conceived that mere mechanical causes could give birth to so many regular motions. . . . This most beautiful System of the Sun, Planets, and Comets, could only proceed from the counsel and dominion of an intelligent and powerful Being.

Of Universal Tolerance

Voltaire

Translated by John C. Jarvis

Voltaire, (1694–1778), born François-Marie Arouet, was a French Enlightenment writer, essayist, deist, and philosopher. The name "Voltaire," which he adopted in 1718, is an anagram of his surname, "Arouet," and the first letters of the tagline "le jeune" ("the younger"). Voltaire is well-known for his sharp wit, philosophical writings, promotion of human rights, and defense of civil liberties, including freedom of religion and the right to a fair trial. He was an outspoken supporter of social reform, despite strict censorship laws in France and harsh penalties for those who broke them. Through satire, he criticized Church dogma, French institutions of his day, and members of noble French families, and this relentless use of satire led to his being imprisoned in the Bastille in 1717 & 1726, as well as numerous periods of exile from France. The adoption of the name Voltaire, after his first incarceration at the Bastille, demarcates a formal separation from his family and his past. He is perhaps best known for his satirical novel, Candide *(1759). In the following selection, written in 1763, Voltaire bases his argument on the belief that, because we are all manifestations of divine creation, we are therefore obliged to tolerate one another.*

It does not demand any great skill or highly developed eloquence to prove that Christians ought to show tolerance for one another. I will go a step further: I will tell you that we ought to look upon all men as our brothers. What! Call a Turk my brother? A Chinaman my brother? A Jew? A Siamese? Yes, without hesitation; are we not all children of the same father and creatures of the same God?

But these people despise us; they treat us as idolaters! And what of it? I will tell them they are quite wrong. It seems to me that I could shake up at least the arrogant assumptions of a high Moslem leader or the head of a Buddhist monastery if I were to say to them something like this:

"This little globe, which is no more than a dot, spins through space the same as countless other globes, and we are lost in this immense vastness. Mankind, at about five feet of height, is unquestionably a rather small thing in all of creation. And yet one of these insignificant beings says to a few of his neighbors in Arabia or in South Africa: 'Listen to me, for the God of all these worlds has enlightened me. There are nine hundred million little ants like us on the earth, but my anthill alone is dear to God; all the others are a source of disgust to him for all eternity; mine alone will know happiness, and all others will be forever miserable.'"

At that point they would stop me and ask who the madman was that spoke such foolishness. I would be obliged to answer them: "It is you yourselves." I would then attempt to calm them down, but that would be quite difficult.

Next I would speak to the Christians, and I would dare to tell, for example, a Dominican Inquisitor devoted to his faith: "Dear brother, you know that each province of Italy has its own way of talking and that people in Venice and Bergamo do not speak at all like those in Florence. The Academy of Crusca has set up the rules of the Italian language; its dictionary is a standard from which one must not stray, and Buonmattei's book of grammar is an infallible guide which must be followed; but do you believe that the consul of the Academy, or Buonmattei in his absence, would have been able, in good conscience, to cut the tongues out of all the Venetians and of all the Bergamese who would have persisted in speaking their own dialects?"

The Inquisitor would answer me: "There is a vast difference; here it is a question of the salvation of your soul: It is for your own good that the Grand Inquisitor orders your arrest upon the testimony of a single person, be he of the worst character and an outlaw to justice; that you have no lawyer to defend you; that the name of your accuser be not even known to you; that the Inquisitor first promise you mercy, and then condemn you; that he put you through five different tortures, and that afterwards you either be whipped, sent to the gallows, or burned at the stake. [Church leaders and influential Christian judges] are of exactly of this opinion, and this holy practice cannot suffer contradiction."

I would take the liberty of answering him: "My brother, perhaps you are right; I am convinced of the good you only wish to do me, but can I not be saved without all that?"

It is true that these absurd horrors do not stain the face of the earth every day, but they have been done frequently, and one could easily compile them into a book that would be much larger than the Gospels that condemn them. Not only is it quite cruel in this short life to persecute those who do not think like us, but I wonder if it isn't rather bold to pronounce their eternal damnation as well. It seems to me that it is not the business of momentary specks of insignificance, such as we are, to second guess the decrees of the Creator. I am far from fighting against the maxim "Outside of the Church there is no salvation"; I respect the Church and all that it teaches, but, in truth, do we know all of the ways of God and the extent of his mercy? Isn't it permitted to hope in him as much as to fear him? Isn't it enough to be faithful to the Church? Must each particular group take for themselves the rights of the Divine, and decide, in its place, the eternal fate of all men?

When we wear clothes in mourning for the king of Sweden, Denmark, England, or Prussia, do we say that we are in mourning for a damned soul that is eternally burning in hell? In Europe, there are forty million inhabitants who do not belong to the Church of Rome. Shall we say to each of them: "Sir, in light of the fact that you are infallibly damned, I will neither eat, nor converse, nor have anything to do with you?"

What ambassador of France, when given audience with a Great Lord, will say in the depths of his heart: His Highness will be infallibly burned during all of eternity because he has undergone circumcision? If he really believed that the Great Lord was a mortal enemy to God and the object of divine vengeance, would he be able to speak to him? Should he have been sent to see him? With what other man could one do business, what civil responsibilities could one carry out, if in effect one was convinced of this idea that he was dealing with the damned?

O schism-loving worshippers of a merciful God! If you have cruel hearts, if, while you adore him whose entire law consists of these words: "Love God and your neighbor," you have buried this sacred and pure law under meaningless arguments and incomprehensible disputes; if you have sown discord, here over a new word, there over a single letter of the alphabet; if you have attached eternal punishment to the omission of a few words, to the lack of a few ceremonies that other peoples could not know of, I would tell you with tears for all of mankind: "Come with me to the day where all will be judged and where God will reward each man according to his own works.

"I see all the dead from centuries past and from our own time appear together in his presence. Are you certain that our Creator and Father will say to the wise and virtuous Confucius, to the lawmaker Solon, to Pythagoras, Zaleucus, Socrates, Plato, the divine Antonians, the benevolent Trajan, to Titus, to the best of mankind, to Epictetus, and to many others, the very models of men: 'Away with you, monsters, go suffer torments that are infinite in intensity and duration; let your suffering be as eternal as I am! And you, my beloved, Jean Chatel, Ravaillac, Damiens, Cartouche, etc. [Christian leaders with reputations for corruption, evil-doing, and villainous treatment of other humans], you who died with the prescribed ceremonies, sit on my right and share endlessly both my empire and my goodness.'"

You draw back with horror at these words; and, after they have escaped me, I have nothing left to say to you.

In Search of Our Mothers' Gardens

Alice Walker

Alice Walker, the youngest of eight children, was born to sharecropper parents in Eatonville, Georgia in 1944. Today she is considered one of the most important writers of the 20th century; her extraordinary success is made more remarkable as she came from such humble beginnings. Her father is said to have made only $300 dollars a year and her mother helped to support the family by working as a maid. When Walker was 8 years old, she was shot in the eye with a BB while playing with her siblings. The family was too poor to get her the immediate medical attention she required and she subsequently lost sight in her right eye. This early tragedy, coupled with the consequences of economic oppressions and racial segregation she experienced in her youth, fueled Alice Walker's scholastic motivation. She would earn the honor of graduating as Valedictorian of her high school and receive a scholarship to Spellman College in 1961. Two years later, she would move to New York to continue her education at Sarah Lawrence. Following her graduation, she married Melvyn Leventhal, a civil rights lawyer, in 1967. The newlyweds settled in Jackson, Mississippi, becoming the only legally married interracial couple in the town. Over the course of the next decade, Walker would teach at Jackson State University and Tougaloo College while also working on her writing career. She published her first novel The Third Life of George Copeland, *in 1970, followed by her first collection of poetry* In Love and Trouble; Stories of Black Women and Revolutionary Petunias, *in 1973.*

Following her divorce from Leventhal in 1976, Alice Walker began writing with a renewed spirit. She earned the National Institute for the Arts Award and a Guggenheim Fellowship. In 1982, she published what would become her most famous work The Color Purple. *She received both the American Book Award and the Pulitzer Prize for Literature for* The Color Purple. *The novel would later be adapted to film, directed by Steven Spielberg. In the Color Purple, as well as in most of her fiction, Walker works to detail the African American experience. Moreover, and to much criticism, she tends to focus on telling the stories of black women. Many argue that while emphasizing the strengths of black women, she portrays black men in a negative light. Instead, she considers herself a "Womanist," a term she created to describe her appreciation and celebration of black women. It was important for her to distinguish her ideas from traditional feminism as she felt that the oppression experienced by black women could not be attributed singularly to reasons of race or gender. In Search of Our Mothers' Gardens: Womanist Prose (1983), is a collection of essays and memoirs that give voice to the search for heritage. Part personal, part universal, Walker claims in the titular essay from the collection "Guided by my heritage of a love of beauty and a respect for strength — in search of my mother's garden, I found my own".*

I described her own nature and temperament. Told how they needed a larger life for their expression. . . . I pointed out that in lieu of proper channels, her emotions had overflowed into paths that dissipated them. I talked, beautifully I thought, about an art that would be born, an art that would open the way for women the likes of her. I asked her to hope, and build up an inner life against the coming of that day. . . . I sang, with a strange quiver in my voice, a promise song.—Jean Toomer, "Avey," Cane.

The poet speaking to a prostitute who falls asleep while he's talking—

When the poet Jean Toomer walked through the South in the early twenties, he discovered a curious thing: black women whose spirituality was so intense, so deep, so *unconscious*, that they were themselves unaware of the richness they held. They stumbled blindly through their lives: creatures so abused and mutilated in body, so dimmed and confused by pain, that they considered themselves unworthy even of hope. In the selfless abstractions their bodies became to the men who used them, they became more than "sexual objects," more even than mere women: they became "Saints." Instead of being perceived as whole persons, their bodies became shrines: what was thought to be their minds became temples suitable for worship. These crazy Saints stared out at the world, wildly, like lunatics—or quietly, like suicides; and the "God" that was in their gaze was as mute as a great stone.

Who were these Saints? These crazy, loony, pitiful women?

Some of them, without a doubt, were our mothers and grandmothers.

In the still heat of the post-Reconstruction South, this is how they seemed to Jean Toomer: exquisite butterflies trapped in an evil honey, toiling away their lives in an era, a century, that did not acknowledge them, except as "the *mule* of the world." They dreamed dreams that no one knew—not even themselves, in any coherent fashion—and saw visions no one could understand. They wandered or sat about the countryside crooning lullabies to ghosts, and drawing the mother of Christ in charcoal on courthouse walls.

They forced their minds to desert their bodies and their striving spirits sought to rise, like frail whirlwinds from the hard red clay. And when those frail whirlwinds fell, in scattered particles, upon the ground, no one mourned. Instead, men lit candles to celebrate the emptiness that remained, as people do who enter a beautiful but vacant space to resurrect a God.

Our mothers and grandmothers, some of them: moving to music not yet written. And they waited.

They waited for a day when the unknown thing that was in them would be made known; but guessed, somehow in their darkness, that on the day of their revelation they would be long dead. Therefore to Toomer they walked, and even ran, in slow motion. For they were going nowhere immediate, and the future was not yet within their grasp. And men took our mothers and grandmothers, "but got no pleasure from it." So complex was their passion and their calm.

To Toomer, they lay vacant and fallow as autumn fields, with harvest time never in sight: and he saw them enter loveless marriages, without joy; and become prostitutes, without resistance; and become mothers of children, without fulfillment.

For these grandmothers and mothers of ours were not Saints, but Artists; driven to a numb and bleeding madness by the springs of creativity in them for which there was no release. They were Creators, who lived lives of spiritual waste, because they were so rich in spirituality—which is the basis of Art—that the strain of enduring their unused and unwanted talent drove them insane. Throwing away this spirituality was their pathetic attempt to lighten the soul to a weight their work-worn, sexually abused bodies could bear.

What did it mean for a black woman to be an artist in our grandmothers' time? In our great-grandmothers' day? It is a question with an answer cruel enough to stop the blood.

Did you have a genius of a great-great-grandmother who died under some ignorant and depraved white overseer's lash? Or was she required to bake biscuits for a lazy backwater tramp, when she cried out in her soul to paint watercolors of sunsets, or the rain falling on the green and peaceful pasture-lands? Or was her body broken and forced to bear children (who were more often than not sold away from her)—eight, ten, fifteen, twenty children—when her one joy was the thought of modeling heroic figures of rebellion, in stone or clay?

How was the creativity of the black woman kept alive, year after year and century after century, when for most of the years black people have been in America, it was a punishable crime for a black person to read or write? And the freedom to paint, to sculpt, to expand the mind with action did not exist. Consider, if you can bear to imagine it, what might have been the result if singing, too, had been forbidden by law. Listen to the voices of Bessie Smith, Billie Holiday, Nina Simone, Roberta Flack, and Aretha Franklin, among others, and imagine those voices muzzled for life. Then you may begin to comprehend the lives of our "crazy," "Sainted" mothers and grandmothers. The agony of the lives of women who might have been Poets, Novelists, Essayists, and Short-Story Writers (over a period of centuries), who died with their real gifts stifled within them.

And, if this were the end of the story, we would have cause to cry out in my paraphrase of Okot p'Bitek's great poem:

> O, my clanswomen
> Let us all cry together!
> Come,
> Let us mourn the death of our mother,
> The death of a Queen
> The ash that was produced
> By a great fire!
> O, this homestead is utterly dead
> Close the gates
> With *lacari* thorns,
> For our mother
> The creator of the Stool is lost!
> And all the young women
> Have perished in the wilderness!

But this is not the end of the story, for all the young women—our mothers and grandmothers, *ourselves*—have not perished in the wilderness. And if we ask ourselves why, and search for and find the answer, we will know beyond all efforts to erase it from our minds, just exactly who, and of what, we black American women are.

One example, perhaps the most pathetic, most misunderstood one, can provide a backdrop for our mothers' work: Phillis Wheatley, a slave in the 1700s.

Virginia Woolf, in her book *A Room of One's Own*, wrote that in order for a woman to write fiction she must have two things, certainly: a room of her own (with key and lock) and enough money to support herself.

What then are we to make of Phillis Wheatley, a slave, who owned not even herself? This sickly, frail black girl who required a servant of her own at times—her health was so precarious—and who, had she been white, would have been easily considered the intellectual superior of all the women and most of the men in the society of her day.

Virginia Woolf wrote further, speaking of course not of our Phillis, that "any woman born with a great gift in the sixteenth century [insert "eighteenth century," insert "black woman," insert "born or made a slave"] would certainly have gone crazed, shot herself, or ended her days in some lonely cottage outside the village, half witch, half wizard [insert "Saint"], feared and mocked at. For it needs little skill and psychology to be sure that a highly gifted girl who had tried to use her gift for poetry would have been so thwarted and hindered by contrary instincts [add "chains, guns, the lash, the ownership of one's body by someone else, submission to an alien religion"], that she must have lost her health and sanity to a certainty."

The key words, as they relate to Phillis, are "contrary instincts." For when we read the poetry of Phillis Wheatley—as when we read the novels of Nella Larsen or the oddly false-sounding autobiography of that freest of all black women writers, Zora Hurston—evidence of "contrary instincts" is everywhere. Her loyalties were completely divided, as was, without question, her mind.

But how could this be otherwise? Captured at seven, a slave of wealthy, doting whites who instilled in her the "savagery" of the Africa they "rescued" her from, one wonders if she was even able to remember her homeland as she had known it, or as it really was.

Yet, because she did try to use her gift for poetry in a world that made her a slave, she was "so thwarted and hindered by . . . contrary instincts, that she . . . lost her health. . . ." In the last years of her brief life, burdened not only with the need to express her gift but also with a penniless, friendless "freedom" and several small children for whom she was forced to do strenuous work to feed, she lost her health, certainly. Suffering from malnutrition and neglect and who knows what mental agonies, Phillis Wheatley died.

So torn by "contrary instincts" was black, kidnapped, enslaved Phillis that her description of "the Goddess"—as she poetically called the Liberty she did not have—is ironically, cruelly humorous. And, in fact, has held Phillis up to ridicule for more than a century. It is usually read prior to hanging Phillis's memory as that of a fool. She wrote:

> The Goddess comes, she moves divinely fair,
> Olive and laurel binds her *golden* hair.
> Wherever shines this native of the skies,
> Unnumber'd charms and recent graces rise. [My italics]

It is obvious that Phillis, the slave, combed the "Goddess's" hair every morning; prior, perhaps, to bringing in the milk, or fixing her mistress's lunch. She took her imagery from the one thing she saw elevated above all others.

With the benefit of hindsight we ask, "How could she?"

But at last, Phillis, we understand. No more snickering when your stiff, struggling, ambivalent lines are forced on us. We know now that you were not an idiot or a traitor; only a sickly little black girl, snatched from your home and country and made a slave; a woman who still struggled to sing the song that was your gift, although in a land of barbarians who praised you for your bewildered tongue. It is not so much what you sang, as that you kept alive, in so many of our ancestors, *the notion of song.*

Black women are called, in the folklore that so aptly identifies one's status in society, "the *mule* of the world," because we have been handed the burdens that everyone else—*everyone* else—refused to carry. We have also been called "Matriarchs," "Superwomen," and "Mean and Evil Bitches." Not to mention "Castraters" and "Sapphire's Mama." When we have pleaded for under-standing, our character has been distorted; when we have asked for simple caring, we have been handed empty inspirational appellations, then stuck in the farthest corner. When we have asked for love, we have been given children. In short, even our plainer gifts, our labors of fidelity and love, have been knocked down our throats. To be an artist and a black woman, even today, lowers our status in many respects, rather than raises it: and yet, artists we will be.

Therefore we must fearlessly pull out of ourselves and look at and identify with our lives the living creativity some of our great-grandmothers were not allowed to know. I stress *some* of them because it is well known that the majority of our great-grandmothers knew, even without "knowing" it, the reality of their spirituality, even if they didn't recognize it beyond what happened in the singing at church—and they never had any intention of giving it up.

How they did it—those millions of black women who were not Phillis Wheatley, or Lucy Terry or Frances Harper or Zora Hurston or Nella Larsen or Bessie Smith; or Elizabeth Catlett, or Katherine Dunham, either—brings me to the title of this essay, "In Search of Our Mothers' Gardens," which is a personal account that is yet shared, in its theme and its meaning, by all of us. I found, while thinking about the far-reaching world of the creative black woman, that often the truest answer to a question that really matters can be found very close.

In the late 1920s my mother ran away from home to marry my father. Marriage, if not running away, was expected of seventeen-year-old girls. By the time she was twenty, she had two children and was pregnant with a third.

Five children later, I was born. And this is how I came to know my mother: she seemed a large, soft, loving-eyed woman who was rarely impatient in our home. Her quick, violent temper was on view only a few times a year, when she battled with the white landlord who had the misfortune to suggest to her that her children did not need to go to school.

She made all the clothes we wore, even my brothers' overalls. She made all the towels and sheets we used. She spent the summers canning vegetables and fruits. She spent the winter evenings making quilts enough to cover all our beds.

During the "working" day, she labored beside—not behind—my father in the fields. Her day began before sunup, and did not end until late at night. There was never a moment for her to sit down, undisturbed, to unravel her own private thoughts; never a time free from interruption—by work or the noisy inquiries of her many children. And yet, it is to my mother—and all our mothers who were not famous—that I went in search of the secret of what has fed that muzzled and often mutilated, but vibrant, creative spirit that the black woman has inherited, and that pops out in wild and unlikely places to this day.

But when, you will ask, did my overworked mother have time to know or care about feeding the creative spirit?

The answer is so simple that many of us have spent years discovering it. We have constantly looked high, when we should have looked high—and low.

For example: in the Smithsonian Institution in Washington, D.C., there hangs a quilt unlike any other in the world. In fanciful, inspired, and yet simple and identifiable figures, it portrays the story of the Crucifixion. It is considered rare, beyond price. Though it follows no known pattern of quilt-making, and though it is made of bits and pieces of worthless rags, it is obviously the work of a person of powerful imagination and deep spiritual feeling. Below this quilt I saw a note that says it was made by "an anonymous Black woman in Alabama, a hundred years ago."

If we could locate this "anonymous" black woman from Alabama, she would turn out to be one of our grandmothers—an artist who left her mark in the only materials she could afford, and in the only medium her position in society allowed her to use.

As Virginia Woolf wrote further, in *A Room of One's Own:*

> Yet genius of a sort must have existed among women as it must have existed among the working class. [Change this to "slaves" and "the wives and daughters of sharecroppers."] Now and again an Emily Brontë or a Robert Burns [change this to "a Zora Hurston or a Richard Wright"] blazes out and proves its presence. But certainly it never got itself on to paper. When, however, one reads of a witch being ducked, of a woman possessed by devils [or "Sainthood"], of a

wise woman selling herbs [our root workers], or even a very remarkable man who had a mother, then I think we are on the track of a lost novelist, a suppressed poet, of some mute and inglorious Jane Austen. . . . Indeed, I would venture to guess that Anon, who wrote so many poems without signing them, was often a woman. . . .

And so our mothers and grandmothers have, more often than not anonymously, handed on the creative spark, the seed of the flower they themselves never hoped to see: or like a sealed letter they could not plainly read.

And so it is, certainly, with my own mother. Unlike "Ma" Rainey's songs, which retained their creator's name even while blasting forth from Bessie Smith's mouth, no song or poem will bear my mother's name. Yet so many of the stories that I write, that we all write, are my mother's stories. Only recently did I fully realize this: that through years of listening to my mother's stories of her life, I have absorbed not only the stories themselves, but something of the manner in which she spoke, something of the urgency that involves the knowledge that her stories—like her life—must be recorded. It is probably for this reason that so much of what I have written is about characters whose counterparts in real life are so much older than I am.

But the telling of these stories, which came from my mother's lips as naturally as breathing, was not the only way my mother showed herself as an artist. For stories, too, were subject to being distracted, to dying without conclusion. Dinners must be started, and cotton must be gathered before the big rains. The artist that was and is my mother showed itself to me only after many years. This is what I finally noticed:

Like Mem, a character in *The Third Life of Grange Copeland*, my mother adorned with flowers whatever shabby house we were forced to live in. And not just your typical straggly country stand of zinnias, either. She planted ambitious gardens—and still does—with over fifty different varieties of plants that bloom profusely from early March until late November. Before she left home for the fields, she watered her flowers, chopped up the grass, and laid out new beds. When she returned from the fields she might divide clumps of bulbs, dig a cold pit, uproot and replant roses, or prune branches from her taller bushes or trees—until night came and it was too dark to see.

Whatever she planted grew as if by magic, and her fame as a grower of flowers spread over three counties. Because of her creativity with her flowers, even my memories of poverty are seen through a screen of blooms—sun-flowers, petunias, roses, dahlias, forsythia, spirea, delphiniums, verbena . . . and on and on.

And I remember people coming to my mother's yard to be given cuttings from her flowers; I hear again the praise showered on her because whatever rocky soil she landed on, she turned into a garden. A garden so brilliant with colors, so original in its design, so magnificent with life and creativity, that to this day people drive by our house in Georgia—perfect strangers and imperfect strangers—and ask to stand or walk among my mother's art.

I notice that it is only when my mother is working in her flowers that she is radiant, almost to the point of being invisible—except as Creator: hand and eye. She is involved in work her soul must have. Ordering the universe in the image of her personal conception of Beauty.

Her face, as she prepares the Art that is her gift, is a legacy of respect she leaves to me, for all that illuminates and cherishes life. She has handed down respect for the possibilities—and the will to grasp them.

For her, so hindered and intruded upon in so many ways, being an artist has still been a daily part of her life. This ability to hold on, even in very simple ways, is work black women have done for a very long time.

This poem is not enough, but it is something, for the woman who literally covered the holes in our walls with sunflowers:

> They were women then
> My mama's generation
> Husky of voice—Stout of
> Step
> With fists as well as
> Hands
> How they battered down
> Doors
> And ironed
> Starched white
> Shirts
> How they led
> Armies
> Headragged Generals
> Across mined
> Fields
> Bobby-trapped
> Kitchens
> To discover books
> Desks
> A place for us
> How they knew what we
> *Must* know
> Without knowing a page
> Of it
> Themselves.

Guided by my heritage of a love of beauty and a respect for strength—in search of my mother's garden, I found my own.

And perhaps in Africa over two hundred years ago, there was just such a mother; perhaps she painted vivid and daring decorations in oranges and yellows and greens on the walls of her hut; perhaps she sang—in a voice like Roberta Flack's—*sweetly* over the compounds of her village; perhaps she wove the most stunning mats or told the most ingenious stories of all the village storytellers. Perhaps she was herself a poet—though only her daughter's name is signed to the poems that we know.

Perhaps Phillis Wheatley's mother was also an artist.

Perhaps in more than Phillis Wheatley's biological life is her mother's signature made clear.

Night

Elie Wiesel

Translated by Stella Rodway

Elie Wiesel was born Eliezer Wiesel in 1928 in Sighet, Romania. His father, Shlomo, was a shopkeeper of Jewish Hungarian descent, and it was he who instilled in his son a love of literature and languages. In 1944, the Jewish community in Sighet, including the Wiesels, was deported by the Nazis to the Auschwitz-Birkenau death camp. Later, Wiesel and his father were transferred to another camp, Buchenwald, where his father died of starvation. While his mother, Sarah, and a younger sister are presumed to have died at Auschwitz, Wiesel survived to be liberated at the age of 16 by the American Third Army in 1945. After the war, he studied Philosophy at the Sorbonne in Paris and worked as a professional journalist. In 1955, he moved to the United States and became an American citizen in 1963. The present selection was taken from the novel Night, *a partly fictitious, partly autobiographical account of Wiesel's experience in the death camps, first published in Yiddish as* Un di Velt Hot Geshvihn (And the World Was Silent), *then condensed and published in French as* La Nuit *in 1958. The condensed version was first translated into English in 1960. It has to date sold millions of copies in many languages and is generally considered one of the most important documents of Holocaust literature. Wiesel has written, in addition, over forty works of both fiction and nonfiction, and was awarded the Nobel Peace Prize in 1986 for his "practical work in the cause of peace." He presently lives in Boston and teaches at Boston University, where he is the Andrew Mellon Professor of the Humanities.*

A week later, on the way back from work, we noticed in the center of the camp, at the assembly place, a black gallows.

We were told that soup would not be distributed until after roll call. This took longer than usual. The orders were given in a sharper manner than on other days, and in the air there were strange undertones.

"Bare your heads!" yelled the head of the camp, suddenly.

Ten thousand caps were simultaneously removed.

"Cover your heads!"

Ten thousand caps went back onto their skulls, as quick as lightning.

The gate to the camp opened. An SS section appeared and surrounded us: one SS at every three paces. On the lookout towers the machine guns were trained on the assembly place.

"They fear trouble," whispered Juliek.

Two SS men had gone to the cells. They came back with the condemned man between them. He was a youth from Warsaw. He had three years of concentration camp life behind him. He was a strong, well-built boy, a giant in comparison with me.

His back to the gallows, his face turned toward his judge, who was the head of the camp, the boy was pale, but seemed more moved than afraid. His manacled hands did not tremble. His eyes gazed coldly at the hundreds of SS guards, the thousands of prisoners who surrounded him.

The head of the camp began to read his verdict, hammering out each phrase:

"In the name of Himmler . . . prisoner Number . . . stole during the alert. . . . According to the law . . . paragraph . . . prisoner Number . . . is condemned to death. May this be a warning and an example to all prisoners."

No one moved.

I could hear my heart beating. The thousands who had died daily at Auschwitz and at Birkenau in the crematory ovens no longer troubled me. But this one, leaning against his gallows—he overwhelmed me.

"Do you think this ceremony'll be over soon? I'm hungry . . . ." whispered Juliek.

At a sign from the head of the camp, the Lagerkapo advanced toward the condemned man. Two prisoners helped him in his task—for two plates of soup.

The Kapo wanted to bandage the victim's eyes, but he refused.

After a long moment of waiting, the executioner put the rope around his neck. He was on the point of motioning to his assistants to draw the chair away from the prisoner's feet, when the latter cried, in a calm, strong voice:

"Long live liberty! A curse upon Germany! A curse. . . ! A cur—"

The executioners had completed their task.

A command cleft the air like a sword

"Bare your heads."

Ten thousand prisoners paid their last respects.

"Cover your heads!"

Then the whole camp, block after block, had to march past the hanged man and stare at the dimmed eyes, the lolling tongue of death. The Kapos and heads of each block forced everyone to look him full in the face.

After the march, we were given permission to return to the blocks for our meal.

I remember that I found the soup excellent that evening. . . .

I witnessed other hangings. I never saw a single one of the victims weep. For a long time those dried-up bodies had forgotten the bitter taste of tears.

Except once. The Oberkapo of the fifty-second cable unit was a Dutchman, a giant, well over six feet. Seven hundred prisoners worked under his orders, and they all loved him like a brother. No one had ever received a blow at his hands, nor an insult from his lips.

He had a young boy under him, a *pipel*, as they were called—a child with a refined and beautiful face, unheard of in this camp.

(At Buna, the *pipel* were loathed; they were often crueller than adults. I once saw one of thirteen beating his father because the latter had not made his bed properly. The old man was crying softly while the boy shouted: "If you don't stop crying at once I shan't bring you any more bread. Do you understand?" But the Dutchman's little servant was loved by all. He had the face of a sad angel.)

One day, the electric power station at Buna was blown up. The Gestapo, summoned to the spot, suspected sabotage. They found a trail. It eventually led to the Dutch Oberkapo. And there, after a search, they found an important stock of arms.

The Oberkapo was arrested immediately. He was tortured for a period of weeks, but in vain. He would not give a single name. He was transferred to Auschwitz. We never heard of him again.

But his little servant had been left behind in the camp in prison. Also put to torture, he too would not speak. Then the SS sentenced him to death, with two other prisoners who had been discovered with arms.

One day when we came back from work, we saw three gallows rearing up in the assembly place, three black crows. Roll call. SS all round us, machine guns trained: the traditional ceremony. Three victims in chains—and one of them, the little servant, the sad-eyed angel.

The SS seemed more preoccupied, more disturbed than usual. To hang a young boy in front of thousands of spectators was no light matter. The head of the camp read the verdict. All eyes were on the child. He was lividly pale, almost calm, biting his lips. The gallows threw its shadow over him.

This time the Lagerkapo refused to act as executioner. Three SS replaced him.

The three victims mounted together onto the chairs.

The three necks were placed at the same moment within the nooses.

"Long live liberty!" cried the two adults.

But the child was silent.

"Where is God? Where is He?" someone behind me asked.

At a sign from the head of the camp, the three chairs tipped over.

Total silence throughout the camp. On the horizon, the sun was setting.

"Bare your heads!" yelled the head of the camp. His voice was raucous. We were weeping.

"Cover your heads!"

Then the march past began. The two adults were no longer alive. Their tongues hung swollen, blue-tinged. But the third rope was still moving; being so light, the child was still alive. . . . For more than half an hour he stayed there, struggling between life and death, dying in slow agony under our eyes. And we had to look him full in the face. He was still alive when I passed in front of him. His tongue was still red, his eyes were not yet glazed.

Behind me, I heard the same man asking:

"Where is God now?"

And I heard a voice within me answer him:

"Where is He? Here He is— He is hanging here on this gallows. . . ."

That night the soup tasted of corpses.

The Ethics of Living Jim Crow: An Autobiographical Sketch

Richard Wright

Richard Wright (1908–1960), the grandson of former slaves, was born on Rucker's plantation near Natchez, Mississippi. When he was six years old, his father, Nathaniel, a sharecropper, abandoned the family, and Wright and his younger brother Leon spent time in a number of orphanages and foster homes as his mother moved about looking for work. The family moved from Tennessee to Arkansas, where Richard grew close to his Uncle Silas, a prosperous builder and saloon-keeper. In 1917, Uncle Silas was murdered by whites, and the crime went unpunished. After working in a series of odd jobs, Wright became the secretary to an insurance agent in 1922; this job gave him the opportunity to travel throughout Mississippi, where he witnessed firsthand the illiteracy and lack of education among African-Americans that would later become the subject matter for his writing and his social protests. Wright moved to Chicago in 1927 and later joined the Federal Writer's Project. In 1933, he joined the Communist Party and became an editor of the party newspaper, the Daily Worker. *In addition, Wright's work appeared in publications of the radical left, such as* Left Front *and* New Masses, *as well as more mainstream publications, like* Harper's. *Wright left the Communist Party in 1942 because of disagreements about the role that civil rights for African-Americans should play in relation to the overall goal of communism. Wright's first novel,* Uncle Tom's Children: Four Novellas *(1938), won him the critical acclaim that led to a Guggenheim Fellowship. His novel* Native Son *(1940) became a best seller and, eventually, a classic in American literature.*

Other books by Wright include Eight Men *(1940),* Black Boy *(1945),* The Outsider *(1953),* Black Power *(1954), and* The Long Dream *(1958). In 1947, Wright, frustrated by the oppressive climate of racism in the United States, emigrated to France, where he died on November 28, 1960 of an apparent heart attack.*

My first lesson in how to live as a Negro came when I was quite small. We were living in Arkansas. Our house stood behind the railroad tracks. Its skimpy yard was paved with black cinders. Nothing green ever grew in that yard. The only touch of green we could see was far away, beyond the tracks, over where the white folks lived. But cinders were good enough for me and I never missed the green growing things. And anyhow cinders were fine weapons. You could always have a nice hot war with huge black cinders. All you had to do was crouch behind the brick pillars of a house with your hands full of gritty ammunition. And the first woolly black head you saw pop out from behind another row of pillars was our target. You tried your very best to knock it off. It was great fun.

I never fully realized the appalling disadvantages of a cinder environment till one day the gang to which I belonged found itself engaged in a war with the white boys who lived beyond the tracks. As usual we laid down our cinder barrage, thinking that this would wipe the white boys out. But they replied with a steady bombardment of broken bottles. We doubled our cinder barrage, but they hid behind trees, hedges, and the sloping embankments of their lawns. Having no such fortifications, we retreated to the brick pillars of our homes. During the retreat a broken milk bottle caught me behind the ear, opening a deep gash which bled profusely. The sight of blood pouring over my face completely demoralized our ranks. My fellow-combatants left me standing paralyzed in the center of the yard, and scurried for their homes. A kind neighbor saw me, and rushed me to a doctor, who took three stitches in my neck.

I sat brooding on my front steps, nursing my wound and waiting for my mother to come from work. I felt that a grave injustice had been done me. It was all right to throw cinders. The greatest harm a cinder could do was leave a bruise. But broken bottles were dangerous; they left you cut, bleeding, and helpless.

When night fell, my mother came from the white folks' kitchen. I raced down the street to meet her. I could just feel in my bones that she would understand. I knew she would tell me exactly what to do next time. I grabbed her hand and babbled out the whole story. She examined my wound, then slapped me.

"How come yuh didn't hid?" she asked me. "How come yuh awways fightin'?"

I was outraged, and bawled. Between sobs I told her that I didn't have any trees or hedges to hide behind. There wasn't a thing I could have used as a trench. And you couldn't throw very far when you were hiding behind the brick pillars of a house. She grabbed a barrel stave, dragged me home, stripped me naked, and beat me till I had a fever of one hundred and two. She would smack my rump with the stave, and, while the skin was still smarting impart to me the gems of Jim Crow wisdom. I was never to throw cinders any more. I was never to fight any more wars. I was never, never, under any conditions, to fight *white* folks again. And they were absolutely right in the clouting me with the broken milk bottle. Didn't I know she was working hard every day in the hot kitchens of white folks to make money to take care of me? When was I ever going to learn to be a good boy? She couldn't be bothered with my fights. She finished by telling me that I ought to be thankful to God as long as I lived that they didn't kill me.

All that night I was delirious and could not sleep. Each time I closed my eyes I saw monstrous white faces suspended from the ceiling, leering at me.

From that time on, the charm of my cinder yard was gone. The green trees, the trimmed hedges, the cropped lawns grew very meaningful, became a symbol. Even today when I think of white folks, the hard, sharp outlines of white houses surrounded by trees, lawns, and hedges are present somewhere in the background of my mind. Through the years they grew into an over-reaching symbol of fear.

It was a long time before I came in close contact with white folks again. We moved from Arkansas to Mississippi. Here we had the good fortune not to live behind the railroad tracks, or close to white neighborhoods. We lived in the very heart of the local Black Belt. There were black churches and black preachers; there were black schools and black teachers; black groceries and black clerks. In fact, everything was so solidly black that for a long time I did not think of white folks, save in remote and vague terms. But this could not last forever. As one grows older one eats more. One's clothing costs more. When I finished grammar school I had to go to work. My mother could no longer feed and clothe me on her cooking job.

There is but one place where a black boy who knows no trade can get a job, and that's where the houses and faces are white, where the trees, lawns, and hedges are green. My first job was with an optical company in Jackson, Mississippi. The morning I applied I stood straight and neat before the boss, answering all his questions with sharp yessirs and nosirs. I was very careful to pronounce my *sirs* distinctly, in order that he might know that I was polite, that I knew where I was, and that I knew he was a *white* man. I wanted that job badly.

He looked me over as though he were examining a prize poodle. He questioned me closely about my schooling, being particularly insistent about how much mathematics I had had. He seemed very pleased when I told him I had had two years of algebra.

"Boy, how would you like to try to learn something around here?" he asked me.

"I'd like it fine, sir," I said, happy. I had visions of "working my way up." Even Negroes have those visions.

"All right," he said. "come on."

I followed him to the small factory.

"Pease," he said to a white man of about thirty-five, "this is Richard. He's going to work for us."

Pease looked at me and nodded.

I was then taken to a white boy of about seventeen.

"Morrie, this is Richard, who's going to work for us."

"Whut yuh sayin' there, boy!" Morrie boomed at me.

"Fine!" I answered.

The boss instructed these two to help me, teach me, give me jobs to do, and let me learn what I could in my spare time.

My wages were five dollars a week.

I worked hard, trying to please. For the first month I got along O.K. Both Pease and Morrie seemed to like me. But one thing was missing. And I kept thinking about it. I was not learning anything and nobody was volunteering to help me. Thinking they had forgotten that I was to learn something about the mechanics of grinding lenses, I asked Morrie one day to tell me about the work. He grew red.

"Whut yuh tryin' t' do, nigger, get smart?" he asked.

"Naw; I ain' trying' t' git smart," I said.

"Well, don't, if yuh know whut's good for yuh!"

I was puzzled. Maybe he just doesn't want to help me, I thought. I went to Pease.

"Say, are yuh crazy, you black bastard?" Pease asked me, his gray eyes growing hard.

I spoke out, reminding him that the boss had said I was to be given a chance to learn something.

"Nigger, you think you're *white* don't you?"

"Naw, sir!"

"Well, you're acting mighty like it!"

"But, Mr. Pease, the boss said. . ."

Pease shook his fist in my face.

"This is a *white* man's work around here, and you better watch yourself!"

From then on they changed toward me. They said good morning no more. When I was just a bit slow in performing some duty, I was called a lazy black son-of-a-bitch.

Once I thought of reporting all this to the boss. But the mere idea of what would happen to me if Pease and Morrie should learn that I had "snitched" stopped me. And after all the boss was a white man, too. What was the use?

The climax came at noon one summer day. Pease called me to his work-bench. To get to him I had to go between two narrow benches and stand with my back against a wall.

"Yes, sir," I said.

"Richard, I want to ask you something," Pease began pleasantly, not looking up from his work.

"Yes, sir," I said again.

Morrie came over, blocking the narrow passage between the benches. He folded his arms, staring at me solemnly.

I looked from one to the other, sensing that something was coming.

"Yes, sir," I said for the third time.

Pease looked up and spoke very slowly.

"Richard, *Mr.* Morrie here tells me you called me *Pease.*"

I stiffened. A void seemed to open up in me. I knew this was the show-down.

He meant that I had failed to call him Mr. Pease. I looked at Morrie. He was gripping a steel bar in his hands. I opened my mouth to speak, to protest, to assure Pease that I had never called him simply *Pease,* and that I had never had any intentions of doing so, when Morrie grabbed my by the collar, ramming my head against the wall.

"Now, be careful, nigger!" snarled Morrie, baring his teeth. "I heard yuh call 'im *Pease!* 'N' if yuh say yuh didn't, yuh're callin' me a *lie,* see?" He waved the steel bar threateningly.

If I had said: No, sir, Mr. Pease, I never called you *Pease,* I would have been automatically calling Morrie a liar. And if I had said: Yes, sir, Mr. Pease, I called you *Pease,* I would have been pleading guilty to having uttered the worst insult that a Negro can utter to a southern white man. I stood hesitating, trying to frame a neutral reply.

"Richard, I asked you a question!" said Pease. Anger was creeping into his voice.

"I don't remember calling you *Pease,* Mr. Pease," I said cautiously. "And if I did, I sure didn't mean. . ."

"You black son-of-a-bitch! You called me *Pease,* then!" he spat, slapping me till I bent sideways over a bench. Morrie was on top of me demanding:

"Didn't yuh call 'im *Pease?* If yuh say yuh didn't, I'll rip yo' gut string loose with this bar, yuh black granny dodger! Yuh can't call a white man a lie 'n' git erway with it, you black son-of-a-bitch!"

I wilted. I begged them not to bother me. I knew what they wanted. They wanted me to leave.

"I'll leave," I promised. "I'll leave right *now.*"

They gave me a minute to get out of the factory. I was warned not to show up again, or tell the boss.

I went.

When I told the folks at home what had happened, they called me a fool. They told me that I must never again attempt to exceed my boundaries. When you are working for white folks, they said, you got to "stay in your place" if you want to keep working.

2

My Jim Crow education continued on my next job, which was portering in a clothing store. One morning, while polishing brass out front, the boss and his twenty-year-old son got out of their car and half dragged and half kicked a Negro woman into the store. A policeman standing at the corner looked on, twirling his nightstick. I watched out of the corner of my eye, never slackening the strokes of my chamois upon the brass. After a few minutes, I heard shrill screams coming from the rear of the store. Later the woman stumbled out, bleeding, crying, and holding her stomach. When she reached the end of the block, the policeman grabbed her and accused her of being drunk. Silently, I watched him throw her into a patrol wagon.

When I went to the rear of the store, the boss and his son were washing their hands at the sink. They were chuckling. The floor was bloody and strewn with wisps of hair and clothing. No doubt I must have appeared pretty shocked, for the boss slapped me reassuringly on the back.

"Boy, that's what we do to niggers when they don't want to pay their bills," he said, laughing.

His son looked at me and grinned.

"Here, hava cigarette," he said.

Not knowing what to do, I took it. He lit his and held the match for me. This was a gesture of kindness, indicating that even if they had beaten the poor old woman, they would not beat me if I knew enough to keep my mouth shut.

"Yes, sir," I said, and asked no questions.

After they had gone, I sat on the edge of a packing box and stared at the bloody floor till the cigarette went out.

That day at noon, while eating in a hamburger joint, I told my fellow Negro porters what had happened. No one seemed surprised. One fellow, after swallowing a huge bite, turned to me and asked:

"Huh! Is tha' all they did t' her?"

"Yeah. Wasn't tha' enough?" I asked.

"Shucks! Man, she's a lucky bitch!" he said, burying his lips deep into a juicy hamburger. "Hell, it's a wonder they didn't lay her when they got through."

3

I was learning fast, but not quite fast enough. One day, while I was delivering packages in the suburbs, my bicycle tire was punctured. I walked along the hot, dusty road, sweating and leading my bicycle by the handle-bars.

A car slowed at my side.

"What's the matter, boy?" a white man called.

I told him my bicycle was broken and I was walking back to town.

"That's too bad," he said. "Hop on the running board."

He stopped the car. I clutched hard at my bicycle with one hand and clung to the side of the car with the other.

"All set?"

"Yes, sir," I answered. The car started.

It was full of young white men. They were drinking. I watched the flask pass from mouth to mouth.

"Wanna drink, boy?" one asked.

I laughed as the wind whipped my face. Instinctively obeying the freshly planted precepts of my mother, I said:

"Oh, no!"

The words were hardly out of my mouth before I felt something hard and cold smash me between the eyes. It was an empty whisky bottle. I saw stars, and fell backwards from the speeding car into the dust of the road, my feet becoming entangled in the steel spokes of my bicycle. The white men piled out and stood over me.

"Nigger, ain' yuh learned no better sense'n tha' yet?" asked the man who hit me. "Ain' yuh learned t' say *sir* t' a white man yet?"

Dazed, I pulled to my feet. My elbows and legs were bleeding. Fists doubled, the white man advanced, kicking my bicycle out of the way.

"Aw, leave the bastard alone. He's got enough," said one.

They stood looking at me. I rubbed my shins, trying to stop the flow of blood. No doubt they felt a sort of contemptuous pity, for one asked:

"Yuh wanna ride t' town now, nigger? Yuh reckon yuh know enough t' ride now?"

"I wanna walk," I said, simply.

Maybe it sounded funny. They laughed.

"Well, walk, yuh black son-of-a-bitch!"

When they left they comforted me with:

"Nigger, yuh sho better be damn glad it wuz us yuh talked t' tha' way. Yuh're lucky bastard, 'cause if yuh'd said tha' t' somebody else, yuh might've been a dead nigger now."

4

Negroes who have lived in the South know the dread of being caught alone upon the streets in white neighborhoods after the sun has set. In such a simple situation as this the plight of the Negro in America is graphically symbolized. While white strangers may be in these neighborhoods trying to get home, they can pass unmolested. But the color of a Negro's skin makes him easily recognizable, makes him suspect, converts him into a defenseless target.

Late one Saturday night I made some deliveries in a white neighborhood. I was pedaling my bicycle back to the store as fast as I could, when a police car, swerving toward me, jammed me into the curbing.

"Get down and put up yur hands!" the policemen ordered.

I did. They climbed out of the car, guns drawn, faces set, and advanced slowly.

"Keep still!" they ordered.

I reached my hands higher. They searched my pockets and packages. They seemed dissatisfied when they could find nothing incriminating. Finally, one of them said:

"Boy, tell your boss not to send you out in white neighborhoods after sundown."

As usual, I said:

"Yes, sir."

5

My next job was as hall-boy in a hotel. Here my Jim Crow education broadened and deepened. When the bell-boys were busy, I was often called to assist them. As many of the rooms in the hotel were occupied by prostitutes, I was constantly called to carry them liquor and cigarettes. These women were nude most of the time. They did not bother about clothing, even for bell-boys. When you went into their rooms, you were supposed to take their nakedness for granted, as though it startled you no more than a blue vase or a red rug. Your presence awoke in them no sense of shame, for you were not regarded as human. If they were receiving men, not a flicker of your eyelids could show. I remember one incident vividly. A new woman, a huge, snowy-skinned blonde, took a room on my floor. I was sent to wait upon her. She was in bed with a thick-set man; both were nude and uncovered. She said she wanted some liquor and slid out of bed and waddled across the floor to get her money from a dresser drawer. I watched her.

"Nigger, what in hell you looking at?" the white man asked me, raising himself upon his elbows.

"Nothing," I answered, looking miles deep into the blank wall of the room.

"Keep your eyes where they belong, if you want to be healthy!"

"Yes, sir."

6

One of the bell-boys I knew in this hotel was keeping steady company with one of the Negro maids. Out of a clear sky the police descended upon his home and arrested him, accusing him of bastardy. The poor boy swore he had had no intimate relations with the girl. Nevertheless, they forced him to marry her. When the child arrived, it was found to be much lighter in complexion than either of the two supposedly legal parents. The white men around the hotel made a great joke of it. They spread the rumor that some white cow must have scared the poor girl while she was carrying the baby. If you were in the presence when this explanation was offered, you were supposed to laugh.

7

One of the bell-boys was caught in bed with a white prostitute. He was castrated and run out of town. Immediately after this all the bell-boys and hall-boys were called together and warned. We were given to understand that the boy who had been castrated was a "mighty, mighty lucky bastard." We were impressed with the fact that next time management of the hotel would not be responsible for the lives of "trouble-makin' niggers." We were silent.

8

One night, just as I was about to go home, I met one of the Negro maids. She lived in my direction, and we fell in to walk part of the way home together. As we passed the white night-watchman, he slapped the maid on her buttock. I turned around, amazed. The watchman looked at me with a long, hard, fixed-under stare. Suddenly, he pulled his gun and asked:

"Nigger, don't yuh like it?"

I hesitated.

"I asked yuh don't yuh like it?" he asked again, stepping forward.

"Yes, sir," I mumbled.

"Talk like it, then!"

"Oh, yes, sir!" I said with as much heartiness as I could muster.

Outside, I walked ahead of the girl, ashamed to face her. She caught up with me and said:

"Don't be a fool! Yuh couldn't help it!"

This watchman boasted of having killed two Negroes in self-defense.

Yet, in spite of all this, the life of the hotel ran with an amazing smoothness. It would have been impossible for a stranger to detect anything. The maids, the hall-boys, and the bell-boys were all smiles. They had to be.

9

I had learned my Jim Crow lessons so thoroughly that I kept the hotel job till I left Jackson for Memphis. It so happened that while in Memphis I applied for a job at a branch of the optical company. I was hired. And for some reason, as long as I worked there, they never brought my past against me.

Here my Jim Crow education assumed quite a different form. It was no longer brutally cruel, but subtly cruel. Here I learned to lie, to steal, to dissemble. I learned to play that dual role which every Negro must play if he wants to eat and live.

For example, it was almost impossible to get a book to read. It was assumed that after a Negro had imbibed what scanty schooling the state furnished he had no further need for books. I was always borrowing books from men on the job. One day I mustered enough courage to ask one of the men to let me get books from the library in his name. Surprisingly, he consented. I cannot help but think that he consented because he was a Roman Catholic and felt a vague sympathy for Negroes, being himself an object of hatred. Armed with a library card, I obtained books in the following manner: I would write a note to the librarian, saying: "Please let this nigger boy have the following books." I would then sign it with the white man's name.

When I went to the library, I would stand at the desk, hat in hand, looking as unbookish as possible. When I received the books desired I would take them home. If the books listed in the note happened to be out, I would sneak into the lobby and forge a new one. I never took any chances guessing with the white librarian about what the fictitious white man would want to read. No doubt if any of the white patrons had suspected that some of the volumes they enjoyed had been in the home of a Negro, they would not have tolerated it for an instant.

The factory force of the optical company in Memphis was much larger than that in Jackson, and more urbanized. At least they liked to talk, and would engage the Negro help in conversation whenever possible. By this means I found that many subjects were taboo from the white man's point of view. Among the topics they did not like to discuss with Negroes were the following: American white women; the Ku Klux Klan; France, and how Negro soldiers fared while there; French women; Jack Johnson; the entire northern part of the United States; the Civil War; Abraham Lincoln; U. S. Grant; General Sherman; Catholics; the Pope; Jews; the Republican Party; slavery; social equality; Communism; Socialism; the 13th and 14th Amendments to the Constitution; or any topic calling for positive knowledge or manly self-assertion on the part of the Negro. The most accepted topics were sex and religion.

There were many times when I had to exercise a great deal of ingenuity to keep out of trouble. It is a southern custom that all men must take off their hats when they enter an elevator. And especially did this apply to us blacks with rigid force. One day I stepped into an elevator with my arms full of packages. I was forced to ride with my hat on. Two white men stared at me coldly. Then one of them very kindly lifted my hat and placed it upon my armful of packages. Now the most accepted response for a Negro to make under such circumstances it to look at the white man out of the corner of his eye and grin. To have said: "Thank you!" would have made the white man *think* that you *thought* you were receiving from him a personal service. For such an act I have seen Negroes take a blow in the mouth. Finding that first alternative distasteful, and the second dangerous, I hit upon an acceptable course of action which fell safely between these two poles. I immediately—no sooner than my hat was lifted—pretended that my packages were about to spill, and appeared deeply distressed with keeping them in my arms. In this fashion I evaded having to acknowledge his service, and, in spite of adverse circumstances, salvaged a slender shred of personal pride.

How do Negroes feel about the way they have to live? How do they discuss it when alone among themselves? I think this question can be answered in a single sentence. A friend of mine who ran an elevator once told me:

"Lawd, man! If it wuzn't fer the polices 'n' them ol' lynch-mobs, there wouldn't be nothin' but uproar down here!"

UN Speech on Education

Malala Yousafzai

Malala Yousafzai was born on July 12, 1997, into a Sunni Muslim family in Pakistan's Swat Valley. In 2008, the Taliban began taking over the region and banned television, music, education for females and other freedoms. In response to the ban on education for girls, Malala was asked by journalists from the BBC (British Broadcasting Corporation) to write a blog about her life in the Swat Valley under Taliban rule. She also began to speak out against the ban and even had the opportunity to meet with the United States special envoy to Afghanistan and Pakistan, Richard Holbrooke, to ask for his assistance. Her activism raised her public profile, and she was awarded the National Peace Award for Youth.

On October 9, 2012, a Taliban gunman boarded a bus of school children and demanded to know which one was Malala. When she was identified, the gunman shot her, and the bullet went through her head and neck and lodged in her shoulder. Malala's shooting garnered international attention, and she was ultimately treated for her injuries in hospitals in Germany and England.

After her recovery, Malala continued to speak out for the right to an education, calling it a basic human right. Her speech before the United Nations on July 12, 2013 called for worldwide access to education for all children, and the day was declared "Malala Day" by the UN.

The text of Malala Yousafzai's speech at the United Nations

In the name of God, The Most Beneficent, The Most Merciful.
Honourable UN Secretary General Mr Ban Ki-moon,
Respected President General Assembly Vuk Jeremic
Honourable UN envoy for Global education Mr Gordon Brown,
Respected elders and my dear brothers and sisters;

Today, it is an honour for me to be speaking again after a long time. Being here with such honourable people is a great moment in my life.

I don't know where to begin my speech. I don't know what people would be expecting me to say. But first of all, thank you to God for whom we all are equal and thank you to every person who has prayed for my fast recovery and a new life. I cannot believe how much love people have shown me. I have received thousands of good wish cards and gifts from all over the world. Thank you to all of them. Thank you to the children whose innocent words encouraged me. Thank you to my elders whose prayers strengthened me.

I would like to thank my nurses, doctors and all of the staff of the hospitals in Pakistan and the UK and the UAE government who have helped me get better and recover my strength. I fully support Mr Ban Ki-moon the Secretary-General in his Global Education First Initiative and the work of the UN Special Envoy Mr Gordon Brown. And I thank them both for the leadership they continue to give. They continue to inspire all of us to action.

Dear brothers and sisters, do remember one thing. Malala day is not my day. Today is the day of every woman, every boy and every girl who have raised their voice for their rights. There are hundreds of Human rights activists and social workers who are not only speaking for human rights, but who are struggling to achieve their goals of education, peace and equality. Thousands of people have been killed by the terrorists and millions have been injured. I am just one of them.

So here I stand . . . one girl among many.

I speak — not for myself, but for all girls and boys.

I raise up my voice — not so that I can shout, but so that those without a voice can be heard.

Those who have fought for their rights:

Their right to live in peace.

Their right to be treated with dignity.

Their right to equality of opportunity.

Their right to be educated.

Dear Friends, on the 9th of October 2012, the Taliban shot me on the left side of my forehead. They shot my friends too. They thought that the bullets would silence us. But they failed. And then, out of that silence came, thousands of voices. The terrorists thought that they would change our aims and stop our ambitions but nothing changed in my life except this: Weakness, fear and hopelessness died. Strength, power and courage was born. I am the same Malala. My ambitions are the same. My hopes are the same. My dreams are the same.

Dear sisters and brothers, I am not against anyone. Neither am I here to speak in terms of personal revenge against the Taliban or any other terrorists group. I am here to speak up for the right of education of every child. I want education for the sons and the daughters of all the extremists especially the Taliban.

I do not even hate the Talib who shot me. Even if there is a gun in my hand and he stands in front of me. I would not shoot him. This is the compassion that I have learnt from Muhammad-the prophet of mercy, Jesus christ and Lord Buddha. This is the legacy of change that I have inherited from Martin Luther King, Nelson Mandela and Muhammad Ali Jinnah. This is the philosophy of non-violence that I have learnt from Gandhi Jee, Bacha Khan and Mother Teresa. And this is the forgiveness that I have learnt from my mother and father. This is what my soul is telling me, be peaceful and love everyone.

Dear sisters and brothers, we realise the importance of light when we see darkness. We realise the importance of our voice when we are silenced. In the same way, when we were in Swat, the north of Pakistan, we realised the importance of pens and books when we saw the guns.

The wise saying, "The pen is mightier than sword" was true. The extremists are afraid of books and pens. The power of education frightens them. They are afraid of women. The power of the voice of women frightens them. And that is why they killed 14 innocent medical students in the recent attack in Quetta. And that is why they killed many female teachers and polio workers in Khyber Pukhtoon Khwa and FATA. That is why they are blasting schools every day. Because they were and they are afraid of change, afraid of the equality that we will bring into our society.

I remember that there was a boy in our school who was asked by a journalist, "Why are the Taliban against education?" He answered very simply. By pointing to his book he said, "A Talib doesn't know what is written inside this book." They think that God is a tiny, little conservative being who would send girls to the hell just because of going to school. The terrorists are misusing the name of Islam and Pashtun society for their own personal benefits. Pakistan is peace-loving democratic country. Pashtuns want education for their daughters and sons. And Islam is a religion of peace, humanity and brotherhood. Islam says that it is not only each child's right to get education, rather it is their duty and responsibility.

Honourable Secretary General, peace is necessary for education. In many parts of the world especially Pakistan and Afghanistan; terrorism, wars and conflicts stop children to go to their schools. We are really tired of these wars. Women and children are suffering in may parts of the world in many ways. In India, innocent and poor children are victims of child labour. Many schools have been destroyed in Nigeria. People in Afghanistan have been affected by the hurdles of extremism for decades. Young girls have to do domestic child labour and are forced to get married at early age. Poverty, ignorance, injustice, racism and the deprivation of basic rights are the main problems faced by both men and women.

Dear fellows, today I am focusing on women's rights and girls' education because they are suffering the most. There was a time when women social activists asked men to stand up for their rights. But, this time, we will do it by ourselves. I am not telling men to step away from speaking for women's rights rather I am focusing on women to be independent to fight for themselves.

Dear sisters and brothers, now it's time to speak up.

So today, we call upon the world leaders to change their strategic policies in favour of peace and prosperity.

We call upon the world leaders that all the peace deals must protect women and children's rights. A deal that goes against the dignity of women and their rights is unacceptable.

We call upon all governments to ensure free compulsory education for every child all over the world.

We call upon all governments to fight against terrorism and violence, to protect children from brutality and harm.

We call upon the developed nations to support the expansion of educational opportunities for girls in the developing world.

We call upon all communities to be tolerant — to reject prejudice based on cast, creed, sect, religion or gender. To ensure freedom and equality for women so that they can flourish. We cannot all succeed when half of us are held back.

We call upon our sisters around the world to be brave — to embrace the strength within themselves and realise their full potential.

Dear brothers and sisters, we want schools and education for every child's bright future. We will continue our journey to our destination of peace and education for everyone. No one can stop us. We will speak for our rights and we will bring change through our voice. We must believe in the power and the strength of our words. Our words can change the world.

Because we are all together, united for the cause of education. And if we want to achieve our goal, then let us empower ourselves with the weapon of knowledge and let us shield ourselves with unity and togetherness.

Dear brothers and sisters, we must not forget that millions of people are suffering from poverty, injustice and ignorance. We must not forget that millions of children are out of schools. We must not forget that our sisters and brothers are waiting for a bright peaceful future.

So let us wage a global struggle against illiteracy, poverty and terrorism and let us pick up our books and pens. They are our most powerful weapons.

One child, one teacher, one pen and one book can change the world.

Education is the only solution. Education First.